WW008369815

The Undersea Discoveries
of Jacques-Yves Cousteau

THE WHALE
Mighty Monarch of the Sea

The Undersea Discoveries
of Jacques-Yves Cousteau

The Whale
Mighty Monarch of the Sea

Jacques-Yves Cousteau
and Philippe Diolé

Translated from the French by J. F. Bernard

ARROWOOD
PRESS

Copyright © 1972 by Jacques-Yves Cousteau
Translated from the French by J. F. Bernard

All rights reserved. No part of this work may be
reproduced or transmitted in any form or by any
means, electronic or mechanical, including photocopying,
recording, or any information storage and retrieval
system, without permission in writing from the
publisher.

Published in 1987 by

Arrowood Press
166 Fifth Avenue
New York, NY 10010

This edition published by arrangement with The Cousteau
Group, Inc., 38 Eleven O'Clock Road, Weston, CT 06883.

Library of Congress Catalog Card Number: 87-71045
ISBN: 0-88486-014-0

Printed in Spain

Contents

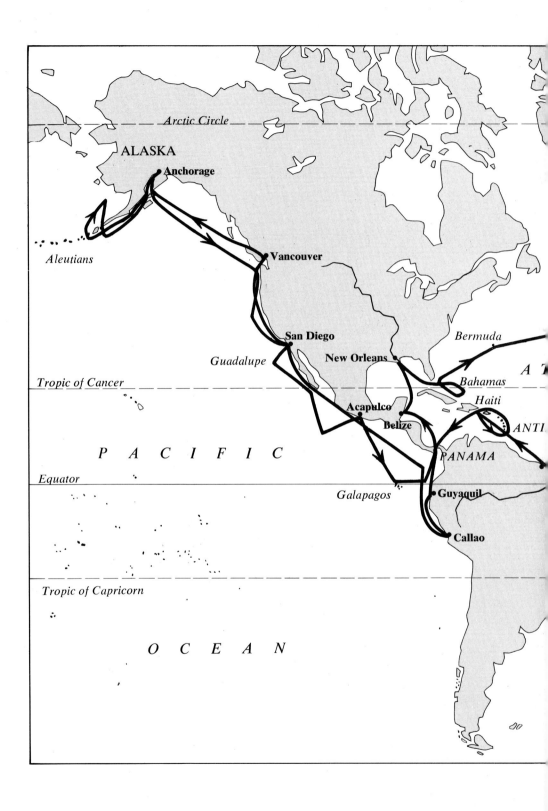

Arctic Circle

ALASKA

●Anchorage

Aleutians

●Vancouver

San Diego

Guadalupe

New Orleans

Bermuda

A T

Tropic of Cancer

Bahamas

Haiti

Acapulco

Belize

ANTI

P   A   C   I   F   I   C

PANAMA

Equator

Galapagos

●Guyaquil

●Callao

Tropic of Capricorn

O   C   E   A   N

Calypso's itinerary, February 1967 to September 1970.

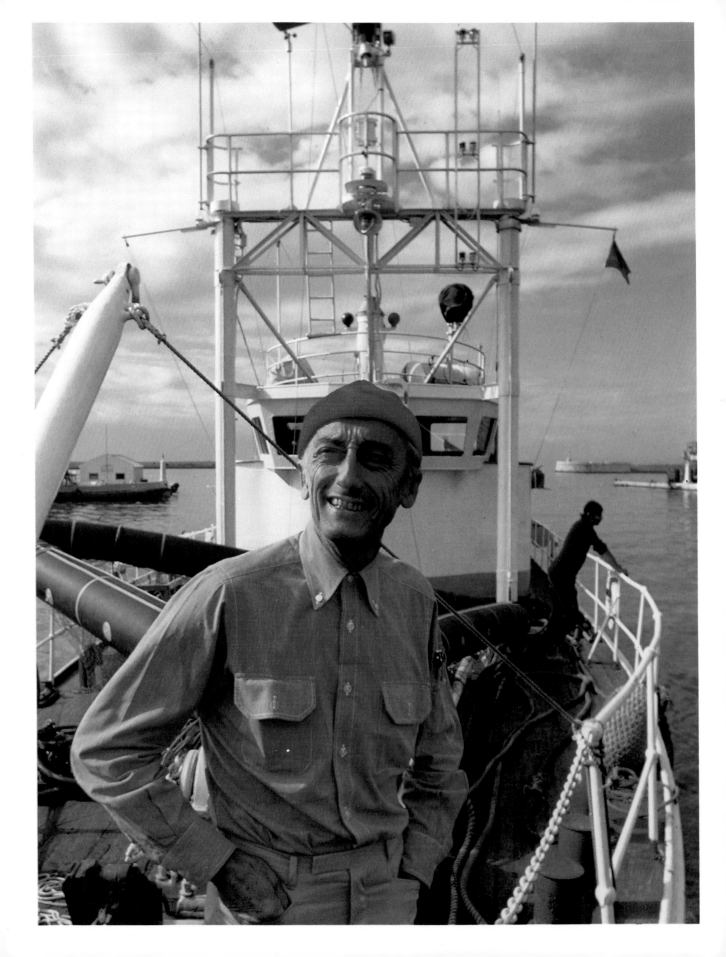

ONE

Meeting a Whale

The seas of the earth are vast. But, paradoxically, in that vastness there are few chance encounters. The waters, like the land, are covered by a network of paths and highways. Every species of life in the oceans has its route, and there are routes for every season. Nothing in this elaborate web of traffic has been left to chance. It has all been worked out in detail. It is all rigorously controlled by biological factors. And it works out greatly to the advantage of seafarers like ourselves whose mission it is to observe, and try to understand, the creatures who inhabit the seas.

In March 1967, *Calypso* was following one of these great underwater highways. Years before, during the spring, we had sighted sperm whales, or cachalots, here in the Indian Ocean near the equator. And again in 1967, during an extended course of observation in the Red Sea and the Indian Ocean, we had seen them once more. I knew, therefore, that we could count on sperm whales being here again at this time of the year.

(Left) Captain Cousteau forward on *Calypso.*

The sighting of great underwater mammals — cachalots, killer whales, pilot whales, and so forth — is always a great adventure for everyone aboard *Calypso*. Now, we have had some experience with all the animals of the sea. We have studied a huge number of species, fish of all kinds, both small and large. We have fed groupers, eels, octopuses, and even sharks. To be sure, these contacts and these tentative efforts at understanding, domestication, and communication were rewarding. But contact with whales — with those enormous warm-blooded beings who bear such a strong resemblance to man, with their lungs, their intelligence, and their talent for communication — this is a uniquely exciting experience.

It is also a uniquely difficult experience. When dealing with fish, we can attract as many as we want simply by offering them food. The effect of such an offering on a whale that weighs perhaps a hundred tons, however, is nil. There seems to be no set formula for establishing a relationship with a whale, and we have to rely upon experience gained from hit-or-miss attempts. For all of our thirty years of living on and in the sea and trying to understand its inhabitants, our experience is still woefully inadequate.

It is astonishing to recall that, after centuries of whale hunting, man knows very little about these giants of the sea.* Until recent years, man had not succeeded in crossing the boundary that separated him from the world of marine life. He had never observed whales, sperm whales, and killer whales in their natural habitat. We are the first to seek them out, in a spirit of friendship and curiosity, in the depths of the sea.

A Marvel of Nature

The relations of man and animals are always mysterious. The gulf separating the two seems virtually unbridgeable. But the most difficult creatures of all in the sea to approach and understand are the great mammals.

Face to face with this mountain of flesh, with the tens of tons of living tissue that constitute a cetacean, man's perplexity has been considerable; and his attitude, variable.

The first emotion was, understandably, terror. And, as always when fear plays a part, legends about whales multiplied. The Leviathan of the Bible story about Jonah† bears witness to man's fear when confronted with a being

*It should be noted, however, that certain whalers — William Scoresby, for instance, — gathered considerable information on cetaceans.

† The narrative is in the second chapter of the Book of Jonah.

so tremendous that it defies human understanding. And the age of Jonah and long afterward was a time when natural phenomena were expressed in myths, or in terms of religious or poetic significance.

Upon the heels of this relatively innocuous era, there came another, less innocent: the age of the hunt. And then, still another, even less harmless: the age of butchery. At this latter stage, whales were regarded as an economic factor, an industrial product; and so avidly were they pursued that, with the development of modern weapons and the tilting of the scales in favor of the hunter, several species of whale were threatened with extinction. The harpoon cannon not only destroyed myth, legend, poetry, and Moby Dick, the white whale; it also brought into question the very survival of the largest beings on the face of the earth.

In the twentieth century, whale hunting has been limited and controlled by national laws and international agreements. This was done at first, for obvious economic reasons, at the insistence of whale hunters themselves. Later, public opinion, catalyzed by more humane reasoning, began to insist on the preservation and protection of whales. Nonetheless, it seemed impractical to leave the whalers unemployed; and so, a certain amount of whale hunting is still allowed. Whales, in other words, are still being killed. And they are being killed, as ridiculous as it may sound, so that dogs and cats may be fed "seafood platters."

Ships of the Soviet Union and Japan hunt whales in order to obtain whale oil. American, British, Dutch, and Norwegian ships, however, have practically ceased all whale hunting. Whaling by French ships — usually at Gabon and Madagascar — has always been at best sporadic. Some were killed during a short period after World War II, when fatty materials were otherwise in great demand and in short supply.

Despite the continuance of whale hunting — which, at least so far as the Western world is concerned, is hardly justifiable from an economic standpoint — the relations between man and whale have changed; and this evolution, which is primarily psychological in nature, is irreversible. The whale is no longer fair game. He is no longer, in man's mind, merely a colossal prey, the handsomest trophy of all. By the same token that it is no longer a sign of virility to fell an elephant with a single explosive shell, it is no longer a manly act to destroy a great whale with a shot of cannon. What has happened is that man has become convinced — and we hope to be able to reinforce that conviction — that the whale is the greatest and most intriguing of nature's marine marvels, the most stupendous form of animal life in the seas.

In Melville's time, it was fashionable to emphasize the "ferocity" of whales. Today, we are astonished at the gentleness of whales, at their extraor-

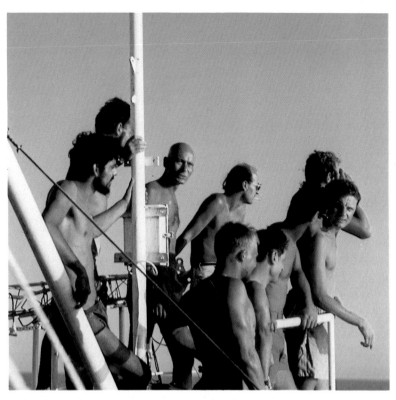

(Left) The entire team watching for whales from *Calypso*'s bow.

(Right) A Zodiac and a launch attempting to encircle a sperm whale. *Calypso* is in the background.

(Below) Falco and Bonnici chasing sperm whales in the Zodiac.

dinary diving ability, at the fact that they have the ability to communicate with one another. And we are touched by their highly developed maternal instinct.

Aboard *Calypso*, we have learned much from our experiences with whales. We know especially that contact with whales is not impossible. We are not forever cut off from our brothers, the mammals who, eons ago, chose the sea rather than dry land for their world. In order to attain even that knowledge, however, it has been necessary for us to tempt fate, to take chances, to run risks; and we have done so. In the course of our contact, the observation that emerges most clearly is this: it is very rare that a cetacean, even one that we have disturbed, or surrounded, or chased, shows any sign of aggressive action. Of course, everything depends on the species of whale, and on circumstances. But, even so, we can say that, up to now, not a single man of *Calypso* has been harmed in any way during our sometimes hazardous encounters with whales. Indeed, we can assert that whales have shown every sign of being docile creatures, every indication of wishing to spare man — and particularly divers — from harm.

This having been said, I must emphasize that there is a great mystery in this apparent respect of whales for man. For there is nothing simple about any aspect of the relations between the monarch of the sea and the ruler of the lands of the earth.

In 1967, *Calypso* left on a three-and-a-half-year expedition.* Once out of the Red Sea and into the Indian Ocean, as soon as we had passed Cape Guardafui, I organized a systematic watch for sperm whales. A sort of crow's-nest — in reality, an elevated platform — had been erected on *Calypso*'s forward, and, from there, two men kept constant watch over a large part of the horizon. My wife, Simone, who always accompanies me on *Calypso*'s expeditions, was, as always, one of our most dedicated observers. She loves to spend hour after hour in the wind and the sun, watching, thinking, trying to unravel the mystery of the sea.

Perhaps the best way to explain our extraordinary rendezvous with cetaceans on this occasion is to reproduce a few passages from my diary. Here is what I wrote upon entering the waters of the Indian Ocean, after we had spent the preceding day diving around the mountainous island of Socotra:

The First Alert

Tuesday, March 14, 1968. At 5:30 A.M. the ship's bell rings, and we all hear the cry, "Whales! Whales!" Our first encounter with them on this voyage! We are all on deck almost instantly. And then we see them: sperm whales, recognizable because of the angle at which they spout water through their blowholes.

In a few minutes, our team is ready. We had intended to use our launch, but it would be too slow. The whales would have outdistanced it almost immediately. Perhaps we will not need a small boat. *Calypso* herself may be able to get close enough to them for our purposes. Cautiously, picking our way, we maneuver into the middle of the herd by following the directions called down to us by the observation team up in the crow's-nest. (Frédéric Dumas, Albert Falco, and Simone were on duty at the time — and I must admit that Simone shows herself to be especially adept in charting a course for *Calypso* through this kind of traffic.)

I send our cameraman René Barsky down to the observation chamber in *Calypso*'s nose. There, he should be close enough to the whales to film from beneath the surface, through the portholes.

A dozen times we try to get *Calypso* close enough for Barsky to do his work. And only three or four times are we successful. But what shots we get

*The story of that expedition has been told in an earlier book, *Life and Death in a Coral Sea,* by J.-Y. Cousteau and Philippe Diolé (Doubleday, 1970).

Portrait of Herman Melville, author of *Moby Dick*, by Francis Day.

then! Once, two whales were swimming alongside *Calypso*, literally wedging themselves up against her hull. On another occasion, Barsky is able to film, almost at his leisure, a mother whale and her calf swimming along only a few yards ahead of our prow. The third time, while we are doing scarcely two knots, *Calypso* brushes against the side of an animal of enormous size. Barsky, filming away down in his little underwater room, is terrified. All he can see through the portholes are these incredibly enormous bodies. And then, suddenly, Barsky is in total darkness. The whales are so close to *Calypso* that they are completely blocking the light from the surface. What has happened is that there are several grampuses among the sperm whales, and these crowded one of the whales so closely that he was unable to maneuver out of our way.

Despite all of our excitement and enthusiasm, it turns out that the film is of poor quality. The water was clearer than it had been for the past few days; but it evidently was not clear enough for really first-rate pictures. We are all disappointed, but there is nothing we can do except continue on our course and hope for another opportunity. At the moment, there is almost a dead calm.

Wednesday, March 15. This morning there is another whale alert, this one lasting from 8 A.M. to noon. There are five or six schools of sperm whales in sight and a few individual whales swimming alone, or in pairs. Circumstances are not favorable to camerawork. The water is clear, finally, but the whales themselves are not co-operating. They seem nervous, wary. Yesterday, they were either swimming around in a particular area, or were heading southeast at about five or six knots, and did not seem to mind our presence. Perhaps today they are feeding. At any rate, as soon as we draw near to them on the surface of the water, they dive — straight down, almost vertically — and disappear without leaving a trace. In their wake, our divers tell us, there seemed to be something like oil; but I think it likely that this is simply the effect of their tail movements upon the water — water vibrations, or what old-time seafarers called *glip*.

The whales remain underwater, swimming along at a depth of twenty-five or thirty feet — even though they are capable of going down as far as perhaps three thousand feet — and surfacing only when they have to come up for air. Once, they stayed under for twenty minutes. What wind they must have!

In spite of everything, we manage to get a few shots. Albert Falco ("Bebert") has taken out the Zodiac — which is faster and more maneuverable than the launch — and is able twice to head off the herd. With him are Deloire, with his movie camera, and Sillner, our photographer, and they capture a whale on film before it gets too far away. The second time, there is enough time to focus the cameras, and Deloire and Sillner manage to get a few good photographs and some excellent frames.

Obviously, we are going to have to find some less timid whales if we are ever going to get good shots. What happened? So far as we can see, there is nothing to account for the difference in behavior between yesterday and today. And yet, yesterday, the whales were indifferent to our presence, while today they are most unapproachable.

We continue the watch all afternoon until dark, but without seeing a sign of the school.

The tail of a sperm whale diving.

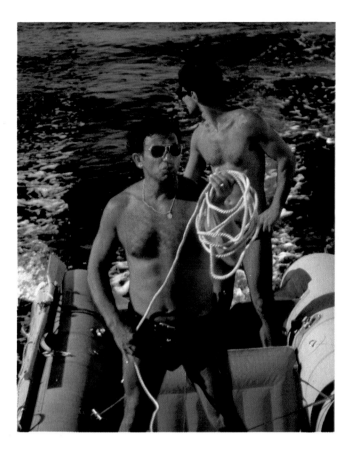

(Right) Falco and Bonnici prepare to confront a sperm whale.

(Below) A diver has jumped out of the Zodiac and is going to latch onto a young sperm whale.

Thursday, March 16. Today, nothing. We are into the fringe of a storm from the northeast. There is a wind, and the sea is rough — force 4, which is not dangerous, but is rough enough to make whale watching impossible. It is too easy to confuse the spout of a whale with the crest of a wave in this kind of weather.

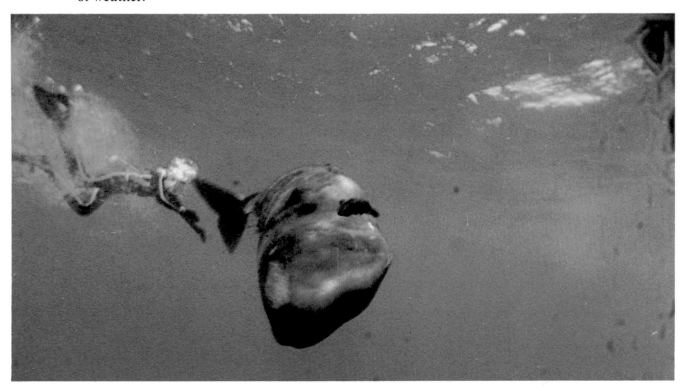

I have worked out and distributed a plan for filming. Barsky, Deloire, Marcellin, Dumas, Bebert, and Didi are reading it, and I have asked them to let me know their comments after they've had a chance to think about it.

We must get to work on the sequences that we have already filmed, and begin to plan others. I am not overly concerned about this aspect of it, though. Barsky is a true artist with his camera, and I have the greatest confidence in him. And Deloire is simply unbelievable. He manages somehow to plan every aspect of his work in the most minute detail, and yet remain so flexible that he is never unprepared when something unexpected turns up. Yesterday, for example, when he went out with Bebert and Sillner in the Zodiac, he lay down in front of the raft with his camera cradled in his arms. Then, as soon as Bebert told him "Go!" he simply rolled into the water, practically on top of a whale, and began shooting instantly. This kind of thing seems to be his cup of tea. He simply radiates contentment and good humor.

March 18. The squall from the northeast is not so rough, and we have once more taken up our watch for sperm whales. We will reach the Maldives, our next port of call, at the earliest on March 20.

The past two days have been taken up entirely with our hunt for whales. There have been many fewer than during the month of April, both in 1954 and 1955, when we were sailing along the equator, north of the Seychelles. We hope to see some more before reaching the Maldives — and I've deliberately charted a crooked course in order to add ten days to our cruise. Even so, there is no certainty that it will have been worth it.

I am struck, as always, by the incredible fertility of the sea. Whales seem to exist in all parts of it. And Japanese fishermen* seem able to drop their lines at just about any spot and haul out tuna and swordfish bigger than the fishermen. Whales, tuna, swordfish — it is no wonder that the waters of the earth abound with such a variety of life forms. Think what resources are necessary to sustain these huge (and hungry) creatures.

We have taken steps to cope with the next whales we sight. We know that sperm whales are able to attain speeds of up to 20 knots, while *Calypso* struggles along at eleven knots. And so, I have had two 40-horsepower outboard motors mounted on one of our launches. This should make it possible for our team to keep up with the great mammals. The problem is that, if the sea is even a little rough, a launch traveling at that speed is in for trouble. Everyone aboard — our divers, cameramen and pilots — are thrown about mercilessly and are in constant danger of ending up in the water.

Calypso had the opportunity to observe these fishermen at work in the Indian Ocean.

(See *Life and Death in a Coral Sea*, Chapter Two.)

It is true that it is often easy to get fairly close to whales — a phenomenon that always surprises me. The trouble comes when we want to capture them on film. It seems that we no sooner get our cameras in focus than the whales dive and are lost to sight. Several times, Deloire, clutching his camera, and another diver, jumped into the water right in front of a sperm whale; but, as soon as the whale sensed their presence, it disappeared. "If one has a great deal of patience, it is possible to film a whale's tail," André Laban says, but without a trace of bitterness. And that is only a slight exaggeration. Even so, it seems to me that a whale's tail is well worth the effort.

From aboard *Calypso*, at any rate, it is this enormous tail that we see most clearly when a whale, having drawn himself up to dive, plunges with a mighty burst of speed into the deep. We see it then, a flat, triangular expanse of living flesh, curving into what seems an ironic salute, for a second before it too disappears where no man can follow. An awe-inspiring sight. Sometimes, an infuriating one. And, occasionally, in spite of ourselves, we burst out laughing.

April 6. We are at anchor off the island of Funidu, one of the Maldives group, in order to take on fresh water. This evening, a party from *Calypso* went ashore to do a bit of exploring, and turned up a few objects of interest: some drums, and a superb dagger the hilt of which is made of whale's tooth. This shows that there are indeed whales in these waters, and that the natives are able to kill them — but how?

A First Meeting.

April 9. This morning, after breakfast, Bonnici, Bebert, and Barsky go to the Zodiac and have a great time romping with a troop of dolphins. The dolphins, who seem to love this sort of thing, make a game of rushing at the Zodiac, at full speed, and then diving just when it seemed that they could never turn away in time. We almost captured a magnificent spectacle on film: a troop of a hundred dolphins leaping along ahead of the Zodiac, seeming to be harnessed to it as Bebert, pushing the Zodiac to its maximum speed of 18 knots, never quite manages to catch up to them.

A Difficult Part to Play

The first thing to do, obviously, is to be prepared; and so, I set up a tight schedule. Our gear must always be ready: suited divers on the foredeck, with

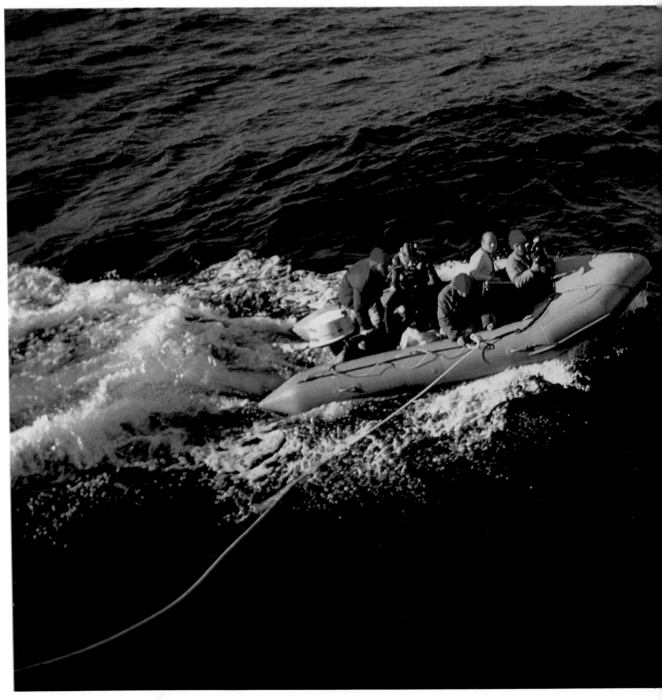

The Zodiac catches up with a fleeing dolphin.

harpoons, nylon line, and buoy within reach. The Zodiac and the launch must be ready to be lowered into the water with their motors in place. Two underwater cameras must always be loaded and ready for use. And a cameraman must be standing by to go immediately to the observation room.

The use of the harpoon gun by our divers requires some explanation. It is

very rare that one is able to follow a particular whale, observe it when it dives, and then pick it up again when it comes to the surface for air. There is usually no way of knowing if the whale that comes to the surface is the same whale that you saw disappear fifteen or twenty minutes before; for one cachalot looks very like another, at least to human beings. Therefore, it is almost impossible to judge the speed of a certain whale by measuring the distance from the point of disappearance to the point of reappearance, unless there is some way of making sure that the whale, in both cases, is the same whale.*

So far as I know, there is only one way to be certain, and that is to "mark" the animal. And for that we intend to use the same method that worked for sharks in the Red Sea. That is, we try to attach a metal marker to at least one whale's dorsal fin — if we can get close enough to those enormous cylinders of shiny black flesh that are spouting and rolling all around *Calypso*.

The job of attaching this marker is reserved for Albert Falco. It is not a task to be undertaken lightly, or to be carried out without trouble; but if there is one man in the world who can handle it, it is Falco. He has been with us since he was fifteen years old. He has shared everything with us, every danger and every risk, for twenty years. But Falco is not only an extraordinarily capable diver and a dexterous athlete; just as important, he is a man with a gift for handling animals. Somehow, he is able to succeed in making himself accepted by marine animals. Others on our team have developed the same talent to some extent — Delemotte, Raymond Coll, Canoë Kientzy, and my son Philippe; but Albert Falco was the first who deliberately undertook to make friends with life forms in the open sea, and he remains the practitioner par excellence of that difficult art.

This aspect of Falco's talent is especially important at this time. The relationship between man and whale is precarious and uncertain. It is true that whale hunting is now practiced on a much smaller scale than formerly, and that whales are no longer looked upon as "ferocious monsters." But we have not yet been able to work out a new relationship, to devise a new approach to these sperm whales which, only yesterday, were considered "Leviathans" existing in a kill-or-be-killed relationship to man. It is very difficult for man to go directly from butchery to sympathy.

April 10. As soon as it is daylight, I am up and on deck checking to make sure that the television camera and the automatic camera are set up and ready to roll in the observation room. By 7:30, Barsky is ready on *Calypso*'s diving platform, at water level, camera in hand, waiting for a chance to shoot some flying fish. And Simone is up in the crow's-nest, keeping a sharp lookout for sperm whales. Then, just at the moment when René Haon climbs up to relieve her, the alarm sounds: Whales!

---

*Whalers were the only ones who ever had the opportunity to keep track of the duration of a cetacean's dive, or of its speed. They, however, observed whales only when the animals' behavior was abnormal; that is, when they were being closely pursued.

Calypso swings about, and our team is galvanized into action. The Zodiac, with its new 33-horsepower motor, is lowered into the water, as is the launch with its twin 40s. Bebert and Bonnici set out in the Zodiac with the harpoon — a weapon designed to mark the whale without harming it, for its spearhead is short and light and it is incapable of going deeper into the whale than its layer of blubber. Maurice Leandri and René Haon pull away in the launch.

The first group of sperm whales comprises four animals, and, in addition, there are two other groups nearby, each with three whales. *Calypso* gets to within fifty yards of them — and they dive. We are too late.

Thirty minutes later, the three groups reappear, but a little more widely dispersed. This time, Bebert is prepared. He fires. One of the whales is hit! Apparently bewildered, it remains motionless a few feet below the surface, and its companion whales stay with it. A good shot, apparently. But then, with a flick of their great tails, all three are gone, and Bebert dejectedly reels in his spear. It seems that the harpoon became entangled in the line, struck the whale at an angle, and then fell out. So near, and yet so far. Everyone is disappointed, except, no doubt, the whale.

Nonetheless, we continue the chase all morning, until at half past noon, the whales disappear for good and we are left facing an empty sea. I reset our course for Mahé in the Seychelles, our next port of call, and everyone turns in for a siesta — everyone, that is, except those on watch on the observation platform.

It would seem that, from dawn to about ten or eleven o'clock in the morning, sperm whales are sleepy, or sluggish, and are easy to sight and approach. Beginning at eleven o'clock or noon, however, they liven up and begin to travel; and then is when we lose them. It is even difficult to see them when they blow. Is it because there is less condensation in midday than early in the morning? Perhaps there is some connection between this phenomenon and the fact that most marine life tends to rise or swim toward the surface during the hours between sunrise and sunset. It is possible that whales prefer to hunt at night, when they are able to find food without diving to great depths. That would explain why they appear to be tired and listless early in the morning. And, of course, we have no way (for the time being) of observing whales except in daylight.

April 11. I am adopting a zigzag course in order to increase our chances of sighting sperm whales.

Our team is aware that they are going to attempt to do something that has never been tried before; and that they are going to attempt it in perilous circumstances. This is the kind of challenge that we love, and everyone senses

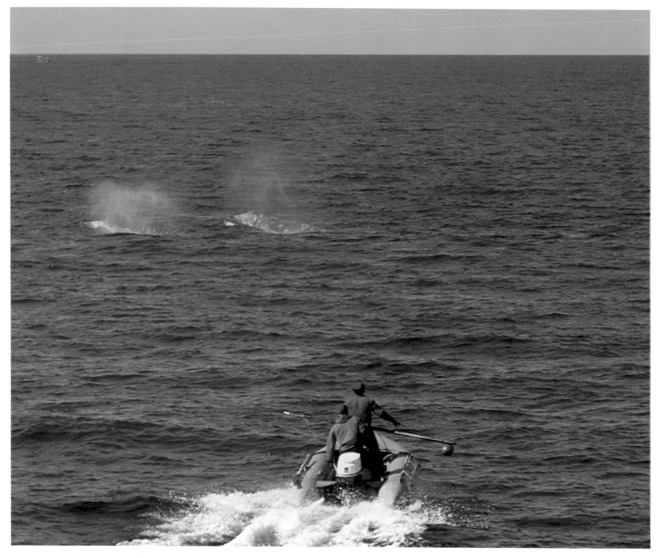

Two gray whale spouts. Canoë Kientzy, in a Zodiac piloted by Bernard Delemotte, is getting ready to throw his harpoon.

that our task requires not only special skills, but also special attitudes and a particular kind of morale. Even Raymond Coll, our almost speechless Catalan, who has never wasted a word in his life, has suddenly come to life and is talking (for him) madly. This is important, for Raymond has an "in" with the great animals of the sea; after all, he was the first man ever to hitch a ride on the back of a whale shark.

Caught in the Trap.

April 16. At dawn, we are where we were years ago, at the "meeting place of the sperm whales." And we are not disappointed. By seven o'clock, Frédéric Dumas has sighted a disturbance in the water on the horizon, an up-

Michel Deloire, our cameraman, prepares his equipment before diving to meet a whale.

heaval like those that we saw here in 1955. Fifteen minutes later, I can make out clearly, dead ahead at about a half mile, the shape of a huge cachalot. To make sure that nothing is able to get by us, I send Bebert, Bonnici, and Barsky out in the Zodiac. They are to stay two miles off our portside. Meanwhile, the launch, with Maurice, Omer, and Deloire, is at the same distance off our starboard. For all practical purposes, nothing can get by us along an eight-mile front.

As it turns out, we still have a lot to learn. It is my intention, thanks to our unsurpassed team of divers, to do what man has never done before: to sail with the whales in the open sea, to come face to face with them in the same way as we have confronted sharks, eels, and groupers. Our encounters with these latter, it is true, gave us a greater familiarity with them than had ever been possible before. What we had forgotten, however, was that even the largest sharks we saw measured around 15 feet — which is quite sizable — while our eels were about 9 feet long, and our groupers, at most, 6 feet. And none of these could begin to compare with a whale 60 feet long. How does one become friendly with a body that weighs over 60 tons? That, of course, is the question that this expedition is intended to answer.

The alarm bell rings. Frédéric Dumas — "Didi," our oldest friend and companion-in-adventure — up in the crow's-nest, has sighted a blow. Apparently, the whale is sleeping. It blows twice more, without showing its back on the surface, and then disappears for eight minutes. The Zodiac goes forward — but is slowed down by engine trouble. After a half hour spent in determining the whale's location, in observing from a distance, and in following slowly, the Zodiac now attempts to close in on the whale. But the animal has awakened and moves eastward at a good speed, closely followed by the Zodiac. We can see the whale's back now, as streamlined as the hull of an atomic submarine, but with a ridiculously small and slanted dorsal fin. The whale is making 12 to 15 knots, and the Zodiac is managing to keep the gap between them at no more than seven or eight yards. In a few seconds, it will be close enough for Bebert to fire his harpoon. Now!

And, at that precise moment, the Zodiac's motor conks out.

Bebert is beside himself with rage. So am I.

Fifteen minutes later, the Zodiac's motor has been changed and the chase begins anew. But the spirit of the thing has been lost, and, although we continue on, we know in our hearts that it is useless.

The reasons for today's fiasco are three: first of all, the breakdown of our new 33-horsepower outboard; second, the sea itself, which, while not really rough, is no longer so smooth as to make use of the Zodiac and the launch very easy; and, finally, *Calypso* herself is slowed down by the absence of her starboard propeller.

After nightfall, I consult my charts in order to try to work out a schedule. It is no use. We must make Mahé, our port of call in the Seychelles, and so our expedition has every chance of having ended with today's failure.

(Facing page above) A sperm whale aground in the Bering Strait. (An engraving from *Histoire des Cétacés,* by Lacépède.)

(Facing page below) André Laban suits up on *Calypso*'s deck.

(Following page) A gray whale, with Canoë's harpoon in its blubber, makes a vertical dive.

The animal that we encountered this afternoon was probably a finback whale, or rorqual. When he breathed, we were able to locate him by his blow; but we could see neither his back, nor his little dorsal fin. He breathed twice every eight minutes, but virtually without moving forward. Once the Zodiac began chasing him, however, he seems to have panicked. He tried to lose the Zodiac by swimming at a speed of 12 to 15 knots — but hardly below the surface; and then he was breathing more heavily, and we could see him very well. His real defensive means became apparent when he began to dive. For an hour he demonstrated the efficacy of his Asdic (sonar), for he obviously knew exactly where *Calypso*, the Zodiac, and the launch were at any given moment, and he always came to the surface where we were not.

I have the impression that the rorqual is somewhat more highly developed and clever than the sperm whale, and that our only chance of getting close to him would have been to catch him by surprise at some point during the first fifteen minutes of the chase.

I must admit that I am discouraged by today's events. Our whale hunt, twentieth-century style, is, it seems, nothing more than a dream. I want to be alone for a while, so I do not go in to dinner with the rest of the team. There is no one I want to see, or to talk to. But there is nowhere I can go in this crowded ship. On the forward deck, one can be seen from the bridge. Sillner and Sumian are on duty in the crow's-nest. And the rest of *Calypso* is one huge resonance chamber for diesels and ventilators. I resign myself to my cabin. I write, I read. And finally I lose myself in a crossword puzzle.

April 18. I am awake at five o'clock and go up on deck to see the sunrise. But everyone else is already there, eager for the sign of land, of islands, of trees. Still smarting from yesterday's fiasco, I find it difficult to share their gaiety.

It does not help that the sea today is what it should have been yesterday, calm as a pond. And here we are, between the islands of Bird and Denis, virtually trapped for the next three days — perhaps the last three days of calm of the entire season. How frustrating. For the next three days I intend to go into a state of suspended animation, and I will not breathe again, so to speak, until we leave these miserable, beautiful islands.

It is two months today that the *Calypso* sailed from Monaco.

The Speargun Sinks

April 20. We left Mahé at 7:30 this morning, and we were no sooner out into the open sea than the helmsman, pointing to a nearby squall, shouted, "There are the trade winds, and they're going to last for six months." This was precisely what I was afraid would happen — that the winds would come, and that that would be the end of our whale hunt.

I set a course for the African islands to take a look at the northern end of the Amirantes. But, as soon as Mahé was below the horizon, the alarm bell sounded. And suddenly it had all been forgotten — the disappointments and failures and discouragement — and I felt a surge of joyous hope. For there was a blow — and another, and another. And the closer we came, the more there seemed to be, slender columns of vapor against the blue of the sky. And best of all, there was no doubt that these were sperm whales, for the spouts were oblique, at an angle of about 45°. And of all the great whales, only the sperm whale has a single blowhole, rather than two.

I order *Calypso* to cut her speed. We must take no chance of a collision that might injure one of our giant friends.

Slowly, cautiously, we draw nearer to the whales. We can see their great backs turning among the waves of the Indian Ocean.

The cachalots are not in a hurry. The noise of our engines — which they no doubt hear very clearly, given the perfection of their auditory sense — does not seem to frighten them or even to disturb them. And yet, they have every reason to be wary of man and his ships.

I check off everything in my mind to make sure that we are prepared for any eventuality. Everyone seems ready, the divers and the cameramen, as well as our sound engineer who will tape, both above and below the surface, the sounds of the whales.

We are now very near. Indeed, *Calypso* is in the midst of them. The Zodiacs are being launched — but ever so cautiously, so as not to frighten the animals. In one of them are our cameramen. They will try to film the whales in the water. I watch from the bridge as they move slowly away from *Calypso*; and at that moment I begin to wonder whether this whole project is not senseless. From the bridge, I can see our tiny men, in their tiny boat. And, at the same time, I see the incredible size of the sperm whales, their mighty backs, the great flat tails that propel these phenomenal creatures. I see their dark silhouettes beneath the surface, more like mountains than mammals.

The men in the Zodiacs, however, seem troubled by no such doubts. I see Falco holding his speargun, to the tip of which a buoy has been attached. His nylon line is neatly coiled in its bucket. In the other Zodiac, Bebert is standing as far forward as he can get, held erect by a special harness so that he may fire his speargun from a standing position even at high speeds.

But now the whale shows signs of being disturbed by the noise from the outboard motors, and begins to swim away. The Zodiac shoots forward, and Falco is very close to the animal. He aims his speargun, and fires.

Aboard *Calypso*, no one breathes. For a few moments, we do not know what has happened. Then we see the other Zodiac skirt around the whale and slow down. Raymond Coll jumps into the water. He is trying to catch hold of one of the whale's fins! This means that Falco's shot was good! And, sure enough, we then see that the spear is in place and that the whale, when he moves, is trailing a red buoy behind him.

The whale's reaction seems initially one of surprise at all the unwelcome commotion around him. Since he is unable to outdistance his pursuers on the surface, he takes the only way out: he dives. We see his huge triangular tail above the surface for an instant, then it is gone. Apparently, our friend is going straight down: a deep dive. The red buoy disappears into the deep at an astonishing speed. This is the critical moment. The line attached to the whale is 3000 feet long — a length that, for all practical purposes, seemed sufficient. But what is practical for us is not necessarily so for sperm whales. The line uncoils, uncoils . . . then reaches its end and snaps like a thread.

Our whale is gone, buoy, buoy line and all. We will have to start all over again.

The main problem is to attach, or implant, a piece of iron, in the form of a spearhead, into the blubber of these animals. Their blubber is so elastic that a harpoon fired from a speargun — or even from a powder-operated gun — penetrates it only with difficulty. And it often penetrates so superficially that the barb cannot hold. I am certain that we shoot as straight as the old-time whale hunters, and from at most the same distance as they did. Why, then, do we fail where they succeeded? The answer, of course, is in our speargun. Our "harpoon" is ridiculously small and light compared to theirs. And yet, we dare not use anything larger or heavier, for fear of harming the whale.

We have learned a few things from our experiences today. We know, for instance, that it is not enough to slow down the animal so that we can film him from the front; we must also be able to guess the direction in which he is going to swim. The trouble is that, once a sperm whale is harpooned, his conduct becomes totally unpredictable. Or rather, in a sense it becomes too predictable: he dives, and that is the end of harpoon, buoy, and line. And the end also of our chance to film him.

Once a cachalot has disappeared beneath the surface, he will not appear again for anywhere from five to fifteen minutes. In the meantime, he is traveling beneath the surface. If we follow him at top speed, we can usually see him when he returns to the surface for air; but, by the time we can get close enough for it to do any good, he has already filled his lungs and dives again.

Watching a sperm whale, one has the impression that he does not move very fast. That impression is wholly incorrect. Watching a whale dive, all of the animal's movements — the movement of the tail, especially — seem desultory, almost casual. What we sometimes fail to take into account is the power in that tail, and the fact that its movements are extraordinarily well   co-ordinated and graceful.

Given the whale's speed once it decides to move away, or to dive, all that we can do is to space out our team along the route that we guess the animal will take. Our cameramen wait, cameras in hand, to film whatever (if any) part of the whale they can, either full face or in profile, as he swims. Then, the Zodiac picks up its men, tries to speed past the whale, disperses them in the water once more, and the whole thing begins again. This is not an easy technique; but everyone seems to enjoy it, even the helmsmen of the Zodiac who must maneuver the craft at the direction of the cameramen.

All in all, the whole operation resembles a bullfight more than a filming session. The trouble is that, in this case, the matador's — that is, the team's — courage and skill are largely wasted. It is not a question of accumulating "points" for daring or technique, but of getting some meaningful film footage of whales in their natural habitat. From that standpoint, I must say that whales are considerably more troublesome than sharks. Using the *corrida* technique with sharks is highly dangerous, of course; but at least there is some return on the risks involved.

Such were our first contacts with sperm whales in the Indian Ocean. We were soon to meet animals even larger than these, for it was not our intention to limit ourselves to close-range observation whenever *Calypso* happened to come within the proper distance to a whale. We set out for the express purpose of making a systematic study of whales in any and every part of the sea. We were going to follow their migrations, and we would observe them mating. We would see whale calves nursing. We would record their cries, their language, their "songs"; and the whole range of sounds emitted by these surprisingly loquacious animals.

The first phase of that project is now complete. It extended over a period of years, and took us from the Bahamas to Alaska to Baja California. And I would like now to report on that expedition.

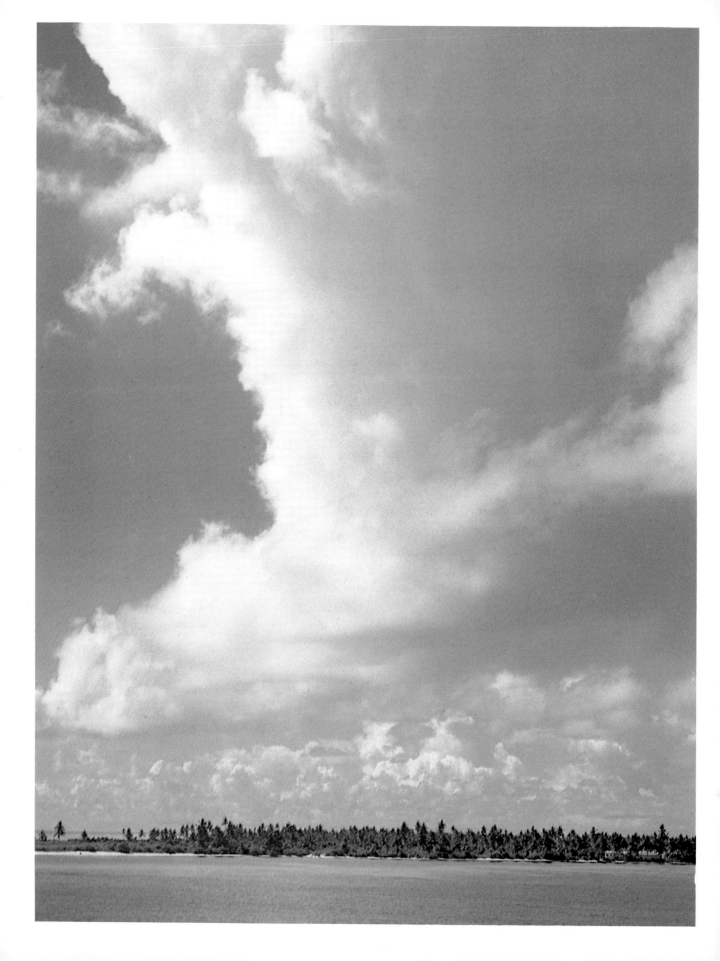

TWO

Fragile Giants of the Sea

During the nearly two days that we remained virtually in the midst of a school of sperm whales in the Indian Ocean, we are able to gain some insight into the scale of life of these giants. It is a scale possible only in the vastness and depths of the sea; for only in the sea could such monstrously huge bodies have evolved, and only there could they exist. There is, therefore, between man and the whale, a difference in scale; a chasm that separates us from them, and that makes them seem not only strange to us, but truly alien.

The whales swimming and spouting around *Calypso* were not a group of unknowing beings, not brutes. They were creatures bound together by ties, by relationships among themselves. Some of them even had distinctive characteristics—they were more daring, or more timid, or more intelligent than the others. Was this intuition? Instinct? Perhaps. But how does one find out when one is dealing with dozens of beings, each one made up of from 30 to 60 tons

(Left) After a long voyage, *Calypso* arrives within sight of the Maldives lying low in the water.

of bone, muscle, and fat?

In the water around *Calypso,* separated from us only by a few planks, there was a fantastic ballet taking place; or rather, a measured, calculated activity that seemed fantastic to us because the performers were a dozen Leviathans. We could see their glistening backs, their tails as large as the sails of a ship, and, rarely, their massive heads. If we had been able to interpret their language, we would very likely have discovered that these turnings and wheelings were not at all random movements, the result of chance, but that the entire school was following a carefully reasoned pattern of behavior. And, indeed, the hydrophones that we used to record their sounds revealed that these whales "spoke," sometimes in dialogue, by means of a series of clicks and vocal sounds.

Strangely, this observation of whales, interesting as it was, had a depressing effect upon me. We found what we came for, it is true, and there were whales all about us. But the very sight of them brought home to me the conviction that we—men and whales—were separated from each other by an impossible gulf, by a too-great disproportion in size between them, cavorting in the sea around a ship hardly bigger than they, and us, who were clustered on that ship like ants adrift on a plank.

In spite of all our techniques, despite our outboards and our Zodiacs and our launches, notwithstanding all the expertise of our teams, it seemed that we were hardly more than specks alongside those islandlike giants swimming, diving, and floating around us. On the surface, they were acceptable by human standards, because we could see only a part of their bodies. But when they dived, they were so immense, so long, and often so fast, that, watching from beneath the surface, it was impossible for us to take in the entire mass of a whale's body at one glance.

I have often felt a sense of bitterness, or rather of impotence, when confronted with the thought that in the final analysis, these marvels of nature are beyond us, beyond our senses, beyond our experience—not because they live in the sea, but because they belong to a race of giants that requires of man an intellectual and emotional flexibility, an understanding, a willingness to break away from traditional concepts, that is perhaps beyond him.

We are trying, with all the means at our disposal—our launches and Zodiacs and divers—to establish contact, to achieve a *rapprochement* with these marvels of marine life. But we are attempting to do so in the sea; and that limitless stretch of water and those great depths are not our natural environment. It is that of the giants we are observing. It was proportionate to *their* size and to *their* strength, and not to ours.

It is difficult to explain what a man's reactions are when he first comes face to face with a whale in the water, with that great living, moving, shining cylinder of black and gray. The first feeling is one of stupefaction at the size of the animal. The whale's dimensions go beyond man's experience with life forms, and beyond his expectations—so much so that incredulity follows upon astonishment. The mind rebels, and the diver wonders whether he is not dreaming, or deluded. On this point, all of our divers agree. The first sight of a whale in the water is terrifying. There is no experience on dry land that can compare with it. Another point on which there is universal agreement is that, when seen from the surface, these animals do not appear to be moving very rapidly; but for a diver in the water to touch a whale, or to grab hold of it, becomes an athletic experience —or a nightmare.

In dealing with such phenomenal beings, we have been able thus far to work out only one technique. As I have already mentioned, it involves the use of two Zodiacs. One Zodiac attempts to get ahead of the whale and, by moving directly in front of it, to slow it down. The other Zodiac puts our cameramen and divers into the water, in front of the whale to watch (and hopefully to film) the creature as it swims around them, or under them, or over them. Nothing that they can do hinders the whale's progress in the slightest. They can climb on its back, grab hold of a fin—nothing seems to bother it; it continues to move forward as though it were alone in the sea. Then, the Zodiac returns, picks up the men, and the game begins all over again. This, unfortunately, is our only method of observation; and, as empirical as it is, and as clumsy, it has had a few good results. That is, we have learned many things.

We have understood, for example, that, if we want to observe a whale for any length of time, or especially to film it, we must by all means slow it down. "We chase it, we jump into the water, we wait a second or two for our masks to clear, and begin shooting," explains André Laban. "And then when we run the film, we see that the only thing on it is the whale's tail — and then only if we were lucky. What happens is that, by the time the water settles after we have jumped in, the whale is gone."

In our attempts to slow down a school of sperm whales, or at least to isolate a single animal, we have tried different tactics with our Zodiacs and lauches. But, so great is the disproportion in size between these cachalots and our craft that we are virtually doomed to failure from the start. It seems that, in the sea, nothing can hope to prevail against these moving mountains of flesh.

An additional difficulty is that there is nothing about a whale, no reaction, no movement, no flick of a fin, no motion of the tail, that man is able to interpret with certainty. We have no idea at any given moment whether a

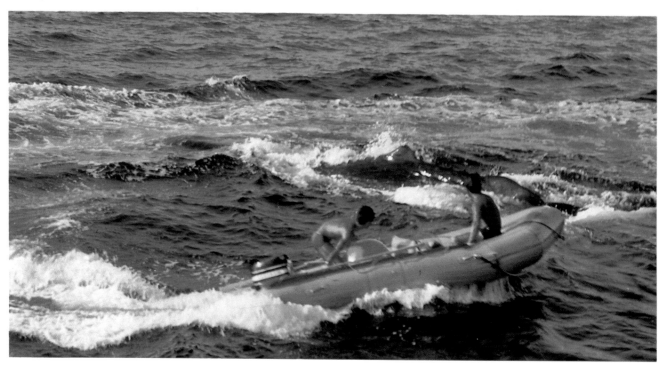

The virazeou technique: a Zodiac literally runs circles around a sperm whale

The whale, disturbed by the noise, tries to pass under the Zodiac.

(Facing page) The sperm whale charges the Zodiac and will overturn it.

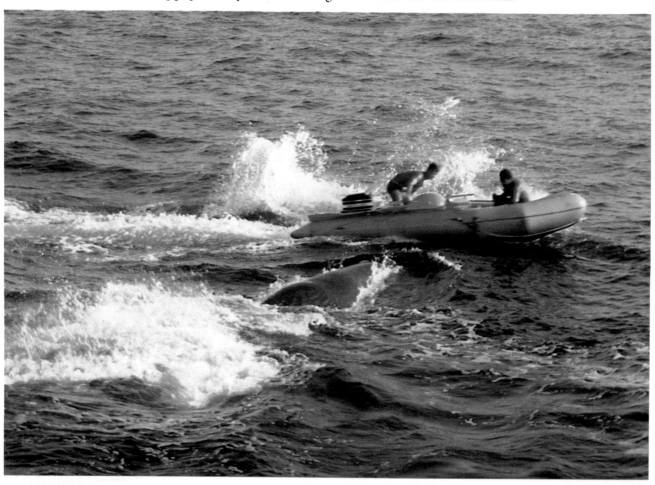

whale is delighted or furious, or neither. When a dog snarls, or a lion roars, or a rattlesnake rattles, you know what to expect. But a whale? A sperm whale could be in a frenzy of rage for an hour before he decides to put an end to us with a flick of that incredible tail, and we would have no way of knowing it. There is no reaction that we are able to interpret as meaning that we have gone too far. For the diver, only the sight of that monstrous square mouth, with its row of glistening teeth, gives warning of what could happen. . . . And yet, we ignored even this, and for thirty-six hours we were able, with absolute impunity, to tease these apparently good-natured behemoths.

In all of this, we have had at least one satisfaction: our method of "marking" whales has been successful. "Bebert" Falco has proved, as we all expected, to be our most daring and effective marker. The helmsmen of the Zodiacs have also risen to new heights of derring-do with their little boats. For example, in maneuvering for an advantageous position for our cameramen, they have learned how to skirt over the back of a semi-immersed whale — the trick being, at the very last moment, to raise the outboard motor

so that its propeller blades do not injure the whale.

Fortunately, the sea is calm and the weather marvelous. Despite that deceptive squall, the trade winds, it turns out, are not yet upon us. And so, we continue our whale hunt and our efforts to mark a whale for observation, using the same technique as before. And we are successful. Our divers manage somehow to jump into the water right in front of the whales. (It is usually the whale who maneuvers to avoid the diver. Is this because he sees the man, or is he forewarned by his echo-location system? We do not know.) And the cameramen are now diving with tanks of compressed air on their backs. This extra weight slows down their movements, but it is necessary for them to use scuba equipment, since a harpooned whale will often dive to anywhere from fifteen to sixty-five or seventy feet. And, of course, the cameramen and divers follow him down. There is something reminiscent of a circus in this; and, as in every animal act under the big top, there is a large element of risk involved.

After one successful marking, we have been able to keep the cachalot near *Calypso* for twenty-four hours, which is a record for us. During that time, the rest of the school — about ten sperm whales — remained in the neighborhood, apparently waiting for their captive companion. Our hydrophones picked up a continual exchange of signals between the marked whale and the others during this period. The waiting whales were not scattered around *Calypso*, but swam a short distance ahead of us, usually to starboard. We could see their spouts rising at regular intervals.

It happened several times to Laban to be able to film the head of a sperm whale; literally to stick the camera into his face. Laban had the impression that the animal, despite its size, was frightened. The noise from the Zodiac's motor no doubt had something to do with it.

There has been no indication of any aggressiveness on the part of these whales during the time that we have been filming them. There are, however, certain signs that may — or may not — indicate nervousness on their part: brusque movements of the head, motions of the tail, and erratic dives.

It seems that the most frequent reaction of a sperm whale, when we try to slow it down, is to continue moving forward and to join its school. He is obviously far more inclined to flee than to confront the Zodiac — though that light craft would be an easy victim.

An Invention: The Virazeou

Bebert Falco has found a way to do what we have been trying to do since the beginning of this expedition: to stop whales long enough for us to be able to observe and film them. Bebert himself has devised a name for this technique. He calls it *virazeou* — a Provençal word that is incomprehensible unless one is familiar with the melodious accents of the South of France, but which Bebert assures us means merely "turn-turn." In any case, thanks to Bebert's virazeou, my morale is much better. This technique — which Bebert has tested on dolphins and grampuses — is fairly simple. He takes out a Zodiac, and with the outboard motor running wide open, he circles around a sperm whale, and circles, and circles. . . The whale finally is enclosed in a circle of noise and bubbles from the Zodiac's wake. His initial reaction seems to be one of annoyance, but he is quickly confused by the noise and the wake. Little by little, he becomes quiet, as though in a stupor.

Sperm whales, like all cetaceans, are creatures with very highly developed hearing. It is likely that the wall of sound with which Falco surrounds him becomes unbearable. Apparently, he reacts much in the same way to the disturbance caused by the Zodiac's wake. In any case, the whale slows, almost stops; and, for the first time in our efforts to approach these giants, we have gained an advantage.

The whale could, no doubt, have chosen to dive, to disappear into the depths in order to elude his tormentors. But he seems paralyzed by the technique of virazeou. I say "seems" paralyzed. For the first time that Falco tried it, we learned otherwise. All seemed to be going well. The Zodiac was circling, the noise was deafening, the water was boiling from the motor's wake, and the sperm whale was lying almost still in the water, just below the surface. Then there was a sudden, monstrous movement in the water. We saw the Zodiac and its passengers thrown up into the air like toys, while the motor, the cameras, and other equipment were all spilled into the sea.

The Zodiac fell back right side up, and Maurice Leandri, who was in the stern, was thrown overboard by the force of the impact, but he succeeded in climbing back aboard.

What had happened was very simple. The whale, whom we thought to be "in a stupor," had tired of the noise and the bubbles, and with one twist of its tail it had sent the Zodiac and all its occupants flying into the air. He could have done much worse. He could have attacked with his great mouth, or crushed the craft and its men with one casual stroke of his tail. Instead, he chose to give a "measured response," but an effective one. And then he continued on his way very calmly, as though the incident were already forgotten.

This power that is so sure of itself, and that little resembles the malevolent aggressiveness of a Moby Dick, is undoubtedly one of the advantages of being a giant. When one is sixty feet long and preternaturally strong, what is there to fear? In my opinion, the so-called "ferocity" of whales, and of sperm whales in particular, is a characteristic invented by man to justify his butchery of the species. Certainly, in our experience with whales, there has been not the slightest sign of any inclination to aggressive violence.

A Delicate Giant

The most striking characteristic of the great whale is its fragility. For its life, its strength, and its effectiveness as a life form, it depends entirely upon the sea. Out of the water, it has no hope of survival. A whale aground in the open air, washed up on a beach, is condemned to death. He has not the

One of the hammerhead sharks that has come to join the school of dolphins.

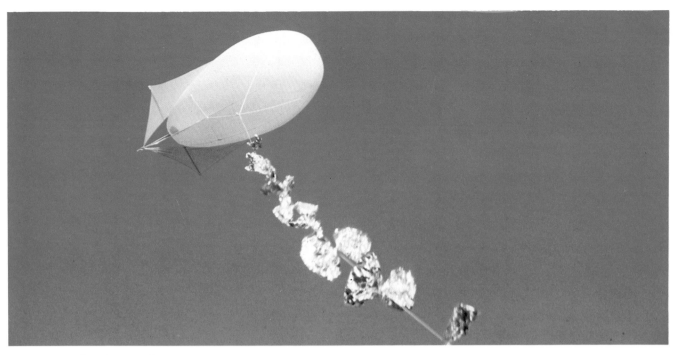

Our kytoon, inflated with hydrogen, is decorated with aluminum butterflies so that we can pick it up on radar.

strength, nor the limbs, to regain the life-giving water. He smothers; and it is his very size and mass that kills him. All of his power, great though it is, is not sufficient to fill his lungs, to move the tons of blubber that cover his body. And he dies of asphyxiation.

The reason for this relative dependency and delicacy goes back far in

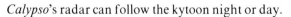

Calypso's radar can follow the kytoon night or day.

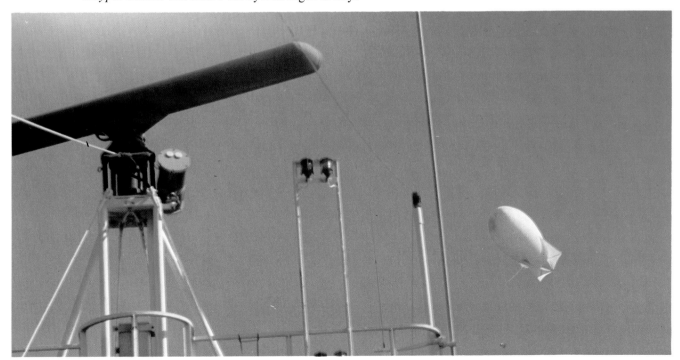

geological time into the Miocene era. Whales first appeared in the Tertiary Era, about 25 million years ago, although their ancestry goes back much farther than that. They were at first land animals — a fact that paleontologists no longer contest. Before becoming lords of the sea, they held a more modest position on dry land. Unfortunately, no one has ever found a fossil trace of the ancestor of whales who walked the earth on four feet; and this point is the only doubtful one in the theory. On the other hand, a good number of complete whale skeletons have been discovered, in fossil form, which are anatomically very close to land mammals. They were considerably smaller than the cachalots and finback whales of today, measuring no more than 18 or 20 feet in length.

The skeleton of the present-day whale shows traces of its land-bound ancestors. There are rudimentary femurs and tibia, and the remains of a pelvic girdle, all surrounded by muscle and not connected to the spine. Moreover, the skeleton of the pectoral fins reveals that the front limbs that are now modified into flippers were once endowed with five fingers. The tail fin is not like that of the Pinnipedia (seals, walruses, and related forms), which evolved from the lower members of a terrestrial ancestor, but is a member found only among cetaceans and *Sirenia* (e.g., the mantee and the dugong).

In its long past, Earth has known creatures of enormous size, particularly in the Secondary Era, when monstrous reptiles roamed the continents — the Diplodocus, the Brontosaurus, the Brachiosaurus, the Gigantosaurus. These were the largest beasts that ever lived on land. But none of them ever approached the 130 tons of the blue whale. None of them, it appears, ever exceeded 30 or 35 tons, for the length of their bodies, though considerable, included a disproportionately long neck and tail, and thereby reduced the weight per foot of length.

These earth-bound giants were reptiles, not mammals. They dominated the life forms of earth during the Secondary Era, which is therefore called (justly) the Age of Reptiles. But, even so, their size and weight compelled them to spend their lives in the water, or at the edge of the water, for a huge amount of energy was required merely to move, on land, a mass of flesh and bone weighing 30 tons. Only in the water could a living being of such size be spared the necessity of using every ounce of its energy to move from place to place.

Among the great Sauria of the Jurassic age, a few species seem to have attained the length of the modern whale — that is, 60 to 75 feet — and still managed to exist on land. The explanation, however, is that, even though they equaled the whale in length, their body mass was much smaller — at most one fourth that of the whale. Nonetheless, a few species — the Brontosaurus, for example — still chose to live in the water; and, for that reason, its nostrils were on top of its head, as are the blowholes of the whale today.

Obviously, for these enormous quadrupeds to be able to move, it was necessary that they have enormous legs. It has been calculated that if an elephant weighed twice as much as it actually does, its feet would have to be so big that they would be wider than the elephant's body. But an elephant weighs only three to six tons — which is the approximate weight of the tongue of some whales. So, one can imagine what sort of legs and feet an animal like the Brontosaurus had.

Dinosaurs disappeared from the face of the earth with a suddenness that has always mystified paleontologists. It is possbile that their very gigantism was the cause of their downfall, for size entails numerous and important disadvantages. In any case, the giants of the Secondary Era were, so to speak, one of Nature's mistake — a mistake that was not perpetuated. Or, at least Nature was able to correct her mistake by transferring her giants to the sea and allowing them to become extinct on dry land.

The problems faced by these enormous monsters on land were virtually insoluble. And movement was not the only such problem. Even breathing was a great effort. To open its thoracic cage, which meant raising a part of its body, a creature of this size had to make an effort that presupposed extraordinarily powerful muscles and a skeleton constructed in a peculiar manner. And this is the reason why a whale out of water, even though it is an air breather, dies very quickly. Despite its incredible power, it simply does not have sufficient strength to breathe in the open air. Its skeleton is not capable of sustaining the weight of its muscles and blubber in the air, although it serves very well in the dense medium of water. On one occasion, we took a whale calf out of the water in order to nurse it, and it was necessary to place its body on a stretcher, or litter. Otherwise, its very weight would have caused even its relatively small body to "collapse."

Another problem faced by the great reptiles of the Secondary Era was that of food. In order to nourish a body such as that of the Brontosaurus, a very large amount of food was necessary. Even an elephant consumes between three and four hundred kilos of food every day. But the Brontosaurus was almost incapable of consuming what was needed, for the reason that its head was ridiculously small in proportion to its body. A beast weighing 30 tons, with a head the size of that of a horse, obviously must eat without stopping if it is not to die of malnutrition.

Both baleen whales and toothed whales have no problem in this respect, since they all have enormous heads and mouths to match. The baleen whales,

The head of the finback whale seen in the water was a pleasant surprise for us.

since they have no teeth, nourish themselves by straining millions of tiny sea animals through the rows of whalebone (baleen) hanging from their upper jaws. This requires no particular effort on their part. They simply swim with their mouths open, collecting their prey on the whalebone plates while the water runs to waste.

Pursuit is more complicated, and more arduous, in the case of the sperm whale, which has teeth in its lower jaw. This whale's natural prey includes the giant squid that live near the bottom of the sea, at depths of 1500 feet and over. In this case, the whale's size is a considerable advantage. One can imagine the amount of energy that is necessary for that massive body to propel

A finback whale's huge tail—with two divers above it.

itself to the bottom for a combat to the death with a squid that may measure more than thirty feet from tip to tip.

The size and power of whales make them monarchs of the sea. But are they monarchs without enemies? That is a moot point. Certainly, man has long preyed on whales, and even on the very largest species, such as the blue whale and the finback whale. The Basques, those early hunters of whales, pursued and killed so many right whales *(Eubalaena glacialis)* — which are particularly vulnerable because of their lack of speed (three knots) — that the species became virtually extinct along their shores.

Until the nineteenth century, however, man's career as a killer of whales was limited by the relatively primitive means of pursuit and slaughter at his command — ships propelled by sails or oars, hand winches, flimsy ropes, and hand-thrown harpoons. At this time, size was a decided advantage to a whale, for man could attack and kill only the smaller specimens. With the invention of the harpoon gun in 1864, however, the balance of power shifted. Man was now able to hunt any whale, regardless of its size; and gigantism was no longer an advantage.

But man is not the whale's only enemy. It has foes in the water as well as on land, and, among these, the most formidable is one of its relatives, the killer whale* — also known as the orc *(Grampus orca)*. The killer whale is a toothed relative of the sperm whale. It is smaller than either the baleen whale or the sperm whale, but what it lacks in size it makes up for in ferocity and in strength, and particularly in its almost diabolical intelligence. Traveling in schools, these killers do not hesitate to attack even the largest baleens.

The Ideal Solution: A Balloon

April 13. At seven o' clock in the morning we set sail toward Shab-Arab, but following a deep curve toward the end of the gulf. We do not hold to that course for very. long, for, very soon, three white whales are sighted about twenty-five yards off the starboard. They are perhaps Belugas, or "white whales." We bring *Calypso* around, but are unable to locate these mammals. Then the alarm bell rings again. Sperm whales! It is incredible what one can find in the Gulf of Aden at this time of the year.

*Chapter Ten is devoted to the killer whale.

(Following page) A diver has just jumped out of the Zodiac and is about to climb onto the finback whale's head.

The pursuit of the whales begins rather badly. Rather than risk losing sight of them, I decide to try to approach them with *Calypso* while the Zodiacs are being launched. Falco therefore has to fire his harpoon from a greater distance than usual. It is a hit — but the harpoon slides off the slippery flank, taking a piece of the whale's skin with it.

Meanwhile, Bonnici is out in the Zodiac and has succeeded in reaching a group of three whales. He manages to isolate a young whale for a few minutes; but the calf's parents will have none of this, and they quickly position themselves to either side of their offspring and lead him away.

We continue trying, in vain, until early afternoon. Then, at two o' clock, there is a new alert. A very young cachalot calf has been sighted, swimming alongside its mother. As *Calypso* approaches, she is sighted by the calf — who leaves its mother's side and makes straight for the ship! I order the engines to be cut immediately. It is just in time, for no sooner have the propellers stopped revolving than the baby whale is contentedly swimming along right next to the hull. The whale mother follows its calf and remains at a cautious distance from *Calypso*, but close enough to be able to protect her baby if there should be any sign of danger.

The Zodiac goes out in an attempt to mark the mother with a light harpoon, but she seems to suspect our intentions and quickly swims away. The calf then joins its mother, and together they return to the school and we lose sight of them.

Immediately after dinner, I have a meeting with Bebert, Laban, Dumas, and Marcellin to discuss our situation. We all feel that we must have more time for whales, and so we decide to abandon our plans for Shab-Arab and devote three additional days to the pursuit of the sperm whale.

When my four friends are gone, I remain alone in my cabin to reflect a bit on our problems. And then, surprisingly, a solution occurs to me: a kytoon!* In other words we will no longer simply attach a buoy to the whale, but a balloon — something that will not merely float on the surface but actually rise into the air. This balloon will be much easier to see from *Calypso*, and especially from the Zodiacs; and we can attach a bit of aluminum to it so that we can pick it up at night on radar.

April 14. Simone is absolutely inexhaustible. She is like a worker bee in a hive. She is not only in charge of our food supply and of the wardroom, but she is spending more and more time on watch for whales. And when she is in the crow's-nest, nothing gets by her. I hope that her luck holds out; I am very eager to try out the kytoon.

* *Kytoon,* for all its exotic appearance, is a term composed from two English words: *kite,* and *balloon.*

The Beauty of the Finback.

Our first sighting on April 14 was not a sperm whale, but a rorqual, or finback whale*, which, after the blue whale, is the largest of the cetaceans. Here are my journal notes for that day:

Early this morning we sighted a large school of dolphins very near to *Calypso*. And, swimming around in the middle of the school, were a large number of hammerhead sharks!

During the morning, we sailed around Cape Guardafui, at the entrance to the Gulf of Aden. After having watched our two Zodiacs cavort with three schools of dolphins for a while, we heard Bebert yell: "A whale! Leave the dolphins alone, and let's go!"

The sea is very calm, and the Zodiacs are able to get up to 15 knots of speed. For two hours, they pursue the whale — a finback, apparently, between 35 and 45 feet long. Speed is absolutely necessary, of course, because the whale stays on the surface for only a short time — long enough to breathe; and then it dives and stays out of sight for ten to twenty minutes at a time. Finally, exhausted by the chase, it slows down, and it begins surfacing at shorter intervals.

Experienced whalers have no difficulty in distinguishing between the sperm whale and the finback because of the sperm whale's oblique spout. For us, however, there is a much easier way: the dorsal fin of the finback whale is large and hooked, while the only protrusion from the sperm whale's back is a sort of low and irregular crest about two thirds of the way down its length. One can also distinguish between the two species by the way they dive. The sperm whale goes straight down, so that the last thing we see before it disappears is its tail protruding from the water; but the finback whale dives at an angle. Moreover, sperm whales seem usually to travel in schools; and our finback whale appears to be alone. Apparently, they travel singly, or in groups of two or three.

Bebert's Zodiac is now in place, almost against the whale's blue-gray flank. He fires, and hits his target. The whale bolts — and we watch the harpoon line unwind at 15 knots. When the 1500 feet of polypropylene are gone, there remain another thousand feet of blue nylon line, which unwind with astonishing speed. We will soon know if the harpoon will hold.

---

* In order not to encumber the text with descriptions of the characteristics of the various species of whales, we have relegated such information to the appendices and glossary. The reader is referred especially to Appendix I for the essential distinction between baleen or whalebone whales (Mystacoceti) and toothed whales (Odontoceti).

Bebert has returned to *Calypso* and begins to secure the Zodiac when, suddenly, the harpoon line goes slack. The harpoon has not held.

Everyone is disappointed, even disheartened. But that does not keep us from getting back to work immediately. As the cameramen's Zodiac and *Calypso* continue the chase, Bebert rewinds his 2500 feet of line and reloads the harpoon gun. By the time we are within sight of the whale again, he is ready. He raises the gun, fires, and hits the whale — but the spear does not penetrate its blubber. He grabs the rubber crossbow and fires — but the steel bowstring breaks. Finally, he picks up the old-fashioned hand harpoon.

By now, the whale is tired and has slowed to eight knots. It can be seen clearly from the Zodiac, only a few feet beneath the surface. And Falco's craft approaches it easily when it rises to the surface to breathe as Bonnici, in his Zodiac, blocks the animal's way. (Bonnici's part is not as easy as it sounds. When he cut in front of the whale after it had surfaced, its great triangular tail struck the water only inches from his boat.) As soon as Falco is close enough, he fires and sticks the finback in the left flank. The spearhead penetrates — but the handle of the spear bends like a straw as soon as the whale dives. It bends — but holds. Falco allows 1500 feet of the line to run, and then he attaches a large red buoy to it. The preceding four hours' work has been only a preliminary. Now, the chase begins in earnest, with Laban and Deloire in the water shooting footage of the whale swimming by and Barsky filming from the surface. Aboard *Calypso*, we are busy making notes on everything that the whale does.

The finback is evidently bothered by the Zodiacs buzzing around her like mosquitoes. And, in view of its size, Falco's little harpoon has about the same effect as a moquito bite. It is constantly changing direction. The two Zodiacs keep the whale between them, with the cameramen on the right and the divers on the left. They jump into the water ahead of the animal and film it as it swims past. The whale is breathing very frequently now, about every fifteen seconds. Despite the heat and the dry air, the vapor of its spout can be seen from a distance.

Late in the afternoon, the cameramen's Zodiac returns to *Calypso*. Falco is already aboard, preparing the kytoon for use. The balloon is filled with hydrogen, and to its top is attached an aluminum butterfly to serve as a radar guide. Then the entire apparatus is attached to the buoy by means of a line.

As this is going on, another ship, no doubt attracted by the kytoon floating in the air, has been drawing nearer and nearer to the whale. *Calypso* diverts her by means of a few maneuvers.

Marcellin and Dumas take their sound equipment and, in one of the Zodiacs, follow the whale very closely. One of their tricks is to hang a

In pursuit of two gray whales, who have a bagful of tricks for getting away from curious humans.

microphone at the end of a pole and hold it over the whale's blowholes. We are rewarded by a tape of the whale breathing — like a series of muffled cannon shots.

This finback whale is truly an exceptional subject. Exceptional, first of all, because of its size, for it is larger than any of the sperm whales that we have seen on this expedition. It is also more handsome, with its marvelous head (which appears rather serpentine when the mouth is closed), and with a body less massive than that of the sperm whale. There is no neck discernible. Altogether, it is a perfect body from the viewpoint of hydrodynamics, and a graceful and elegant one. Its color is also lighter, more silky and "luxurious" than the sperm whale's.

Aboard *Calypso*, everyone is delighted with "our" whale. It is the consensus that finbacks are much more easily approachable than cachalots. This, no doubt, has something to do with the fact that this particular whale is traveling alone. It does not belong to a group from which it would be unwilling to be separated.

"There seems to be only one thing that sperm whales want," Michel Deloire, says, "and that is to get away from us so that they can rejoin their school. They would even push us aside in order to get back to their friends. Our whale, however, is much more casual about the whole thing. She seems to have all the time in the world, and has no appointment to keep with her friends. And, aside from that, this whale is a truly remarkable animal; ten times, or a hundred times, more beautiful than a sperm whale. I could swear that, with its flat head, it looks as though it is always smiling. If you see a finback directly from the front, it looks like one big smile — as though there were something friendly about it, or as though it has a sense of humor. In fact, this whale of ours is the only animal I have ever seen that really astonishes me."

During the night, a duty team remains in the Zodiac to keep an eye on the buoy and the kytoon. Naguy has installed a blinking light on the kytoon so that it is easily visible. All through the hours of darkness, we were aware of what the whale was doing. At times, she halted completely. And sometimes she would sprint forward at six or seven knots.

Saturday, May 13. Today we have organized our time so as to be able to take advantage, as much as possible, of our whale's presence. At dawn, Barsky and Deloire are at work taking pictures of the kytoon and *Calypso.* This is followed by underwater photographs of the whale, using the same technique with the Zodiacs as yesterday. That is, the Zodiac pursues the whale. The whale dives, reappears slightly to the north, and begins swimming eastward. All this Deloire films from a Zodiac with an underwater camera. Barsky is in the other Zodiac with a regular camera.

Everything is going very well. Too well, I suspect, for it to last. And, sure enough, the unforeseeable occurs. The finback executes a half turn around one of the Zodiacs and the harpoon line becomes entangled in the propeller blades of one of the Zodiacs. An extraordinary scene follows: the whale dives, and begins dragging the Zodiac down with it. One can imagine how much power is required to submerge a large inflatable raft like the Zodiac! Fortunately, Falco, with great presence of mind, knows exactly what to do. In an instant, just as the Zodiac is beginning to go down, he quickly hands all the cameras and equipment to the other Zodiac and then cuts the line. The whale is now free — but the alternative would have been to lose the Zodiac.

Perhaps yesterday we were guilty of a bit of anthropomorphism in describing our whale as "friendly." Obviously, she cares very little for us; and right now, no doubt, she is swimming merrily on her way without giving the slightest thought to us.

Falco, however, is more faithful than his whale. As soon as the line is untangled from the Zodiac's propeller, he sets out in hot pursuit — and succeeds in implanting another harpoon. We are back where we started yesterday, as *Calypso* follows as best she can the gyrations and maneuvers of Zodiacs and whale.

Deloire, taking no chances, is now using his Tegea in the water, and the results are sensational. For the first time, a finback has been observed and filmed under the surface. It is a great moment for Michel. Also for Bonnici, who has jumped into the water, latched onto the whale's dorsal fin, and is being towed as by some nightmarish locomotive. Another first! And Barsky, not to be outdone, joins in the fun and films Bonnici's acrobatic exploits.

Laban and Bebert, meanwhile, are in the water with their still cameras. The results show a long, supple body. At one point, they were so close that they saw an enormous eye staring at them from only three feet away.

Late in the afternoon, Barsky's Zodiac starts back to *Calypso* — and once more the harpoon line becomes entangled in its propeller. This time, Falco is taking no chances. He cuts the line immediately and Barsky — by now standing on *Calypso*'s deck — films our farewell to the valorous finback as it swims away on our portside, as indifferent to us as ever (or at least so we think).

After dinner, Bebert, Dumas, Laban, and the cameramen meet to go over their shots and sequences and to determine what remains to be done. "The finback," Laban says, "is more impressive than the sperm whale because it is bigger. This one must have been fifty feet long. And, for a diver, the sperm whale's big square head has something monstrous about it — it makes up almost a third of the whale's body. It looks like someone made a mistake in judging proportions, and then gave up before finishing the job. But that well-shaped and handsome finback head — that comes as a pleasant surprise when you are used to sperm whales."

The finback whale's apparent gentleness is also in its favor. Regardless of whether or not it is naturally gentle, the fact remains that it cannot really bite, since it has no teeth. The divers took advantage of this to the extent that they approached the finback more freely, and treated it more familiarily, than they would have a cachalot. They were not deterred, as they always are in dealing with sperm whales, by the sight of those great teeth gleaming in the water. Even so, the finback is not a helpless creature. It has a weapon, and a terrible weapon, for use against sharks and killer whales: the enormous flukes of its tail — what Bebert calls its "fly swatter." This fly swatter is capable of crushing a man with one blow.

"As long as you stay in front of the animal," Deloire says, "there is nothing to be afraid of. Its front part is not frightening at all. Once half of its body has swum past you, though, you must begin to be careful, and remember that you move more slowly in the water than on land. When you see that huge tail waving in the water and covering a large area of it, it's time to get out of the way. Otherwise, it's like being hit with a ton of bricks."

Humpback Whales and Gray Whales.

All whales do not look alike in the water. There are differences, even among the giants. Finback whales, as we just observed, are enormous — and indifferent. Humpback whales — such as we already filmed in Bermuda — are endowed with a suppleness and a grace that are reminiscent simultaneously of a swallow and a Boeing 707. Their flippers are white and very long and, in the water, look like wings. The humpback uses them to turn. These whales do not swim, like the finback, in a straight line. And, unlike sperm whales, they are easily approachable and sometimes brush against divers as they swim around, turning and circling back, probing with their long cylindrical heads and slightly receding chins. What the humpback whale does not have, however, is a humped back. They got the name from their practice of showing the napes of their necks and their backs when they dive.

It should come as no surprise that our divers have favorites among the different species of whales. They have lived with whales, and they found some species disappointing; and others, delightful and admirable.

The whale that our team has the greatest affection for is the gray whale of California, with whom we lived for several months.

"The first time I saw a gray whale," Philippe Cousteau says, "I jumped into a Zodiac and grabbed a camera. As soon as I was in front of the whale, I dived into the water — forgetting to put on my diving equipment. I practically landed on top of it, but it didn't seem a bit disturbed, and didn't try to turn away. I could see, somewhat fuzzily, its immense mouth — a mouth unlike any that I had ever seen before. And then I saw its body as it swam past me. Its movements seemed incomparably supple; they were not separate motions, but one beautifully co-ordinated action. I was struck by the hydrodynamic perfection of its power, by its invincibility . . . It disappeared, finally, because I simply could not swim fast enough to keep up with even its casual pace. I climbed back into the Zodiac and put on my mask, and then dived again. But the spell had been broken. I had to worry about the camera, about angles, about my breathing equipment; I could no longer give myself over

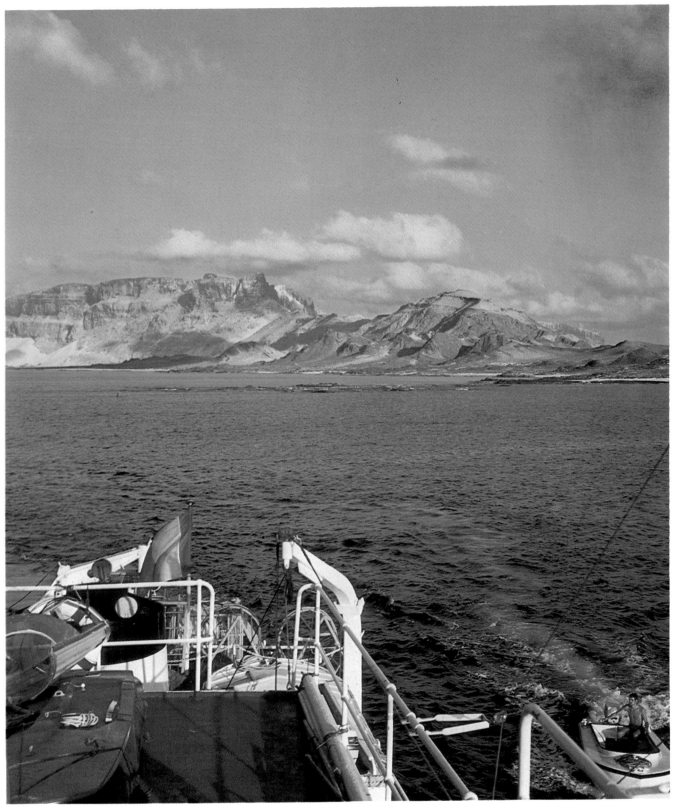

The bleak mountains of the African coast around Cape Guardafui. *Calypso*'s aft is in the foreground.

entirely to the feeling of admiration. But, for a brief time there, it had seemed that whale and I had reached a perfect understanding."

Approaching a whale *beneath* the surface of the water — that is, while diving — is very different from doing so on the surface. Zodiacs, spearguns, and buoys no doubt have an effect upon an animal's reaction to man, even though we do not know exactly what that effect is. We do know, however, that whenever we approach a whale in his own element, without such apparatus and equipment, we experience a feeling of understanding, or sympathy, or empathy.

Philippe states categorically that he has never encountered a whale that showed the slightest sign of hostility. But then, we must add that no whale encountered by Philippe had just been harpooned, even by a light spear such as that used by Bebert. (Understandably, Philippe dislikes the idea of "marking" whales. At Bermuda, for example, he was strongly opposed to our doing so to the humpback whales we saw there.)

"I could swear that they know how weak we are," Philippe says. "One stroke of the tail, or of a fin, or a bump with the head — that would be it as far as a man is concerned. But they've never done anything like that. The impression I've always gotten is one of extraordinary gentleness. They usually try to avoid us, but when they swim away they move slowly, gently — not suddenly, the way that fish do. . ."

It is not impossible that there is an element of sexuality in a whale's behavior. Once, Philippe encountered a gray whale who was behaving rather strangely, swimming back and forth and turning over on her back. She was obviously not pregnant, but her sexual organs were turgid, inflamed, she was possibly "in heat." Perhaps she was hoping for sexual contact with these strange new forms of marine life — the diver, or the Zodiac. (We have recorded the same phenomenon with Dolly the Dolphin, whose sexual appetites were, to say the least, obvious.)

In any event, I can say that, in these underwater encounters, there exists an element of attraction to one living being from another, from one mammal to another. Despite the great difference in size between man and whale, we are not indifferent to one another.

THREE

When Whales Travel

Whales love to travel. A very strong instinct leads them to winter in equatorial seas, where the water is warm, and to summer in the arctic and antarctic regions.

Whalers used to take advantage of these migratory habits to attack schools of whales, and succeeded in slaughtering large numbers of the animals. Despite this contact, we know very little about the details of these migrations or about the behavior of cetaceans while traveling thousands of miles through the oceans.

It was our intention to follow the whales and, making use of every means at our disposal, to get as close to them as possible — not only with our Zodiacs, but by diving among them — and to film them.

The gray whales of California, who leave the Arctic in January for a southward migration to Baja California, where they mate and give birth, seemed to us to offer a splendid opportunity for the observation of whales in migration.

Here is a transcript of Bernard Delemotte's account of one of the most

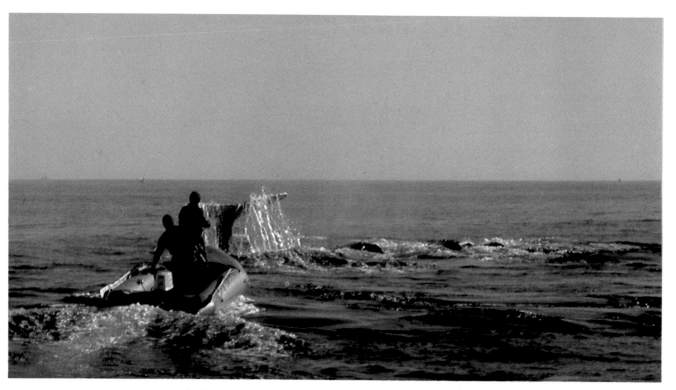

A gray whale tries to elude its pursuers by diving.

dramatic episodes of this three-month expedition to the Pacific:

"*January 23, 1968.* It is 2 P.M. The Zodiac is in the water and the cameras are in place on their foam-rubber pads. Yves Omer is our cameraman on this occasion. He has already suited up and taken his place in the Zodiac, on the portside, ready to grab his camera and dive at a moment's notice. Falco is all the way forward.

"We set out after our subject, a large gray whale who, unfortunately, is swimming very fast. So much the worse for us. We must still try; for in two hours there will no longer be enough light for underwater filming.

"We manage to keep up with the whale by maintaining a speed of five or six knots, and then accelerating whenever she comes up to breathe. Yves has already been over the side three times, but conditions have not really been ideal. In order to get full shots of the animal's head, we have to time ourselves almost to the split second. If the diver goes down too soon, the whale turns aside to avoid him; and if he dives too late, the film will show only the body and tail.

"We have decided not to dive from the Zodiac unless we are absolutely certain of our timing, even if this means missing a few opportunities offered by the whale's surfacing.

"The chase continues. Very exciting — despite the fact that, whenever we hit a wave, it is like running into a stone wall. Each time the whale surfaces, we are in a slightly better position. Now, we are only 150 feet away.

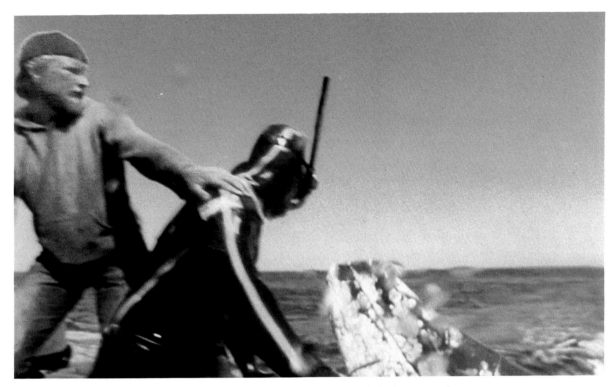

An accident: the gray whale charges the Zodiac while Bernard Delemotte tries to protect Yves Omer by pulling him toward the rear.

"She surfaces, and I speed up, We are almost even with her. She dives — but we can still see her. She can't be more than 25 or 30 feet beneath the surface, and we can make out the movements of her enormous body.

"Bebert Falco, from his vantage point forward, can see her better than I. He guides me by gestures so that the Zodiac can remain directly above her. Yves already has the camera in his hand, for the whale will have to come back to the surface to breathe at any moment now. And we intend to be there when she does.

"She is quite obviously bothered by the Zodiac's engine noise. She turns first to the right, then to the left. She speeds up, then slows down. Thanks to Bebert's sharp eyes, I am able to keep the Zodiac directly over her. Now the whale seems to be rising. I cut the motor and immediately Yves Omer is over the side, camera clutched in his hand.

"Then I hear Bebert's yell: 'Watch out ! . . .'

"But it is already too late, I hear an incredible sound, like a giant waterfall. Is it the whale spouting? Is it merely the water that she is displacing as she breaks the surface?

"I see a gigantic, monstrous head above the water, only ten or twelve feet from the Zodiac and looming up over it. Then I see a great black mass rising next to the boat, and, somewhere between me and the whale's body, I catch a glimpse of one of Yves's legs. . .

"I never did figure out exactly what caused the roar of water that I heard.

The next thing I knew, the whale's body had struck the Zodiac and Omer and I were both thrown violently into the water. I could tell from the water pressure in my ears that we were going down, deep.

"I knew that I was still alive, and I had my eyes wide open. But all I could see was blackness. I tried to swim, but, somehow, I could not move a muscle. I was squashed flat against a living wall of flesh. Against my left cheek, I could feel soft skin. I was pinned against the whale's body. But that was only on one side of me. I was being held there — by what?

"I realized what must have happened. The Zodiac and I had gone down together; and we were both trying to get to the surface at the same time and from the same place. I was trapped beneath the Zodiac and the whale's stomach.

"My first reaction was one of anger. I was furious to think that, after surviving a head-on collision with a whale, I might drown because an inflatable raft was holding me *under* the whale.

"Then, suddenly, my arms and legs were free. I kicked, and began to move. I rose straight up, as though I were climbing a ladder. It seemed to take forever, and I needed desperately to breathe.

"Finally, my head was above the surface, and I heard a yell: 'My leg, my leg!' It was Yves. He had been hooked to the Zodiac by a line, and had risen to the surface with it. But now he was thrashing around about thirty feet from the Zodiac, entangled in pieces of clothing and a coil of line.

"I yelled back, 'Hold on, I'm coming!' I grabbed his hand with one of mine and, with the other, pulled myself onto the Zodiac. Then I helped him climb aboard. All the while, I avoided looking at his legs. I was afraid to see one of them crushed. . . or missing. Fortunately, it was not nearly that bad. At the moment of impact, Yves's leg was caught between the whale and the Zodiac; but it was an inflatable section of the Zodiac, and the air had cushioned the leg somewhat. Even so, it was quite a blow; but there seemed to be no broken bones.

"Bebert had been just a bit more lucky. He had had time to jump overboard — but he had forgotten that he was also tied to the Zodiac by a harness. He had been dragged along for about sixty feet, until the snap hook had broken because of the violence of the traction.

"The second Zodiac soon picked us up and towed us back to *Calypso*. Our friends, somewhat pale, were waiting for us on deck. They had been able to see everything that was happening in the water, while we had been otherwise occupied. They saw the whale leap out of the water and fall back with an immense splash. When the water had calmed, they said, there was nothing to be seen on the surface. No whale, no Zodiac, and no men. At least fifteen

Canoë Kientzy, ready for a dive.

Bernard Delemotte, Philippe Cousteau, and Jacques Renoir during our stay with the gray whales.

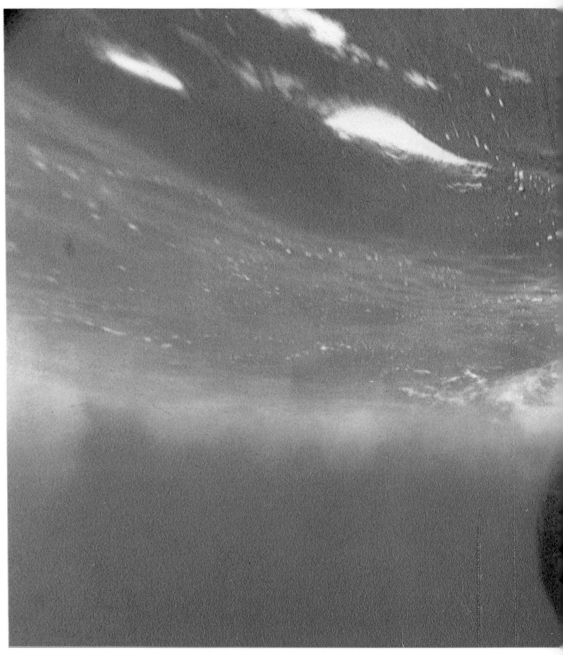

A diver has succeeded in grabbing onto the tail of a finback whale.

seconds had passed before the Zodiac reappeared, 150 feet away from where it had gone down. Then one head appeared above the surface. Then another. And then another.

"We are being very offhand about the whole thing, but we are all rather shaken.

"The final tally shows that Yves Omer has a dislocated knee. The Zodiac: an inflatable section has been ripped off and punctured, the flooring has been reduced to kindling, and the gas tank has been smashed flat."

The Salvation of a Species

One may gather from Bernard's account that whale chasing is not always a safe occupation. Up until then, the whales we encountered had always seemed rather gentle; but, on this occasion in the Pacific, we were dealing with gray whales.

At the beginning of 1968, my son Philippe had heard some talk about these gray whales, *Eschrichtius glaucus.* This species, threatened with extinction during the nineteenth century and at the beginning of the twentieth, is now protected by international agreement. The measures taken have been so effective that the species is now flourishing — so much so that, in the past few years, hunting permits have been issued for 600 gray whales. The total number of these whales, worldwide, is estimated at 20,000 specimens.

Gray whales winter in the Arctic, feeding on plankton off the Siberian coast, in the Bering Sea, and in the waters of Korea and northern California. In winter, they migrate to the warm waters of Baja California, off the Mexican coast.

Since gray whales swim close in along the California coast, their migrations have been observed more carefully than those of other species. And there are always crowds of people who gather to do so. It is known as the "Moby Dick Parade," and it is undoubtedly the best free show On the West Coast: 40, 50, and sometimes 75 whales a day swim by on their way to Baja California.

In San Diego, interested persons have formed an association for the conservation and defense of the species, and also to lead them back out to sea when they lose their way inside a port.

"Whale watchers" follow the course of the migration with great interest from watch towers, and help the whales whenever help is needed.

Gray whales migrate southward for a well-defined reason: some of them are going to mate, and others are going to give birth, in the shallow, warm water of the Mexican lagoons. In the nineteenth century, whalers — and particularly one Captain Charles Melville Scammon, who discovered the secret of the gray whales' destination — slaughtered many of these animals. But, since the species has been protected, both males and females have returned in large numbers to these sheltered lagoons. And it was there that we hoped to be able to observe them at close quarters.

Our rendezvous, it seemed to us, could be scheduled in advance, for one could almost set a clock by the gray whales' migratory schedule. On the same date of any given year, they are always at the same spot. And they always pass through the Bering Straits on the same day.

Philippe Reconnoiters

In February 1967, Philippe was in San Diego on the first leg of his reconnaissance of the gray whales. At that time, *Calypso* was in the Indian Ocean, and unavailable. Philippe therefore rented a Cessna. He then invited Wally Green, and Professor Ted Walker, a specialist in gray whales, to accompany him on a flight down the West Coast to Mexico.

Philippe's primary interest in this flight was to determine whether, and where, we could film the gray whales. In that respect, he gathered much useful data. It was too late in the migratory season, however, to mount an expedition to follow the whales, and Philippe concentrated on finding the lagoon in Baja California that seemed to be the most promising for observation and filming of the whales.

When his work was done, Philippe joined us aboard *Calypso* in the Indian Ocean, and he quickly persuaded me that it would be worth our while to organize an expedition the next year in order to film the gray whales of California. His enthusiasm was contagious.

We first planned to follow the whales from the time they reached San Diego, in January, during their migration southward. But *Calypso*'s heavy schedule made it impossible for her to be in San Diego at that time. I therefore decided to rent another boat, *Polaris III* — a small boat that seemed adequate for the expedition — and to turn the project over to Philippe.

It Begins

The *Polaris III* left San Diego on January 16, 1968. Aboard with the regular team was Ted Walker, a gray-bearded scholar with a passionate interest in whales, who was to be of great help.

The migrating whales were traveling in small groups, and generally were swimming in water not over 650 feet deep. The *Polaris III* was exactly on time, and it had no trouble in sighting many groups, all visible and recognizable by their spouts.

As soon as a group of whales realized that they had been seen, they all dived together. But this was a trick. While the group as a whole was making a 90 turn underwater, a solitary gray whale remained on the surface, directly in front of the *Polaris,* to lead the boat on a merry chase.

This strategem — which I do not find described in any of the accounts of the whalers — demonstrates an extraordinary amount of understanding and communication among the members of the group of whales. How else does one particular whale know that it is his responsibility to distract the pursuers while the other whales escape?

Even more surprising was the fact that this ruse was put into effect immediately, as though it had been rehearsed, or used, many times in the past.

Whales know more than one trick. It happened on one occasion that the decoy whale made a great show of diving and then reappearing to the rear of the *Polaris,* hoping no doubt to throw us even further off the track of the group. Sometimes, the whale would pop up to port, and then to starboard. There were many variations. It was by no means a fixed, invariable plan. The decoy whale's behavior seemed to be largely extemporized according to the requirements of the situation.

It seems to me that such varied behavior presupposes that whales are able, to a certain extent, to exchange abstract concepts, such as "left," "right," "up," and "down," and to communicate an order to maneuver — that is, to reverse their direction.

They Sleep, But Not Much

Faced with this new and clever species of whale, the *Polaris'* team had to start almost from scratch, forgetting what we had learned so painfully in 1967, in the Indian Ocean, about cachalots.

First of all, it must be said that no one ever succeeded in filming a gray

A gray whale spouts at the surface.

whale migrating toward Baja California. Every time a diver jumped into the water, the whale was somehow, and immediately, 35 or 45 feet away from him. It always takes about five seconds after a diver jumps into the water from the Zodiac for his mask to clear and for him to get his direction. And that is plenty of time for a gray whale to flick its tail and disappear, leaving the diver, to all appearances, alone in the sea.

The cruise down the California coast took a relatively long time. It took the *Polaris'* team a full month before they were able to mark a whale so as to slow her down and be able to track her during the migration. This particular whale was the source of some important data; for example:

That gray whales sleep in half-hour "naps," six or seven times a day;

That they swim all night long, without stopping;

That they eat while they are migrating — a fact that was in doubt up until then. There can be no mistake about it. When a whale starts swimming in circles in shallow water, where there is plankton on the surface, it is obvious that she is eating. It seems that the California coast has their favorite foods in abundance.

The tail of one of Matancitas Bay's gray whales.

To give an idea of the problems that Bernard Mestre's team encountered on this first gray-whale expedition, I would like to quote from the expedition's journal:

A Near Shipwreck

January 23. In the open sea off San Diego we have run into vast areas of kelp — that is, giant algae of the Pacific that measure no less than 65 feet in length. We have noticed that gray whales like to roll around in kelp, and there are two of them doing so at this moment.

We intend to film them, and we are very fortunate. The water is absolutely calm. A short distance away, we can see several spouts. The *Polaris* is proceeding at reduced speed. The Zodiacs are launched noiselessly and are rowed among the algae. Meanwhile, the whales are still rolling around, showing not the slightest intention of running away. This will be a great scene on film.

January 24. At 9 A.M. a whale passes under the *Polaris,* and every amateur cameraman on board is hanging over the railing.

Around 10 A.M. we begin pursuing an isolated whale swimming southward. Falco manages to sink a harpoon to which is attached a bag of fluorescein. The fluorescein will allow us to track the animal and even to know beforehand where she will surface. This is a new device that we are trying to perfect.

The whale's dives are becoming shorter and shorter: 35 seconds now. She is worried and nervous. Going past Minson Bay — a large beach near San Diego — we had a scare: we thought that she would go aground in 20 feet of water.

At a given moment, the Zodiac catches up to the whale's tail by going forward at full speed, and then cutting the motor and letting the boat's momentum carry it the last few feet. The men can see the whale below them in the water, 10 or 12 feet below the surface. She is almost absolutely still. Then, suddenly, she moves upward toward the Zodiac and turns on her side. Delemotte and his men can see her eye, which appears to be watching them. It even seems that there is a flicker of interest in that shining orb. Then she rises a few more feet until she is up against the Zodiac, as though to get a closer look at its occupants. Next, using her left flipper, which she has slipped under the Zodiac, she raises the craft, and the men, three feet out of the water — and then suddenly pulls away the flipper. The Zodiac comes crashing down; but the men foresaw the attack and lay down in the boat, and were able to keep from being thrown overboard. In fact, there is no damage at all.

Jacques Renoir, aboard the other Zodiac, was filming the whole spectacular scene.

January 25. We continued southward almost the whole night; and, at the first light of dawn, the *Polaris* was surrounded by whales!

About a mile to the south, we can see a whale jumping. At least once her entire body was out of the water.

We begin by pursuing a group of four whales, who react, as usual, in an apparently disorganized manner, This is around 8 A.M. and we hope that, by the end of the morning, we will have harpooned one of them.

The shoreline has changed its appearance considerably since yesterday. Then, we were sailing along an inhabited coast; but now the shore seems empty, desolate — but beautiful nonetheless. We must be in Mexican waters. The land seems flat, but directly in front of us are some islands, high out of the water, among which we will have to maneuver in order to follow our whales.

At 10 A.M. we notice a group of five whales in the water, swimming about in all directions, surfacing often, and showing their flippers more than they usually do. Ted Walker, stroking his salt-and-pepper beard, explains that they are probably trying to mate — "trying," he says, because it is not easy for whales to do so.

We try to get in closer and harpoon one of the females; but the animal shakes off the harpoon within ten seconds, after having twisted it into a pretzel.

We have often discussed why our harpoons always seem to become dislodged. Is it because the barbs are too short? Or too long? Yet, the harpoon does sink into the whale's blubber.

In this particular instance, the harpoon entered at an angle, and was probably pulled out by the traction of the water. After quick consultation, it is decided to continue using this type of harpoon and gun.

Philippe wants to try the harpoon himself, and we begin pursuing another group. (We have a wide selection to choose from.)

The sky is now cloudy, and the sea absolutely still. It will probably rain tonight. We are only about a quarter mile from shore, and a crowd of porpoises is accompanying us.

At 4 P.M. Philippe has his chance and throws the harpoon. It appears to be a miss, and the whales disappear. When we retrieve the harpoon, however, we see that it was not a miss at all. The head penetrated the whale's side, but then came out without the barbs being able to fasten into the whale's blubber. It is possible that the barbs are not spread out enough. It seems that we are jinxed.

An hour later, we see another group, this one with four whales, and we try to catch up with them. But it seems that we may have already tried this group. (How do you tell one group of gray whales from another?) In any case, they will not let us near them.

The *Polaris* is now in shallow water, over a rocky bottom. The Zodiac is close by. We are using sonar, and moving very slowly and carefully to avoid an accident on the rocks.

At 5:20 we are informed by radio that Canoë has shot a harpoon, but that the line caught in the Zodiac's propellor and was cut. Ted Walker says that a 40-hp motor is too loud and too fast, and so it is impossible to come to a quick stop — hence, today's accident.

January 26. This morning the weather is gray and chilly. There is a large swell from the southeast that sprang up during the night, and it is doing some minor damage — broken dishes, etc.

Several groups of whales are swimming in front of us at 170°.

We spent the night at anchor near a small island called Saint Martin. This island is inhabited by birds — millions of birds, especially pelicans and cormorants — and by a colony of sea lions. There are a few human residents, too: a few fishermen, who inhabit the end of the island where there are no birds or sea lions. It is an edifying example of peaceful coexistence.

Despite the unpleasant weather, Canoë scores a hit with his harpoon, and we see the red buoy bouncing along on the surface. But, once more, the line breaks — perhaps cut, this time, by barnacles, the parasites that attach themselves to the backs of gray whales and give them a mottled appearance.

We add 250 feet of new line and decide to try again. We pass within touching distance of a submerged bank where the water is only five feet deep. It is easy to tell where these are: there are breakers.

Thousands of birds are perched on a tiny spot of land in the water. When they see us, they take wing with a deafening screech.

The Hand Harpoon

We follow a group of five whales, and then a group of three. It is a fine shot — but the harpoon does not hold. Everyone on board, all the harpooners or aspirant harpooners, vow never again to use our Norwegian harpoon gun — or, at least, never again today. It is decided that we will use the good old

(Right) A diver exploring the kelp forest off San Diego Cape.

hand harpoon that nineteenth-century whalers used. We have one aboard the *Polaris.*

Ted Walker who, I believe, has never run across such a totally committed team, is very enthusiastic about the experiment.

A group of eight whales appears in the distance — at about two miles — and is immediately pointed out by the men on watch. The Zodiac is on their trail at once, and tries to keep one animal always in sight. At 2:15, Canoë, standing forward in the Zodiac, in the traditional harpooner's stance, throws his weapon — with such force that he breaks the harpoon's stem and almost falls overboard onto the whale's back. Even so, the harpoon's head remains embedded in the whale, and we can see a trail of red ribbons — another one of our tracking devices — streaking through the water. But the ribbons do little good. The whale dives, taking her ribbons with her into the mysterious depths. Perhaps we will see her again in a lagoon of Baja California, still with the ribbons.

January 27. We are now near the lagoons. We can see the high sand dunes, that give this area its desert appearance, along the coast. Immediately in front of the channel into Scammon Lagoon, there is an island looming high out of the water: Cedros. We anchored off of Cedros last night.

At seven o'clock, we are under way, going south, past the mountains of Cedros whose red and yellow cliffs look like copper in the morning sun. The crests of the mountains are hidden by billowing white clouds.

The whale chase begins for the Zodiacs. But we are distracted. A friendly and photogenic sea lion wants to play, and Philippe and Bernard Delemotte cannot resist him. They cut the motor in sufficient time not to frighten him by its noise, and they dive and cavort with the animal for a while. It is a fine sequence — but, unfortunately, not the one that we came to Baja California for.

It seems that the island of Cedros is the point at which the migrating gray whales divide into two groups. Some of them swim between the island and the mainland and almost all enter Scammon Lagoon. Those who continue swimming in the open sea go on to the Matàncitas lagoon or the Bay of Magdalena. A few of them even go down to the southernmost point of Baja California.

The *Polaris* follows those who are going farther south, and we inaugurate a new tactic for the Zodiacs. We sneak up on the whales, as it were, without ever accelerating the motor or racing it, but by maintaining the same speed even when the whales slow down. This seems to be working very well. A Zodiac gets to within 25 or 30 feet of a whale — the closest it has ever been. But then the Zodiac's helmsman becomes nervous and speeds up. The result is instantaneous: the whale disappears.

Another tactic: we cut the Zodiac's motor and try to row to two whales not very far off. But they see us, or sense us, and are gone in a flash.

At one o'clock we head back to the *Polaris,* tired, hungry, and a little discouraged. Have we come all this way for nothing? No, we decide, we have not. This afternoon, come what may, we are going to harpoon a whale.

And we do. By the middle of the afternoon, we have had a successful shot. The harpoon penetrates into the blubber, and the whale streaks off with the buoy trailing behind it. The line holds — for all of two minutes.

Our "jinx" is beginning to curb our enthusiasm a bit.

A Tap on the Head

If there is a man aboard the *Polaris* who is a part of everything that we undertake, it is Ted Walker. By his advice and his almost intuitive knowledge of whale behavior he has become indispensable. Philippe and his friends find him untiring, always pleasant, and always ready to answer questions. Moreover, his affection for whales is contagious.

To our young divers, Professor Walker is an "elderly gentleman," a respected authority on a mysterious subject. But Ted is also an expert on putting people at ease and making them forget the generation gap.

He does not seem to mind at all that we are all jammed into the *Polaris* like sardines into a can. I think that the sight of a whale spouting makes him forget everything else in the world.

Ted, no doubt to warn our divers against taking foolish chances, has told them the story of his friend Rick Grigg, who almost lost his life diving. Rick had gone down with an aqua-lung one day, and when he surfaced he saw a gray whale so close that he could simply stretch out his hand and touch it. And he did. He felt the flesh quiver, like a horse's flesh; and then the sea exploded into blackness.

The next thing Rick Grigg knew, he was lying on the deck of his diving companion's boat, with a serious wound on his forehead. He still has the scar from that light tap of a whale's tail — a tail encrusted with barnacles.

Techniques of Marking

The kind of marking that the *Polaris* was trying to accomplish among the gray whales of Baja California was exactly the same kind that we succeeded in doing with cachalots in the Indian Ocean. It is a very superficial kind of

A finback whale tows a diver holding onto its dorsal fin.

wound, that does not harm the animal in the slightest. In fact, the harpoon markers that we use do not penetrate the whale's skin as deeply as those used by the International Whaling Commission; and even the Commission's harpoons do not do any damage to the whale. These harpoons have been found not only buried in a whale's blubber, but even enveloped and hidden by new layers of blubber.

If we have had so much trouble making our harpoons stick and attaching a buoy to a gray whale, it is because we absolutely refuse to use any sort of weapon that might actually injure a whale. Instead, we use a very light harpoon — so light, it seems, that the whale is able to shake it off almost immediately.

Little by little, however, we are learning to do our marking as quickly, and as gently, as possible. We have discovered that the best method is to stay about forty feet behind a whale while it is under the surface, and then to wait until it surfaces. It is also helpful occasionally to cut the engine for a few seconds in order to confuse the whale as to the Zodiac's distance from him.

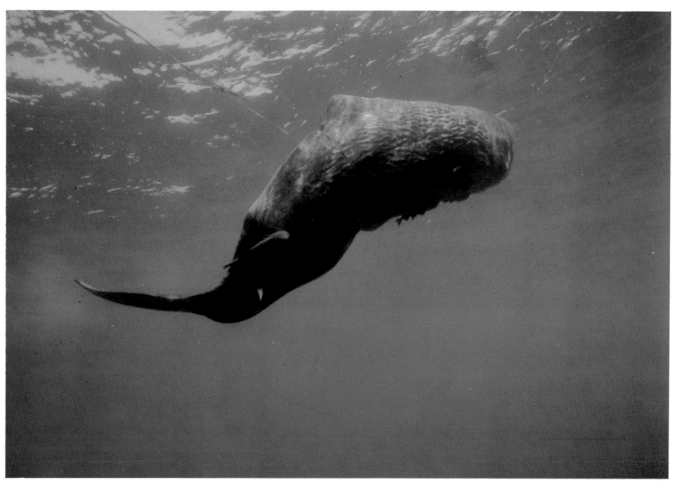

A sperm whale near the surface.

There is, however, no absolute rule in whale chasing. Everyone on the team brings his own particular qualities to it. Some have ingenuity; others, quick reflexes, and others, strength. What it requires of everyone, in addition, is nerves of steel.

The Parasites

Everyone aboard the *Polaris III,* including myself when I brought *Calypso* to join the expedition, ended up by developing a special affection for gray whales — and this despite all the tricks they played on us. It is difficult not to sympathize with beings of such intelligence — in the same way as we are attracted to a brilliant, but difficult, child.

Even so, we must admit that gray whales are not the handsomest of creatures. Their bodies, and the huge triangular tails, are covered with spots which are parasite scars.

The presence of parasites on whales is related to their migratory habits. In warm waters, they pick up barnacles, that look like (and are often mistaken for) mollusks. They are, however, small crustaceans: *Cirripedia*. These fauna drill deep into the delicate skin of the cetaceans in much the same way that a relative of these parasites, the acorn barnacle, attaches itself to rocks. But, as soon as the whales enter the colder waters of the Arctic, the parasites drop off. Fortunately, birds also help to rid the unhappy cetaceans of these "whale fleas."

Among these scars, there are other marks, semicircular in form, that seem to be left by lamprey bites.

Along the coasts of Siberia, some gray whales have found a clever method of ridding themselves of all kinds of salt-water parasites. They literally take showers at the foot of the cliffs from which fresh water pours into the sea.

Perennial Travelers

A common but erroneous belief is that whales have taken refuge in cold waters because they have been so much hunted by man. Actually, their migrations have to do with temperature and nourishment rather than safety. Plankton, the crustaceans favored by baleen whales, is plentiful in the Arctic and Antarctic during the summer. Tropical seas, on the other hand, offer ideal conditions during the winter for mating and giving birth. And in the Antarctic, during the summer, when the water is at a temperature of 0°C, cetaceans find an abundance of krill *(Euphausia superba)* which is their staple diet. The whales who go to the Antarctic, like their cousins who go to the Arctic during the summer, also, when winter comes, migrate; but they migrate northward, toward the warm equatorial waters.

"We now know," Professor Budker writes, "that there are two populations of baleen whale, one in the Northern Hemisphere, and the other in the Southern Hemisphere; and we know that the two groups do not mingle."

Humpback Whales

Humpback whales, remarkable for their large white flippers and their songs, have unusual migratory habits. Between January and March, they go to the Caribbean, in the area of Puerto Rico, the Bahamas, and the Virgin Islands. In April, May, and June, they are off the American coast near the

Carolinas, to the west of the Gulf Stream. They remain in the shallow water around Bermuda, where we have had the opportunity to film them and record their extraordinary sounds. This stopover in Bermudan waters allows them to rest in preparation for their migration to the northeast, which will take them toward Iceland and Norway.

Because their migrations are so predictable, humpback whales have suffered a great deal from whalers, particularly in the vicinity of Newfoundland, along the southern coast of Labrador, and around New Zealand and Australia.

Humpback whales have certain characteristics that leave them at the mercy of whalers. They swim slowly along in coastal waters, near to shore; and when they are feeding or mating, they do not flee when approached — as we learned at Bermuda.

Until recently, humpback whales were hunted relentlessly by whalers using helicopters, sonar, and harpoon cannons to destroy what is left of the last schools. And, as humpback whales tend to sink when they are dead, their carcasses are inflated with compressed air to keep them afloat. No group of animals can survive this sort of technological slaughter. If the humpback whale is to survive, it will only be because the whaling industry, in condemning a species to extinction, also condemns itself to extinction.

A 500-Horsepower Engine

In every account of an encounter with whales, as well as in the hundreds of photographs that we have taken, it is easy to see how important the tail is to all cetaceans. It is at once a weapon (which is sometimes used against divers), and a means of locomotion which enables them to migrate. It has been estimated that the tail of a whale is the equivalent of a 500-horsepower engine.

No one who has ever encountered a whale in the water will think that this is an exaggeration. A diver who brushes against a whale has the impression that he has just had an encounter with a speeding locomotive. Moreover, the passing of the whale's enormous body creates great turbulence in the water, while its tail stirs up a trail of waves in its wake. So much water is displaced that a camera cannot be used for several seconds after a whale has passed; it is knocked around too violently by the water.

Deloire has drawn a judicious distinction between the way that a shark swims and the motion of a baleen whale or a cachalot. The shark throws himself forward like a rocket, propelled by a twist of its whole muscular body.

A cetacean, on the other hand, goes forward smoothly, rhythmically. Its horizontal tail is so powerful that there is no need for violent motions; it beats slowly, gracefully, almost floating in the water around it.

One exception to Deloire's rule is the whale shark *(Rhincodon typus),* with whom we have had some experience in the Indian Ocean. The whale shark, which is not a whale at all but a shark, with a vertical tail, has the same slow, graceful rhythm of the cachalot. The reason probably lies in its size, for the whale shark is the largest of the sharks, measuring from 40 to 50 feet in length. For an animal of this size, regardless of whether the tail is vertical or horizontal, it is probably physically impossible to move the tail rapidly because of the resistance of the water.

One must have seen a sperm whale dive in order to appreciate the utter grace of its tail movements. Of all the cetaceans, the cachalot is the only one who, in preparing for a dive to the bottom, jackknifes and, as he goes beneath the surface, raises his tail, like two great wings, out of the water.

A Surface Leap

The whale's tail is used not only to propel it in the water, but also to propel it above the surface. In my journal of January 24, 1968, I have this notation:

"At the end of the day, when there was not enough light for filming, we saw a whale leap, twice, completely out of the water. It was an unforgettable sight; but, unfortunately, a brief one. We must keep constant watch, and never become discouraged — even when it seems that nothing will happen."

On this occasion, it is not a cachalot, but a baleen whale; and probably a gray whale. All of the large cetaceans probably dive in order to feed, and their horizontal tails enable them to go back and forth from the surface, where they breathe, to the depths, where they eat. The tail is, in fact, both a rudder and a stabilizer or stern oar placed flat in the water. An ideal appendage for a marine life form.

Whale Speed

The speed of a whale depends, among other things, upon the species of whale. We have had ample opportunity to clock the whales that we have encountered in the Indian Ocean and in the Pacific. Here are some of the data that we have gathered on the subject:

Sperm whales, again, are the speed champions of the world of whales. Left to themselves, they swim at only three or four knots; but, once they are disturbed or irritated, they speed up to ten or twelve knots. It is recorded that, in the Azores, a cachalot that was being pursued was capable of towing a boat at 20 knots.

A blue whale weighing 100 tons and 90 feet in length swims at a speed of 14 to 15 knots for two hours at a time; and he can sustain a speed of 20 knots for ten minutes.

Finback whales have been known to attain a speed of 18 knots.

It is reported that Sei whales* are capable of speeds of up to 35 knots, but we have never had any demonstration of this ability.

Humpback whales are relatively slow-moving animals. Their normal speed is 4 knots; if they are disturbed, they may exceed 10 knots.

It should be noted, however, that a female with a calf slows down in order not to lose her offspring; and that the school slows down to match her speed also.

The gray whale that we observed over a long period, from the *Polaris* and *Calypso* as well as from the Zodiac, normally moved at 4 or 5 knots. We ascertained, however, that when she was frightened she could swim at 10 knots, and perhaps more — in any case, at a speed greater than the 7 or 8 knots usually cited by cetologists.

Finally, we have calculated that, for a whale to leap entirely out of the water as they do (for reasons that we do not yet understand), he must be able to attain an accelerated speed of 30 knots. Males, apparently, leap more frequently than females; and the dive which follows a leap lasts anywhere from four to fifteen minutes.

Despite the power of their "engines" and their massive musculature, whales are far from being the fastest animals in the sea. Smaller cetaceans — the killer whale, the dolphin, the porpoise, for example — attain incomparably higher speeds.

*See Appendix I.

The spout of a gray whale off Baja California.

FOUR

The Breath-Holding Champions of the World

The Cachalot: Our Master

The cachalot, or sperm whale, is a marvelous diver. He is, in that respect, our undoubted master. Although cachalots are, like us, warm-blooded and lung-breathing, they seem immune to the physiological perils that are the lot of men in the sea: rapture of the depths, and decompression accidents. This immunity is, thus far, one of the mysteries of the sea. In trying to solve it, we may be able to better man's situation in the sea and expand the range and competence of the diver.

When a sperm whale dives, apparently using every muscle in his body and raising his great tail above the surface of the water, to what depth does he go?

Once more, I must have recourse to my journal and refer to *Calypso*'s expedition in the Indian Ocean:

Monday, May 22. We drifted only five miles last night. This morning, we set a course for Shab-Arab; but we did not get far. We soon made a detour to inspect a school of dolphins.

To be sure, dolphins are not what we are looking for. Yet, we have often had occasion to notice that there are spots in the sea where life seems to congregate — assembly areas which exist, no doubt, because food is abundant there. The food may consist of microscopic forms — plankton, or tiny crustaceans. Nonetheless, it seems to attract everything in the sea, even sperm whales. And this is the case today.

At 10:30 A.M. we sight a group of cachalots calmly going about their business. Instantly, Deloire is on the harpoon plaftorm; Barsky backs him up; Falco is at the prow with one of our new hand harpoons, which are heavy but, unfortunately, have weak heads. Li is in the observation chamber. And Jack and Alan are excitedly filming away with every camera they could find aboard the ship.

As *Calypso* picks her way toward the school of cachalots, we find our first subject: a young — or rather, an adolescent — whale. Falco sinks his harpoon in the youngster's side on the first try; but the whale reacts violently and succeeds in shaking loose the point.

The second subject is an adult, and he is well within range; but the harpoon strikes him sideways and bounces off harmlessly. Indeed, the trouble with our harpoons is that they are *too* harmless.

The third whale we select is enormous, the largest of the school. Falco throws the harpoon with all his strength. I am standing next to him, and I can see the harpoon strike the whale on the left side. Then we hear an extraordinary noise — a loud clap. The cachalot's skin has been split like that of a drum. And yet, it seems so tough and so thick!

I am certain that the harpoon's head has not reached the sensitive flesh underneath. It is embedded in the thick layer of blubber under the skin — a layer 20 to 25 inches thick, while our harpoon's point is only 16 inches long. The cachalot very likely is only vaguely aware of our harpoon. Even so, he stops swimming, and begins turning in a circle, his head held above the surface as though he is looking around to discover the source of that annoying pin-prick.

Then, he suddenly decides to leave, and begins moving away very rapidly. The polypropylene line uncoils so fast in its basket on the forward deck that it fairly whistles. When 1500 feet of the line have uncoiled, the red buoy attached to it is dragged overboard, and we follow it with our eyes as it leaps and bounds over the waves at high speed. A promising beginning.

Deloire sets out in the Zodiac with the 35 mm. Tegea, as we keep the whale in sight from the *Calypso*. He has been swimming toward his companions and, by now, has rejoined them. There are seven or eight whales altogether. When Deloire reaches the school, he jumps into the water in the middle of them, camera whirling. We should have some footage of the school as a whole.

For almost an hour, our captive cachalot swims quietly around the red buoy at the end of his 1500-foot leash. At first, his companions remain near him. But, after a while, they swim away, leaving behind, as company for our whale, another adult of almost the same size as the captive whale. But, before long, this one leaves too, and our whale is alone. We are somewhat surprised, and disappointed — prematurely, as it turns out — at this apparent lack of solidarity among the cachalots.

Our divers, who have already had a taste of broncobusting with whales, would like to try it again with a sperm whale. It seems easy enough: our cachalot is circling quietly around like a performing horse under the big top. But this one is no performer. He senses the divers approaching him, and, with a single stroke of that incredible tail, shoots sixty feet away from them. Then he goes back to his circling pattern.

The divers exhaust themselves trying to catch up to him. When they are ready to give it up, the Zodiac picks them up one by one. It would take ten divers, lying in ambush around the whale, for someone to be able to climb on his back.

By radio, I instruct the Zodiac to call the whole thing off. All of the divers are being worn out with nothing to show for it.

The Whale's Dive

Around four o'clock, the sperm whale decides to change his tactics. He dives. The 1500 feet of line disappear beneath the surface. Then the red buoy also disappears.

I should explain the significance of the buoy being dragged beneath the surface. Our buoys are actually balloons, made of thick plastic and inflated with air. The particular model we use was developed by Gaz de France for the purpose of holding up its underwater gas lines while they are being laid. On the surface, these buoys have a volume of 60 liters; therefore, in order for them to be dragged beneath the surface, a pull of at least 135 pounds is required. These buoys, however, are not crushed by water pressure. Since the plastic skin is flexible, they resume their form, and retain their floatability, when they return to the surface.

The whale therefore went down to at least 1400 or 1600 feet, and remained at that depth for about fifteen minutes He then rose to the surface

— and, a few minutes after, we see the buoy bouncing gaily on the water.

I immediately dispatch a Zodiac to attach a second buoy by means of 1000 feet of line. Then, we inflate a kytoon with helium and attach bits of aluminum foil to it so that we may track our whale by radar during the night.

The kytoon is attached to the second buoy by a hundred-foot line. And scarcely is the line taut than the whale dives again. The first buoy goes under very quickly. As we watch anxiously from *Calypso*'s deck, it is followed by the second buoy. Then, in consternation, we see the kytoon being dragged down also, until it is level with the surface. Suddenly, it begins to rise into the air again; and rises, and rises, and rises until it disappears from view into the sky, trailing a streamer of broken line behind it.

We Lose Our Whale

The sperm whale has obviously reached, or exceeded, a depth of 2500 feet. Hoping against hope, we add another 1000 feet of line and a third buoy. Then we begin inflating another kytoon. As soon as the whale surfaces, Bebert sinks another harpoon and we attach the new buoy.

The whale dives again; and this time the first two buoys are dragged down with him, but the third one remains on the surface, moving slowly forward.

It is not possible for us to determine precisely what depth the whale has reached on this dive, since he apparently has not gone down vertically. Even so, when he comes to the surface, he is still rather close to the spot at which he dived — which means that, while it may not have been an absolutely vertical dive, it was not far from it. I think we can say that the depth of the dive was more than 2500 feet, but less than 4000 feet.

At nightfall, we begin tracking the cachalot by radar, as we did on May 12 and 13 with our other whale. But the wind soon rises, and the choppy water interferes with reception. We can no longer locate the kytoon on our screen. Hastily, we organize a "Zodiac watch" near the third buoy. Bonnici has the duty first, and he notifies me by radio that the wind has blown the kytoon down onto the surface — no doubt because, when we launched it, we had nothing with which to make a rigid frame for the stabilizer. At any rate, Bonnici unhooks the kytoon from the buoy and attaches it to the Zodiac, where he can keep an eye on it.

In the middle of the evening, Bonnici informs me that the third buoy has suddenly stopped moving. Either the whale has shaken off the harpoon, he says, "or else he has fallen asleep." Taking no chances, we continue the Zodiac watch until dawn.

(Right) A sperm whale passes in front of *Calypso*'s bow in the Indian Ocean.

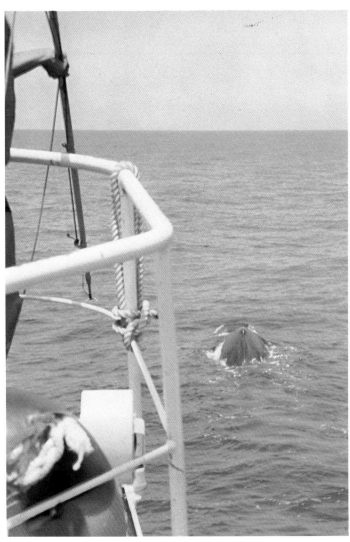

(Below) The Zodiac heads toward the spouts of two gray whales.

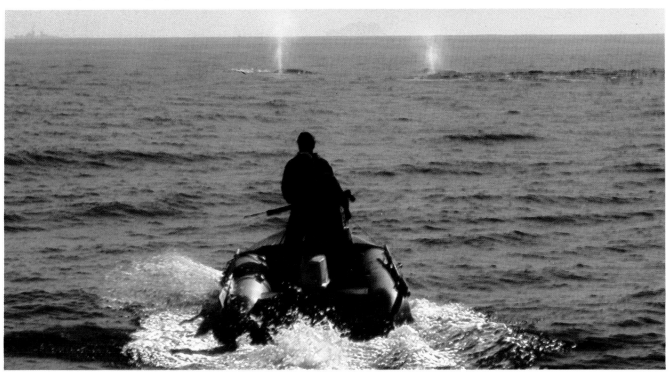

Tuesday, May 23. At daybreak, we begin hauling in our lines and discover that our cachalot has, in fact, freed himself. An examination of the harpoon reveals that the last of the three bards, which we were counting on to hold the harpoon in the whale's blubber, is gone, and the stem is broken. The steel line by means of which the nylon line is attached to the harpoon is about two thirds cut through, but apparently it was still holding. Obviously, it was the harpoon's head, with its three sharp ridges, that cut the surrounding flesh and allowed the harpoon to work itself free.

That the whale should be free was no surprise. What is astonishing is that our flimsy little weapon, with its bits of steel and nylon line, should have held such a Leviathan for so long a time.

In the Trap

Experts on whales have had much discussion on the maximum depth to which a sperm whale can dive. In 1900, a German scholar, Kukenthal, declared that they could go down to 3250 feet.

Kukenthal's opinion was apparently corroborated by a curious incident. In 1932, an American cable layer, the *All America,* was working on a telegraph line in the open sea off British Columbia. The ship's crew was amazed when they raised the defective line — with great effort — to find the carcass of a cachalot tangled in the line. The animal had obviously been trapped by the cable, and had drowned. The interesting fact was that the cachalot's body had not been crushed by the water pressure — even though the cable had been laid at a depth of 3330 feet.

Professor Budker writes: ". . . it now seems to have been proved that sperm whales often swim at depths of around 3000 feet. It seems plausible therefore to conclude that sperm whales when they become entangled in underwater cables are in search of food. That is, they are swimming with their lower jaws hanging open, stirring up the upper layers of sediment on the bottom."*

So far as the length of a line attached to a harpooned whale is concerned, we cannot say that it gives an exact indication of depth, since there is always a certain amount of horizontal slant involved which must be taken into account.

*Kenneth S. Norris, in his *Whales, Dolphins, and Porpoises,* records that, in 1957, another sperm whale was discovered caught in an undersea cable — this one at a depth of 3850 feet. Several other cases of this kind have been discovered since that time.

Some relatively precise experiments have been performed by a group of Norwegian investigators who, in observing humpback whales, used harpoons equipped with pressure gauges. The greatest depth registered in the course of five experiments was 1180 feet. The humpback whale who established that record returned to the surface with such vigor "that he towed the boat for a full half hour and finally had to be slowed down by a second harpoon." *

Our own observations indicate that the depth to which whales dive varies according to species. The large marine mammals dive out of necessity, in order to find food. For that reason, baleen whales do not dive as deep as sperm whales. We will see, for instance, that cetaceans who feed on krill (a crustacean that remains near the surface — sometimes in great abundance — and is never found at depths of more than 325 feet) are the ones who do not dive deep.

Sperm whales, who feed on the giant squid found at depths of 1500 to 2500 feet, are apparently the champion divers of the world. It is also possible, however, that the bottlenose whale is an even more brilliant performer.

It is worth noting that diving ability seems to be to some extent a function of size. The larger the individual whale, the better diver he is. In practice, this means that adult male whales are more proficient at diving than young whales, or females.

Ninety Minutes of Apnea

How long can a sperm whale remain beneath the surface without breathing? There is a considerable amount of data available on this point, and the consensus seems to be that large males can remain in apnea — that is, do without breathing — for between sixty and ninety minutes.

It is true, however, that in almost every case the whale in question was being hunted or chased, and that he was seeking to escape. He therefore remained under water for as long as possible. His dives, therefore, cannot really be regarded as "normal."

The cachalots that *Calypso* has pursued have probably never been really frightened, in the sense that they fortunately have never been fighting for their lives and been compelled to remain without breathing to the limit of their endurance.

---

*These experiments are described by Professor Paul Budker in his *Baleines et baleiniers,* p. 76.

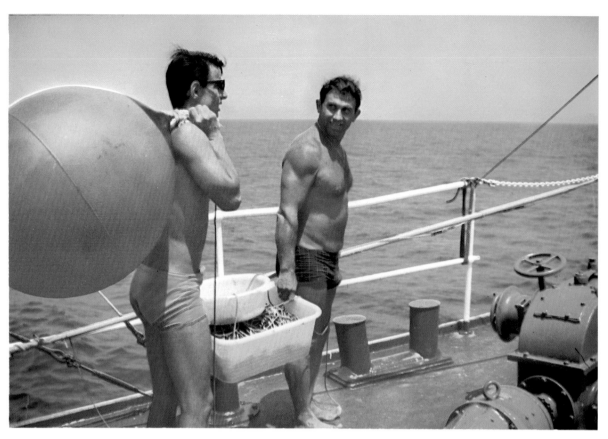

Bonnici and Falco prepare the buoys and the nylon line that are attached to the harpoon.

In my journal, I find the following entry, written at sea off the island of Socotra:

March 14. During the morning, we sight five or six groups of cachalots. Sometimes there is only one group at a time, and sometimes two. Whenever we approach, however, they dive; but several times we are able to follow their

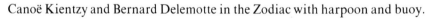

Canoë Kientzy and Bernard Delemotte in the Zodiac with harpoon and buoy.

Two launches attempting to encircle a sperm whale.

trail. This "trail" is a sort of slick, similar to an oil slick. I am more and more convinced that the trail is the result of the movement of the whales' tails.

They are swimming only 15 to 30 feet beneath the surface, but they are capable of infinitely greater depths than that. They often remain twenty minutes without breathing, even when there is no particular reason for them to be wary of coming to the surface.

Obviously, there is no absolute rule in a whale's behavior. The spectacular sight of a sperm whale jackknifing to dive and thrusting the whole of his tail out of the water usually indicates a deep dive. And yet, we have seen on several occasions, cachalots also dive without that foregoing maneuver. In such cases, they seem to go down only to a moderate depth.

In general, baleen whales do not perform deep dives while they are migrating — unless they are disturbed or frightened.

Our observation of gray whales from both *Calypso* and *Polaris III* leads us to believe that these toothless cetaceans remain in a dive for much less time than a sperm whale.

We have an exact record of the length of apnea among gray whales encountered along the Pacific coast, and also of the probable depths of their dives. The record dive lasted 8 minutes and 27 seconds, while the average dive lasted between two and four minutes. The greatest estimated depth was

500 feet. Bernard Mestre was in charge of these records and calculations, and he fulfilled his responsibilities with scrupulous care.

Humpback whales seem somewhat better endowed as divers than gray whales. We have timed their dives at between ten and fifteen minutes.

Apparently, only the finback whale rivals the sperm whale in the durations of its dives, as was demonstrated by the specimen that we marked and tracked in the Indian Ocean.

What amazes me even more than the length of a whale's dive, or its depth, is the fact that, in some mysterious way, a whale under the surface — no matter how great the depth — seems always to know what is happening at the surface and to act accordingly. We had a startling example of this ability with our finback whale near Mahé, who so dexterously gave us the slip (see Chapter One). During his dives, he seemed to know the exact location of *Calypso*, of the Zodiacs, and of the launch — even if their engines were not running.

Myoglobin

Not all mammals are able to hold their breath for the same amount of time. Cats, dogs, and rabbits can remain in apnea for three to four minutes; muskrats, twelve minutes; seals and beavers, fifteen minutes.

It is obvious that the cetaceans' apneic abilities are shared to some extent with their relatives on land. Land mammals have simply developed that ability to a smaller extent. And even this is not always true; for beavers can hold their breath longer than gray whales. To what does the sperm whale owe its undisputed superiority in this respect?

The obvious answer would be: to its lungs. But that is not so. The cachalot's lungs are not especially well developed in proportion to the animal's overall size.

On the other hand, the sperm whale ventilates its lungs, while it is on the surface, much more than other mammals do. When it surfaces, it renews 80 percent or 90 percent of the air in its thoracic cage — compared to 20 percent for man. (One inhalation by a whale is the equivalent of eight for a man.)

Moreover, a cachalot's respiratory rate is extraordinarily slow: six times a minute. But the rate is even less for baleen whales: who inhale at the rate of once every minute.

The skin of the large cetaceans is very dark, almost black. We have mentioned this coloration is peculiar to mammals who are good divers. The reason is that the color is due to the presence of myoglobin in the system, which stabilizes oxygen in the mammal's muscles. And this is one of the most plausible explanations that can be advanced for a whale's ability to go for long periods without breathing.

According to Professor Grassé, the oxygen that a man uses when he dives comes from the following sources: 34 percent from the lungs, 41 percent from the blood, 13 percent from the muscles, and 12 percent from other tissues. For a whale, the breakdown is : 9 percent from the lungs, *41 percent from the blood, 41 percent from the muscles,* and 9 percent from other tissues.

It remains to be explained how cetaceans, who are, after all, lung-breathing mammals like us, seem to be immune to the perils that the human diver runs because of nitrogen in his system. This immunity, which we envy so much and which has haunted my dreams for so many years, seems to be due to a complex of physiological pecularities.

The first of these is the whale's very unusual circulatory system;* a system which one finds also among certain Pinnipedia and among sea otters. This system includes a complex of blood vessels running on both sides of the spine down to the tail. These networks are of two kinds: arterial and venous.

The advantage conferred is that these vessels assure the proper distribution of blood to the brain and the heart during a dive. It is possible, too, that it serves as a temperature regulator. It has also been said that the whale's aptitude for diving is due to the size of his venous sinuses. And it has been pointed out that cetaceans' thick layer of blubber may contribute to the absorption of nitrogen during apnea. (This same function may be filled by the oily emulsion that we have noted in the whale's lungs, and which would also be the cause of the whale's visible "spout.")

A possible clue: the heartbeat of cetaceans is as slow as that of the aquatic reptiles — snakes, or the marine iguanas of Galapagos — who also remain in apnea for long periods.

There is nothing certain about any of these explanations. They are all hypotheses. What is missing is true experimental knowledge. But are experiments possible with animals of this size?

The Spout

After Philippe had spent some time reconnoitering the lagoons of Baja California in search of gray whales, he returned to San Diego by air and flew over the interior coast of the Gulf of Cortes. He was accompanied by Ted

---

*The scientific name of this system reflects its quality. It is called *reta mirabilia* — "wondrous networks."

Walker and Wally Green.

Along the Mexican coast, they flew over the Canal de las Ballenas (Whale Canal) which lies between the shore and the island of Angel de la Guarda. From the air, they saw a school of finback whales which, if they were not permanent residents of the canal, seemed at least very much at home there.

Philippe, Ted, and Wally immediately landed near a fishing village and rented a boat. Here is Philippe's account of the day:

"It was a beautiful day, and we set out early to find the school. The scenery alone was well worth the trouble. Along the coast there were high cliffs, reddish in color, majestic, but completely denuded of any sort of vegetation. There was not a tree or a blade of grass. It was an untouched desert; but a desert of rock. The cliffs descended vertically to the sea that lay 150 feet below.

"The sea was like a lake, and our motorboat was surprisingly quiet — as quiet as only Americans can make a motor. We had no trouble in finding the whales, and, when we drew near, we cut our engine. In the almost total silence that followed, an enormous spout shot up from a finback not ten feet from our prow. It seemed for a moment that the universe was filled by that geyser. I am certain that it was a finback. We were in the Gulf of Cortes, and there are no gray whales there.

"Ted began shouting and pointing, and we quickly saw why. We were completely surrounded by finbacks, one on each side of the boat. We started the engine and advanced slowly. Our whale escort stayed alongside of us, moving at the same speed, remaining at a distance of 15 or 20 feet from us. From time to time, they sank gently below the surface, and then rose again. We continued moving forward, and we noticed that the water in front of us was filled with bubbles, like soda water. They came from a school of tiny fish that kept diving and then coming to the surface to empty the gas from their swimming bladders.

"Then I understood what was happening. The finbacks around us were using our boat, and the sound of our engine, to round up the little fish. And, for the first time, I experienced, and saw in operation, the intelligence of these animals. Moreover, it had not taken them long to devise this plan. We were not there for more than twenty minutes before they arrived and stationed themselves aound the boat.

"The water was cloudy, and I was unable to dive to shoot some film, but I

(Left) Cameramen trying to film a sperm whale that is already out of range.

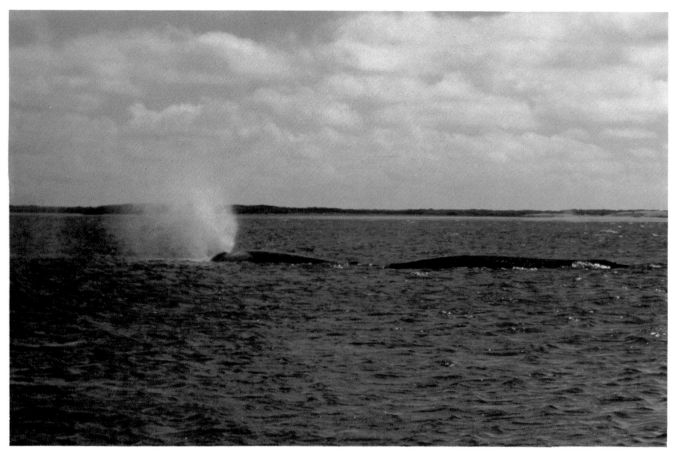

Gray whales spouting in Scammon Lagoon.

did not really regret it. I don't see how I could have found anything beneath the surface to equal the scene that we witnessed from our boat. What an extraordinary sensation it is, in the silence of a desert, to see a whale — to say nothing of several whales — swimming alongside more slowly than a man walks. One of these giants, the one on our starboard, was three times the size of our boat. Ted estimated its length at 85 feet. The one to port was smaller.

"This was my first real contact with a whale at close quarters. Of course, I have seen whales since I was a child aboard *Calypso*. But that particular day, I could see and hear the spouting, and the whale was very close. It was very different from anything that I had experienced before. The noise, especially, amazed me. It was as though we were in a cave, listening to the repeated echoes of a mysterious sound.

"All in all, it was one of the most unforgettable days of my life. I was

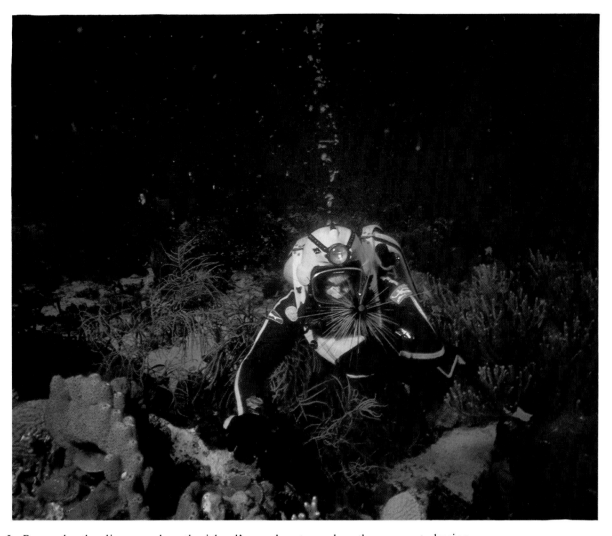

In Bermuda, the divers explore the island's coral waters when they are not chasing humpback whales.

able to understand how so many legends are told about whales, and to understand how they began.

"Up to that time, I had not known very much about whales. I had heard more or less romanticized stories, seen drawings, read books. But to see a whale in real life, and especially to *hear* a whale — that is beyond imagining. And to think that, in the midst of that monstrous sound there is a life form even greater. . . .

"One of the most memorable things about that afternoon was that I actually *breathed* the whale's breath. Its spout rained down on us like a gentle drizzle, and a fog covered my face and hands and the boat itself. Surprisingly, there was no unpleasant odor, but a slightly musky smell; one which only the sovereign authority of a nearby giant could impose on us whether we were willing or not."

Halitosis?

A very widespread opinion has it that the spout of cetaceans has an unpleasant odor. However, our divers have often been sprinkled by this spray, and they have rarely complained of its smell. It should be noted that, in their contacts with whales, their minds were usually occupied with matters other than whether or not the whale had halitosis. Even so, there was no trace of an unpleasant smell on their diving gear, or on their bodies, on such occasions.

It is possible that the spout of a sperm whale has a more disagreeable smell than that of a baleen whale, since the cachalot's diet is very different.

As far as gray whales and finbacks are concerned, it may be recalled that Philippe was abundantly sprinkled by their spout, and he denies absolutely that there was any disagreeable smell whatever. According to Philippe, whalers are responsible for the story that cetaceans have halitosis; and he points out that the only whales that whalers have contact with are those who are either exhausted by a long chase, or wounded.

An Asthmatic Whale

"Thar she blows!" is the ritual cry by means of which the sighting of a whale is announced. It was also the alarm given aboard *Calypso* when we were whale chasing in the Indian and Pacific oceans. (That is, we used the French version: *Elle souffle* — which means exactly the same thing.)

When a whale surfaces after a dive, his blowholes are the first thing to break water. Out of them (or it, as the case may be), comes the spout, a white column of vapor that resembles a steam geyser and which is perfectly visible above the water. That it is necessary for a whale to spout is an unfortunate arrangement of Nature, for the spout makes it possible for the whale to be sighted from a good distance away. And the spout is accompanied by a rush of air the sound of which can be heard at 800 feet. This was the "repeated echoes of a mysterious sound" that, heard from close up, made such an impression on Philippe.

The *Curlew*'s* team, during their expedition in the waters around Bermuda in pursuit of humpback whales, had the opportunity to record this sound on many occasions. Our sound engineer, Eugène Lagorio, noted that, so far as sound itself is concerned, there is a considerable amount of difference between the spouts of different whales.

*The *Curlew* was the boat that we rented for our Bermudian adventure.

On one occasion, conditions were particularly favorable for this kind of observation. The day had been spent in exterior shots, and, toward evening, the *Curlew* was at anchor, with its engines cut. Seven or eight whales had remained in the ship's vicinity, apparently unworried by the presence of the hull in their waters. Even when divers went down, the whales seemed hardly to notice them. This was in relatively shallow water, and it is likely that the whales were quietly, and even somewhat lazily, feeding. They remained on the surface a good deal of the time, diving occasionally and always reappearing near the *Curlew*. Lagorio was therefore able to tape-record their spouts individually. There was one whale among them whose spout was noticeably different, harsher and louder.

Lagorio, who is *Calypso*'s reigning deadpan, remarked: "An asthmatic, I presume."

A Fifty-Foot Spout

Cetaceans are able to dive only after they have inhaled and exhaled a certain number of times on the surface; and the number depends upon the species. Dr. Budker says that "the blue whale breathes only three to five times; the finback, five or six times; the Sei, ten to fifteen times. The sperm whale, during its ten to eleven minutes on the surface, breathes sixty to seventy times, which shows a respiratory rate much faster than that of baleen whales."

The spout of a whale emerges from its blowholes under considerable pressure and sometimes rises 50 feet into the air. The longer and deeper the dive, the higher the spout that follows it. Experts have devised the following rule of thumb: a sperm whale sixty feet long, weighing 60 tons and remaining in a dive for 60 minutes, will breathe sixty times.*

Experienced whalers are able to tell, from a whale's spout, the species, age, and even the size, of the whale.† The finback whale, for example, has two blowholes, both of which spout; but since the two blowholes are very close together, the spout becomes a single jet of vapor. The spout of the right whale, on the other hand, is actually two distinct jets, and is aimed forward. And the spout of the humpback whale is a single straight column that spreads at the top, like the spout of a fountain.

---

* Cited by Kenneth S. Norris, *Whales, Dolphins, and Porpoises,* p. 698

†See the word "Spout" in the Glossary.

A shipboard chore: cleaning the portholes of *Calypso*'s observation chamber.

Another Riddle

Contrary to what is commonly believed, the whale's spout is not simply a jet of water. Professor Budker places great emphasis on this point. "Anatomically," he writes, "it is impossible for a whale to eject water through the blowhole, for among marine mammals there is no connection between the respiratory and digestive tracts. Breathing and digestion take place independently of one another, and water absorbed through the mouth has no way of being ejected through the blowhole."

What gives the spout its appearance of white steam? The most feasible explanation is that air, compressed in the whale's thorax by his dive, expands at the moment of exhalation. The air's temperature is thus lowered, and it condenses into water vapor.

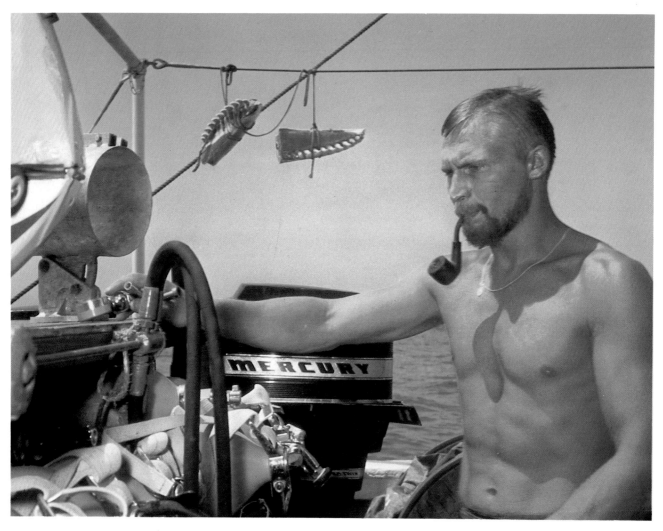

Bernard Delemotte is our resident tooth-collector. Here, he has just put a killer whale's jawbone out to dry.

Among the smaller cetaceans — dolphins and killer whales, for example — the spout is invisible.

The Misadventures of a Cardiologist

There is a connection, it seems, between the spout and the rate of a whale's heartbeat — as there is between that rate and the amount of time spent in apnea. An American cardiologist, Dr. Paul Dudley White (among whose heart patients was President Eisenhower), has actually succeeded in running an electrocardiogram of a whale. Dr. White, who is a friend of Ted Walker's, had already taken electrocardiograms of an elephant (30 beats per minute), and of a bird (1000 per minute). Apparently, the larger the animal the slower the heartbeat.

Ted Walker explained to us that Dr. White had chosen gray whales for his experiment because he considered that species more accessible than others. He got together a team, organized an expedition, and equipped a boat. Once in the water, however, his team, which had little familiarity with the customs of gray whales, attempted to install their electrodes on a mother whale accompanied by her calf; and mother whales are always touchy. This one reacted violently to their impertinence. She charged the boat, smashed the rudder, bent the propeller, and left a gaping hole in the hull. It was all the crew could do to pump out the water fast enough to keep the boat afloat until help could arrive.

Dr. White finally found a 30-ton subject in Scammon Lagoon, installed his electrodes without mishap, and took a reading of 27 per minute. The fact that the whale was grounded at the time obviously had some effect upon the reading, for the normal rate has been established at nine beats per minute.

FIVE

They Talk, They Sing—and They Listen

The fact that certain cetaceans "speak" is not a recent discovery. Aristotle knew it, and wrote about it. His record, however, was ignored and passed off as a legend until the day, during World War II, that the American navy began using underwater microphones (called sofar — sound fixing and ranging) to detect the presence of enemy submarines. The device immediately picked up a series of grinding sounds, clicks, and mewings along the American coast. And thus were discovered the voices of the World of Silence: the noises of the crustaceans, the groaning sounds of the fish, the whistles of the porpoises, the squeaking of the dolphins, the calls of the sperm whales, and the trills of the baleen whales.

Certainly not all the sounds made by cetaceans are part of a "language." Some of them are not a means of expression, but a method of orientation and detection.

Man was not the first mammal to use sonic and ultrasonic guides in the depths of the sea. Cetaceans have a natural sonar device.

The sonar system of marine mammals, by means of which they detect

The head of a humpback whale. One can almost make out the expression on its face.

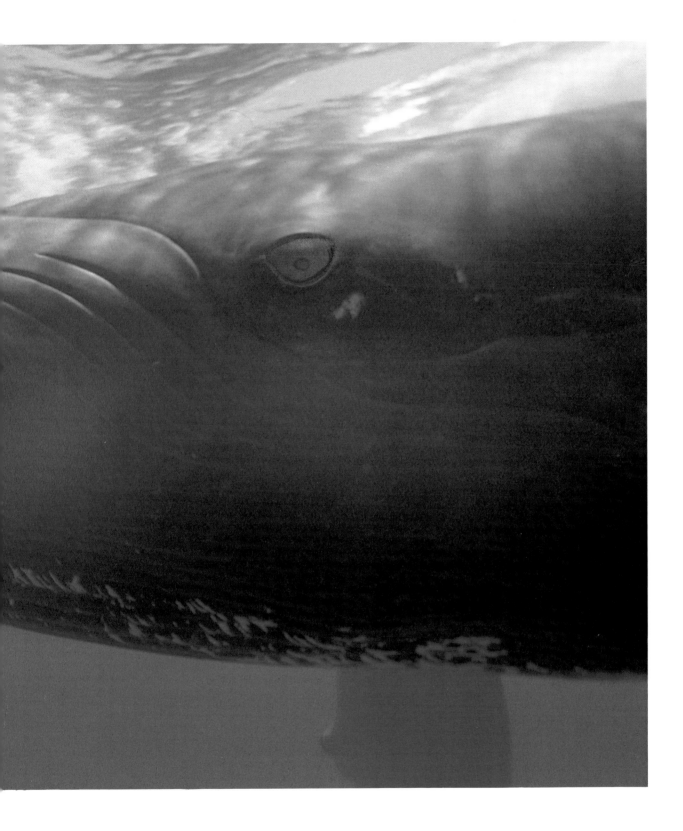

obstacles and locate their food and their enemies, is more complex than one may think. Today, it is believed that this system functions at two levels. The lowest frequencies, for example, seem to be used by cachelots to locate squid in very deep water, or by dolphins to locate prey or obstacles from afar, while the high frequencies seem to serve as a means of communication among individuals of the same species.

A New World of Sound

Sight, which is so important to land mammals, is not the sense upon which cetaceans rely most. Hearing is most important for them. Baleen whales and cachalots live, and organize their lives around, a world of sound. And, even though they have no vocal chords, they speak, and they sing. They also listen; and they send out sonic signals that, by their echoes, give information on the cetaceans' surroundings.

Cachalots *grunt* in order to communicate with one another, and they emit a series of rhythmic *cracking* noises, at a very high sonic level, to explore the area around them. They hear one another, and are able to locate one another, at distances of over three (marine) miles.

This explains why one occasionally finds a whale calf alone, far from its parents. For the parents know perfectly well where their offspring is at any given moment; and the calf also knows where its mother and father are located.

This ability to locate, this sonar device, is not automatic, and not merely passive. Whales broadcast and receive, in my opinion, directionally; and it seems probable that they must rotate, like a radar antenna, when they are exploring their surroundings. This would explain why *Calypso* is able to approach whales from the rear without disturbing them.

On the other hand, when whales want to know what is going on around them, they assume a vertical position with their heads protruding above the surface. This is not in order to be able to watch *Calypso*, as we once thought. The angle of transmission (and perhaps of reception also) is perpendicular to the whale's cylindrical body; and, no doubt, there is a special "ear" which is kept turned toward the ocean bottom.

On the surface, sperm whales are constantly attuned by sonar to the depths. If their constant crack-crack-crack discloses the presence of one or more sizable squid at 2000 or 2500 or 3000 feet directly underneath, then they dive vertically and go straight to their prey. The hypothesis that they transmit vertically seems to me to explain the *vertical* dives of cachalots and pilot whales.

THEY TALK, THEY SING 109

Whales apparently find the noise of outboard motors especially annoying. This is probably a question of frequencies. And it is also probably because of overlapping frequencies that our tactic of the virazeou, using outboard motors, seems to work.

In the center of the circle of noise, the sperm whale's sonar reception may be garbled; and he would therefore have to remain stationary (and furious) on the surface. And, since he relies upon his sonar for diving, he would not be able to dive. (It would very likely be improper to suggest that a cachalot would dive "by reflex," since he is sufficiently well developed to have a choice of alternatives in his behavior.)

Before we began to understand the effectiveness of their auditory equipment, we foolishly accused cachalots of disloyalty, and we were completely wrong. When a cachalot is in trouble, the head male orders the school to withdraw. But the school then remains within sonar range — a range that may extend for several miles. If the whale in question is unable to get away, the school sends one or two members to investigate — the mother, if the whale is a calf, or another adult if it is a full-grown whale. On several occasions, the school disappeared about a mile to the east of the captive, and then reappeared a mile to the west of him thirty or forty minutes later. To travel that distance, it ordinarily takes a whale less than twenty minutes. Which means that the school apparently spent some time within sonar range of the whale on the surface, calling him and telling him that they were waiting for him to rejoin them.

Bermuda

Philippe spent two months observing and recording the most loquacious, and the noisiest, of all cetaceans: the humpback whale.

Bermuda seemed the ideal place for such an undertaking, because Bermuda is one of the regular stopovers of humpbacks in the spring, when they are en route to the Arctic for their summer feast of small crustaceans. During this particular year, however, the weather was very disagreeable, and working conditions were proportionately unfavorable.

The largest boat that we were able to rent was an old sailer, the *Curlew*, whose ballast had been removed so that it could travel in shallow water. It therefore rolled so violently that it was impossible for anyone to stay at sea on the *Curlew* for more than one or two days at a time.

On the first day, everyone was enthusiastic. The *Curlew* began by crossing the lagoon, where the water was very calm. Then it got out into the open sea, where there were waves six to nine feet high. Almost everyone aboard

The humpback whale is recognizable by its large white flippers.

was instantly seized with *mal de mer*. And, of course, whales began popping up all around the ship. Despite their discomfort, the divers began to prepare to go down. As soon as the *Curlew* was in the proper position, however, the rudder broke. Fortunately the *Curlew* was able to hold the course on its own, with one engine running at reduced speed. Otherwise, she would inevitably have smashed into one or more of the submerged coral reefs in the area and sunk.

Bernard Delemotte and Philippe took turns working in the hole, trying to repair the rudder pulley, with the help of the ship's captain, Philippe Sirot. Finally, the *Curlew* was able to limp back into port.

Several days later, the *Curlew*'s rudder was as good as new, and she put out again with Philippe and his friends. Alongside a level reef, they encountered a group of seven whales who began swimming and playing around the boat, rubbing against one another and emitting a series of extraordinary

(Right) Humpback whales are specialists in underwater acrobatics. Note the shape of the mouth as seen from above.

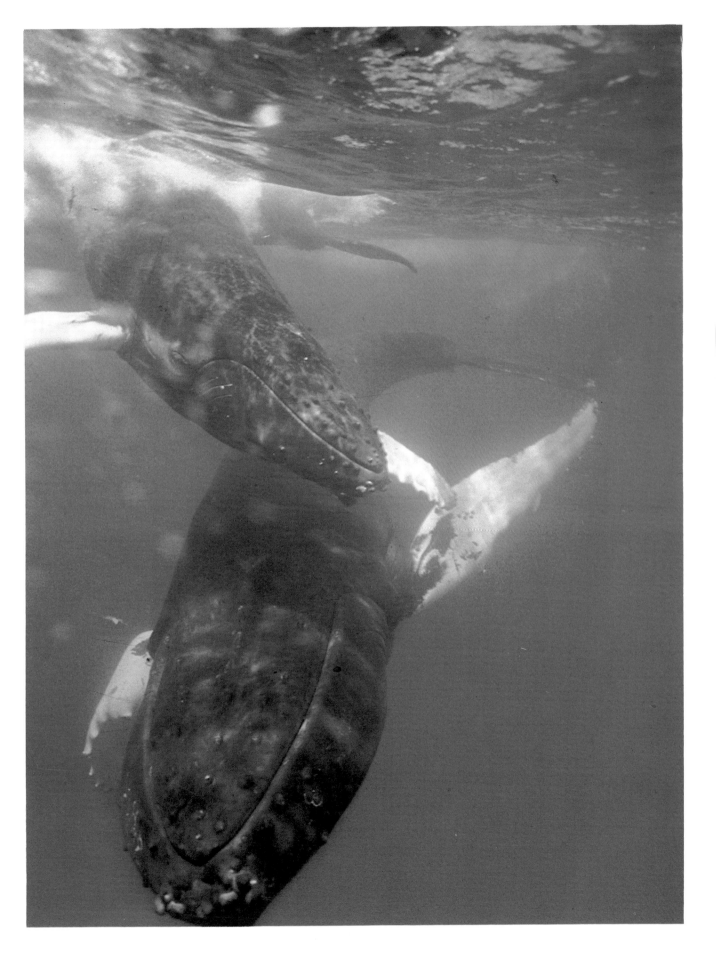

sounds: modulated, and very audible sounds.

Philippe, who had already suited up, dived immediately into the middle of the school. The water was cloudy, and all that he could see were "large wings" passing, waving. The flippers of humpback whales are white, and very large, measuring one third the length of the whale's body. (The body itself is black.) They do, in fact, look like wings — or, as they pass in a cloudy sea, like ghosts in white sheets.

A Concert

The weather finally improved, and the sea became calm. It was now possible to tape-record the "songs" of the whales. It was decided to do so at night, for humpback whales are much more communicative after dark than in the daylight hours. Apparently, they are able to transmit more strongly then; and indeed they speak to one another over considerable distances.

As their recording site, the team chose an underwater canyon. The *Curlew* was moved to that location, and microphones were placed 60 to 75 feet from the surface.

On certain nights, Eugène Lagorio, our sound engineer, was able to record what amounted to a veritable concert. There must have been, he says, a hundred whales over a more or less extended area, all "talking." Early in the evening, there were only a few sounds, scattered, uncertain; as though the musicians were tuning their instruments.

Then one whale began to sing; and a second; and a third. Soon, the mewings, creaks, and whoops filled the water. Some of the performers were close, and some were far away. And, because of the underwater canyon, the sounds echoed two or three times at intervals of five or six seconds. It seemed almost that one was in a cathedral, and that the faithful were alternating the verses of a psalm. . . .

Lagorio's recordings show beyond a doubt that whales communicate with one another. The whale nearest to the *Curlew* would make a series of sounds, and others, farther away, would answer. The sounds alternated, just as in a conversation; but it was a mysterious conversation, and an untranslatable one.

A Thousand Different Sounds

The sounds made by humpback whales are different from those of any other animals. They extend over a much wider range and have a variety of expression greater even than that of birds.

I think that we could probably distinguish a thousand different sounds, each one individually audible to the human ear. The timbre, the volume, and the frequencies present an almost infinite variety. There are trills, creaks, janglings, and very short mouselike squeaks. Sometimes we heard a bellowing, like the belling of a deer. Occasionally, these bellowings overlapped; but almost always they seemed addressed to another whale. They were weird, alien sounds, exchanged — it seemed to us — on secret wave lengths.

Lagorio, who has been part of our team for many years, had found the job of his life. Sitting in the darkness, twirling his dials and flicking his switches, he was like a wizard summoning monsters who, from the bottom of the sea, were answering with moans, sighs, and clanging chains. No sound engineer has ever undertaken a more modern project, or one more evocative of ancient myths.

On certain unusually calm nights, the songs of the humpback whales blended into what Lagorio called "choirs." These sounds, which were very near the *Curlew*, were truly polyphonic, an "ensemble" of voices. And the bass section always was taken by a sound like the creaking of rusty hinges.

A few of the men aboard the *Curlew* were of the opinion that the whales might be making noise for the sheer joy of making noise. And yet, not even the birds sing entirely without reason.

There have been cases in which it seemed possible to attach a particular meaning to a whale sound. One night, when they were talking more than usual, and they could be heard very clearly over the microphones, they surfaced near Lagorio's boat and began looking him over. Lagorio was sitting there, in the open, earphones on his head, surrounded by his wires and lights and dials and all the paraphanelia of his trade, and they seemed quite interested. They came very close, and began making little squeaking noises, like mice. Lagorio was convinced (and still is) that they were talking about him. And that they were saying flattering things.

"I could feel somehow that they were discussing what they saw in the Zodiac," he says. "Maybe they were wondering whether I was dangerous or not, and if they should run away."

Conversations

Lagorio is very proud of the fact that the whales finally decided to stay. They must have concluded that he was a friend.

(Following page) A diver has been allowed to latch onto a humpback whale's tail — but only for a moment.

Even though one may know intellectually that it would be foolish to give too human an interpretation to the acts and sounds of another species, it is nonetheless difficult to ignore one's immediate impressions. When one hears whales "talking" in the night, it seems quite obvious that they are able to communicate with one another; that they are not simply indulging in a series of sounds without meaning, but that they are actually exchanging thoughts and opinions.

My friends and I have perhaps spent too much time with whales; we may be the victims of an illusion. But how can we explain those alternating voices, and such a diversity of modulation, except by concluding that it is actually conversation? In any event, it cannot be denied that there are signals of some kind being exchanged — perhaps signals that are acknowledged from a distance by the cetacean equivalent of "roger"; or even that one whale "speaks" and that another answers.

The most startling transmissions are those, like Lagorio's choirs, that are group manifestations or forms of collective sound. Sometimes they sound like a rumbling, or buzzing, which varies in intensity. The overall effect is the same as a group of children reciting their lessons aloud.

Is it possible to define any of those sounds? Can we say that such and such a noise is an obvious cry of surprise? This, of course, is entirely subjective. The sounds of "surprise" that Lagorio heard one night were heard again on other occasions; and there is no doubt that, when the whales discovered the presence of the *Curlew*, or of a Zodiac, they gave little cries that may well have been expressions of curiosity. And they did not run away. They swam slowly around the craft, while squeaking softly. It was obvious that they were interested in us; and it is possible that was the meaning of the noise they were making.

It does not seem that whales have a special sound for alarm, as the birds do — the crow, for example. In any case, we have never recorded any whale sound that was followed by a withdrawal of the school.

A Bellowing Male

One night, while the *Curlew* was at anchor, Philippe and Lagorio were able to spend an hour — from 11 P.M. to midnight — in an extraordinary recording session. I say "extraordinary" because they were able to get an excellent recording of the sounds of a school of whales that was "talking" as its members swam slowly on their way. Occasionally, a loud bellowing would drown out the other sounds. We cannot say for sure that it was actually the bellowing of a male. And yet, that seems the most plausible explanation, for, on another occasion, it was possible to record a nearby bellow, and then one far off, as though the second was answering the first. Was it a mating call? A challenge? We know too little to be able to tell.

So far as humpback whales are concerned, it should be noted that, at the time that we were in Bermuda, it was not the mating season. Humpbacks mate at the end of winter and in the spring; and they do so around the Bahamas and the Antilles. Bermuda is merely a port of call for this species; they come to feed and to rest before resuming their northward trek. It does not seem likely, therefore, that the bellows we heard were addressed by a male to a female.

Bermuda has an abundance of the kind of food that humpback whales favor; and this, of course, is why they stop there. Through our earphones, we could hear perfectly well the crackling of the crustaceans that they were eating. Sometimes it was so loud that it garbled the sounds of the whales themselves.

These recordings, in fact, presented a number of problems. Underwater microphones give faithful reproduction only when the water is at a dead calm. If there is a swell, we get a lot of interference, in the form of the swell's noise, on the tape. And Bermuda seems to have more than its share of bad weather.

When the sea was not calm, Lagorio's Zodiac, obviously, rose and fell with the swell. And, just as obviously, the microphones rose and fell with Lagorio's Zodiac. . . and that section of tape was garbled. Lagorio tried everything that his not inconsiderable ingenuity could devise to compensate for this surface motion: buoys, floaters, springs, and, finally — which gave the best results — a Rube Goldberg arrangement of springs and pipes that, somehow, worked.

The chief disappointment of the *Curlew*'s team during their stay at Bermuda was their failure to record the sounds exchanged between a whale mother and her calf. It was impossible to get close to any of the mothers and to keep them in one spot. They could have used the virazeou on the calf; but then the Zodiac's noise would have prevented them from recording, because the sound of its motor would have drowned out any exchange between the mother and its calf.

Among the recordings made of humpback whales at Bermuda, there is nothing that goes beyond the range of the unaided human ear. The highest frequencies used by the whales were 8000 or 9000 cycles per second. Lagorio was prepared to record up to 35 kilocycles, but there was nothing taped that went into the ultrasonic range.

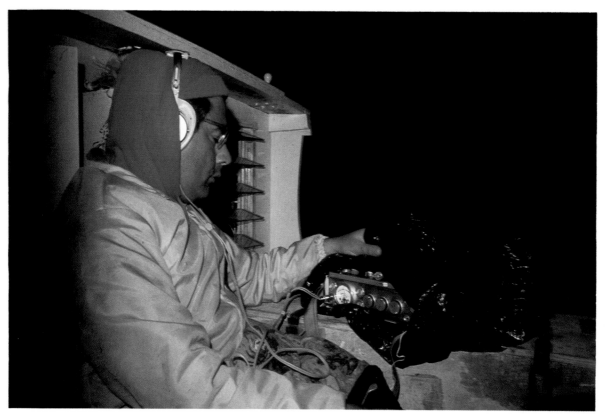

Eugène Lagorio, called "Gegène," with all his gear for recording the sounds of whales.

(Right) *Calypso*'s team listening to the whale "talk" recorded by Lagorio, who is to the right and wearing earphones.

Gray Whales

In the lagoons of Baja California, the water was extremely dirty; so much so that at the entrance to the lagoons we could scarcely see the whales. But we compensated for this by being able to hear them very well indeed.

It was again Lagorio who taped their voices. Usually, he stationed himself in one of the launches at a certain point, and lowered his microphones. Then, earphones in place, he would wait. He could locate the whales by sound as they approached his boat, and he could see the waves that they made on the surface. But the water was so cloudy that he could scarcely see what they were doing. Indeed, visibility was so poor that he often had the frightening

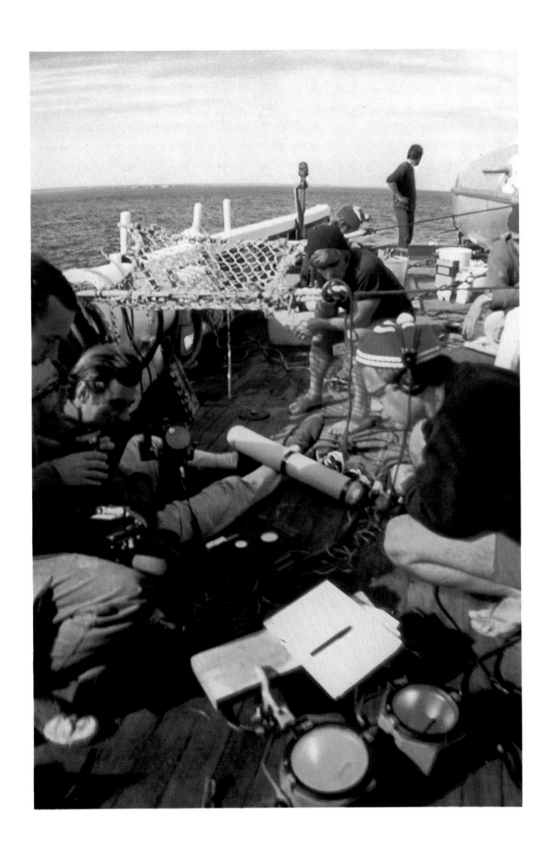

impression that the animals were heading straight for him and would ram the boat.

Then, at a given moment, the frequency of the whales' sounds increased perceptibly. They had sensed the boat in the water and were establishing its location and its shape by their echo-location system. The sonic waves they sent out sounded like ta-ta-ta-ta. . . . Then the transmission ended by a continuous trilling sound: trrrrr.

The animals increased their sounds in order to obtain more precise information on the object in their path. And, finally, Lagorio, without being able to see the school, could hear them turning away and swimming in another direction as their sounds decreased to a normal rhythm.

Lagorio and his team ordinarily went out in their launch very early in the morning, before dawn, because we had noticed that this was often the time that the gray whales entered the lagoon. (At night, they went out into the open sea, and returned to the lagoon at daybreak.)

It was therefore the best time to listen to them. But, again, there were problems in recording. The microphones drifted in the current, while the launch was blown in the opposite direction by the wind. Moreover, the choppy water striking the boat's hull garbled the sounds of the whales on the tape.

Despite these obstacles, Lagorio succeeded, on one occasion, in recording the sonar exchange between a mother whale and her calf. Their two trills are clearly recognizable. The mother's "clicks" are louder than those of the baby whale. And Lagorio saw their two dark silhouettes gliding alongside the hull of his boat.

These sonar messages were not the only sounds picked up by the microphones. Gray whales also emit the short mouselike squeaks that we had heard among the humpback whales of Bermuda. But gray whales are less talkative than their humpback cousins, and their voices are less strong.

A Time for Silence

An observation of Philippe's on gray whales deserves to be reproduced here:

"In the Matancitas lagoon," he says, "we would lower a Zodiac into the water, and then put down a microphone. If we listened for a while, we would hear a large number of very diverse sounds. The whales were there, all around us, but invisible. They had increased their sonar transmissions, however, because they were in such dirty water.

Eugène Lagorio, our sound engineer, records "the song of the whales".

"We dived with aqua-lung equipment, and the whales located us from far off. They passed under us; but visibility was so bad that we could hardly make them out, and they quickly disappeared into the gloom.

"What was strangest about the whole thing was that, as soon as they had located us, it seemed that all whale sounds in the lagoon ceased instantly. All that we could hear through the earphones was the noise from the bottom — especially from the crustaceans. Obviously, there was a rule of silence; a rule that one of the whales had invoked. And it worked, for there was instant and general silence. The tapes are a record of this phenomenon. At a given moment, there was not a sound to be heard from a whale on any track.

"Very likely, the 'silent treatment' was a security measure that the gray whales had developed as protection against marine animals whose hearing is as keen as their own; against killer whales, for example."

A Long-Distance Conversation

It has been said that the cry of a humpback whale in the Arctic Sea can be heard by another whale at the equator; but this, of course, has never been demonstrated. Whatever the case, we know for a fact that the sonic range of whales is fantastic.

How far do their sounds really carry? It all depends on the species, and perhaps on other circumstances: migration, the mating season, and so forth. There are certain empirical data that may begin to answer the question. We know, for example, that gray whales swim at an average speed of 5 to 6 knots.

Now, we hear gray whales one hour before we see them, and we can hear their sounds one hour after they have passed our position. It should be added that the cries of gray whales are far from being as loud as those of humpback whales.

Dr. Payne, an eminent American authority on humpback whales, is of the opinion that this species uses sound corridors — "deep sound channels," they are called — to communicate with one another over long distances. Moreover, water is a better conductor of sound than air, and it is an excellent transmitter for the sonic emissions of whales. It seems likely that humpback whales choose the place, and the depth, that is especially favorable to the dissemination of their sounds. It is also possible that a particular sound may be relayed from one group of whales to another throughout the course of a migration.

Another Mystery

What organ produces the sounds that a whale makes? How are the sounds made? No one knows for sure, and the experts are still studying the problem. One complicating factor is the fact that cetaceans, noisy as they are, have no vocal chords. They do have, however, a larynx, and a respiratory tract, and a blowhole — all of which may be used to produce sounds. But these are very complicated organs and systems which we have hardly begun to understand.

The problem has been studied especially with dolphins in captivity, and researchers have been able to distinguish two basic kinds of sound: "cracks" and whistles. The cracks are produced regardless of whether the blowhole is open or closed, but their frequency is different in each case. But high-frequency sounds apparently can be produced only when the blowhole is closed. From this, one can conclude that cetacean sounds are produced by a

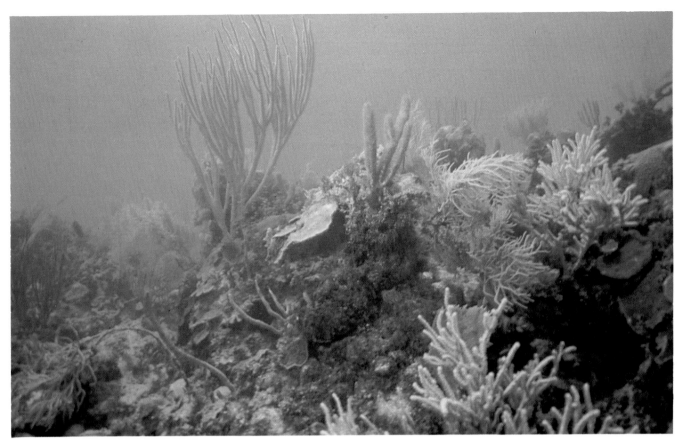

A sight familiar to *Calypso*'s men: sea fans and coral—this time on the level reef that surrounds the main island of Bermuda.

complex of anatomical factors, of which the blowhole is only a part.

We could hardly hope to resolve this mystery of sound merely by observing sperm whales and baleen whales in the open sea. Nonetheless, I remember Philippe's excitement during a dive when he saw a stream of modulated bubbles emerging from a humpback whale's blowhole — which meant that the whale was there, in front of Philippe, talking. Perhaps it was even talking to *him* — a dialogue of the deaf.

The Invisible Ear

Cetaceans, even though they have no visible external ear, have a great advantage over fish: they have a middle ear, and an internal ear. Fish, on the other hand, have only an internal ear, and they cannot locate the origin of a sound that they hear. Cetaceans, however, do have an external ear — one which we cannot see because it is buried in the animal's skin.

The middle ear and the internal ear have properties that no doubt assure very keen hearing. The middle ear is partially surrounded by a substance that resembles beaten egg whites; and the internal ear has sensory cells that are especially well developed — like those of animals who hear ultrasonic noises (bats, mice, cats).

Another very important peculiarity is the unusual size of the auditory nerve in cetaceans. In the human brain, the centers of vision and hearing are of the same size. Among cetaceans (and bats), however, the acoustical centers are larger than those of sight. It should be noted that both cetaceans and bats at one point in their evolution abandoned life on land and adapted to another way of life: bats, to a nocturnal life in the air; and cetaceans to a life in the water which reduced visibility.

Cetaceans and Language

We know that society and language are related. We know also that whales are social animals, and that they communicate with one another. It is our ambition not only to listen to, but also to understand, the conversation of these social animals among themselves.

With land animals, the human voice has a function: it warns, it quiets, and, sometimes, it commands. What can it do, however, with cetaceans? One day, we will know. Man is trying — *we* have tried — to enter into verbal communication with these animals. But these have been clumsy efforts and vague attempts. Nonetheless, the cetaceans do not run away when we try. They stay; and we might even say that, in certain instances, they seem to be willing to co-operate. All of man's experiences with dolphins and killer whales in captivity indicate this. We have recorded their voices and sounds on miles of tape. It is not likely that we will learn to interpret their language very soon; but we are at least in a position to begin studying it.

It seems likely that, when man and cetacean communicate, it will be by means of sound, by voice. But communication does not consist in the mutual production of sound. Dr. Lilly has tried, in vain, to teach English to dolphins. But dolphins speak only dolphinese. If anyone is going to learn a new language, then it must be man. And there is no obvious reason why man cannot learn the language of the dolphins.

Nearsighted Whales

Baleen whales and sperm whales guide themselves by their sonar equipment, and hearing is the sense that is most important for them. Sight also plays a part in their sensory system.

The eyes of most cetaceans are blue, and slightly clouded. But they are eyes, as divers will tell you, that are full of life. Seen from close, they are quite beautiful — blue-black orbs that shine like crystal. But the eyes are small, and have the appearance of nearsightedness. This is true at least of baleen whales and cachalots. Killer whales seem to have excellent vision.

The size of a whale's eye in proportion to the body is almost unbelievable. One would say that everything grew except the eye. Man's eyes constitute one seventieth of his body; those of a mole — traditionally a nearsighted animal — are one eightieth of its body. But the eyes of a whale are only one six-hundredth of its overall mass. Perhaps he does not need more; for even when a whale is swimming on the surface, his eyes remain in the water.

Some divers claim that whales — especially humpback whales — seem careful not to disturb a man in the water. It is not known for sure whether or not that characteristic has anything to do with a whale's vision. And, for that matter, humpback whales, when they take action to avoid running into a man in the water, do so by raising their flippers. This means that they are probably aware of the man's presence in front of them through sonar, and not by sight; for their eyes are on the sides of their head and they do not have front vision.

None of this means that the whale's eyes are useless. His vision may be different from ours, or it may be bad; but a whale sees nonetheless. We have taken photographs of whales from as little as three feet away. And the eye that we see is not that of a blind creature.

"In the water," Canoë says, "there can be little doubt that a whale sees you, and that he is looking at you. Sometimes you even feel that it is *not* a kindly look; but that may be because there are several folds of skin under its eyes that make it *look* mean.

"Whenever I met a whale in the water, I always had the feeling that he saw me. And the look that a whale gives you is very different from that of a shark. A shark only glances at you. It passes with the appearance of not having seen you at all. But a whale's look is quite open. He doesn't look at you out of the corner of his eye."

Canoë is a man who has not only encountered cachalots, humpbacks, and gray whales in the water, but who has touched them, and even been towed by them.

Michel Deloire, who has filmed whales — sometimes in rather acrobatic circumstances — says this:

"Several times, I have caught the eye of a whale. I mean that there was no doubt at all in my mind that the whale *saw* me. Of course, that is a purely personal and subjective impression.

"So far as the cachalot is concerned, what gives him such a strange look is that his eyes are so inconspicuous and so hard to locate. They are far back in his head, and very low, almost at the corners of his mouth. Because of their location, these eyes cannot have binocular vision. Do the zones of vision of each eye overlap in front of the whale? For baleen whales, perhaps they do. But I doubt that this is the case for the sperm whale. Because of his enormous head, he must have a blind area in front of him.

"It would seem easy enough to find out about this by a simple experiment. In other words, when a diver is fifty feet in front of a sperm whale, does the whale see him? But it is not that simple. There is always a time when the diver is a bit to the right or to the left — and therefore within the range of those eyes."

A Sensitive Skin

The sense of touch, it seems to me, is third in the order of importance among cetaceans. Actually, I am not talking about "touch" in the same sense that man has that sense, but rather of a special sensitivity that extends over the whole body. The skin of cetaceans is different from that of land mammals: the epidermisis and the dermis are both thinner. Even among the largest whales, they are only about two and one-half inches thick. On the other hand, the layer of blubber which covers the entire body is exceptionally thick. The thinness of the skin probably entails great tactile sensitivity and thus sensations which it is difficult for land creatures to imagine. . .

We have, on several occasions, seen whales rubbing against one another. This action is almost always the preliminary to mating. Whale calves also seem to thrive on physical contact with their mothers; and they seem to enjoy rubbing against the hull of *Calypso*.

Lagorio was a witness to the following scene: in Scammon Lagoon, a baby whale left its mother's side to rub against *Polaris III*. The mother immediately went after the calf, pushed it far away from the ship — and then struck it several times with her flippers. The blows had every appearance of being slaps, and they were obviously administered in order to teach the baby not to confuse a ship's hull with a mother's stomach.

There is no doubt in my mind that cetaceans, like land animals, love to be petted and stroked. Dolphins, pilot whales, and killer whales in captivity seem to enjoy physical contact with humans. According to trainers and keep-

(Right) Between whales, our divers enjoy the splendid coral waters.

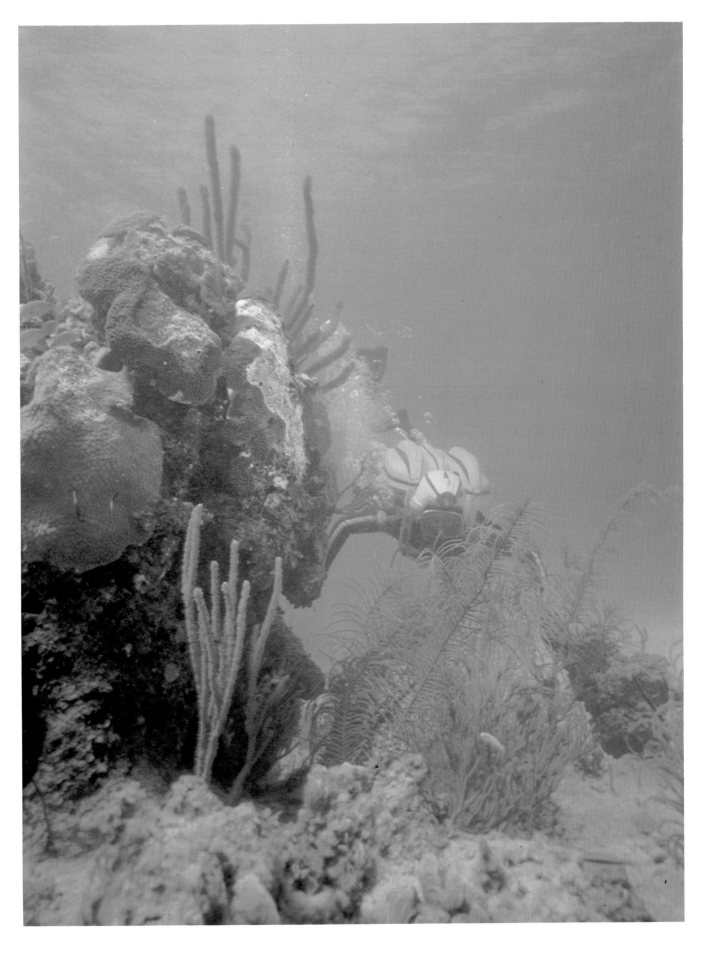

ers in aquatic zoos, the best way to domesticate one of these animals is by touching it, or brushing it.

There are other aspects of cetaceans' tactile sense that we know almost nothing about. Finback whales, for instance, have small bumps at the end of their snout; and several species have very sensitive "whiskers" on their cheeks. And the cells that are found in different organs may indicate the presence of another sense, one related to the perception of variations in water pressure or turbulence.*

So far as we can tell, cetaceans are not especially well endowed with respect to the other senses. At the base of their tongues, as in the case of man's tongue, they have "buds" — taste buds. We may therefore believe that whales are capable of appreciating the taste of krill, or squid. But we cannot say that cetaceans are difficult to please when it comes to food. They are not equipped to be gourmets; for the "taste nerve" which runs from the tongue is very small, and probably does not convey very intense taste sensations.

The sense of smell, which is well developed among fish, is very weak, or nonexistent, among marine mammals. It is completely absent in toothed cetaceans, and only rudimentary among baleen whales. In their blowholes — which are their nostrils — cachalots do not have the equivalent of the nerve cells that humans have. Baleen whales, however, have retained a certain number of olfactory cells.

Them and Us

The little that we know certainly does not allow us to form an adequate idea of the sensory life of cetaceans. We can say, however, that life is very complex, and occupies an important place within the framework of animal psychology. (Let us remember, for example, that the cachalot's brain is the largest of any animal in existence, and that its skull also contains an extraordinary and mysterious organ: the "tank," in which the spermaceti is enclosed.)

We have no way of knowing what the emotional life of these giants may be. We can hardly even imagine what it must be like to live in the water, and guide oneself by sonar, to depend more on sound than on sight. We can only resign ourselves to the fact that we will never be able to feel what a whale "feels."

---

*The "whiskers" seem to be the only capillary growth on the whale's body. The embryo does, however, have some hair growth.

A Whale's-Eye View of Man

Naturalists, as well as novelists, have always been concerned with what man knows and thinks about whales. But no one has ever wondered what whales think about man. This question has been much discussed aboard *Calypso* and everyone has his own opinion.

Philippe says that "when you latch onto a whale's back, it is like performing a trick on the trapeze or going up in a balloon. It is exciting for man. But I doubt that it does anything at all for the whale. They simply continue on their way. We probably annoy them somewhat, like a fly buzzing around a man. I doubt that they find us amusing. But they are so powerful that they do not even find it necessary to react, or to show any resentment or aggressiveness."

It would be interesting to know what whales think about us, what kind of creatures they believe we are, what sort of mental image they have drawn of us through their nearsighted view and their sonar equipment.

In the sea, they go out of their way to watch divers. They are, obviously, curious. A veteran diver in Bermuda assures us that a whale used to pay him regular visits while he was working on a particular job. I believe him. Whales, like dolphins, seem to seek out human company. We, unfortunately, are not in the same position. We cannot disappear when we wish. But whales can lose a diver in ten seconds by one swish of its tail, or dive straight down and vanish. So long as we are not able to go where they go and to stay by their side, we will never bridge the gap that separates us.

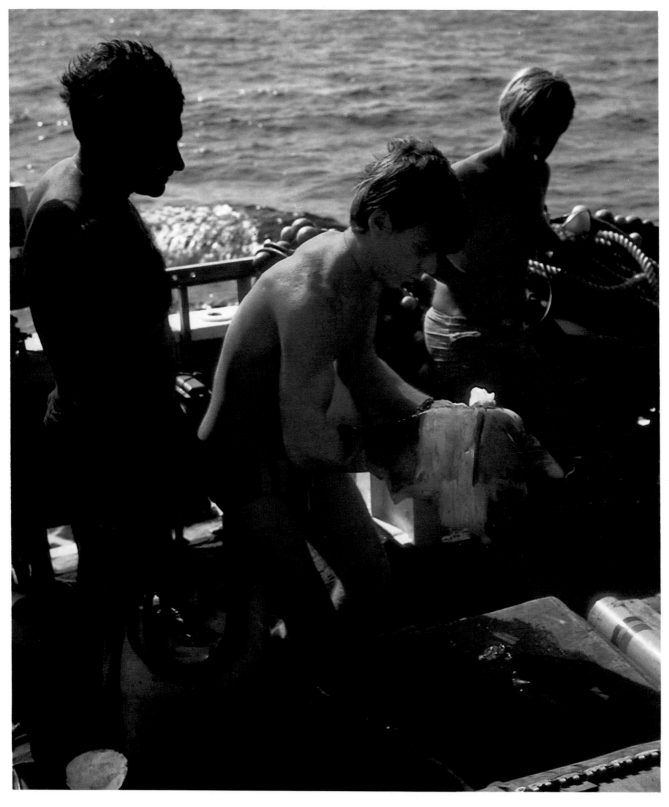

A piece of tail fin from a giant squid, which we found floating in the sea, is an object of great curiosity. It is being held by our chef—who plans to serve it for lunch.

SIX

The World's Greatest Flesh Eaters

It is May 20. We are in the Indian Ocean, and the weather is almost beautiful. Dawn is just breaking — and Didi Dumas reports a whale spouting off *Calypso*'s stern. Soon, we see others, many others, ahead of us on the horizon.

At eight o'clock, Dominique Sumian, who is on watch in the crow's-nest, calls out:

"Captain, there is something white floating to port."

Instantly, everyone is alert. On the sea, the most ordinary object may be a clue to what we do not see, or do not understand; to something that is happening, or has happened, beneath the surface. Any seaman worthy of the name must have in him the soul of what we call in French a *badaud* — that is, an unhurried browser in the marketplace of life, curious, eager for the unexpected, on the alert for something that will dissipate (or create) a mystery.

I take the binoculars and look. Dominique was right. There is something, a large white object. But what is it? It never occurs to us not to find out. Bebert takes one of the Zodiacs and brings back the object, holding it at arm's length. It is a large, heavy piece of flesh, white and flaccid — a piece of a giant squid's tail. The front part of it is torn, and it is covered with punctures similar to those inflicted by the teeth of a cachalot or a pilot whale.

Everyone is excited. We are no doubt close to a school of sperm whales. Apparently, there has just been a battle at the bottom of the sea, for the piece of squid is still fresh. In fact, it is so fresh that our chef announces that we are going to have it for lunch. It doesn't seem to bother anyone that we will eat the crumbs from a cachalot's table.

Bebert has also brought back a piece of flesh shaped like a saucer, or rather like a plate. It is one of the squid's suction cups. Dr. François measures it, and announces that its diameter is 24 inches. This, obviously, was a "small" giant squid. Its body probably measured between 8 and 10 feet — in addition to the large arms, of course. A handsome specimen, no doubt, and a worthy opponent.

As it turned out, it was also inedible, except by a cachalot. Our chef cooked the piece of the tail with garlic, but it was so tough that we could not cut it. And as for the suction cup, it was too horrible for us to describe. It was as though we had tried to make a meal out of a hunk of soft rubber.

Sperm whales apparently have no objection to this kind of diet. In fact, being devoted flesh eaters, they prefer squid to anything else. They find this delicacy in very deep water — between 2000 and 3500 feet — where the squid sometimes reach a length of forty feet. But cachalots will eat not only squid and octopus, but also just about anything else. So far as diet goes, they are easy to please, and consume quantities of giant crustaceans, seals, rays, and even sharks 10 or 12 feet long. Even so, they show a marked preference for cephalopods. We can therefore conclude that sperm whales, which are capable of remaining below the surface for as much as two hours, dive down to the bottom and swim for several miles there in search of anything edible. Their natural radar undoubtedly plays a great part in this hunt in the darkness of the deep.

The "monster squid" of the depths, the fantastic "Karken," is not a creature of legend. It exists in reality, but it is little known because it is almost impossible to capture since it comes to the surface only rarely, and then only at night. This is above all the case with the *Architeuthis,* the largest of the giant squids. No man has ever seen an *Architeuthis* except as food not yet digested in the stomach of a sperm whale. In the stomach of a whale killed near the Azores, a squid was found whole and intact, with its tentacles. It was 35 feet long and weighted 397 pounds. The sperm whale itself measured 47 feet in length.

The giant squid is by no means an easy prey for a cachalot. It has a well-developed nervous system, excellent eyes, and salivary glands that secrete a poison. We can surmise that a sperm whale's attack depends upon surprise. It tries to rush in and swallow the squid before the latter has time to resist. From the remains that we found today, it is evident that he does not always succeed. And when this is the case, the battle between these two giants, with such different weapons, must be on a scale beyond our power to conceive. The squid attempts to position his tentacles on the eyes and the blowhole of the cachalot, and rips at his attacker with his beak; and the whale, in the meantime, is trying to regain the surface while holding the squid's enormous weight on its head. One can imagine the whale tearing at the squid's soft body with those terrible teeth, as pieces of the victim float to the surface. But the battle continues still, for the squid's vital organs are not easy to reach, even for a cachalot.

We can only imagine what these battles must be like in the blackness of the great depths. Both the squid and the cachalot must use wit as well as force; for they are both magnificently (though differently) armed; and it is likely that their intelligences, though also different, are comparable. To the terrible jaw of the cachalot, the squid opposes its tentacles, suction cups, and beak. And, because of their highly developed nervous systems and senses, cephalopods are able to move as quickly, and with as much precision, as vertebrates. Moreover, given their undoubted intelligence, in combination with these weapons, they are adversaries worthy of the great sperm whales.

A Collector of Teeth

Calypso's divers, whenever they meet a cachalot in the open water, are always struck most by the animal's enormous square head, in which the eyes are situated far to the rear. The mouth also is strangely placed. It is far down from the whale's rounded muzzle, and, indeed, might almost be described as being on the whale's underside. The lower jaw is comparatively narrow and thin, and it carries the whale's teeth: sixty of them, in two parallel rows. Some of these teeth weigh six or seven pounds and are eight inches long — which, given the size and weight of the cachalot, are rather modest dimensions. These teeth fit into sockets in the upper jaw, where there are only tiny vestigial teeth.

The cachalot's teeth are all alike. That is, there are no incisors or molars, and they are used only for seizing the whale's prey. For this great animal, who to all appearances is so well armed and a flesh eater, does not have the teeth of a carnivore. The cachalot does not pulverize his food, nor does he chew. He does not even really bite. Instead, he swallows his food whole, in a gulp.

Aboard *Calypso*, everyone has more or less specialized in a particular area of marine life, and this specialization often has little to do with one's assigned job on the ship. The consuming passion of Marcellin, our electrician, is coral; and Laban, the engineer, dives to paint underwater landscapes. Delemotte has a special calling as a collector of teeth. He has brought back walrus teeth from the islands of the Pacific, and killer-whale teeth from Alaska. To these treasures he now adds cachalot teeth from the Maldives. His collection is actually quite instructive, and even beautiful. It is a pleasant pastime to look at these handsome bits of polished ivory — so long as they are not attached to a monstrous jaw.

We spend much of our limited leisure time discussing these various specialties and avocations among ourselves, and there is much sagacious nodding and much stroking of beards. For, in the ancient maritime tradition, *Calypso*'s men have always distinguished themselves by their personal adornment as well as by their accomplishments. There was the era of turn-of-the century mustaches. Now, we are at the stage of beards and long hair. And everyone, of course, is perfectly free to experiment as much as he likes, since there is no one to witness either failure or success in this line except seals and cormorants and whales.

Bernard Delemotte's beard, which serves as a resting place for his curved pipe, is reddish blond, and Philippe's is brown and curly. Some of the divers sport the royal beard of King Louis XIII; and others, a more modern style of short, square beard. There are even some who favor the elaborate sideburns and mustaches of the Emperor Franz Joseph. It is something of a shock to see these time-honored decorations protruding from a diving mask. . . Only Laban has remained faithful to hairlessness of face and skull (and one is as unnatural as the other, for he shaves his head every day).

What would Jonah think of all this, I wonder. The truth is that his own story is not entirely a myth, and that for Jonah, certainly, it was a miracle. It has actually happened that a man who fell into the sea was swallowed by a whale. And, like Jonah, he was not chewed or ground up. He did not, however, emerge alive after three days. His chest was crushed, and by the time his body was recovered, the whale's gastric juices had begun to work on the corpse. This modern-day-Jonah story was recorded by the man who performed the autopsy on both the man and the whale, Dr. Egerton Y. Davis of Boston, in the 1947 issue of *Natural History* magazine. Shortly afterward, Dr. Davis, his scientific curiosity piqued, found a man who was willing to play Jonah experimentally. The man crawled, feet first, into the mouth of a sixty-five foot (dead) sperm whale. The throat, however, was so narrow that he was able to get through it only with difficulty. According to Davis, a man would be

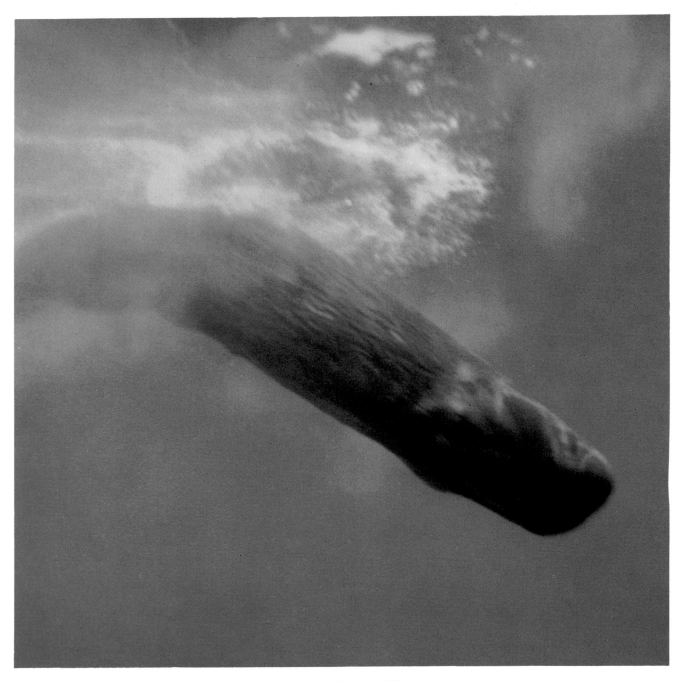

The massive, indescribable form of a sperm whale, seen diving.

dead before reaching the whale's stomach. And as for spending three days alive in a whale, that would be absolutely impossible.

The "Teeth" of Toothless Whales

All cetaceans are carnivorous and consume an enormous quantity of living flesh. It would be impossible for them to feed their giant bodies if they lived on dry land. (And, in fact, even in the age of the dinosaurs, there never existed creatures of comparable size.) Whales can survive, and find the incredible amount of nourishment that they require, only in the living wealth of the sea; for a whale's mouthful of food can weigh more than a ton.

In order to feed itself, a baleen whale, while continuing to swim along, opens its gigantic mouth. The under-jaw is lowered; and the pleated crop—which is half the length of the whale's body—swells up as it takes in several tons of water, along with whatever food is in the water. The mouth then closes. The baleen in the upper jaw acts as a sort of strainer and, as the crop contracts, the water is forced through the baleen. The whale then swallows the solids that have remained in its mouth: crustaceans, jellyfish, small fish. But, even knowing this, to see a finback whale feeding, with its gigantic mouth open, is one of the most astonishing and awesome spectacles that a diver can witness. Bonnici saw it once, in the Indian Ocean. Our handsome finback whale – the one on whose dorsal fin Bonnici had hitched a ride – was the animal in question. When its mouth was closed, one could see only the lips, and a rather elongated and almost flat muzzle. On a single occasion, when Bonnici was present, that mouth opened. He could see the baleen grill, laid out in a circle of black and white, like something out of a nightmare. Then, the cavelike orifice closed without a sound, without a ripple. The head was flat once more, and the baleen was once more a secret. But the whale had not eaten, and we have no idea why it chose that particular occasion to exhibit its oral equipment. Was it a yawn? Or was it a sign of irritation – of resentment against Bonnici's antics? That is not important. What is important is that we succeeded in seeing and in photographing the toothless whale's baleen.

These whalebone fixtures are one of the strangest attributes of the *Mysticeti,* or toothless whales. They sometimes measure nine or ten feet in length, and seem to be closer in composition to fingernails than to teeth. (This was the "whalebone" of whalebone-corset fame.) They are tough, but flexible, and are found only in the upper jaw. Moreover, they are edged with a fringe , the spacing of which depends upon the size of the crustacean that the particular species of whale eats. Thus, the finback, who eats very small lifeforms, has a filter as fine as wool. And the blue (or sulphur-bottomed) whale, who subsists on larger crustaceans and on small fish, has a more widely spaced fringe.

Regardless of what whales eat, the fact remains that they require tons of food every day. And their primary task is to find this food. In summertime, they seek it in the highest latitudes, in the Arctic and Antarctic where the extended daylight of the long days causes the development of a photoplankton that entails the production of a zooplankton which whales devour.

At this time of year, whales gorge themselves twenty-four hours a day in the polar regions. They will need this nutrition when they begin their polar migration, in the course of which they do not eat at all. The subcutaneous layer of blubber which is formed is a reserve food supply for this trek; but it is also an indispensable form of insulation for these warm-blooded animals. (Indeed, whales are so well insulated that their bodies remain warm as long as thirty-six hours after their death.) Moreover, this layer is composed of tissues that are lighter than water, and which therefore offset the weight of the whale's body. In combination with the air in the whale's lungs, the layer makes it possible for the whale to float.

To give one an idea of the amount of nourishment that is involved when whales feed, let me mention that a young finback whale, while he is growing, eats about three and one half tons of plankton a day. An adult finback consumes between a ton and a ton and one half — which means that he takes into his mouth, and filters out, approximately one million cubic meters of water every single day.

An Orgy of Krill

The basic food of the baleen whale is krill *(Euphausia superba),* a crustacean that is never more than two to two and a half inches long. Krill are found in greatest abundance at about depths of between 35 feet and 350 feet, even though they exist as far down as 3000 feet. In the waters of the Arctic and Antarctic, during the summer months, veritable blankets of krill cover hundreds of square miles of surface — so much so that the water takes on a reddish-brown color from the carotene (rich in Vitamin A) in their bodies. For the whales, of course, this is a feast without limit. They are surrounded by food, and have only to open their mouths in order to eat their fill.

Their menu is not limited to krill. In addition to this unique dish and the plankton, the whales sometimes swallow fish — and occasionally even a penguin, perhaps in the course of a yawn. In the stomachs of our humpback whales, for example, naturalists have found mackerel, herring, whiting, cuttlefish, and even a cormorant.

"Even though there are at least eight species of toothless whales," Ted Walker remarks, "each species seems to prefer a kind of crustacean that is not found everywhere in the oceans. Thus, the various kinds of whales do not conflict in their search for food."

Front view of a sperm whale. This is what our cameramen and photographers see coming toward them in the water.

The Nightmare of the Toothless Whale

Our friend the gray whale is very eclectic when it comes to food. During the summer, along the coasts of Siberia, it eats crustaceans from the bottom: amphipods. During the winter, in the lagoons of Baja California (where we observed it), it eats shellfish, clams.

When Philippe was diving in the lagoon of Matancitas he saw how the whales "fished" for their favorite mollusks. They always did so at low tide, and when the tide was slack, they slept. When the tide was either going out or coming in, the whales could be seen grouping and then swimming in or out against the current. They found food by holding themselves toward the side at a 90° angle and digging trenches on the bottom with their bodies. They would take sand and water into their mouths along with shellfish, and then rise to the surface and, with their heads sticking straight above the surface, filter out the liquid through their baleen by using their tongues as pistons. The sand was expelled with the water, and the shellfish were swallowed — partly by the force of gravity, and partly, no doubt, by the action of the esophageal muscles.

Observers have long wondered why gray whales thrust their heads up above the surface as though they were inspecting their surroundings. They are able to maintain this position for about a minute at a time — a position that is called "spyhopping." Old-time whalers believed that the whales were watching them. It is more likely, however, judging by what we have seen, that they do this for convenience in eating. Gray whales are able to swallow while in a horizontal position, but a vertical position allows them to filter the debris out of their mouths and to swallow rapidly whatever remains.

It is not entirely safe to watch a whale clam-fishing from too close. This Delemotte, Philippe, and Chauvelin learned the hard way. They had rowed one of the Zodiacs to a position directly over a whale busily engaged in rooting around the bottom. The whale suddenly decided it was time to come up for air, and when she did so the Zodiac was overturned and the three curious inspectors thrown into the water. We all agreed that it was unintentional on the whale's part; an accident. But I suspect that there may be times when a whale, like any other intelligent being, wants privacy. If so, this one made her point.

February 19. We are in Scammon Lagoon. The sky is relatively clear, and so is the water. The weather seems to have put our whales in a good humor, and there is a lot of leaping and playing all around *Calypso*. Is it the same whale who is doing all the jumping, or do they all have spring fever? Our cameraman, Jacques Renoir, sets his camera up on deck and succeeds in filming a sequence that we have attempted many times before without success: a whale leaping completely out of the water, not once but twice in succession. It is likely that when they jump in this way they begin by supporting themselves on the bottom with their tails, and then thrust upward. But this is not absolutely necessary. Blue whales have been seen to leap out of the water in spots where the bottom was 250 feet below them. (This was off the coast of Gabon in Africa.) This sort of "spyhopping," therefore, is not necessarily linked to the whales' feeding habits.

One can imagine what it is like to see a great whale leaping out of the water to become silhouetted against the sky for a moment, and then to fall back with a cataclysmic splash and a noise like a thunderclap. It is no wonder that everyone aboard *Calypso* is intrigued and excited by these gymnastics, and that Ted Walker is bombarded with questions: Is it a game? Or a sexual rite of some kind?

Ted, stroking his gray beard, answers: "Perhaps, perhaps." He himself inclines to a less romantic explanation and believes that these leaps have something to do with the whales' digestive process. They jump, in other words, to help the food go down into their stomachs. This would be true particularly of mollusk shells which whales cannot break because they lack teeth. Moreover, as Ted points out, they have such disproportionately small throats that "sometimes what they eat cannot go down by itself."

Three Stomachs

The whole digestive apparatus of whales is, by human standards, very strange. As I have already mentioned, whales do not chew. Cachalots cannot do so because they have no molars; and baleen whales because they have no teeth at all. Since they all swallow their food whole, whales must necessarily have strong stomachs. And, in fact, many of them have three separate stomachs, or gastric pouches. The first one, or forestomach, produces no gastric juices, but serves to pulverize the food by means of a very sturdy muscular wall (which among finback whales attains a thickness of two and one half inches). This stomach also contains sand and pebbles, which helps in crushing the food.

The forestomach and the stomach are sufficiently large to hold a ton of krill — about a cubic meter of food. An inventory of an 80-foot finback whale's stomach revealed that it contained five million shrimp weighing two tons.

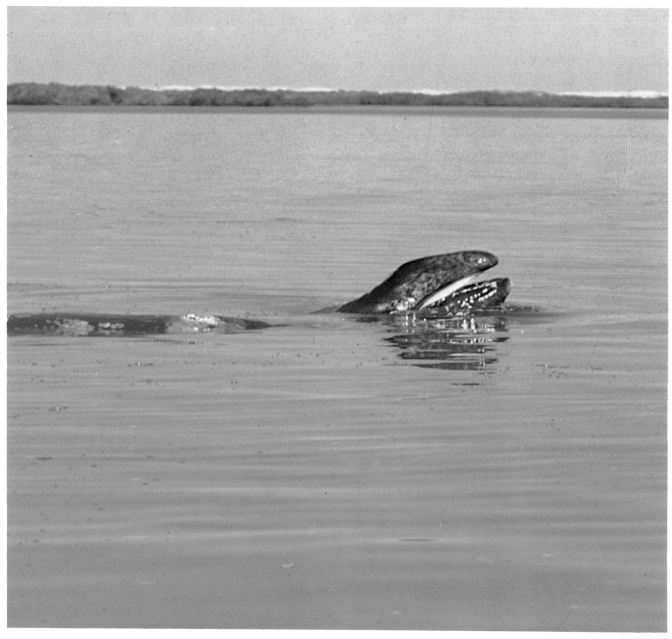

The head of a gray whale submerged in Matancitas lagoon.

The third stomach, which secretes digestive juices, is called the "pyloric stomach." It opens into the intestine by means of a circular aperture (the pylorus) — an arrangement which the whale has in common with man.

Sperm whales have only two stomachs. They may swallow a squid in one gulp; but squid have soft flesh that does not require mastication. There is only one hard part to a squid: the beak.

Our chef's experiment with squid meat taught us a lesson that every

Gray whales seem to raise themselves out of the water to look around. This is known as "spy-hopping."

cachalot probably knows from birth: one does not attempt to chew a squid, but swallows it whole. The trouble was that, having swallowed it, we needed two stomachs to digest it, like a sperm whale; and, unfortunately, we had only one apiece.

If we had succeeded in swallowing the squid's beak along with the rest of the animal, it is possible that we might have turned into producers of ambergris, that precious substance indispensable in the manufacture of expensive perfumes. Ambergris is found only in the intestines of sperm whales, and it very likely is formed from the beaks of squid that have been digested. The largest block of ambergris ever found in a cachalot's intestine weighed close to a thousand pounds and was worth a fortune.

The chances are that cachalots would have fared better at the hands of the whalers if it had not been for ambergris; for their flesh is mediocre and their oil inferior to that of baleen whales. Ambergris ("gray amber"), however, has always been highly regarded, first for the medicinal qualities imputed to it, and, now, for the strange quality that it has of causing a scent to linger. In addition, sperm whales offer another treasure: an exceptionally pure wax, called spermaceti.

A whale's digestive tract terminates in the intestine — and what an intestine it is, being much longer, proportionately, than that of man or of any land animal. The human intestine is five or six times the length of a man's body. That of a cachalot is twenty-four times the whale's length.* In a whale 55 feet long, the intestine measures over a thousand feet. That of a dolphin is less developed; it is only twelve times the length of the dolphin's body.

A Visit to the Pantry

However familiar we may be with whales — and no team has approached as many whales as we have in the waters of every sea of the world — our astonishment never lessens at their size, their strength, their gentleness, and their appetites.

Whales are the only creatures truly created on a scale worthy of the seas themselves. But are the nutritional resources of the seas equal to the task of feeding whales? Do whales struggle to find the necessary food, or is it easily available in sufficient quantity for them?

In the Arctic and Antarctic, as we have seen, whales find their tables already set, and groaning under an indescribable load of food. When they leave the polar regions to mate in the tropical zones, however, they eat hardly at all, and perhaps not at all. This is generally true — although we have noticed that gray whales and humpback whales do not turn up their noses at an occasional mollusk or crustacean.

Sperm whales, those mortal enemies of the giant squid, are another matter. Their principal habitat seems to be between 40°north and 40°south; and

*According to Sarah R. Riedman and Elton T. Gustafson, in *Home is the Sea for Whales.*

these are the farthest limits of their migrations. Unlike baleen whales, they cannot simply open their mouths and swallow a few million tiny crustaceans whenever they wish. They must seek out their prey, and sometimes they must fight in order to eat. They are not only meat eaters, but flesh eaters.

From this, two questions arise: Do sperm whales find enough victims in the sea? And do they find them in the comparatively restricted area in which they live?

It is my impression, from what I have seen in the Red Sea and the Indian Ocean, that cachalots move about with their sonar systems tuned toward the bottom, apparently in search of prey. This is probably also true of other cetaceans: dolphins, grampuses, and pilot whales. We can use *Calypso*'s sonar device in much the same way, in order to discover the layer below us that is richest in life forms. And it is my ambition not only to find the pantry of the whales, but to visit it, and if possible to make an inventory of it.

Plankton Soup

During our expedition in the Indian Ocean, I noticed that there were certain places, at about the level of the equator, where we were almost certain to come across killer whales, sperm whales, pilot whales, dolphins, and sharks, all in the same area. It seemed to me that these large marine animals all gathered there because of the abundance of food, and I wanted to investigate the truth of this supposition. For this sort of undertaking, we have aboard the SP-350 — the minisub — which would be ideal in determining the density of life at various levels of the sea.

Here are my journal notes:

April 8. Our first day on the high seas after leaving the Maldives.

In order to make sure that we will not miss anything, I have the automatic camera in the observation chamber checked in the morning and again in the evening. This camera records every living being passing within range of the *Calypso*'s prow, beginning at 6:30 A.M.

Saturday, April 9. We are traveling practically along the equator. Right now, my intention of running an inventory of the biological resources in these waters seems almost ridiculous. The job is simply too great to be undertaken. From the surface, one would think that the sea is empty; but we do not know what is going on 200, 300, or 3000 feet beneath the surface. It is my old dream — to see beneath the surface, to see and understand what no man has yet been able to see and understand.

After dinner we have our first minisub dive in the open sea. We have

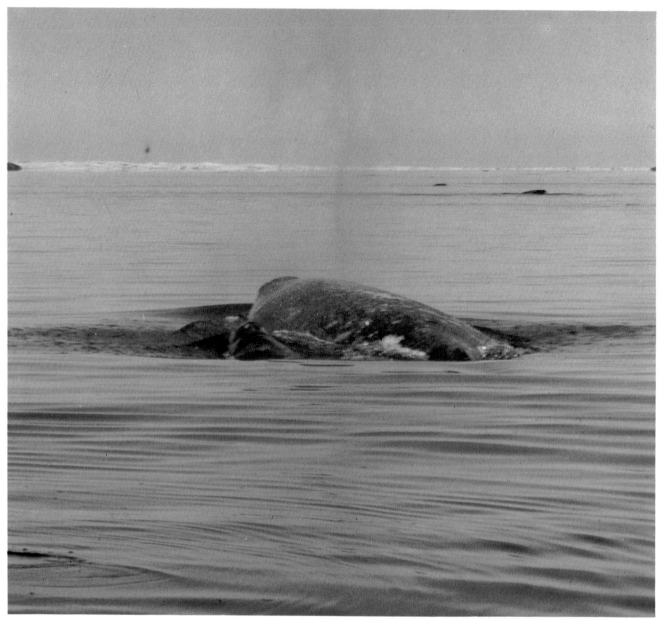

A gray whale, accompanied by her calf, in Matancitas lagoon.

often talked about doing this, but we have never done it before. We lower the minisub into the water and attach it to our launch by a nylon line 1200 feet long. Bebert is in the minisub, and Maurice Leandri in the launch. Aboard *Calypso*, I am in touch with the minisub by sonar, and with the launch by walkie-talkie. What we intend to do is to allow the minisub to go down to about 1000 feet, and then to climb. (The purpose of the nylon line is to make sure that we do not lose the minisub.)

There are times — and this is one of them — when I feel that I am wasting

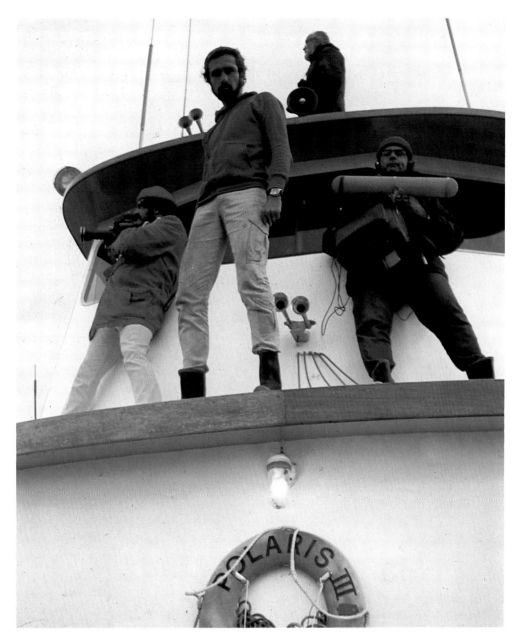

Aboard *Polaris III:* Philippe Cousteau (center) and (right) Eugène Lagorio, our sound engineer.

my time on something absurd. It is almost certain that we will see nothing. The ocean is vast, and the chances are against there being anything to see. Even from our observation chamber, it is very rare that we see anything. To send down the minisub is like looking for the proverbial needle in a haystack, unless — unless the layers of water below *Calypso* are richer than we think. And, of course, at night, when there is a general migration upward toward the surface, we may discover something interesting.

I set the sonar for 12 KC and note two DSL, two layers registering at 100 fathoms and 150 fathoms. At 34 KC, there is only one layer, at 150 fathoms. We shall see what we shall see.

Here is what we find:

75 feet: a plankton soup clouding the water. Little silvery fish from the deep. Tiny shrimp and crustaceans.

150 feet: an even thicker plankton soup. Two small squid who are very curious about Bebert. There are some fish with luminous organs, but it is hard to see them clearly because the water is so cloudy.

300 feet: still plankton soup. A seven-foot shark is circling the minisub and gives it a push.

450 feet: the water is clearing, but there is less life here.

525 feet: shrimp, with very long antennae.

850 feet: nothing. Clear water.

1200 feet: released ballast, and the minisub begins slowly to rise.

700 feet: a very large cephalopod, absolutely immobile about 30 feet from the minisub, is staring fixedly at Bebert. This is sperm-whale bait. Is it sleeping? Dreaming? If a whale comes along, the monster will be swallowed whole.

625 feet: released the second ballast. As the minisub rises, it is escorted by two sharks.

The minisub vertical reconaissance, lasting about one hour, has been very helpful. We now have information on several points:

The registering layer that rises to the surface at night is a cloud of plankton, crustaceans, and small fish from deep water. This cloud rises and falls at a speed of from 2 1/2 to 4 1/2 inches per second.

The water is more cloudy and more filled with small life forms at 150 feet than at 75 feet. And this confirms what we learned during Operation Lumen in the Mediterranean.

Large animals: three sharks, two squids, and an enormous cephalopod. Its great eye is perhaps luminous.

All in all, the dive was successful, and we will have to make more use of the minisubs in this fashion. Unfortunately, the SP-350 cannot go down far enough, and, in the future, we will use the SP-500 and the SP-3000.

One curious thing: the deeper layer, at 150 fathoms, seemed to vanish as the minisub approached it. I saw the same thing happen in the Indian Ocean in 1954 when we used the first automatic cameras with an Edgerton flash. On that occasion, we could see the layer dissipating on the depth finder. Perhaps our huge cephalopod is a part of that mobile layer characterized by negative phototropism.

Squid in Layers

April 11. Everyone in the deck and saucer teams is up at 4 A.M. By 5 A.M., the SP-350 is in the water for a dive that we will call "S-15." Dawn has not yet broken.

Here are our tentative conclusions. Last night's dive (S-14) was made a bit too late in the day. The various layers had probably finished rising. Dive S-15, however, produces results that are more typical: there is a layer at 125 feet, another at 400 feet (which has already sunk). The minisub catches up with the third layer at 725 feet, and finds that it is made up of shrimp and siphonophores swimming toward the bottom as fast as they can.

If we were going about this in a strictly scientific manner, we would have to make hundreds of dives of this kind; and then I would collate all the data as elements toward a study of DSL. But we are here in order to work with film; and, from this standpoint, dives early at night — say, one hour after sunset — seem to be those that find the most life forms (and the strangest) within range of the minisub.

There are two things that we must do better with. First, we must tow the minisub more slowly during its descent and ascent so that its pilot can observe as much as possible. Second, the kind of thing we are going to film will require that we improve our lighting drastically. We will have to work something out.

After dinner, there is another minisub dive, but this time the nylon line is attached to *Calypso* rather than to the launch. In order to assure that the line will not be too slack in the equatorial current, we double the minisub's ballast; and we also fasten the line to the forward bumper, so that the minisub will move front-forward.

The minisub is put in the water at 9:35 P.M., about two hours after sunset. At 10:25 P.M. it is at its maximum depth of 900 feet. At 11:15 it is back on the surface.

This dive is interesting, but disappointing so far as filming is concerned. I hoped to find zones of life corresponding with those expanded and deep layers. Everywhere there were one or two layers of squid. And often there were sharks. And yet, the minisub goes down at random, and its range of visibility is very limited. The tens of thousands of squid are probably the destined prey of the large animals, dolphins, cetaceans. For food to float downward from

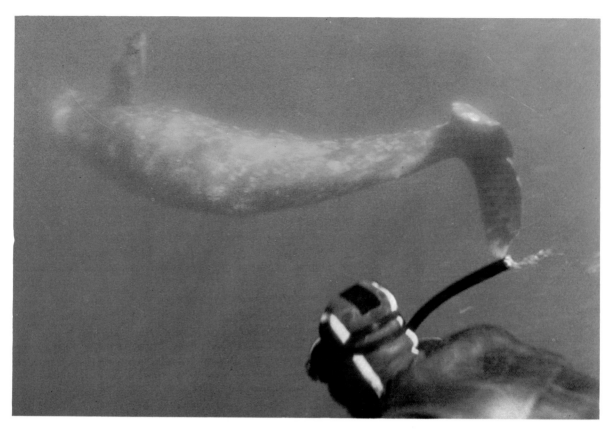

A diver manages to come close to a gray whale.

(Facing page) Launching of the SP350 in the Indian Ocean in order to study the various quantities of food available at different depths.

Canoë and Captain Cousteau are pleased after a good day's work.

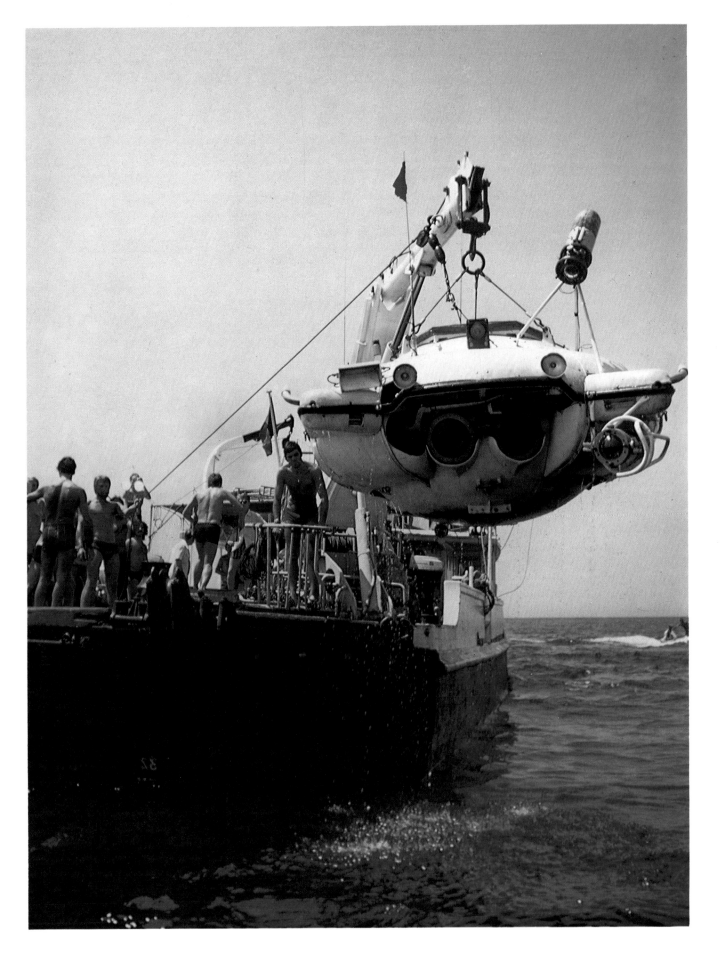

those fields of microscopic algae that comprise the upper layer, the yield (in weight) that is passed from one echelon to the next echelon in the nutritive chain must be greater under water than on dry land.

This, apparently, is so, for almost all the animals are cold-blooded — which means that they do not have to expend calories to maintain their body temperatures (unlike men, cattle, or dolphins). Weight does not exist; and therefore no calories have to be used to keep one upright. Calories are used only to move (and the bodies are designed to make movement as easy as possible) and to *grow*.

Is the whole thing an illusion? These minisub dives have given us unexpected results and have given me a new and broader outlook on marine life. It also seems to me to be a more logical outlook, because we have seen and photographed the huge cephalopod and the schools of squid on which the cachalots feed — which explains the squid's presence here. It is as though someone had given us the key to the pantry that I have been looking for, for so long.

SEVEN

The Art of Love

Love, it is said, makes the world go round. Certainly, it makes the whales go round. Love, or at least sex, is the reason why whales leave the glacial waters of the Arctic for the warm lagoons of Baja California. For, once they have completed the migration, they mate.

The age of sexual maturity among cetaceans varies according to species. For the blue whale, it is five years; for the porpoise, seven years. For most baleen whales, the age at which they are able to reproduce is between two and three years. Sexual maturity, however, does not mark the end of growth among these giants. Having attained puberty, they continue to grow.

In the school of gray whales that Philippe and his team followed southward aboard the *Polaris III*, in addition to the whales who were looking forward to mating, there were also expectant mothers who would give birth to their young in the tranquil waters of the Mexican lagoons. Having carried their calves for almost a year, they sensed their time was near,* and, accord-

---

*The length of the period of gestation among whales depends upon the species in question. For the gray whales, it is twelve months; for sperm whales, it is sixteen months.

Bernard Delemotte succeeds in establishing contact with a gray whale.

ingly, they seemed in great haste to reach their destination. It would have been unthinkable for them to give birth in the open sea. They required shallow water, a protected lagoon, warm waters. And they knew where there was such a place. The pregnant whales formed the advance party of the migrating school. They would be, as they always were, the first to reach Baja California. The others traveled more slowly; they were not expecting, and they could afford a more casual pace.

It was the latter group that the *Polaris III* followed, with our friend Ted Walker aboard. All along the California coast, the team was busy trying to mark and to film individual specimens of the school. And it was with these, the last to arrive, that Philippe and his companions reached the Mexican shores and the Gulf of California.

The coast of Baja California is studded with gray dunes on which no vegetation grows. It forms a complicated network of channels and passes and presents an appearance of strangely beautiful but savage isolation. Al-

Full-face view of a gray whale's head. This photograph was taken in Scammon Lagoon.

together, it is an ideal place for whales in search of privacy, for there is little chance of intrusion by strangers. The marked preference of gray whales for this kind of locale, for sand and solitude, has caused them to be nicknamed "desert whales."

It seemed to Philippe, who was on hand when the whales reached their destination, that they were perfectly familiar with the place. For many of the school, this was not their first visit. They had been here every year over a long period of time, and they remembered the "secret passage" — the inlet — that led to the lagoon; or, if this was their first trip, they followed the older and more experienced members of the school. In any event, they all seemed to know, beyond a doubt, that, just beyond that narrow neck of water, there lay a personal paradise ideal for giving birth, or for practicing the art of love.

These places are so well hidden that, until the middle of the nineteenth century, they were unknown even to the most avid whalers. They were finally discovered in 1852, by Captain Charles Melville Scammon, commanding the brig *Mary Helen.* Scammon had been attracted by a series of spouts seen from afar, and, in his search for their origin, it occurred to him to enter the lagoon. There, he discovered a concentration of whales such as he had never dreamed existed.

Over a period of nine years, Scammon and his harpooners slaughtered whales in the hundreds and filled thousands of barrels with whale oil. Naturally, they kept strictly to themselves the secret of this windfall — the fact that Scammon had happened upon the pass leading into the most populated of the lagoons of Baja California, into what today is known as Scammon Lagoon.

In the tenth year, Scammon's competitors, consumed with envy and determined to share in this good fortune, had spies set upon Scammon's ship. In a short time, his secret was in their hands. Thereafter, the slaughter of gray whales reached such proportions that, by the beginning of the twentieth century, the species was on the verge of extinction. It was saved only by a series of international agreements — agreements which the government of Mexico enforced with commendable severity. Even so, it took almost fifty years for the species to recover from the havoc wrought by Captain Scammon and his fellow whalers; and it was not until the middle of the twentieth century that the gray whale began to be found again in appreciable numbers.

Today, most members of the school are less than thirty-five years old, and they average 50 feet in length. If they are left alone, they will live for another half century or more, and will reach lengths of 55 to 60 feet.

Captain Scammon differed from his associates to the extent that he combined an ardor for whale hunting with a taste for zoological curiosities and a certain talent for writing. He was the author of a book on the subject that he knew better than any of his contemporaries: *Marine Mammals of the Northwest Coast of North America.*

Scammon recorded that, when the female whales were about to give birth, they withdrew to the farthest reaches of the lagoon, which lay about thirty miles inland from the coast. My own observations indicate that expectant mothers seek out isolated spots where the water's greater salinity offers increased floatability, and where the abundance of food enables them to produce adequate amounts of milk. Nonetheless, many of these whales remain near the pass while giving birth.

When I first entered the lagoon, I suspect that my astonishment was at least as great as Captain Scammon's. There were spouts in every direction, almost as far as I could see, rising toward the gray sky. Everywhere, whales were floating on the surface, immobile, apparently asleep. There were at least a hundred of them in sight at that moment.

The Bay of Solitude

After one passes through the channel, Scammon Lagoon comes into view in all its immensity. It is not easy to explore, for channels branch out in every direction. Sandspits, which are exposed at low tide, make navigation difficult. Philippe, when he first reconnoitered the Baja California coast by airplane and boat, selected for us a lagoon other than Scammon: Matancitas, which appeared to be better suited to our work. Matancitas is a narrow strip of water separated from the sea by sand dunes. Entry into Matancitas is feasible only through Boca de la Soledad: the passageway of solitude. There is another channel, but it leads into Magdalena Bay and is very long and winding.

The whales themselves use only Boca de la Soledad, and the *Polaris* chose to follow their lead. In its explorations, it wandered up tiny channels, followed the line of mangroves that border the beaches, and investigated Magdalena Bay. The *Polaris* has a draft of five or six feet, and it often touched bottom in the course of its wanderings. Fortunately on such occasions, the bottom was always of sand or mud, and no damage was done; but the ship's local crew, unaccustomed to this sort of touch-and-go navigation, spent their days in a state of near panic.

As isolated as the region appears, there is a small town in the vicinity, Matancitas, which gave its name to the area. The town comprises nothing more than a canning factory, some fishermen's houses, and a landing field. And, over the whole, there reigns an incredible odor; an odor so strong that those who tried to sleep there for the first time — the *Polaris* was too small for everyone to be able to sleep aboard — found it virtually impossible to do so. The stench is due to the canning factory, whose main product is anchovies, and whose waste is dumped into the lagoon.

The First Dive

The first time that our divers went down into the Matancitas lagoon, they received an unpleasant surprise: the visibility was practically zero. The presence of sand and mud in the shallow water makes it perpetually cloudy.

There was one advantage at Matancitas, however, that made the *Polaris'* team willing to put up with the cloudy water. The fact that the lagoon, lying as it did between two dunes, and comprising the maze of waterways that it

(Following page) A gray whale diving in a lagoon of Baja California.

did, enabled the ship to creep up on the whales without being noticed. The first group of gray whales that the team approached, in fact, was taken completely off guard. Undoubtedly, the animals had been sleeping; but then they awoke with a start, one after the other and, in a great uproar of splashing and spray and gigantic tails smashing about in the water, they disappeared beneath the surface.

Obviously, the team would have to perfect its technique before it could accomplish what everyone was aiming at: the filming of the mating of gray whales.

Gray Whales and Gray Scars

In approaching a whale, the main thing is to proceed as silently as possible and to avoid alarming the animal. The *Polaris,* therefore, now remained at anchor near the entrance to the lagoon while teams of cameramen and divers went out in Zodiacs; and, in order to avoid disturbing the whales with the sound of outboard motors, they were usually Zodiacs propelled by oars.

The whales were drowsing near the center of the lagoon, with their backs barely breaking the surface. Neither their heads nor their tails could be seen; but, every once in a while, the animals would rise slowly to the surface to breathe and then sink again — no doubt without being more than half awake.

Our team had ample opportunity to observe that gray whales are not actually gray, but black; and even the calves are very dark. The skin of the whales, however, has gray markings. These are not natural markings, but scars, caused by barnacles and lampreys. Our divers noted that these parasites do not remain permanently on a whale — but remain long enough, nonetheless, to leave a conspicuous, marbled-gray spot on the mammal's soft, smooth skin. These scars are particularly evident on older whales, since the older ones are those who have suffered the most from these parasites.

The impression received upon approaching a sleeping whale is above all one of enormity. The whale's physical presence is overwhelming, overpowering. From time to time, one hears it breathing, and is perhaps sprinkled by its spout. At that moment, man realizes that he is approaching a life form beyond the scale of human reckoning; a mysterious presence, embodied in an incredible black cylinder. One must picture it in one's mind: a vast black bulk moving very slowly in the metallic-gray water of the lagoon, under Baja California's gray skies. Seen in life, it is a vastly impressive spectacle; and also a somewhat frightening one.

Plane and Parachute

Several days of shooting gained our team hardly more than a few feet of usable film. Despite all imaginable precautions, it was extremely difficult to get close enough to the whales for good shots. One problem was that the Matancitas lagoon, although not as large as that of Scammon, was too extensive to be covered by oar. The divers often attempted to start out from shore and to row out to a group of whales swimming nearby; but they never succeeded in reaching the whales before they disappeared.

At that point, Philippe decided to reconnoiter the lagoon from the air in order to locate groups of whales and to guide the Zodiacs to them.

He therefore began a systematic air search of the lagoon in a Cherokee 300 in the hope of finding a pair of whales mating, or a female giving birth. He was also able, by flying the length of the bay several times a day, to keep an approximate tally of the number of whales entering or leaving the lagoon, to observe the entry channel, and to have an overall view of the daily life of these gigantic mammals that had escaped completely the teams in their Zodiacs.

The Cherokee, however, had a rear door from which a cameraman — well strapped down, with his legs hanging out into the air — could film anything of interest below.

The airplane had one major disadvantage: it made too much noise. It allowed Philippe and the cameraman to find and take the whales by surprise; but the racket from its engine quite obviously upset and frightened them.

Philippe next attempted to solve this problem by using a vertical, or ascensional parachute; and the attempt almost ended in tragedy. The traction cable broke, and its buckle struck Philippe in the face with such force that he had to be fished out of the lagoon, unconscious. In any event, this sort of parachute was useless at Matancitas, for it requires that one leave the ground and land facing the wind. But the Mantacitas lagoon, which is long and narrow, lies at a 90°angle to the prevailing wind.

A Solution

The final solution lay, as it happened, in Philippe's hot-air balloon — a vehicle that he had already used successfully in the Red Sea and also in the Indian Ocean, at the island of Europa.*

*See Life and Death in a Coral Sea, Chapter Six. The balloon used in Baja California, however, was twice the size of that one.

Our team—trying not to disturb a finback whale at night.

The balloon is of the traditional type — a classic Montgolfière, no less — and the hot air is provided by a fuel-oil burner. The chief problem is that it is difficult to handle because of its thermic inertia. It tends to rise and descend at a rapidly accelerating rate, and it requires considerable dexterity on the part of the pilot to keep it at the desired altitude. Moreover, its effective operation requires that there be no wind to speak of.

Philippe took advantage of an exceptionally fine day to go up in his balloon with a battery of cameras — and with his wife, Jan, who insisted on accompanying him.

"In my mind's eye," Philippe reports, "I can still see the balloon's shadow on the lagoon. The air was unusually calm, and it was a spectacular day. I could see the whales below me as they rose to the water's surface. And, from my vantage point, I could also make out some rays and sand sharks on the bottom. It would have been impossible to see them from the Zodiac.

"It was an absolutely magnificent experience. I got many shots that we could never have gotten even from an airplane, because a plane travels too fast and because its noise panics the animals.

"Of course, the balloon makes noise too, but only when it is being launched. The flame from the fuel-oil burner — it's about three feet high — roars like a lion. But, once the balloon is stabilized, we need only a small flame to keep it going. So, we are able to remain over one spot in the water for as long as we want without disturbing the animals. To them, we probably look like part of the landscape."

After Philippe had been in the air for a period of time, however, the wind rose and began pushing the balloon out to sea. He then dropped a line to a waiting Zodiac, and the balloon was towed back to the *Polaris*

Philippe's balloon ascent uncovered several important things, among them the locations where there were the largest concentration of whales, and also the sheltered spots to which they went to give birth to their young.

From the air, he was able to observe the technique of a young male who quite obviously had designs on the virtue of a female accompanied by a calf. The female would have none of it, and kept pushing away the male with her head while his tail thrashed violently in the water. The male, however, was difficult to discourage, and his advances continued.

"It was quite a spectacle," Philippe said. "The male would literally hurl

Aerial view of a group of gray whales during the mating season in Scammon Lagoon.

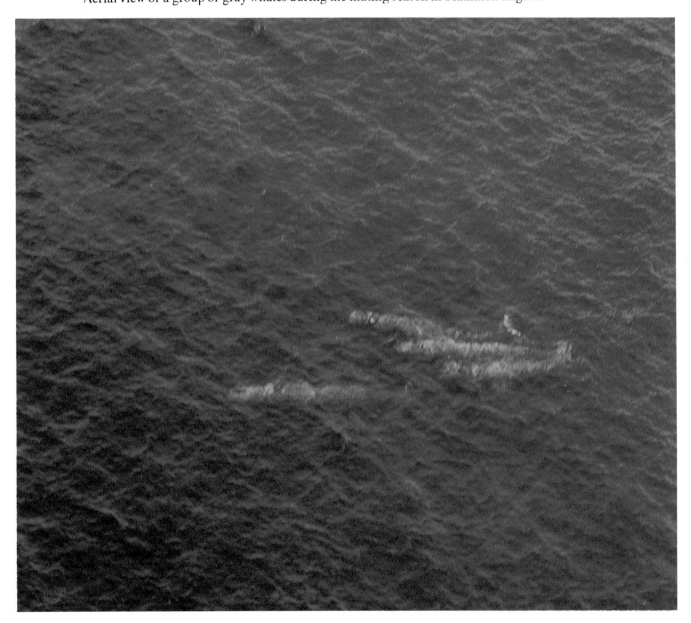

himself upon the female at a high speed. It was like watching two ships col-lide. The calf, who was unlucky enough to be between the two when the male charged, was actually lifted out of the water by the force of the charge.

"The matter was finally settled when the female, her patience apparently exhausted, gave the male a great swat with her tail, and sailed away with her calf in tow."

An Amorous Trio

Ted Walker had already described to us the gray whales' technique for coupling. The two animals lie side by side on the surface on their backs. Then, they turn over on their sides and there is the first attempt at penetration. (This position, awkward as it sounds, is at least more comfortable than that of other species of whales, who couple standing vertically on their tails.) The male's organ, which is curved like the handle of a cane, is proportionate to the whale's size — generally, one tenth the length of its body — and it is placed far back on its body.

Ted has had a vast amount of experience with the behavior of whales; and he has an extraordinary instinct for recognizing the significance of a par-ticular act, gesture, or position. He keeps special watch, for example, over the tail and the flippers; and he is hardly ever wrong in his interpretations.

One day, toward noon, Ted was watching the lagoon from *Polaris'* rear deck. "Look! Look!" he yelled. "Hurry up, everyone. They're mating!"

Bernard Mestre, one of the cameramen, and a diver jumped into a Zodiac, very excited, and shot out to the spot that Ted had indicated. There, they found not two, but three whales, all rolling around together and stirring up a sea of foam.

It took a while to understand what was actually happening. It seemed at first that the two males* were competing for the female's favors. Each one apparently was trying to displace the other — a situation that did not seem designed to facilitate mating. But Ted explained that, in the sexual encoun-ters of whales, there are almost always two males. The second male has a specific function: he lies across the male and female who are coupling, in order to help them maintain their position in the water.

*Ted Walker is very competent at distinguishing males from females by the shapes of their heads. The males' heads are narrower. It is true, however, that, in the present instance, there were other ways of telling one from the other.

Philippe Cousteau as director of "Project Gray Whale."

Be that as it may, by the time the Zodiac arrived at the scene, the second male's function seemed to be limited to swimming in great agitation around the other two whales, who were making a great deal of noise.

The Zodiac team could see that the female was using her flippers to hold the male in an embrace. It was a strangely touching sight.

It is probable that the team arrived at the very beginning of the mating process. The preliminaries, and the initial attempts at penetration, went on for a long period of time. Finally, the whales coupled, or attempted to do so, perhaps ten times.

Meanwhile, the Zodiac was only a short distance away, and our team was fascinated by the sight. The overall impression conveyed was one of an alien sexuality, a sort of erotic nightmare. It was an act of love on such a gigantic scale, and so difficult, as to be almost pathetic. There was an element of pain, almost tragedy, in the repeated attempts of these leviathans to

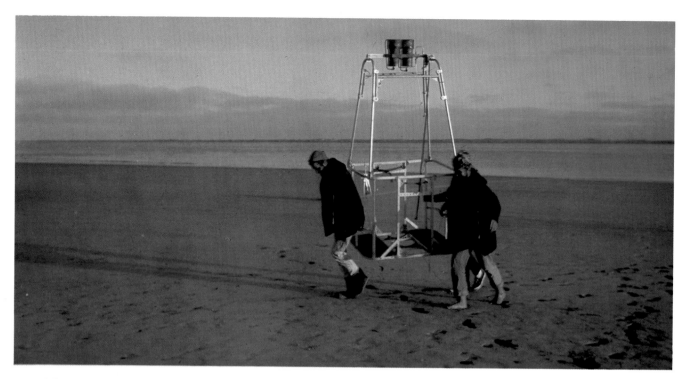

Philippe and two other men carrying his balloon's nacelle.

Philippe has become particularly adept in handling his hot-air balloon.

The balloon enabled us to observe and film the gray whales without frightening them.

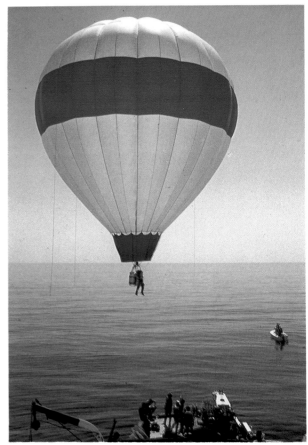

The balloon is deflated and folded aboard the *Polaris*.

achieve penetration — an element reflected in the frenzied gyrations of the third whale around the mating pair.

The team in the Zodiac — the cameraman and the diver — had intended to get into the water, but the scene was so violent that they thought it better to go no closer than they already were. The action of the whales, however, was so complicated and confused that they were unable to shoot any good footage. And, of course, the movements of the whales made the water even cloudier than it already was.

What would have happened if the men had decided to dive into the water for a closer look at the whales? There is no way of knowing for sure. What is certain is that the three whales were in the grip of violent emotions and no longer conscious of what was going on in the water around them. Gray whales are not particularly aggressive, except when it is a matter of defending their young; but, in this instance, there would have been a serious danger of being struck, unintentionally, by a flipper or a tail — a blow capable of crushing a man.

After a while, Ted Walker noticed a large spot of froth on the surface, covering an area about a hundred feet long. In his opinion, it was probably the sperm of the male whale; or perhaps a substance secreted by the female. Another possibility is that the water of the lagoon, containing as much organic matter as it does, had been simply whipped into a foam by the movements of the whales.

It is certainly possible that the mating had not been successful, and that the male's sperm had been lost in the water. According to all the experts, it is relatively rare that the male succeeds in penetrating the female. And this, no doubt, is the reason why the attempt is repeated at such brief intervals and lasts such a short time.*

The main obstacle in the mating of whales is the fact that it is necessary for them to rise to the surface in order to breathe. Sexual contact takes place in the water, when the two whales are partially submerged; and the pair must co-ordinate their breathing in such a way as to be able to rise and sink together.

It seems that when whales dive deliberately, they are able to remain submerged longer than when, half asleep, they merely sink back beneath the surface, or when they do so in the process of mating. Before a dive, in order to

---

*According to K. S. Norris, the sexual act lasts for only ten to thirty seconds, and may be repeated every eight minutes for an hour and a half. There are numerous contacts between the male organ and the stomach of the female before penetration is finally achieved.

Maintenance of the balloon is time-consuming and complicated.

be able to remain as long as possible beneath the surface, a whale prepares itself by hyperventilating its lungs. However, when it sinks beneath the surface, either while it is sleeping or when it is excited, it does not hyperventilate, and it must necessarily breathe again in a short time.

For males, the act of coupling is a rare and important phenomenon. According to Ted Walker, a successful penetration is the exception rather than the rule in the love life of the whale. Success requires the simultaneous realization of several conditions: the proper time of year, a suitable place, a female in heat, victory over one or more rivals, and, of course, the consent of the female. Under the circumstances, mating is impossible during the migratory trek from the Bering Sea. All the energies of the school must be devoted to swimming, for the time available for the voyage to Baja California is relatively brief.

Not all cetaceans mate in the same way, and the behavior of gray whales is somewhat exceptional. It happens frequently that the female rather than the male is the initial aggressor, in that she shows the male that she is in season. Since whales have virtually no sense of smell, the male must rely upon his sight.

Humpback whales mate facing one another, chest to chest, and the climax occurs as they rise together, at considerable speed, to the surface. A technique as acrobatic as this one can only be effective when sexual contact is very

A humpback whale. Its mating habits are particularly arduous.

brief, lasting no more than a few seconds.

During the *Curlew*'s observation of humpbacks in the waters around Bermuda, there was no opportunity to witness this technique in action. But our friends did see humpback whales making fantastic leaps out of the water, and these may have been part of the mating ritual; or they may even have been the last phase of an unsuccessful attempt at copulation.

Humpbacks are the acknowledged champions of this sort of high jumping. Their bodies leave the water completely, and then they fall back, onto their backs, with a loud noise and an enormous splash. Altogether, it is an impressive demonstration of the power of these 40- or 50-ton giants.

At Bermuda, Philippe witnessed another episode of love-making among whales, and this one did not involve humpbacks.

"One especially fine day, we had just taken the *Curlew* outside the lagoon when we saw one spout, and then two, in the distance. When we got closer, we put the Zodiac into the water, and Bernard Delemotte, Dominique Sumian, and I set out to investigate.

"We saw two whales. At first, we thought that they were gray whales. They were not quite as dark as the humpbacks that we were used to, and they had no dorsal fins.

(Right) Gray whales are champion acrobats. In order to make such leaps, they must attain a speed of 25 miles per hour.

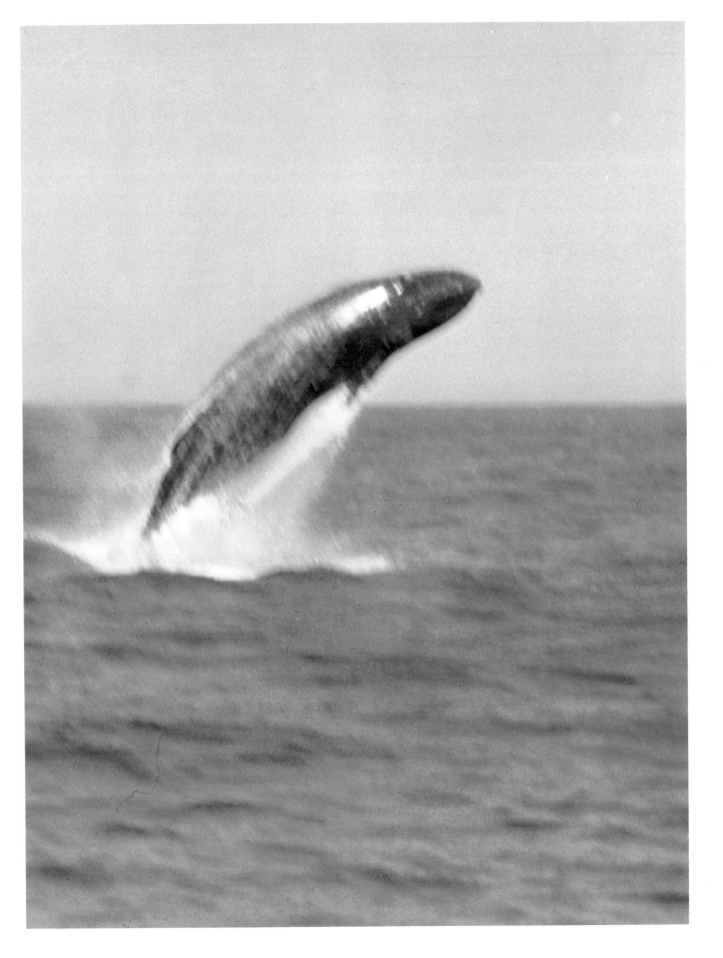

The habits of the sperm whale are quite different from those of the baleen whale. Their love-making is much more violent, and the males are devoted polygamists. It is not unusual for a large male to have gathered around him a combination harem-household comprising twenty to fifty other whales — females and offspring.

The lord and master of this family unit may, sooner or later, find himself dispossessed. There seems to exist among cachalots the same sort of rivalry for females that one finds among sea elephants and seals; and there are always young males around the fringes of the reigning male's household.

A dethroned male is left alone in the sea and, to escape his shame, he takes refuge in the waters of the Arctic and Antarctic. It was in polar waters that whalers used to find those immense and very old solitary males whom they called "Emperors."

"We stopped the Zodiac about 200 yards away so as not to frighten them, and Delemotte and I swam the rest of the way. Unfortunately, the water was cloudy. Nonetheless, we saw clearly enough what was happening. There were two whales — right whales — mating. There was no mistaking it. They were rolling one on top of the other, caressing each other the length of their bodies.

"It all happened very quickly. They were not so caught up in each other as not to be aware of our presence. As soon as they discovered us, they disappeared. I was able to shoot only about thirty-five feet of film.

"There is no doubt that these were actually right whales. They had short, well-defined triangular flippers, and no dorsal fins. Their mouths were enormous; and their stomachs were spotted. Their appearance was very different from that of any other species of baleen whale that we had ever seen. They looked like great cows, swollen and heavy."

Whales generally are monogamous to the extent that a male will remain with the same female for at least one season. In any case, during the mating season one meets whales in couples or in trios. It is possible that gray whales, who are the "liberals" of the cetacean world, practice polyandry. We saw some indications of this in Scammon Lagoon. So far as the other baleen whales are concerned — the finbacks, humpbacks, etc. — they seem to play in couples what Professor Budker describes as "games designed to assure the continuation of the species."

EIGHT

The Nursery of the Leviathans

After the excellent work done by Philippe and his team in Baja California's Matancitas Lagoon aboard the *Polaris III,* I decided to wind up our observation of gray whales with a visit to the bay of Scammon. Philippe had decided that this lagoon was too large to be studied with the equipment that he had on hand on the *Polaris.* With *Calypso,* however, and our launches, Zodiacs and other equipment — to say nothing of our twenty-nine men, including divers — I thought that we would well be able to undertake the observation of the gray whales that, we were told, were everywhere at the bay of Scammon.

One of our fondest wishes was to be present at the birth of a whale calf. The *Polaris* team had been able to watch whale mothers nursing their young, and even to film the scene. But no one had yet witnessed the birth of a whale or of a cachalot, although dolphins in their tanks had been observed, and filmed at length, bearing their young. It seemed to us that whale maternity would be a marvelous subject.

Generally, baleen whales have a calf every two years, and they nurse the calf for nine months. Among cachalots, however, gestation lasts sixteen

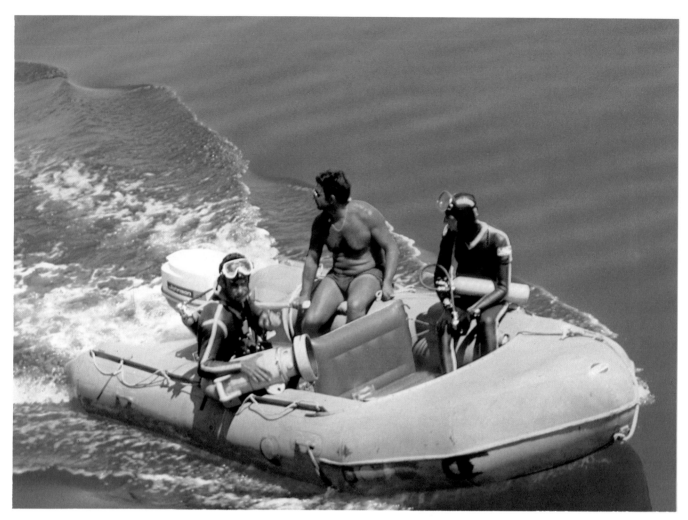

A camera team, in the Zodiac, follows in the wake of a whale.

months rather than a year, and there is a birth only every three years.

We know that almost all cetaceans are born tailfirst from the belly of their mothers. This is a rather striking trait, for all other species of viviparous mammals* bear their young headfirst. Among cetaceans, being born tailfirst prevents the calf from drowning during birth; and then, as soon as the process of birth is complete, the mother very quickly takes the calf to the surface for its first breath of air. She is aided throughout by one or more females — midwives, or, as they are called in California, "aunts" — who continue, after the calf's birth, to act as "mothers' helpers." There is every indication that these surrogate mothers are bound to the calf by emotional as well as practical ties.

Bringing *Calypso* into Scammon Lagoon was not an easy operation, nor an entirely safe one. The only entrance is quite narrow and shoaled. The

*The only other exception are the *Chiroptera* (bats).

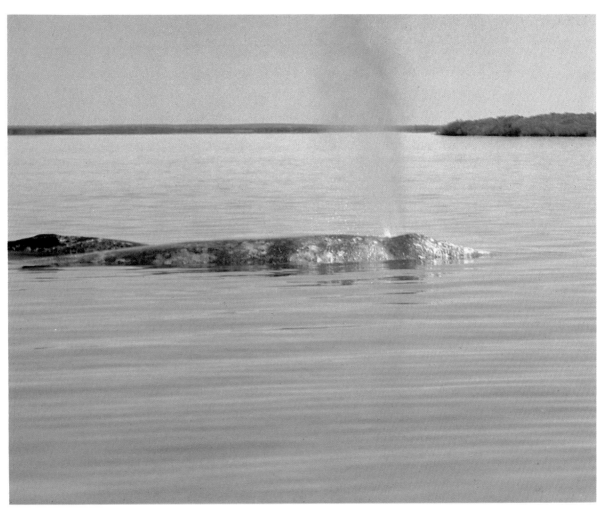
Two gray whales in Matancitas Bay.

channel is a series of twists and contains a number of sandspits, and its configuration varies from tide to tide. Moreover, the first part of the lagoon is filled with salt marshes and would be totally impossible if buoys had not been placed, in a zigzag pattern, to mark a channel.

Calypso touched bottom twice; but, fortunately, the bottom was muddy in both places, and she was able to extricate herself without difficulty.

After we had found good anchorage within the lagoon, the two Zodiacs and two launches went out every day to reconnoiter the area. There were gray whales everywhere, and the small craft had to maneuver among them constantly and as quietly and inoffensively as possible.

Many of the whales seemed to be asleep, with their calves lying alongside of them. Some of the calves were even resting their heads against the mothers' chests near their mammary glands. But they were not nursing. Sometimes, mother and child seemed to play by rubbing against one another.

Like all infants, whale calves seem to be unaware of danger and to have confidence in the goodness of all creatures. They are also very curious.

When gray whales sleep, they keep their heads and tails under the surface, and all that can be seen from above are their round, spotted backs. When they must breathe, the head rises very slowly, and the sound of their breath breaks the silence momentarily. Then the great head sinks again slowly. Meanwhile, the calf continues playing alone near the mother.

The whales reacted in various ways to the Zodiac's approach. We noticed first that, when the craft approached a sleeping gray whale from the rear, she did not seem to notice it, or at least had no reaction to it. But if it came from the front, she awoke with a jump — which, if the Zodiac was close, was not very comfortable for us. Apparently they are much less sensitive to noises from the rear than from the front. Their alarm systems seem to be aimed forward.

The reaction of the baby whale was not the same as the mother's. While the mother slept, the calf was often awake; and, if a Zodiac came near, he showed the greatest curiosity about both the craft and the men in it. And then he reacted in one of two ways: either he came joyfully swimming out to play — or else he showed every sign of fright.

A gray whale spouting, followed by its calf. The calf's blowholes are clearly distinguishable.

An Outraged Whale

It often happened that a calf would leave the sleeping mother and swim toward the Zodiac for a closer look. So far as we were concerned, we were willing to satisfy its curiosity; but within limits, for a curious whale, even a "baby" only 15 to 20 feet long and weighing a few tons, can present a few problems for a small, light craft like our Zodiac. On one occasion, the mother of one of these young and curious animals awoke suddenly to find her baby gone. Then she saw him — making friends with Philippe, Delemotte, and Serge Foulon, and, for all she knew, with the Zodiac. The mother was upon the Zodiac in a flash, and everything — men, equipment, and the boat itself — ended up in the air, and came crashing down into the water in the midst of a sea of foam. Then the mother gently herded her child back to safety without even a glance to see what she had done. She felt no particular animosity for *Calypso*'s men; all she was interested in was the well-being of her offspring. Mother love is extremely well developed among the great marine mammals.

Sometimes a mother whale will correct her baby without resorting to physical means. In the Bay of Matancitas, a calf came to rub itself against *Calypso*'s hull. When the mother awoke and saw what was happening, she lifted her great tail out of the water and came rushing over to get her offspring and towed him off hurriedly, in a very human spirit of love and indignation combined.

It happened occasionally that a calf reacted to the Zodiac's presence not by trying to satisfy his curiosity, but in fear. In one such case, the baby tried desperately to awaken the mother by swimming over and around her and pushing her with his head, all in a state of obvious excitement. When none of this succeeded, he decided to dive; and this, finally, awakened the mother, and she followed her calf into the depths. So far as the Zodiac was concerned, this was the best possible solution. I wonder what would have happened to us if the baby had succeeded in awakening his mother sooner.

Panic in the Lagoon

In Scammon Lagoon there were a number of protected coves, pockets of water hidden by dunes, which mother whales seemed to favor. The divers quickly became aware of this, and called that part of the lagoon the "nursery."

We had to be especially careful when we ventured near the nursery in our Zodiacs, for the mother whales were easily upset by any potential threat

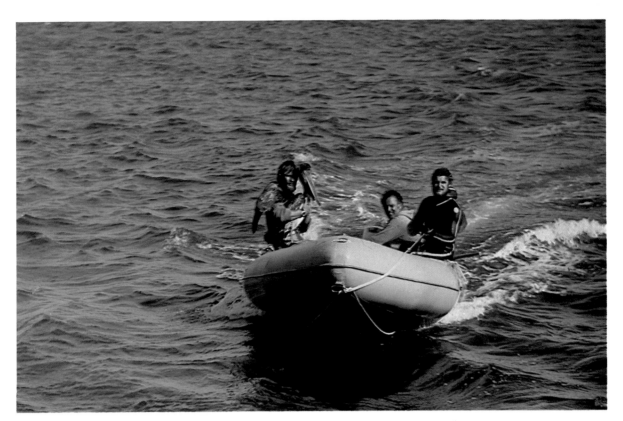

(Above) In a Zodiac piloted by Canoë, Bernard Delemotte has rescued a wounded pelican and is bringing it back to *Calypso*.

(Right) This particular pelican has developed a great affection for Bernard Delemotte who is holding him.

(Facing page above) Pelicans always gather at the same time and on the same sandbanks.

(Facing page below) Pelicans are excellent underwater fishermen.

to their young ones. When they were awake and we came near, they were immediately ready to charge. And, in every instance, they would immediately place themselves between the Zodiac and their calves.

On one occasion, Bonnici and Delemotte unwittingly caused a great uproar in the nursery. Several mothers were sleeping, while their calves were playing in the water near them. As soon as the Zodiac appeared, two of the calves swam over for a better look at this strange apparition. But, at that moment, the mothers awoke; and all that Bonnici and Delemotte could see were indignant spoutings emerging from a minor hurricane in the cove. By the time the water was calm again, the calves had been forcibly returned to their mothers.

Everything had happened so quickly that the men in the Zodiac had not even had time to react. The cameraman, on instinct, had waved his camera around — but the film, when developed, showed nothing more than an enormous splash of water.

In earlier times, whalers often took advantage of whales' maternal instincts in order to meet their quota. Captain Scammon, for example, for whom this bay is named, used to begin by firing upon the calves, which inevitably led the mother whales to charge the whaling boat; his men could then throw their harpoons at close range. It was a dangerous game, however, for it is not always easy to evade the charge of a furious 40-ton animal; and, in fact, Captain Scammon had many boats crushed by mother whales mad with rage. But he also succeeded in killing a great number of gray whales.

The Cradle

After a while, we became more and more adept at approaching whales without disturbing or frightening them. Our teams would maintain absolute silence, and would always approach a whale from the rear. This tactic allowed the teams, on several occasions, to see mothers nursing their calves — an extraordinary spectacle, and a moving one. Even among giants, the act of nursing one's young has an air of tender familial intimacy about it.

While the calf is nursing, the mother whale's flippers play such a large role that they almost seem to be arms cradling the young one. The whale lies on her side and holds the baby with her flippers while he nurses. As long as she is not disturbed, she rises and descends slowly in the water, carrying the young one with her. At the same time, she keeps the baby's head above the surface, and he nurses a few seconds at a time.

The breasts of the mother whale are in proportion to her body and, al-

Delemotte force-feeding his pelican.

(Following page) A mother humpback whale supporting her calf.

The grateful pelican cannot tear himself away from Delemotte.

though located in a fold of skin, they are very large. A muscle squeezes the breast and sends out a jet of milk under a pressure sufficient to carry it straight up for six or seven feet.

We have had the opportunity to see this milk on the surface, and even to taste it. It is yellow rather than white, with a strong taste and an oily flavor. It is extremely rich in fat — 35 percent, as contrasted with 3.5 percent for cow's milk.

A baby whale grows at a rate that is almost incredible: about 230 pounds a day, or almost 10 pounds every hour. A ton every nine days. No other animal in the world grows at a comparable rate. (We are of course talking about the infantile rate of growth.) A blue whale calf reaches a length of about 50 feet in three years; and its "youth" breaks down as follows: infancy lasts 7 months; adolescence, 17 months; and another year passes before he reaches sexual maturity.

A Rubber Doll

In spite of our best efforts, it was impossible for us to witness a birth. It was not because the whales were particularly shy, but because we never managed to be in the right place at the right time in that gigantic maze which is Scammon Lagoon. The actual birth is probably very brief in duration. The calf must be free of the mother's body very quickly, otherwise it will die. Infant mortality, indeed, is high, if one may judge by the number of bodies of baby whales that we have seen along the banks of the lagoon.

Ted Walker tells us that gray whales give birth in shallow water, lying on their backs, and that they push their offspring to the surface so that they may breathe immediately after they are born.

The new-born calves that we have seen have all been in very shallow water with their mothers. When they are that young, their bodies are very soft — like foam rubber — and they cannot swim. Even when they move their tails, they remain in the same spot. Nor do they float. Their density is too great at that age for them to do so, and their thoracic cages are not yet sufficiently developed for the air from their lungs to keep them afloat. Their mothers must therefore hold them on the surface. I have often seen, from the Zodiac, a mother whale carrying her baby with her flippers, either against her chest or below her head. The baby rolls in the water like a barrel, and spends more time on his side or back than on his stomach; but the mother always sets him right side up again and keeps his head above the surface.

The fact that baby whales can neither swim nor float explains why the gray whales of California travel four or five thousand miles to Baja California's shallow waters in order to give birth. If their offspring were born in the open sea, they would almost surely drown.

February 17. The whole day has been spent getting ready for a dive tonight. The diving suits have been painted phosphorescent red, and strips of the same color have been attached to the Zodiacs and launches. The reason for making this dive at night is that Ted Walker believes gray whales may give birth only after dark.

We begin at two o'clock in the morning. The Zodiacs and launches set out into a night so dark that it is almost opaque. Everyone watches for disturbances in the water, and for spouts. The cameramen are in the water, and the divers have lighted their floods. Ahead of them, we see silhouetted the motionless bodies of whales asleep. Nothing moves. The divers remain at a slight distance. It would be pointless to disturb the animals — especially since we do not know how they might react.

We look over the sleeping whales very carefully, but, so far as we can see, no female is giving birth.

We shoot some film and then return to *Calypso.* By now, dawn is breaking, and the dunes are pink in the morning light.

The Pelicans

We learned gradually to understand and love this "desert" of Baja California, in which a secret animal kingdom flourishes in the dry sand, at the foot of the cliffs with its mangroves whose roots twist like serpents into the water.

Our primary purpose in going to Scammon and Matancitas was to study gray whales. But, once there, we discovered the pelicans, and found them only slightly less interesting than the whales. We could hardly miss them, and it was a revelation to discover how intelligent they are, and how beautiful in flight. They resemble bombers in formation. When they land, they put their feet out in front and water-ski a bit before settling into the water, sometimes for as much as thirty feet.

The pelicans were with us every day. Every morning and every evening, at the same time, when the light was reddish pink, they would fly in single file over the pink and gray dunes as though this was a planned maneuver which they were obliged to perform.

They had a particular place during the day, and one for the night, and they assembled in those spots in numbers that must occasionally have

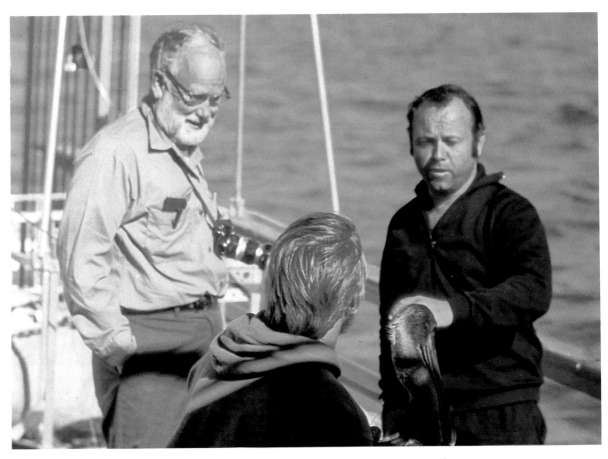

Ted Walker talking with Bernard Delemotte and Dr. François aboard *Calypso*.

reached a thousand. Sometimes, as though on a whim, they flew in a straight line only a bit above the surface of the water.

When the pelicans fished, each one of them was accompanied by a sea gull. The sea gull followed his host pelican closely, eating whatever the pelican would not eat or what he let fall. When the pelican dived, the sea gull dived also.

We found a pelican with a broken wing and took him aboard *Calypso*; but the next day he escaped over the side and fell into the water, crying pitifully, unable to fly. Serge Foulon jumped overboard and rescued him, and brought him back to us. Up to that time, the pelican had shown no enmity to any of us; on the contrary, he seemed friendly and easy to train. But, from the moment that Serge brought him back aboard, the bird could not bear the

(Left) A humpback whale and her calf seen from beneath.

sight of his rescuer. Everyone else could pet the pelican except Serge. If Serge went near him, there was an uproar, screams, and a great clacking of the pelican's beak. A pelican's beak is a rather dangerous weapon, ending as it does in a pointed and very sharp spur.

It was Delemotte's job to feed the pelican. He named it Alfred (in honor of Alfred de Musset), and Alfred returned the favor by eating, very gently, out of Delemotte's hand.

As soon as Alfred could fly again, of course, we released him.

A Sewing Job

No sooner was Alfred out of sight than we had another resident pelican aboard. This one we found on the beach, weak and thin, and very sad-looking. Philippe caught him and brought him aboard, where we examined him and discovered that his pouch had been ripped from top to bottom.* He could no longer eat, since all of his food would fall through the tear. The bird's condition was not the result of an accident. We learned that the children of Matancitas, when they catch a pelican, slit open its pouch with a pocketknife.

Dr. François, our ship's doctor, selected a spool of heavy thread and a large needle. After sterilizing them in alcohol, he sewed up the pouch. The next day, the animal was able to eat. A few days later, Dr. François pronounced him fit to travel, and he was released.

In a surprisingly short time, we had all developed an attachment for our two pelican patients. The pelican's combination of natural dignity and natural humor is hard to resist.

After living for weeks in close quarters with the birds, after seeing them flying and hearing their cries daily, we looked upon them as an inseparable part of the locale, along with the spouting whales and the sand and mangroves. They became a symbol of this place that is at once so desolate and so full of living things. The entire atmosphere of the place makes one think that this is the way it must have been at the dawn of time.

Pelicans and whales live here cheek by jowl, as it were, but without interfering with one another. The pelicans do not touch the bodies of dead baby whales. That is left to our local carrion-eaters, the turkey vultures *(Cathartes aura)*.

*The lower half of a pelican's beak is very long and contains a flexible pouch which can be distended to accommodate a large amount of food.

A Devoted Aunt

Calypso left Baja California when the gray whales began to emerge from the lagoon and enter the waters of the Pacific for their northward migration. The older specimens, who knew the way, went first, and the rest of the school followed them. They were headed for the Arctic Ocean, 4000 miles beyond the horizon. They were leaving their desert for the marine fields of plankton that flourish in the cold polar waters. Even the young whales, those who survived the perils of infancy, undertake the voyage, with the help of their mothers and their "aunts."

It was at this time that we noticed the sharks — large white sharks, some of which must have been thirteen feet long — lying in ambush at the mouth of the channel. They were waiting for any young whales who might be more or less in trouble. On their own, they would not dare have attacked. They are much less aggressive than killer whales, and less intelligent.

We sent down our anti-shark cages and, despite a strong current, our divers and cameramen prepared to film the passage of the whales — hoping in their hearts that they would also be able to film a battle among giants. But they were disappointed. Nothing happened; and, in any event, the water was very cloudy.

We therefore began following the school of whales who, at a slow pace, had begun their migration to the arctic regions. Their moderate speed was due, of course, to the presence of the calves, of whom the adult whales were extremely solicitous.

The family unit is the basis of a school of whales, and maternal love is at the root of the family. We know for certain that a new-born whale, from his birth until several years later, needs constant protection. But the mother by herself cannot defend him against all dangers and teach him everything that he must know. Apparently it is another female, and not the father, who helps her in this task. This second female is called the aunt.

There is a physiological foundation for the phenomenon of the aunt. Whales cannot give birth every year, since the gestation period lasts twelve months. During the year that follows the period of nursing and the time when the calf is more or less "on his own," the female is at loose ends, and her maternal instinct drives her to care for the calves of other females. This is a peculiarity common to all the great marine mammals, and also to certain large land animals.

Elephants, too, have "aunts." And there are other points of similarity between whales and elephants, perhaps because both species have such long gestation periods and because their young mature so slowly.

A diver getting ready to pass a line around a young sperm whale's tail.

We have had occasion to see for ourselves how effective the aunt's protection can be. We once found two large female whales standing guard, one
on either side of a calf. When we tried to maneuver in such a way as to isolate
the young whale, one of the two whales always succeeded in getting between
our Zodiac and the calf. (The calf was too young to be able to dive.) One of
the two females kept spouting, turning, and seemed very excited. Curious
about her reactions, we tried to get close enough to her for a good look, but
she always succeeded in staying just out of range.

It was not until we looked around and saw that the mother and calf had
disappeared from our sight that we realized that the whole thing had been a
trick to get us away from the calf — a trick that had succeeded very well
indeed. At that moment, the aunt dived, and she too disappeared. We had
been outsmarted.

The sperm whale has been lassoed.

Humpback whales, like gray whales, also have aunts, who fulfill the same functions. Philippe Sirot, who was captain of the *Curlew* during our expedition to Bermuda, noted that when a school of humpback whales is chased, the entire school will flee if there are no calves in the school. But, if there is even a single young one who cannot swim at the same speed as the adults, the school waits in the vicinity while one adult whale — perhaps the aunt — takes on the job of leading the pursuers away.

Something similar occurred on one occasion when the Zodiac team had almost succeeded in cutting off a young whale. The calf was obviously exhausted from the chase and on the point of allowing himself to be captured. The mother seemed unable to help him. It was the aunt who charged the Zodiac, and kept the men occupied while the mother led her offspring to safety.

"They Could Have Killed Us"

The *Curlew*'s team passed several uncomfortable nights anchored off Bermuda over an isolated reef, while rough water tossed them about unmercifully. the boat was small and everyone was crowded into tiny quarters. The entire team suffered from mal de mer, except Philippe, Delemotte, and Davso. The fact that they had no beds, but only sleeping bags, made the effects of being seasick particularly unbearable.

One day, they were rewarded for their pains. The sea calmed and became as smooth as glass. And then, a short distance away, someone sighted a whale spouting; and, next to it, another, smaller spout. A humpback whale mother and her calf. The Zodiac shot out and began circling the pair, enclosing them in our famous "magic circle." On previous occasions, humpback whales had seemed immune to this technique and had always escaped. Now, however, it seemed to work very well. And the explanation, of course, was that the mother would not escape and leave her calf.

Philippe and Delemotte slid into the crystal water and, for a half hour, they witnessed an incredible whale ballet as they struggled frantically to keep the mother and calf within camera range. "From beneath the surface," Philippe told us later, "it was a very calm, and very graceful spectacle. The mother whale had her huge white flippers extended like wings, and she was wheeling, stopping, starting again — and all the while she was holding up her calf and taking him to the surface to breathe."

In our film footage of that day, we can see the mother whale and the calf swimming straight toward Philippe. Then Philippe passes between them with his camera — and the mother pulls back one end of a flipper so as not to hit Philippe!

This extraordinary gesture was not a matter of chance. On another occasion, a humpback whale lifted her entire flipper to avoid a photographer.

"They could have killed us twenty times over," Philippe reported. "I think that those were the most beautiful hours that I have ever spent in the water in my whole life."

Usually, no matter what we did to isolate a calf, the mother would never give up trying until the situation had been resolved in one way or another — usually to our disadvantage.

When a mother and her calf had been encircled, the mother helped the calf by pushing it. When two adults and a young whale were encircled, the mother remained with the young one while the other adult escaped, but remained nearby, swimming around us. Then, when we released the calf and its mother, the three of them regrouped and swam away together.

A diver swims out to the sperm whale to set it free.

Falco, with a stroke of his knife, cuts the line and releases the prisoner.

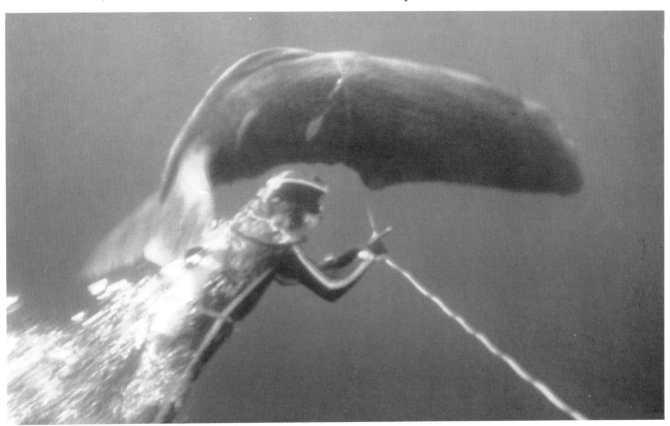

Sperm whales

The family ties of cachalots or sperm whales seem even stronger than those of baleen whales. The reason is that a school of cachalots may be composed of a hundred individuals, all of whom belong to the same family. And the family is presided over by one large male.

Here are my notes describing our encounter with cachalots in the Indian Ocean:

Monday, May 15. At 8:35, a number of whales are sighted, and the Zodiac goes out immediately. They are sperm whales, swimming in small groups. Whenever the Zodiac approaches a group, they dive and remain under for twenty or twenty-five minutes, and then come up some distance away. The Zodiac rushes from one group to another without being able to put its Virazeou technique into operation. Now Bebert tries another group of whales, and these begin jumping first to the right, and then to the left, quite near *Calypso*. If I didn't know better, I would think that they are playing with us.

At 11:21 A.M., one of the groups dives and comes up after nine minutes. Ahead of *Calypso*, to both port and starboard, two other groups are spouting. How funny. Bebert is rushing from one group to another without being able to catch any of them. And here the whales are, surfacing all around us and swimming calmly alongside our ship.

At 1:53, Bebert gives up.

A superb coryphaena swims through the clear water at our feet.

Tuesday, May 16. During the afternoon, Didi goes down to his bunk for a nap and, through the porthole, sights a school of sperm whales. (I wonder what those who were awake on deck were doing at that moment.)

It is 2:05 P.M. We try to approach several different groups of the cachalots in our Zodiacs, but without success. *Calypso* tries now; but the whales are too wary to allow her to draw near.

The Zodiacs try once more; and twice they are almost capsized by a giant tail striking the water directly in front of their bows.

A Young Whale Escapes

Finally, Falco spots a "young" whale weighing only about three tons, and his Zodiac manages to overtake it, circle around it, and establish the Virazeou ring of noise and water. The whale seems confused. He remains on the surface, turning first in one direction then in another. Soon, confusion gives way to irritation, and, mouth open, he attempts to seize the Zodiac on every pass and close his jaws on it. At first, he attempts to do this from the normal surface position, with his mouth downward; but then he turns onto his side and exposes his mouth. Twice, Falco fires his special marking harpoon at the angry whale, and twice the spear bounces off the whale's skin.

Maurice and René come to the rescue in a launch and, while Falco loads his harpoon again, they distract the now thoroughly disoriented animal.

Then, gathering his strength (and his wits) for a final charge, the whale throws himself at the launch and strikes it with a great crash.

The outboard motor falls off into the water and remains hanging behind the boat. Maurice Leandri is also thrown overboard by the impact; but, propelled by terror, he is back in the launch in an instant. And the whale, now free and apparently satisfied, dives peacefully and disappears.

But Falco and Maurice do not give up so easily. As soon as the outboard is back in place, the two craft are once more in hot pursuit — so hot that they find the whale about a mile away. Once again, the circling begins; and, once again, the whale becomes a prisoner on the surface, as though by magic.

Calypso is only a few meters away from the marine battleground, and Barsky is filming away. We can hear Falco's shouts, and excitement grips everyone aboard. Everyone grabs a camera and rushes to the prow.

The whale once more tries to attack the launch and the Zodiac with his jaws. And everyone holds his breath when Maurice falls overboard a second time. The whale rushes, weaving to the right and then to the left — and bites an iron bar that is protruding from the launch's stern. Then he veers off while Maurice scrambles aboard.

Twice, Falco's Zodiac was struck by the whale tail; and both times it was lifted out of the water but, fortunately, came down right side up.

Falco now fires a short, harmless harpoon by gunpowder; and the spear bounces off of the whale's side as though it were made of rubber. He fires again, aiming at the blubber of the whale's stomach. This time, the harpoon penetrates the whale's skin.

The whale remains motionless for a moment, then he begins to swim westward at eight knots. By 5:05 P.M., the buoy at the end of 1500 feet of polypropylene line is leaving a long serpentine wake on the surface, and we begin preparing a kytoon for tonight.

The whale's breathing is now normal: once every fifteen minutes. And he is still heading directly west. Soon, we see two spouts rising in the distance, undoubtedly from the whale's parents. By sunset, the young whale has rejoined his family. The kytoon has been attached, and we are looking forward to an interesting evening.

But, suddenly, the buoy stops moving, and the kytoon floats quietly over the water. Bernard and Falco rush out to the buoy and pull in the line. It has not broken, and, at the end of it, they find the harpoon intact.

"These are remarkably intelligent animals," Bebert declares. "Unless someone proves otherwise, I will always believe that the adult whales pulled the harpoon out of that young whale's stomach."

This is not impossible. There are stories of whales helping one another; and one hears of cases where whales who had been harpooned were freed by their companions.

And, as though to overcome any doubt that we still might have, we catch sight of the three whales, swimming quietly away into the twilight.

The Baby Whale Who Lost His Head

We had one more adventure with a baby whale whose group was determined to protect him.

Calypso was heading toward Djibouti for supplies. We were all very enthusiastic about our encounters with whales so far, especially since we had just seen the films recording these encounters.

Tuesday, May 24. Sperm whales have been sighted. *Calypso* has tried four times to get close to them. The first three attempts were filmed by Li from the observation chamber. But we were not close enough at any time for Falco to be able to shoot his harpoon from *Calypso*'s prow.

We have put two Zodiacs into the water, and they are beginning to close the circle around a young animal. For an hour and a half, the Zodiacs keep him there while Bebert is feverishly preparing his weapon. At 10:30, the young sperm whale is harpooned. At 11:00, the launch pulls away from *Calypso* carrying the equipment for underwater filming.

In a short time, the young whale is joined by two adult cachalots (perhaps his parents) and then by an entire school. We can now count eleven sperm whales around *Calypso*, some of which seem to be enormous. Very impressive.

From 11:25 to 12:30, there is a constant coming and going between *Calypso* and the whale as we take exterior shots, underwater shots, sound recordings, and underwater photographs.

Lagorio, our sound man, wires hanging down from every part of him, his head covered with earphones and a tape recorder dangling over his stomach, is jumping from one launch into the other, shouting "Silence!" in his deep singer's voice, and making more noise than anyone else.

Nineteenth-century whalers used to engrave pictures of what they loved most on sperm whales' teeth—usually their girl friends or their ships. On the one to the right, we see the American flag, the lance used to give the death-blow to sperm whales, and a whaling scene in which a boat has been overturned. *Collection Jean-Horace Chambon.*

Finally, the young whale succeeds in escaping.

We examine the harpoon's point and conclude that we are very poorly equipped for this kind of work.

From *Calypso*'s deck we can see that there is great excitement in the school of whales. Three cachalots leap into the air — a sign of joy, no doubt, because the young whale, either alone or with the help of adults, has rejoined his family.

They are celebrating too soon, we think. The Zodiac once more cuts off the young whale and immobilizes it. And, at 2:40, Falco once more harpoons the animal. But it turns out that we have made a mistake. This is not the same whale. It is slightly larger than the other, and there is no trace of an earlier harpoon wound. But the fact is we have little time to discuss our mistake. For five minutes later, the harpoon is dislodged and the whale dives and is swimming away.

By 3:15 we have caught up with him again, and Falco sinks a harpoon into the middle of his back, where it sticks up like a small mast. And this time it holds. We set about the same routine as before: a buoy, 1500 feet of nylon line, a kytoon. Filming and sound-recording.

Meanwhile, the young whale's relatives are swimming forward of *Calypso*, to starboard, waiting and, at regular intervals, emitting sounds as though to encourage the captive, or to show him the way to them. Another cachalot, close by, seems to answer the cries of the young whale.

Through our underwater microphones we are picking up three distinct levels of sound from the whales: the young, captive animal; then the young whale's mother; and, finally — and perhaps — the chief male of the school.

This time we will have no trouble following the kytoon by radar. The weather is beautiful.

Tuesday, May 25. At dawn, the school of whales is still with us. They followed *Calypso* for twenty miles to the north during the night.

We are picking up a radar echo from Aden, 56 miles at 313.

We are going to try to lasso our young captive's tail so that we can remove the harpoon and release him. This is easier said than done. Bonnici and Alan try again and again, but fail, and they are exhausted. Then the whale himself takes over and, by twisting and turning continually, manages to wrap the line around his tail. He has succeeded where we failed.

But how will we be able to get the line off of him?

Bebert, in his Zodiac, tries next to remove the harpoon, but the handle breaks and it falls into the water where it, too, becomes entangled in the line.

Lagorio, meanwhile, is near the launch, taping everything that is being said in the water. There seem to be many whales "talking" nearby. The entire school apparently is waiting to see how we are going to get out of this.

Finally, Bebert and Alan, who have now rested a bit, try to cut the line around the whale with a knife so as to free him. But the whale squirms so much that they cannot get hold of the flipper to cut the line, and they are afraid of cutting him by mistake.

At 4 P.M., there is a very solemn moment when Deloire films, under water, two divers who hack away the snarls and knots of the line and release the animal. It is all over.

We see the young whale swim away toward his school; and Gaston, from the crow's-nest, watches through his field glasses the joyful demonstration with which the whale family greets the return of their prodigal son.

Ted Walker has gone to find water in an effort to save the grounded baby whale.

The wounded calf is sprinkled with water.

With the greatest care, the animal is placed in a net.

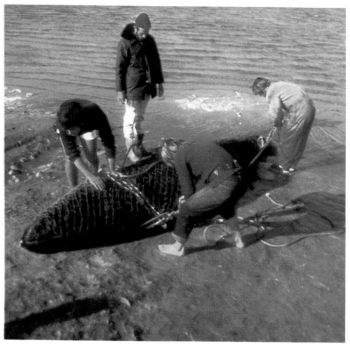

NINE

The Baby Whale Who Wanted to Live

February 24. Before leaving, I want to take a last look at Scammon Lagoon which, by now, has become so familiar to me, with its nursery, its love chambers, and also its cemetery. Philippe takes me up in the Cessna for a ride over the whole lagoon.

Just before leaving, I ask the *Polaris* and *Calypso* to take a census of the whale population in the various lagoons. I would also like to know how many bodies there are of baby whales, so as to be able to estimate the rate of infant mortality.

At birth, a gray whale calf is about eleven feet long and weighs nearly a ton. Three months later, it is strong enough to undertake its first northward voyage, and now measures about twenty feet. That is, if it survives.

Whale calves are subject to a number of diseases, and they also have natural enemies — grampuses and sharks. And, in fact, from the air we can see about ten dead whale calves lying in the lagoon. Among the mangroves bordering the beach, we can see whale skeletons. The roots of the mangroves have grown and, sometimes, disturbed these bones.

Not all of these cadavers are the result of disease or sharks. Whales, unlike man, follow an inexorable law of nature. If a whale calf seems, at birth, to suffer the slightest defect, it is immediately abandoned by the mother and, of course, dies. Heartless? Perhaps, but only by human standards. In nature, death goes hand in hand with life, and it might be more cruel to prolong a defective calf's life than to allow it to end as soon as possible after birth. The calf's presence in the school would expose all the members to attack by enemies and slow its migrations. And it would be all for nothing, for, even if cared for by the mother, a defective calf's chances of survival would be negligible. In the sea as in the jungle, nature's law is still in force, and only the fittest of each species survive adolescence.

Baby Whale in Distress

On February 28, the pilot of our reconaissance plane signals us by radio that a whale calf has run aground at the entrance to the lagoon. Dr. Walker, Philippe, and Michel Deloire set out immediately in the launch to examine the whale.

The weather around the lagoon is, as usual, leaden and a bit foggy. Then, suddenly, the sun breaks through the low-lying clouds and fog. Philippe sees in the distance, on a finger of sand, a dark shape. The launch heads for it. It is undoubtedly the baby whale. But is the whale still alive?

Ted Walker and Philippe begin the examination as soon as they arrive, while Michel handles the camera. There are still signs of life, but they are weak. Dr. Walker, who has managed to look into the calf's eye, reports that there is a glimmer of life — and of intelligence. Frantically, Walker ransacks the launch for cloth or canvas — anything that can be dampened and used to cover the calf's body.

Out of the water, a beached whale succumbs very rapidly to the heat. It dehydrates, and the sun burns its skin. It can also happen that, once it is weakened, it will drown in the rising tide.

Seen from close up, with its long flat muzzle stretched out on the sand, its rubbery skin slightly tinged with blue, its eyes closed, the calf looks for all the world as though he were already dead. Lying there, trapped by its own weight, crushed against the spit of sand only a few yards from the blue water that it needs to live, this son of giants can do nothing but wait helplessly for the end to come. Unless we are able to do something to save it, its fate is sealed, and it will shortly become nothing more than food for birds.

The calf seem to get a certain amount of relief from the water that is poured over it. Ted Walker, sweating and out of breath, his beard dripping, carries buckets of water from the sea to the sand spit, pours them over the suffering whale, and then goes back for more, his wet sneakers squishing audibly. And the calf stirs a bit.

An Orphan?

Philippe has alread notified *Calypso* by radio of the situation, and has asked them to send out a team immediately with a net and lines.

The whale, meanwhile, is again still, its eyes closed to protect them from the sun. It seems that he is already dangerously dehydrated. And on his head there is a large open wound, bleeding, inflicted by birds — probably sandpipers, who are voracious little animals.

From the size of this wound, Ted concludes that the calf has very likely been ashore for several hours, perhaps since last night. We really have no idea of exactly what happened to him. It is hardly likely that he would have been taken off guard by the tide. At his age, the mother whale is usually able to extricate her baby from any such difficulty — even from being trapped by a retreating tide.

It is not impossible that this baby is an orphan. Or that it is unhealthy and has been abandoned by its mother. In any case, it is thin and obviously undernourished. Later on, we discovered bits of clam in his excrement, which leads us to surmise that perhaps he was trying to feed himself; or that, even though he was nursing, he tried to eat clams. It is not possible to know for sure.

Ted Walker is almost beside himself with impatience, waiting for the rescue team to arrive. In his nervousness he is not unlike a father in a panic over his sick son.

First Aid

The rescue team arrives at full speed in the Zodiac: Delemotte, Bonnici, Delcoutère. They have brought a large net and some line; and now the struggle begins. The baby whale must weigh over two tons. He is extremely difficult to handle, and the job is not made easier by Ted's absolute insistence that this 4000-pound baby must be handled very gently, and also by Philippe's frequent orders to "Hurry! Hurry! We have to get him back into the water immediately!"

Slowly, painfully, the six men roll the inert mass onto the net, and then drag the net a few yards to the life-giving waters of the lagoon. At the moment when the whale feels the coolness of the water, he breathes a sigh that causes his whole body to shudder. But he is not yet safe. He is again in his natural element, but he is too weak to stay afloat. His blowhole is under water, and he is in imminent danger of drowning.

Working frantically, the team rigs up a litterlike contraption alongside the launch by suspending the ends of the net, which is still around the whale, from a spar. The calf is now alongside the launch, held by the net at surface level, with his blowhole above water. By the time the job is completed the broiling sun is high in the sky; but the whale is alive, and breathing normally. Ted Walker, standing above the whale in the launch, is petting him and talking to him in a soft voice.

Slowly, very slowly, the launch begins the trip back to *Calypso*, with Ted insisting, every few yards, that Philippe reduce his speed even more. Everyone now feels that there is a fair chance of saving the whale. It all depends on how severely he was dehydrated before we were able to reach him.

A Moral Obligation

This incident with the whale calf has become a psychological and philosophical adventure for everyone aboard *Calypso*; and for me it has also taken on the dimensions of a personal challenge.

The whale's presence here is a measure of our sensitivity, and it is fascinating to see how each of us reacts. Some of us pretend a hardhearted indifference — but sneak over to the side every once in a while to make sure that the baby is still breathing. And some of us are overly emotional about the whole thing; but this is rare. *Calypso*, after all, is a hard school. The most interesting reactions, however, are those that are the coolest, that produce the most ingenious and effective ideas for handling the situation. And it is from that aspect that I have been able to realize how difficult it is for a man to keep his sense of proportion in dealing with animals.

Certainly, we — thirty humans and a ship — are not there for the purpose of attempting to repair nature's accidents by saving dying animals, or by trying to reverse infant mortality — which is one of nature's methods of conservation. Still, whether or not it seems reasonable, the fact remains that this whale is, somehow, our responsibility. It was on the verge of dying, and we took it and, we hope, saved it. That act represents a sort of commitment on

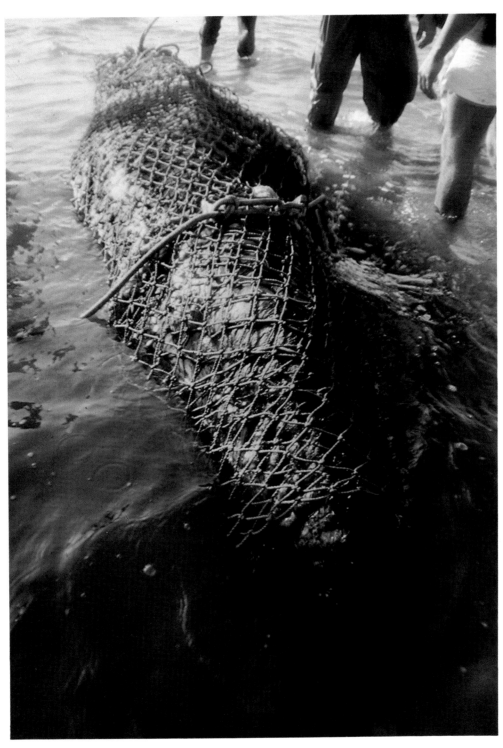

The team succeeds in getting the victim back into the water.

our part. We now have an obligation to do everything that we can to make sure that it survives.

For the three days that the baby whale is with us, an unprecedented sense of well-being reigns aboard *Calypso*. Everyone volunteers to stand extra watches at night. And everyone is aware of the smallest change in the whale's breathing, and of its slightest movement.

The day that the whale was found and brought to *Calypso* it seemed best to me for it to remain suspended in the water in its net alongside the ship. In that way, I reasoned, it would slowly regain its strength. And I hoped, above all, basing myself upon experience, that his mother would come looking for him and, no doubt, hear his cries. This would have been the ideal solution from our standpoint. We could then have turned him loose, restored to his mother.

Until then, however, it seems best to have a full-time guard assigned to our ward, for he would be an easy prey for the many sharks in the lagoon. The guard, who is armed with a loaded rifle, will be relieved every two hours, throughout the night. He is also instructed periodically to check the baby, and to notify me immediately if the mother should show up.

The first night passes without incident. In the morning, the calf is still alive, but there is still no sign of the mother.

Jonah

In the wardroom we decide on a name for the baby: Jonah. It is a logical choice, for we know for certain that this creature at least has emerged alive from the belly of a whale.

Jonah now seems better. His eyes are open, and they are no longer glazed, but clear; and he watches us as we watch him. He shows signs of becoming more lively.

The first thing we must do is to feed him. And now I understand how great is the responsibility that we have assumed from the moment that we lifted Jonah from the sandspit and brought him to *Calypso*. What, and how, does one feed a baby that weighs two tons? Ted Walker is at work whipping up a sort of puree made of all our condensed milk, of flour, and of vitamins. When it is ready, he carries it over to Jonah.

The whale, showing no sign of surprise, watches Ted approach him, and politely opens his mouth when Ted thrusts some of the puree toward him. But the food will not go down Jonah's throat, and it spills into the water.

Next, we rig up a giant baby's bottle, made of a barrel and a length of hose. When Ted has transformed the puree into a more liquid form, we put the nipple end of the hose into Jonah's mouth, hoping that he will instinctively draw the food into his mouth. He does — but is still unable to swallow it.

He Loves Me!

Ted has now concluded that Jonah is very likely old enough to require solid food, and, with a group of volunteers, he has made up a mixture of clams and squid. This, Jonah swallows; and he shows every sign of enjoying it. Ted continues until all the food is gone, putting it, handful by handful, onto Jonah's enormous tongue, which, for the occasion, the whale rolled into a cylinder-shaped trough. Jonah, when he has finished eating, holds onto Ted's hand, refusing to let it go. And Ted Walker, who has tears in his eyes, begins to shout:

"He understands that we want to feed him. He understands . . . he loves me!"

Ted, having spent his life studying animals and loving them from afar, has been deeply touched by Jonah's gesture, by his appeal for help.

I order the camera and sound to be cut off. It seems somehow wrong to record the great emotion of this lover of animals.

It has taken a day's work to feed our baby whale 25 pounds of mollusks, for four men had to gather up the clams and squid from the bottom of the lagoon. And 25 pounds is not much food for even a baby whale.

Obviously we will have to continue.

Calypso's daily routine is now a thing of the past, and life aboard her revolves around Jonah. Meals are no longer served at regular hours, and our work schedule is completely disrupted. Everyone gathers around Ted Walker, who knows so much about whales, offering to do whatever they can to help him save Jonah. And everyone, according to his temperament and background, is searching his mind for a way to keep Jonah alive.

I must confess that we are poorly equipped for this kind of thing. Even the food we have, except for mollusks, is intended for men rather than for whales. And this will be a serious problem. Nonetheless, for the moment Jonah seems to be growing stronger. I seriously believe that he is trying to help us help him.

What we need above all if Jonah is really to recover is a large pool where we can look after him. And, of course, we need medicines and a veterinary expert. We have none of these things, and no way of getting them. On im-

The calf has been tied alongside the launch and is being taken very slowly to *Calypso*.

(Facing page) On the rear deck, the wound inflicted by the birds is examined.

The young whale is hoisted aboard.

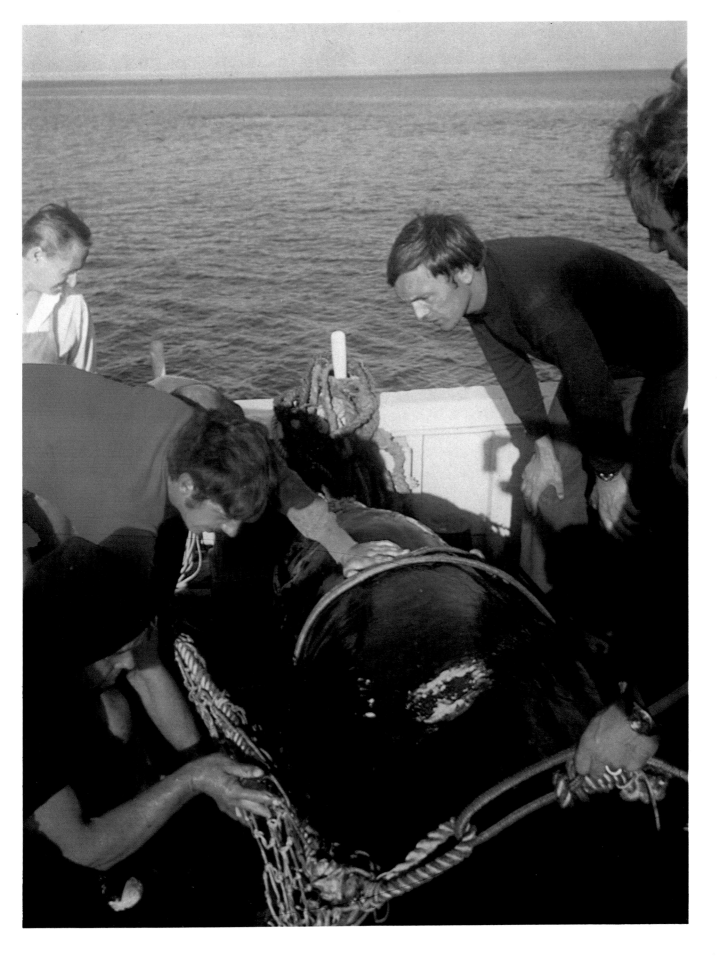

pulse, I telephone the Marine Zoo of San Diego. The director of that institution assures me that they would be delighted to take care of Jonah, until he is well enough to be turned loose again. This really seems to be the best, and perhaps the only, solution. It would be difficult for us to part with our baby whale, to turn him over to strangers. Yet, it would be inexcusably selfish for us to keep him, knowing that we may very likely not be able to save him. Besides, we know that at the San Diego zoo he would receive the best of care from expert hands, and that what could be learned about whales from observation of Jonah, by scientists with the latest equipment at their disposal, would benefit not only Jonah himself, but other whales in the same predicament. And so, we have no choice.

But now another problem presents itself: how do we get Jonah to San Diego? He would never survive being towed that distance, even at slow speeds; and it is essential that we get him there as quickly as possible.

A Whale Harness

For the moment, however, our immediate problem is to care for Jonah's head wounds, which are showing signs of becoming infected. Maurice and Henri have had the idea of making a sort of webbing for Jonah so that he may ride alongside *Calypso* more comfortably than in his net. And when — or if — he regains his strength, he will have greater freedom of movement. So, it is decided to hoist Jonah aboard *Calypso*'s rear deck so that simultaneously we may install this harness, and Ted may care for Jonah's wounds.

Lifting a whale out of the water is a delicate undertaking. A whale, even a baby, can "break" under his own weight unless he is evenly supported at all points. By the time we are ready to begin hoisting, a stretcher has been built. We attach this to our pneumatic hoist, very painstakingly move it under Jonah's body; and then, as slowly and gently as possible, the whale is lifted from the water and deposited on *Calypso*'s deck.

Ted gets to work at once. He determines that the sensitive lips that protect the baleen have been lacerated by birds; and there are other wounds around the blowhole as well. He keeps a close watch on Jonah's breathing, and also tries to listen to his heartbeat with a stethoscope; but the layer of blubber is too thick for anything to be heard. Next, he applies a paste of antibiotics and silicone to Jonah's wounds.

Jonah's presence aboard *Calypso* has a strange effect upon us all. We can see him there, hear him breathing; and we sense the existence of life under that dark mass of flesh. We even feel the heat radiating from his body. He is as warm-blooded as we. It matters little that, out of water, Jonah seems nothing more than a rubbery sack of bones. We have seen whales in the water, and we know what marvels of grace and suppleness they are in their own element.

Far from being an alien, anonymous being, Jonah appears to us to be a familiar animal, and we feel toward him as one does toward a beloved pet who has been struck by an automobile. But with this difference, that it was by the merest stroke of luck that we happened along in time to save Jonah; without us, he would surely have died.

The Blowhole

At this moment, no one thinks to wonder whether or not it is possible for men and whales to communicate with one another, whether or not there is an unbridgeable gap between us. We are aware only of the necessity of saving Jonah's life. And we might say that Jonah himself is trying to make us aware of that necessity. He is pathetic; and most pathetic of all is the blowhole through which he breathes, its lips trembling as it draws in the vital air. A whale's breathing is hardly more than a man's breathing amplified, and that similarity is at once more striking and more moving than any other reaction of marine life.

Once Jonah's wounds have been dressed, he is placed gently in his harness and lowered over the side into the water. Never has our hoist been handled with such loving care.

In the water, Jonah stirs and, as though he wants to tell us that he is all right, and to show his gratitude, he gives a few strokes with his tail. The harness apparently is much more to his liking than the net.

By the end of the day, Ted Walker seems convinced that we will be able to save Jonah. But the question still remains of getting him to San Diego. Perhaps we can get a seaplane. Watching Jonah, it appears that he is improving. But I can see that he has trouble keeping his balance even in the light current of the tide.

Never has the landscape appeared more inhospitable than at this moment. Everything is still, deserted, bearing the stamp of desolation as though it were part of another world. It is an appropriate setting for Jonah, whom we have adopted, but for whom we can do no more than we have already done.

The baby whale seems to give no sign of life.

(Facing page) Ted Walker administers first aid.

Ted Walker opens the whale's mouth to try to feed it.

A Night of Watching

The young orphan whale is fighting as well as he can for his life. We have now done all in our power for him, and I want at least to continue protecting him from the killers who roam the water at night. Therefore we again set up a relay of armed guards.

At three o'clock in the morning, I am awake and go on deck to see Jonah. He seems comfortable. The water is calm.

At five o'clock, Canoë, who is on duty, awakens Caillart, our ship's captain, who rushes to the rear deck. He sees Jonah rolling over on his back, and notices that he is breathing only with difficulty.

Canoë then comes to awaken me. I go up immediately. And I find that Jonah is dead. We had not found him in time. He had been too badly burned, too dehydrated for us, with our primitive means, to be able to save him.

I look up at the light of dawn. The pelicans are awake now, wheeling in the sky.

Everyone aboard, as though awakened by a mysterious alarm, gathers

Ted takes the whale's measurements.

on the rear deck. Jonah has already found himself a place in the history of *Calypso*. For these men, most of them very young, Jonah embodies the great mystery of life and death. He was one of the marvelous works of nature that nature, with a callousness that man finds shocking, destroys on a whim. We have seen great animals of the sea die before; but nothing has moved us as we have been moved by the slow agony of the baby whale who did not want to die, and to whom we had wished to give life. And yet, our reaction is that of creatures of land. In the sea, there is no room for pity or for sorrow.

As in the case of human suffering and death, Jonah's demise released us from our trancelike state of fascination. *Calypso* has resumed the daily routine that was so dramatically, and so tragically, interrupted.

Our first job is to dispose of the calf's body. It is towed out by the launch, weighted, and then sunk in deep water. We have not removed the harness that we made for him. And we do not want to see what will happen to Jonah when the sharks find his body.

Coming out of our dream, we find that the exodus of whales for which

The patient is treated with affectionate care, but its eyes remain shut.

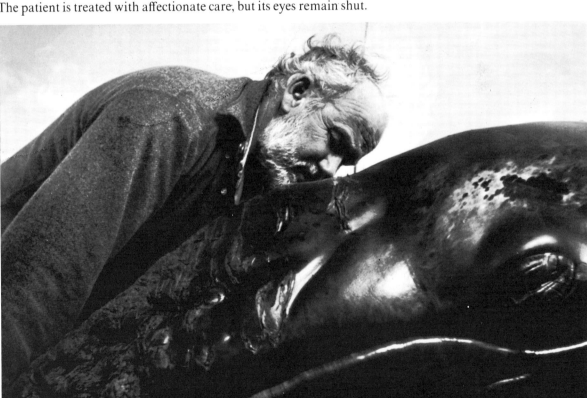

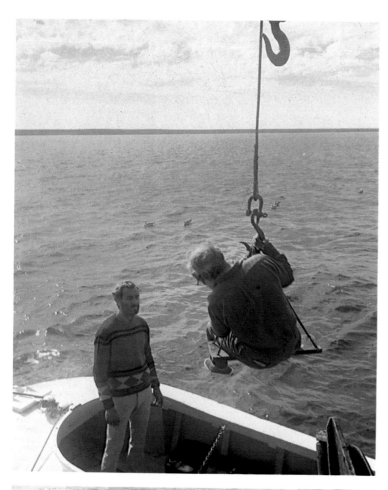

Ted Walker, hanging from the crane, will try to feed the animal, which has been put back into the water.

A funnel and a rubber hose serve as a baby bottle.

(Facing page above) Ted Walker forces open the calf's jaws.

(Facing page below) Jonah now refuses to let go of Ted's hand.

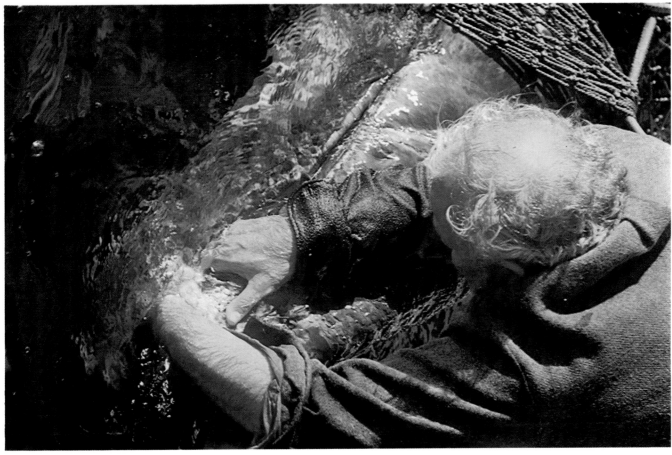

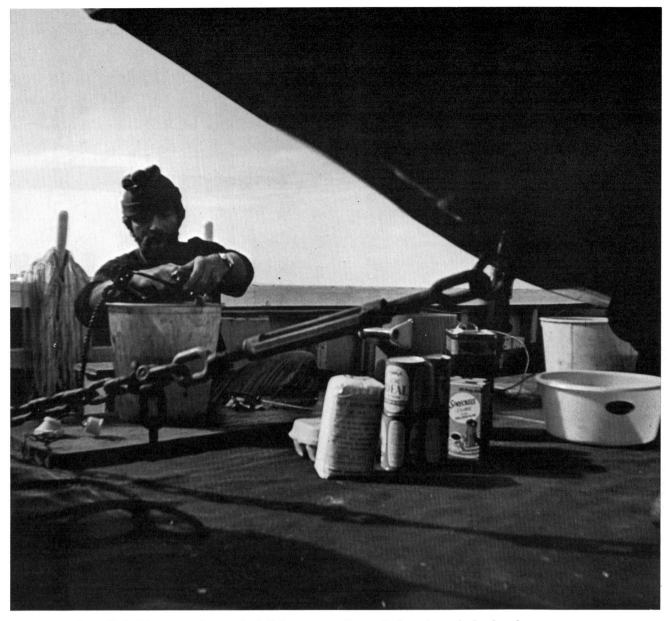

Jean-Clair Riant uses almost all of *Calypso*'s supplies to devise a formula for Jonah.

(Left) A futile attempt to listen to the whale's heartbeat with a stethoscope.

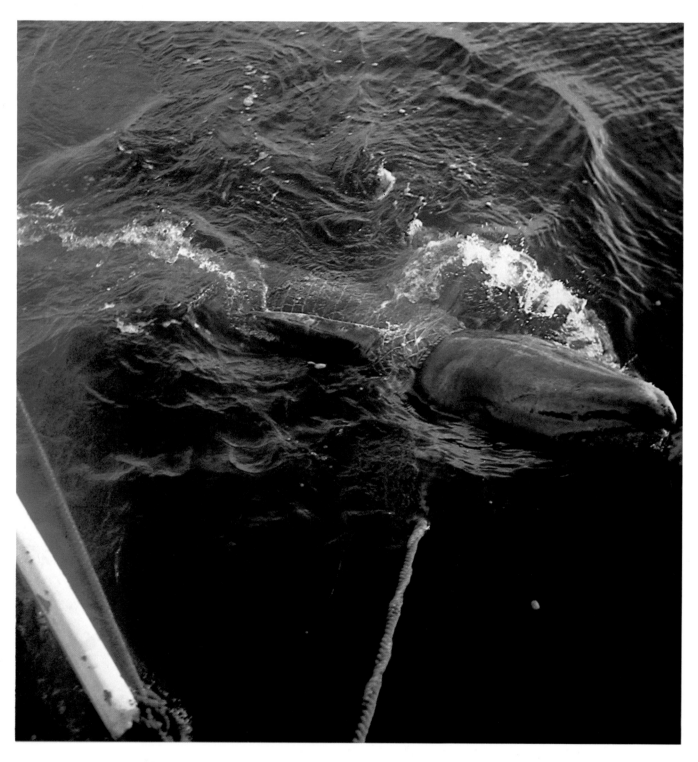

The baby whale has just died, and Ted Walker and Jacques Renoir are deeply affected.

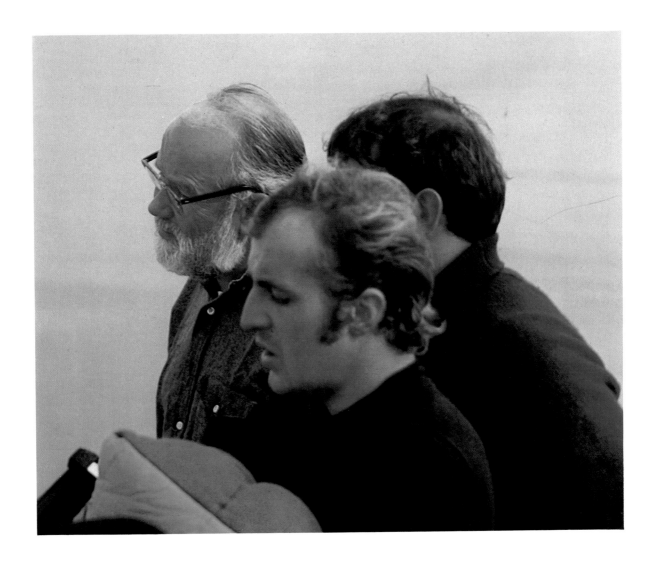

we have been waiting has already begun, and indeed is well underway, without our even having been aware of it.

No matter. They will return every year for centuries to come, to spend here the most important hours of their lives — the hours of love, of birth, and of death.

We have been the respectful, and often astonished, witnesses to all of this. The cycle of life and death is especially impressive when embodied in these giants of the deep. These creatures, with their fifty-foot bodies and their forty or fifty tons of flesh, are not built to a human scale; and yet, they breathe, they love, and they suffer as we do. Our lives and theirs, though different, are not finally distinct.

Will the great adventure of the gray whales continue for long in the modern world? These animals are now protected by law, and they will not be subjected to the massacres that were common in the nineteenth century. But will their refuge in Baja California always be a deserted area? Will their bay forever deserve its name: the Bay of Solitude — a solitude peopled by contented whales?

TEN

The Strongest and Most Intelligent of All: The Killer Whale

Between the enormity of the cachalot and the blue whale, and the sleek grace of the dolphin, there is a whole range of animals of intermediate size who are also marine mammals, and who are intelligent and physiologically similar to man. They all make sounds which, it seems, convey meaning. There are the blackfish (or pilot whales), killer whales (orcs or prampuses), and bottlenose (also called beaked whale) — all of whom are toothed whales.

The relatively small size of these animals makes them rather easy to approach so far as man is concerned. For sperm whales and baleen whales, however gentle they may be, occasionally show signs of not knowing their own strength.

Until very recently, these medium-sized cetaceans were but poorly understood. We knew almost nothing about their behavior, their intelligence, their social instinct. The stories of whale hunters, and the prejudices of man, attributed terrible reputations to some of them; to the orc or grampus, for example, who became known as the "killer whale." It did not help his reputation that nature had endowed him with a set of from twenty to twenty-eight formidable-looking teeth.

A twenty-five-foot killer whale. Its blowhole is clearly visible at the top of its head.

(Right)Dolphins are very clever in devising ways to escape when they are being chased.

In the course of our expeditions aboard *Calypso*, we have met a fair number of blackfish and killer whales.

In the Red Sea, while *Calypso* was at anchor near a reef, our divers reported a school of blackfish playing near the ship. Michel Deloire immediately went down with a camera, but he was able to shoot only a few feet of film. As soon as he began to mingle with the school, they would disperse and reassemble a short distance away. We had the impression that it was their mating season, and that they were engaged in prenuptial rites. If that was so, they no doubt regarded us as intruders.

On another occasion, when we were returning from our other expedition,

we ran across a school of blackfish midway between the Aleutians and Anchorage. They were instantly recognizable because of their round heads (shaped like basketballs) and their uniformly dark color. (Unlike the killer whale, which has large white markings.)

These small whales were less timid than those we had seen in the Red Sea. They remained on the surface until *Calypso* was quite close, and then they swam slowly away. The largest of them were between fifteen and twenty feet long, while the maximum size for the species is about twenty-five feet. This particular school comprised about twenty animals; but schools of several hundred animals are not uncommon.

These schools of blackfish are actually marine harems, for the male of the species, like the cachalot, is polygamous. They attain maturity late: the female at six years, and the male at thirteen.

When migrating, blackfish or pilot whales follow their leader blindly — a characteristic that sometimes leads to catastrophe. It happens occasionally that a leader, frightened by something or the other, goes aground and is immediately followed by the entire school.

Pilot whales eat cuttlefish and squid. The memorable night that we filmed the mating of the squid in the Pacific, off Santa Catalina, pilot whales were constantly circling around that enormous assemblage of cephalopods.* The presence of the divers, however, and the floodlights that we used to film the squid in ecstasy, kept most of the mammals at a respectful distance. Nonetheless, they remained in the vicinity throughout the night; and, occasionally, the bravest of them would rush in, sneak a forbidden mouthful of squid, and then disappear. They are very timid creatures — as distinguished from the sharks, who, ignoring lights and divers alike, threw themselves upon the stars of our film and swallowed them in great mouthfuls.

Public Enemy Number One

In 1967, in the Indian Ocean, we met a school of killer whales. We were frightened of them — more frightened than we should have been, as it turned out. At that time, nothing was known about their behavior in captivity or semicaptivity; and we, along with the rest of the world, considered killer whales to be the most fearsome creatures of the sea, the avowed enemies of all life forms to be found in the water, including divers. So far as we were concerned, the killer whale — even when known by the less ominous names of orc and grampus — was the most dangerous animal we could possibly meet. It was more feared even than the shark; for we knew that it was a very intelligent creature.† Also, its teeth were most impressive, numerous, and enormous.

We knew that killer whales were social animals, and that they traveled and attacked their prey in groups. So, as soon as we saw this school of them, we concluded that the sea around us was being subjected to a reign of terror.

*A television film, called *Night of the Squids* was distributed internationally as part of the series "The Undersea World of Jacques Cousteau." The subject of squid and octopuses will be covered in the next book of the present series.

† The shark's intelligence, on the other hand, is comparable to that of the rat — which is not to be dismissed lightly.

Here are my journal entries from that period:

April 12, 1967. At 5:30 in the afternoon, a school of small dolphins — a species that we know to be almost unapproachable — is reported. Bébert, Bonnici, and Barsky go out immediately in the Zodiac and chase them until sunset, without being able to catch up. The tricks that these dolphins use are fantastic. First of all, they separate into two groups that swim in different directions. The group that is followed then splits up into two more groups. When the team that is being chased tires, they dive — and are replaced by the other team. When a single dolphin is isolated, he begins by feinting according to a pattern: first to the right, then to the left, and back again. As soon as the pursuer becomes accustomed to this rhythm, the dolphin changes it brusquely — by diving, or by swimming away in a new direction.

It is likely that this sort of behavior, which is very different from that of our ordinary friendly dolphins who are always ready to play around *Calypso*, is due to the presence of killer whales in the neighborhood. These tactics, which are so effective that they threw our Zodiac off the track, were no doubt designed to have the same effect on the predators.

I think I can conclude that dolphins and whales are almost always followed closely by groups of sharks who feed off their leavings, and who sooner or later attack the infant, young, or sick dolphins and whales. As far as the killer whales are concerned, however, they no doubt create a circle of destruction around themselves, butchering any creature who dares to claim a share of their food.

Even so, we must make every effort to approach these creatures by using the same method we have used with cachalots: send out a Zodiac with a harpooner and a cameraman who is ready to jump into the water with the killer whale.

April 13. As soon as I awaken Simone, the alert sounds. Everyone rushes up on deck, and the Zodiac is lowered into the water. From *Calypso*, we can see very clearly what is in the water: killer whales.

They are easily recognizable by the white markings behind their eyes and on their stomachs, and also by their triangular dorsal fin.

Everyone is excited by the sight. It is still early, the weather is magnificent, and it promises to be a splendid day.

As usual, our visiting killer whales seem to be very quick-witted, and very wary of us. The school includes a huge male who must weigh several tons. His dorsal fin protrudes above all the others, like a standard of a chieftain. Another dorsal fin, slightly smaller, next to his must be that of an adolescent whale, no doubt the son of this giant. Sooner or later, the young one will do battle with his father to obtain control of the harem. It brings to mind the

A school of killer whales, photographed by Dr. Millet in the Bering Strait.

case of certain Arabian sheikdoms in which succession is often determined by parricide.

There seem to be eight or nine adults, each weighing between 1500 and 2000 pounds, and a half dozen younger whales. Like the school that we chased to the south of Socotra in 1955, this one is trying to get away from us, apparently under orders from their leader. They want no part of man or his machines, and *Calypso* is too slow to be able to catch up with them.

Bebert and Bonnici take a Zodiac with a 33-horsepower motor and go out after them, while *Calypso* follows at a distance. At nine o'clock, after a hell-for-leather chase at 15 or 20 knots that lasted ninety minutes, and after persevering through an elaborate series of feints and tricks, Bonnici sees a massive black-and-white shape surface right next to the Zodiac. He throws his harpoon. Bull's-eye. The killer whale takes off, very fast at first, trailing the red buoy. These mammals are capable of speeds of over thirty knots (35 miles per hour); but, as streamlined as they are, they are built for pure speed and not for towing. Even an object of moderate weight, like the buoy, will cut their speed in half.

(Right) The killer whale has an impressive dorsal fin.

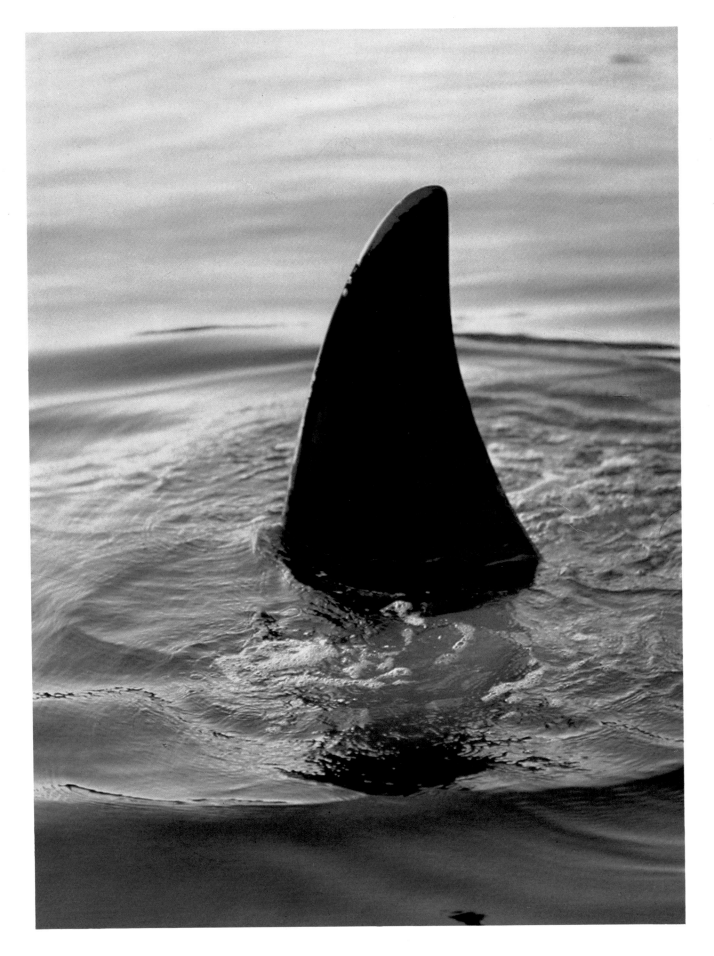

The rest of the school, noticing that one of the members was slowing, also cut their speed for about ten minutes, to give him a chance to catch up.

Then, when the leader decides that they have waited long enough, they disappear in a burst of speed. Bonnici, touched by the predicament of his captive, cuts the harpoon line; and the lightweight harpoon disengages itself from the whale's skin. The killer whale then sets out on the trail of his friends.

A Surprise: No Attack.

April 15. Another alert at eight o'clock this morning, and the Zodiac takes off. It returns shortly. The mammals sighted were more of our very shy little dolphins.

A few minutes later, Simone sights a school of blackfish, or pilot whales. We slow down, but the Zodiac is a long time getting into the water. We chase the school, but without success, for over two hours. For some reason, these blackfish, instead of letting us come near as they usually do, flee with every sign of fright. What is the matter with them? This is the first time that we have seen timid blackfish.

A large shark is following *Calypso* close to her stern, but when we slow down it flees.

After lunch, we try once more to catch up with our unapproachable dolphins, but, again, in vain. Something is wrong here. Everything that we have seen for the past three days seems terrified of something. Are there Japanese whalers at work here, exterminating all the mammals in this area? Upon reflection, however, we reject this idea. There are *many* animals in these waters. They have not been exterminated; they have been terrorized.

We think that this situation has prevailed since our encounter with killer whales on April 12. Is it possible that these animals, usually as rare as they are terrible, are present here in large numbers?

By the end of the afternoon, we sight a school of killer whales. The Zodiac is lowered immediately, and the chase begins, to continue until nightfall.

The school is composed of an enormous male (at least three tons, 25 to 30 feet long, with a dorsal fin four and one half feet high), a femal almost as large as the male but with a smaller fin, seven or eight medium-sized females, and six or eight calves. This is not the same school that we saw a few days ago; in this one, there is no young male. But the number of members is about the same. It is a nomadic school, comprising females and children, and with a single male as lord and master of the group. This presupposes the elimination of male competition in a school, and I expect that other males are either killed by the chief or driven off. The latter alternative is hardly better than being killed outright, because I doubt very much that a killer whale, alone and on his own, can find enough food to keep himself alive.

The Zodiac chases the school for two hours, sometimes guided by radio from *Calypso*. Nothing escapes our men on watch in the crow's-nest.

At the beginning of the chase, the killer whales are very sure of themselves, diving every three or four minutes and reappearing about a half mile away. Ordinarily, this would be enough to lose any marine attacker, and to shake off a whaler. But the Zodiac is doing 20 knots on a sea of glass, and is capable of turning on a dime. A few seconds after the grampuses surface to breathe, they hear the Zodiac's wasplike buzzing coming up from the rear.

After a while, the mammals try a new tactic. They surface every two or three minutes now, and increase their speed. But the Zodiac keeps up with them.

The time has come for evasive tactics: the whales dart to the right at 90°, then to the left and back again; then they make simulated turns at 180°. finally, they play their trump card: the male remains visible, eminently so, swimming along at 15 or 20 knots, and occasionally leaping out of the water. He is accompanied only by the largest female. His purpose, obviously, is to lure the Zodiac into following him — while the rest of the school escapes in the opposite direction.

When the Zodiac is about a mile away from the school, but quite close to the male, the latter dives and disappears in the water. Guided by the voices of his companions, he swims straight toward them. From *Calypso*, we are watching all of this with great interest. We, unlike the Zodiac, have never lost sight of the main body of the school. And suddenly we see the leader surface in their midst, certain, no doubt, of having done his duty and played a good trick on the pursuer. We would be compelled to agree with him — except for the fact that he surfaced practically alongside *Calypso*.

This chase has taught us a great deal about killer whales, and has allowed Barsky to get some marvelous (and rare) footage. Nonetheless, we must regard the whole adventure as a failure. The purpose of the pursuit was to mark the huge male, but the light harpoon twisted in flight and struck sideways. Bebert tried four more times, and the same thing happened each time. So, we will abandon this system.

Here is one important observation: during the chase, the Zodiac, traveling at 15 or 20 knots, happened to pass over the back of one of the whales just as it was surfacing. The craft actually took off, like an airplane. Everyone was thrown to the deck and the camera, still running, shot up into the air and

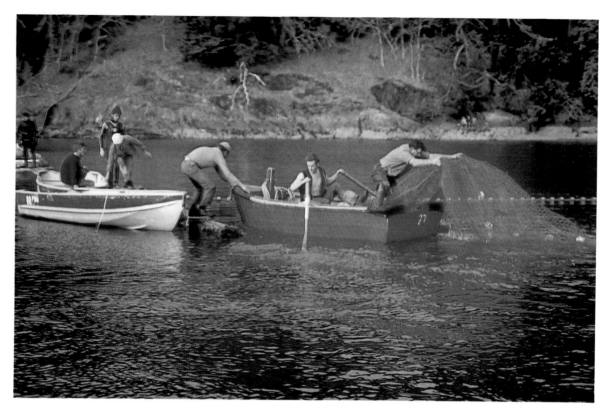

Laying nets in the Juan de Fuca Strait, near Seattle.

(Facing page above) The albino killer whale of the Juan de Fuca Strait.
(Facing page below) The killer whale's teeth are fearsome weapons.

Two killer whales (one is an albino) in the nets.

then fell back into the Zodiac. That will be an interesting shot. In spite of the irritation that an incident like this must have caused the whale, and in spite of all the other annoyances that the Zodiac undoubtedly caused, the killer whales did not once take any aggressive action. These animals, certainly ferocious, terribly powerful, and very intelligent, and moreover armed with a legitimate complaint against the Zodiac, never attacked the frail little boat that was irritating them so. If they had wished, they could have made a single mouthful of Bebert, Maurice, and Barsky. But they did not.

When the Zodiac returned, Bebert told me: "I don't know why, but I had the feeling that they wouldn't do anything."

Ambush

In the lagoons of Baja California, where we spent three months with gray whales, we saw not a single killer whale. We would have sighted them easily by their large triangular dorsal fins, which project above the surface when they swim. We were surprised at their absence, for they could have wreaked havoc among the gray whales there — as much as a whaling ship. And yet, we did see killer whales lying in ambush just at the entry of the lagoon, at the mouth of the channel. Obviously, they were waiting for the gray whales and their calves to leave the lagoon's protection.

They were difficult to see from the surface when the water was rough, but they could easily be seen from the air. And Philippe also saw them from his hot-air ballon.

Some divers claimed that a male gray whale was stationed in the channel to keep the killer whales out of the lagoon. It seems more probable, however, that the mammals, since they are group animals, are unwilling to risk an encounter in a narrow lagoon, in shallow water, where they would have no place to maneuver. Their superiority over gray whales rests on their skill in group strategy; and that strategy would be seriously hindered in a restricted space blocked by sandbanks.

The killer whale is a fearsome adversary. It is capable of diving to depths of over 1000 feet and is able to remain beneath the surface for as much as twenty minutes. Also, its vision is better than that of the baleen whale (its eyes are larger), and it sees as well in the air as in the water. On the whole, its visual acuity seems about equal to that of the cat.

The killer whale, except for man, is the only enemy of the whale. They always attack in groups and sometimes cover their prey from one end of its body to the other. A single killer whale would have no chance against the

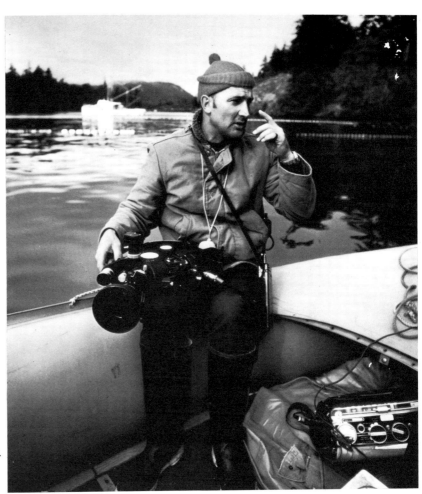

Ron Church, our photographer.

strength and the enormous tail of a full-grown baleen whale. Their attacks are always well co-ordinated and tactically effective. Some of the killer whales bite the victim in the stomach and in the genital area, causing it great pain. Others force the baleen whale to open its mouth and they seize its tongue. It is a pitiless and savage onslaught, and the attackers have numbers on their side. In order to discourage such attacks, baleen whales form a defensive circle, or try to beat off the predators with blows from their tails. Killer whales therefore prefer, as their victim, a whale calf, or a young whale; and, when they find such a victim, they mount a diversionary attack against its mother.

Whales are not their only prey. They also attack squids, sea elephants, seals, narwhals—and even dolphins which although they are able to master predatory sharks, seem comparatively helpless against killer whales. (They will also occasionally attack schools of salmon and tuna.)

There are witnesses who state — though I cannot, from my own experience, support that statement — that they have seen a group of some twenty killer whales encircle a school of a hundred dolphins and then slowly close the circle. Next, a single killer whale threw itself into the midst of the dolphins and killed one of them, while the rest of the whales continued to

A diver feeds one of the killer whales of Juan de Fuca Strait.

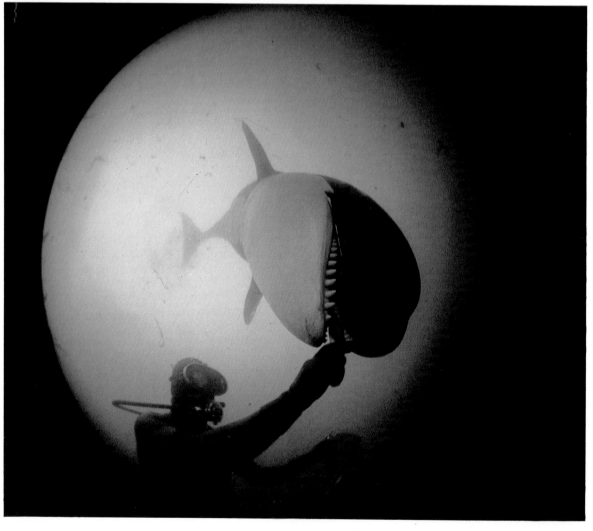

maintain the circle. Each of the predators then took its turn in attacking a victim, until the water was red with the blood of the dolphins.*

It is my opinion that almost all stories about killer whales are somewhat exaggerated. These animals are, after all is said and done, somewhat rare; and, despite their intelligence and strength, they have never become the dominant species of the seas.

Today, we know for certain that there is no "man-eating" cetacean. Killer whales, whose legendary ferocity has, for centuries, struck fear into the hearts of seamen, never attack divers. In fact, they have proved to be remarkably easy to tame.

Killer Whales in Captivity

I am always terribly depressed at the sight of an animal in captivity, and especially when it is an animal of the size and intelligence of the killer whale.

Even though the behavior of animals in captivity tells us little or nothing about their behavior in their natural environment, the fact remains that the only way man has at present of familiarizing himself with killer whales is to observe them in the great marine zoos. Captivity, therefore, may be a necessary evil. But it may not always be so.

This having been said, let me go on to assert that an animal in captivity deserves our respect; and he also deserves that we try to make him as comfortable and as happy as possible under the circumstances.

The first killer whale to be exhibited in captivity was named Moby Doll, and was at home in the aquarium of Vancouver, British Columbia.† How it came to the aquarium is an unusual story. A Canadian sculptor had been commissioned, in March 1965, to execute a statue of a killer whale; and, in order to have a model, he intended to kill a specimen. After two months of trying, he succeeded in harpooning a whale; but, when the moment came for the *coup de grâce,* the artist could not bring himself to do it. Instead, he brought his victim to the aquarium, nursed her back to health with penicillin, gave her the name of Moby Doll, and, to everyone's astonishment, won the whale's affectionate friendship. This was in 1965, when the killer whale was still regarded as the most savage of marine animals, the "tiger of the sea."

Moby Doll became a celebrity. The Duke and Duchess of Windsor came

* This account is taken from *Home Is the Sea for Whales,* p. 116.

†The whole story is told in the work by Riedman and Gustafson cited above.

to see her and to watch her savior and friend scratch her stomach with a stiff-bristled brush. When Moby Doll died, the (London) *Times* devoted two columns to her obituary, and she was mourned throughout the English-speaking world.*

A few months after Moby Doll's death, the Seattle aquarium purchased a killer whale from two Canadian fishermen for $8000. Delivery, however, was not included in the purchase price, and Edward Griffin, director of the aquarium, went to the mouth of the Bella Coola river, near the village of Namu, to supervise the operation. His whale, he found, was twenty-three feet long, and weighed about four tons.

After considering the problem from every angle, he decided to encircle the whale with a floating net and to tow him back to Seattle within the net. Using forty empty oil barrels as floaters, and with the help of 200 volunteers from the village of Namu, the net was completed, and in place, in a few days. And, in recognition of the help given by the villagers, the whale was christened Namu.

A ship now began towing the net and its resident slowly along Queen Charlotte Strait, Johnstone Strait, and Georgia Strait. As the net moved, it was followed by a school of killer whales. It appeared that they wanted to free their companion; but they did not attack. Only one male and two females, who were no doubt members of his family, communicated with him by means of a series of whistles and cries. In response, Namu moved his dorsal fin; but he did not try to escape.

Two weeks later, the whale passed through customs at the American border and was placed in a tank at the Seattle aquarium. There he was treated royally. While he was being moved, he had refused to eat for about a week. At the end of that time, however, he accepted two salmon. He seems to have enjoyed them enormously, for he would never touch any other kind of food as long as he remained in Seattle — an unexpected idiosyncrasy that proved to be expensive for the aquarium.

Namu died after a year, in July 1966. He, like Moby Doll, had evidenced much intelligence and a surprising gentleness. This "tiger of the sea" had turned out to be friendly toward man.

During the past few years, about ten killer whales have been captured and placed in marinelands in Seattle, San Diego, and Vancouver. Edward Griffin, aided by a friend, Gerald Brown, has become a specialist in the techniques of capture. Mr. Brown has spent some time aboard *Calypso* as a

---

*When an autopsy was performed upon Moby Doll, it was discovered that "she" was a full-fledged male.

diver and a specialist in marine life. He has had much experience with killer whales, and he has this to say about them: "They are really something to see in the water. They make up underwater ballets, twisting, rising up from the bottom, jumping. When they were first captured, they were restless and skittish; but when I put my hand out and petted them, and told them that they were beautiful animals, they calmed down. Domestication is not a question of food, but of contact."

A killer whale can be trained and become attached to man without receiving food from the human being. No doubt, this is unique in the annals of animal training.

In fact, the most difficult thing about keeping a whale in captivity is getting him to eat. Killer whales do not really care for fish, Moby Doll being an exception to the rule. They prefer the flesh of warm-blooded animals —

The Juan de Fuca killer whales, at dusk.

which puts the aquarium personnel on the horns of a dilemma, for they cannot feed him their seals.

The first whales captured were traumatized, and it was necessary to allow them to adjust to their tank. The keepers brought this about by going down into the water, waist-deep, and "walking" the whales; or rather, pushing them gently. Left to themselves, they would not budge. In this way, they familiarized them with the walls of their tank. Then, little by little, the whales began to move around by themselves. But they still would not eat.

The keepers began by offering them a sort of pâté made of herring, milk, and vitamins, which they refused. The keepers then propped the whales' mouths open with pieces of wood and tried to place the mixture down their throats; but the animals held their tongues across their mouths and would not allow the food to enter.

Louis Prézelin, with Serge Foulon, gives a guitar concert for the killer whales. The whales seem to appreciate the performance.

"We were sure," explained Brown, "that if we could get one of them to eat, the others would follow suit. When a whale bites, its teeth make noise in the water. And as soon as another killer whale hears that noise, he rushes over to eat whatever is left.

"We experimented first with a young whale. We rubbed a herring against his lips, and then we put it into his mouth and began pulling it out immediately. He reacted exactly as a dog would react: he bit on it and held it. The other whales, of course, heard the 'crunch,' and they came right over and began eating."

The killer-whale family is a closely knit unit. Usually, there is only one calf at a time, and the offspring is enveloped in a maternal love that seems highly developed. When a mother whale has reason to be afraid for her young, she comes close and "speaks" to it.

There are many reliable witnesses to the phenomenon of mother love among these mammals. A mother who was mortally wounded spent her last hour, and her last ounce of strength, circling around her calf in order to protect him as long as possible. Another mother wandered for three days off Hat Island, near Puget Sound, after her calf was killed there.

There have been several instances of mating in captivity, at Seattle and Vancouver. The whales copulate, after extended caresses, in a frontal position, chest to chest. The gestation period lasts from thirteen to sixteen months.

The sexual life of killer whales seems particularly intensive, and includes a powerful attraction for human beings. And they are perfectly capable of distinguishing between human male and female. Our friend, Jerry Brown, discovered this in the whale tank at Seattle.

"We had a female in a tank there for about a year, teaching her the usual tricks. One day, when the water was especially clear, I went down to take some underwater pictures. As soon as I was in the water, this female — Shamoo was her name — came over to me, pushed me up against the tank wall, and began rubbing against me. I called to a friend of mine to throw some herring into the water at the other end of the tank, but this didn't work. Shamoo wouldn't let me go, and I stayed there, pinned against the wall, for an hour and a half."

The skin of killer whales is especially soft and smooth. When they are swimming in groups, they remain constantly in physical contact by sliding against one another. This may well be a form of sex play.

A final and important characteristic: According to everyone who has worked with both killer whales and dolphins — including experts from the U. S. Navy — the whale is much more intelligent than the dolphin. They understand, and learn, twice as fast as their smaller cousins.

A team from *Calypso*, made up of our photographer, Ron Church, André Laban, and Louis Prezelin went recently to visit Griffin and Brown's killer whales at Juan de Fuca, near Seattle. The dean of all captive killer whales lives there, and he is now in his fifth year of residence.

Prezelin had brought his guitar, and played a few tunes while standing alongside the whales' enclosure. The animals immediately came over to the side closest to Prezelin and listened attentively, and then showed their satisfaction at the man's performance by spraying him from their blowholes.

Our team next tried to teach the whales to sing, with Prezelin accompanying on the guitar. This was less than successful; but there is no denying that killer whales are sensitive to music, and that one can get their attention, and their appreciation, if one is sufficiently fastidious in the choice of melodies.

In the water, Brown's whales ran through their entire repertoire of turns, loops, and leaps for our divers and cameramen.

Falco, after having chased so many killer whales over the water in his Zodiac, now hoped to be able to establish more peaceful relations with them. He went to visit two females at the Marine World of California.

Falco reported that both of the females were obviously very sensitive to the sounds coming from a loudspeaker over their tank. These sounds were the dialogue that had taken place when they were captured, between them and the other members of their school. This exchange, which was composed of clicks and trills, had been taped at the moment of capture and was now being played back to the female whales. The captives were quite obviously moved by the sounds. They swam quickly around their tank, but always returned to a spot near the loudspeaker and replied to it by a series of various sounds.

Falco swam for a while with a female killer whale named (for some obscure reason) Clyde, and he took the opportunity to try a few experiments. For example, he held out a fish to her, but, when she came to take it, he placed a thin plank between the whale and her food. The whale immediately turned away — apparently warned by her sonar of an obstacle.

The language of killer whales, like that of dolphins, remains incomprehensible to us, despite the best efforts of Dr. Lilly and several other researchers. At least we now know that these cetaceans do have a language of some kind, and that we must attempt to discover the meaning of the sounds that they make. This, perhaps, is one of the most exciting challenges that we have to face. It is not impossible that the killer whale, more intelligent than the dolphin, will one day provide us with the means of establishing communication between animals and man.

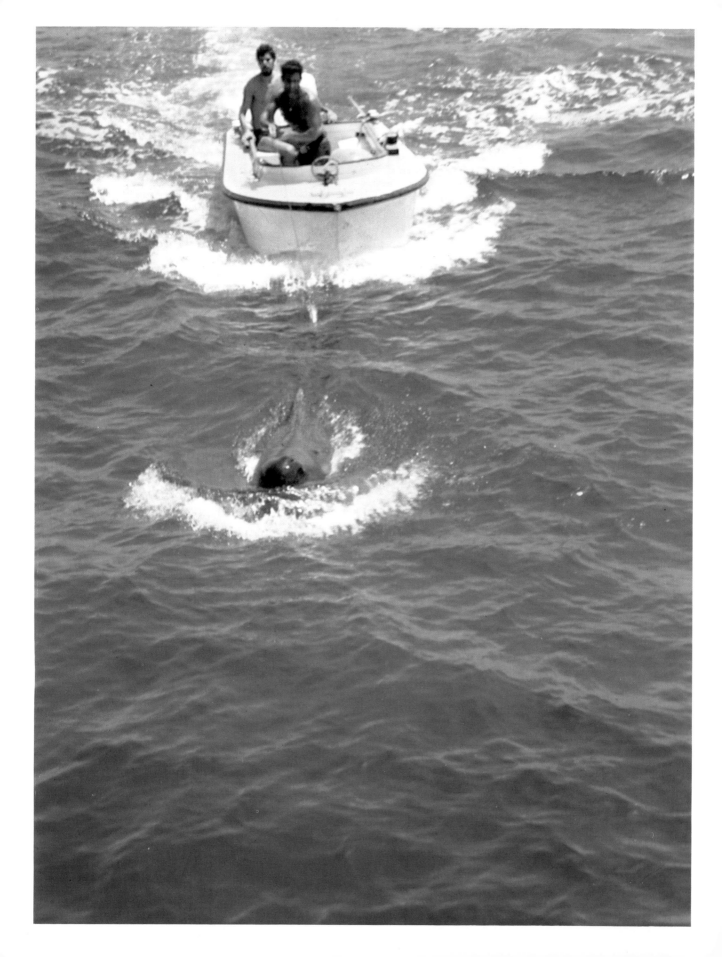

ELEVEN

A Time for Respect

It is March 8, and we are in Baja California's Bay of Solitude. The weather yesterday was atrocious, the sky covered with low-lying clouds. And, of course, it rained. It was impossible to shoot a single foot of film. To cap it all, the tape recorder fell out of the Zodiac and into the water when a whale decided to romp nearby. It was in the water only a few seconds; but that was enough to ruin it. We had to send Eugène Lagorio to Los Angeles by plane to have it repaired. Fortunately, yesterday was the day for our regular air liaison plane.

And then, last night, one of our camera batteries exploded. . .

Today, vengeance is ours. It is a glorious day, thanks to Bernard Delemotte.

Bernard spent the morning trying to lasso the tail of a whale calf. He would grab the calf, hold it in his arms, and, at the same time, try to get his lariat over the tail. The water was as muddy as that of the Mississippi, and he

(Left) A sperm whale has been overtaken by the launch.

couldn't see a thing. We all thought that he had succeeded, but he was not fast enough with the rope. By then, the calf had tired of the game. With a shrug and a rear upward that would have done credit to a mustang, it freed itself from Delemotte's embrace and disappeared in a cloud of foam, leaving Delemotte standing there with his lasso. (In all fairness to Bernard, I should mention that his "little" whale was about twenty-feet long.)

Our underwater cowboy was disappointed, but not discouraged. During the afternoon, he presented another spectacle for our entertainment and delight; and this time he was truly sensational.

Having succeeded in grabbing and holding on to a whale calf this morning, he conceived the idea of — stunt-riding on the back of a whale, as on a horse. For his prospective mount he chose an animal that appeared to be sleeping. Wearing his flippers and mask, but not breathing apparatus, Bernard swam slowly toward the whale, every movement a study in graceful efficiency. He was now next to her, and she was still asleep. In a single motion, Bernard hoisted himself onto her back and stood. He was mounted.

Michel Deloire was filming away as though it were the end of the world, and we were all watching in complete fascination. How long could Bernard stay on? And, more important, if he succeeded in staying on, how would he manage to get off?

The outcome was not long in doubt. The whale awoke and shook herself, more in surprise than irritation, and moved her head brusquely. Delemotte was off and lost in the commotion. By the time he regained the surface, his whale was far away.

From that moment on, the most vital question aboard *Polaris* has become: who will be the first to be towed by a bucking whale-bronco? Bonnici and Serge Foulon both succeed by using what they learned from Bernard's experience. Gradually, they perfect their technique, and they learn to ride with apparent facility, and even elegance. Each one of the riders approaches his whale and mounts in a manner consonant with his temperament. Delemotte is stern, resolute, his muscles tense, his brow furrowed, and he approaches the whale as though he were going to wrestle with it. Bonnici is intuitive, alert, agile; he observes the situation for a moment, then leaps upon his mount gracefully and rides with the professional smile of a circus bareback performer.

Moby Dick Revisited

Such, briefly, is the new relationship between men and whales. I cannot state categorically that whales have an entirely happy memory of our contact

A whale harpooned during a dive. Nineteenth-century engraving. *Bibliothèque Nationale.*

with them, or even a very lively recollection of it. But I can say that Delemotte's exploit marks a new departure in our relationships with whales. It has an almost historical character, and one that will have many repercussions. Once people see, on television, *Calypso*'s men riding on the back of a whale, they will no longer be able to preserve the old point of view with respect to whales. Man will no longer be able to be as limited, as utilitarian, and uncomprehending as our grandparents were in the nineteenth century. They will no longer believe in the "ferocity" and "malevolence" of "underwater monsters."

It bothers me enormously to read the traditional accounts of whaling in the era of sailing ships. These are recitals of deeds of bravery, and even of heroism; but they are also monuments to human incomprehension and misunderstanding. There, one reads only of the "ferocity" of sperm whales — of living, intelligent beings transfixed by eight or ten harpoons, their flesh torn, their eyes gouged out, mad with pain, flailing about in agony.

Thanks to Delemotte's experiences with the gray whales, ·to those of Raymond Coll with cachalots, to those of Philippe with humpback whales and of Bonnici with finbacks, misunderstanding may give way to admiration and comprehension. In mv opinion, man will honor himself finally in being able to feel respect for the largest creature on the face of the earth, in being able to touch it, in being able to understand that it is an innocuous being.

When we drew near to a humpback whale in the water, we imagined that he gave us a friendly look.

A shark's look is more steady, and more misleading, than that of a whale.

Cetaceans may now no longer be relegated to that area of the human psyche which causes human beings to feel obliged to react, out of fear, with violence and death.

Until the twentieth century, the relationship between man and whale was that of killer to victim. When limits were finally established to the massacre of whales, they were limits dictated neither by pity nor by a feeling of respect for these "marvels of nature." What happened was that whale hunters realized at one point that they were finding fewer and fewer whales. And, in fact, there *were* fewer and fewer. The constant and continuing improvement of weapons for hunting, the use of fast boats and of "factory ships," was taking a toll far greater than anyone realized. The whalers now saw that if they continued slaughtering whales at the same rate, soon there

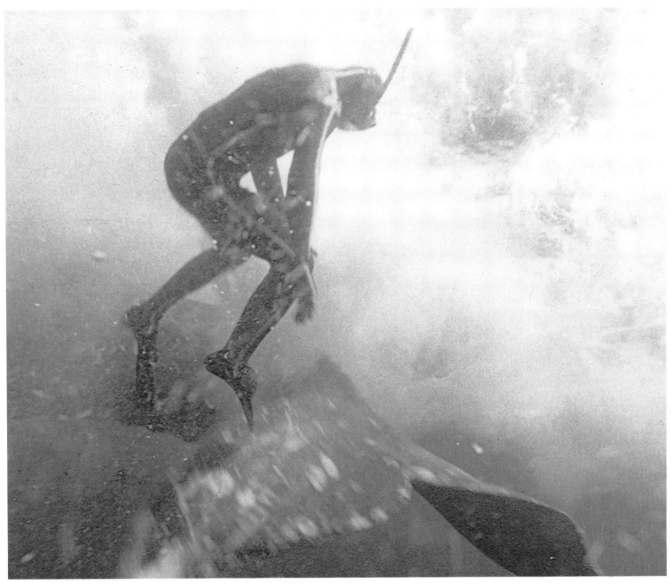

Bernard Delemotte manages to stand up on the back of a gray whale.

would be no whales left to slaughter. They therefore decided, or felt compelled, to exercise moderation so as to conserve their whale "capital" in the oceans. They had already seen what unrestricted whale hunting could, and would do: the whale population of the Bay of Biscay had already disappeared — either through extinction or flight.

It was the twentieth century, however, and not the nineteenth, that produced the greatest slaughter of whales. At the beginning of the century, whale hunting was extended to antarctic waters, and the butchery of these great mammals was intensified until it resulted in the virtual extinction of the right whale *(Eubalaena glacialis)*. Our century, as it turned out, was much more destructive with respect to whales than the period of the great romantic hunts as described in the work of Herman Melville. A hundred years ago, a whaler's three-year expedition netted him thirty-seven whales. Today, a whaler's modern weapons and fast boats give him one whale a day; and sometimes three or four.

At the present time, whale hunting is a regulated industry, and in principle, all species are protected by international agreements arrived at by the International Whaling Commission.*

A Continuing Threat

The fact of regulation does not mean that whales are now safe from extinction. Regulation has come much too late for that.

Right whales, unless they are spared completely, will probably become extinct because of the way they were hunted early in this century.

Blue whales, the largest animals ever to live on the planet, also constitute an endangered species. The hunting season on them is now limited, and, in certain areas, they are completely protected. But conservation experts tell us that it will take fifty years of such protection for blue whales to be out of danger as a species.

The finback whale, or common rorqual, even though it is now hunted on a reduced scale, will also have to be more adequately protected if it is to survive.

From year to year, a different species of whale becomes the principal victim of the whalers. In 1964-65, for example, it was the Sei whale — a very migratory whale of relatively small size — that was butchered. The total count for this period was 24,453 Sei whales, or double the total for the preceding season. For the Sei whale, this was the beginning of the end.

Humpback whales have been an endangered species for a considerable period. They are smaller than Sei whales but, unfortunately for them, their bodies produce twice as much oil. Humpbacks have been hunted with such intensity by Soviet and Japanese whalers that it was necessary to grant them absolute immunity for a two-year period. Even so, it will take half a century before the species is able to re-establish itself.

The International Whaling Commission, in the interest of a more effective protection of each species, has now decided to abandon the quota system based on the famous "BWU" — Blue Whale Unit — and to establish a quota for each separate species during each individual hunting season.

*See Appendix II, "Whale hunting."

Front view of a gray whale.

Converts and Missionaries

What is true of coral and of all other forms of marine life is also true of whales. We are no sooner able to approach them, to learn to admire them, to observe them in the water, than we realize that they are in danger of becoming extinct.

Calypso's men are perhaps more aware of this, and more struck by it, than anyone else. We have seen the eye of the whale. We have admired the delicate muzzle of the finback and the white flippers of the humpback. And we have been converted. We are now on the side of the whales.

Like all converts, we wish to convert others. Will we succeed in changing public opinion? Will we be able to reverse the trend, to assure a place on the earth, in the seas, for whales?

We must try.

Surely whales have more to offer us than "seafood" for our dogs, or oil (which we now get in abundance from other sources), or stays for corsets and ribs for umbrellas. We can learn much from their extraordinary diving ability, and about the depths that they reach, and from their ability to suspend breathing for comparatively long periods of time. Instead of being man's victims, whales should be his guides and teachers in the exploration of the marine world that has just been opened up to human investigation.

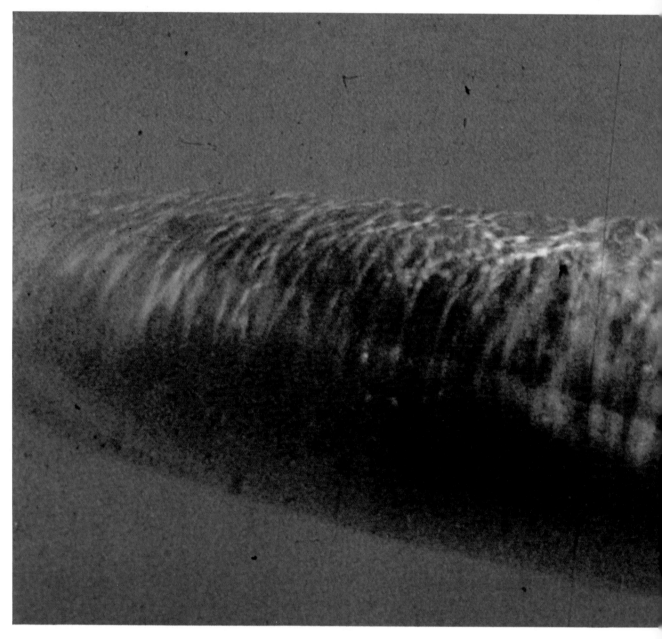

A diver holding onto the dorsal fin of a finback whale.

We now know that there exists a certain link among mammals. This mysterious sense of unity, and solidarity once it has been acquired, can never be lost. Something has changed in the sea. Cruelty and indifference to marine life will henceforth be regarded as intolerable by the vast majority of men.

It is evident that people everywhere are disturbed by what has happened to whales, and that whaling has come to be regarded as a foolish anachronism. Californians, for example, have the opportunity to see migrating whales near their shores, and they have developed a decided affection for these creatures.

Reaching an Understanding

The sympathy that is developing between man and the cetaceans still has an element of distance, of the abstract, about it. It is based more on common sense than on true understanding and affection. But we can hope that things will continue to change for the better; and that they will change especially when man and the whale meet under the surface of the water. Man must learn to know the cetaceans in their own element, in the water; and then the survival of the whale will be seen in its proper emotional and moral context. Right now, public opinion regards the killing of a dolphin as a crime.

Very soon, the same thing will hold true for the killing of a whale.

There is a great difference between seeing a gray whale on the surface of the water and seeing her beneath the surface, constantly maneuvering to keep herself between her offspring and a diver. Right now, we may deplore the massacre of humpback whales that took place at the turn of the century; but from now on we will react with sadness and anger, once we have had a chance to hear a humpback whale "talk"* or glide through the water or turn on its great flippers.

Can we go even further? Is it possible that one day there will be a true "understanding" between men and whales?

Our encounter with the great marine mammals was hampered from the outset by the fact that we knew absolutely nothing about the behavior of whales with respect to man. Little by little, however, we learned. We made overtures, we tried to approach these animals. And, once we discovered that contact was indeed possible, we became more daring and increased our efforts. *Calypso*'s divers eventually were able to confront these mountains of flesh without fear. They had learned to behave in such a way as to be tolerated by creatures whose weight was a thousand times their own.

Man took into the sea with him his desire to impose his will, to make himself understood, to make other animals obey him. During our expeditions in the Red Sea, we demonstrated that we were able, if not to assert our authority, then at least to awaken the respect of an animal such as the shark.

With whales, however, the situation was different. There is no longer any reason for us to feel fear. All that separates us now is a difference in scale. I mean that a man in the water is too small to assume much importance in the eyes of a whale, while, for an average-sized shark, he is big enough to be worthy of the shark's attention.

Despite all the problems of understanding and interpretation, the divers of *Calypso* were able to discern nuances in the whale's attitude toward them. We are beginning to open up, and to explore, a psychological domain in which direct observation is no longer out of the question.

But where will this lead?

That is the essential question. If we are successful in limiting, or even abolishing the practice of whaling, we will have to do the same thing for dolphins and blackfish and grampuses. Will we then put all animals in cages, under the pretext of "saving" them? Will we end up with nothing more than a succession of zoos and marinelands?

* Dr. Payne has put together a commercially available phonograph record, which reproduces the "speech" of humpback whales.

In California, biologists are already worried about the large number of cetaceans in captivity, not all of whom survive. Dr. Scheffer has asked the crucial question: is it not only legal, but is it moral and "human" to hunt grampuses? Since 1965, just in Seattle, six grampuses, or killer whales, died as a result of attempts to capture them. And many others have been mortally wounded by harpoons, by bullets containing narcotics, or by nets. In Dr. Scheffer's opinion, however, killer whales, because of their high degree of social evolution and their intelligence, may learn to avoid the areas where they are in danger. If this is true, then the shores of California will no longer have these animals which people have learned to enjoy, and which have become friendly because they knew that they had nothing to fear in those waters. Then, it will no longer be possible to see these magnificent mammals in their free state, or to approach them. As a solution, Dr. Scheffer suggests that a special permit be required to capture a grampus, and that the permit be given very rarely and only for good reason.

There are other, and specifically modern, dangers that threaten the whale. The gray whale, for example — who is a relic from another age, a true fossil, the oldest of all the species of whale — has had its habitat limited more and more every year. At the present time, there are only three or four lagoons in which it can spend the winter.

The lagoons of Matancitas and Scammon are, for gray whales, a miraculously preserved universe, with their deep waters and their beaches bordered by mangrove plants. But this is the last refuge of the whales. So far, these lagoons are intact; but, already they are threatened by the insidious danger that has already affected so much of the world: pollution. The waters of northern California are already infected, but the pollution has not yet reached Matancitas or Scammon. The latter is visited only by a few fishermen and, except for a small number of salt marshes, has retained its primitive purity. But any amount of pollution would exclude the gray whales from this paradise where they come to mate and bear their young.

But that is not the worst of it. The worst is that recently the various navies of the world have begun to take an interest in whales. Their interest is not purely scientific. It is their intention to "recruit" whales, to use them as underwater detectors, as spies and liaison agents. No sooner has man discovered that whales are intelligent creatures than he tries to involve them in his own stupidity, in his wars and battles. As long ago as 1963, L. Harrison Matthews, an English authority on cetacean life, was writing: "As intelligent as these animals are, they are not intelligent enough to refuse to co-operate, or to address to their trainers some of those underwater clickings which, translated into human language, might convey their profound contempt."

Two divers on the back of a finback whale.

Perhaps the time has come to formulate a moral code which would govern our relations with the great creatures of the sea as well as with those on dry land. That this will come to pass is our dearest wish.

If human civilization is going to invade the waters of the earth, then let it be first of all to carry a message of respect — respect for all life.

Acknowledgments

We owe a special word of thanks to M. Charles Roux, Deputy Director of the Laboratoire des Reptiles et Poissons at the Musée National d'Histoire Naturelle of Paris, who was kind enough to read the manuscript of this book and to offer some very constructive criticism.

Professor Paul Budker, Director of the Laboratoire de Biologie des Cétacés et autres mammiferes marins, at the Ecole Pratique des Hautes Etudes in Paris, once again gave us the benefit of his incomparable experience and advice in the preparation of this book.

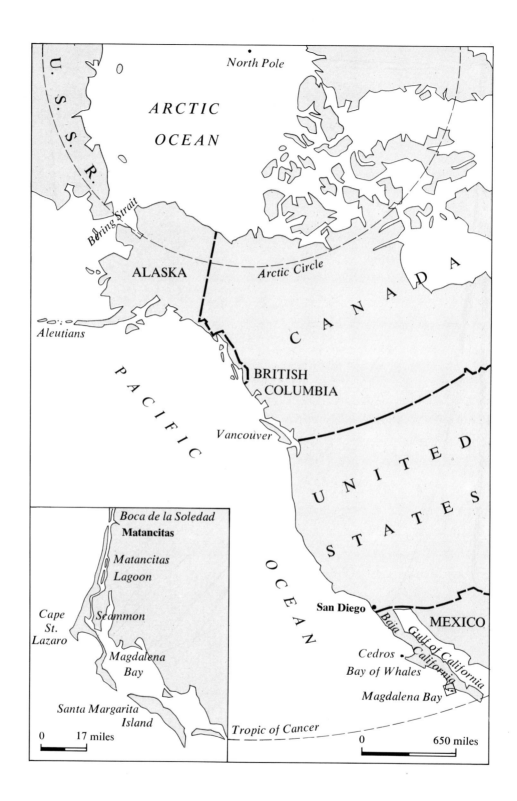

The migration of gray whales from the Arctic to Baja California.

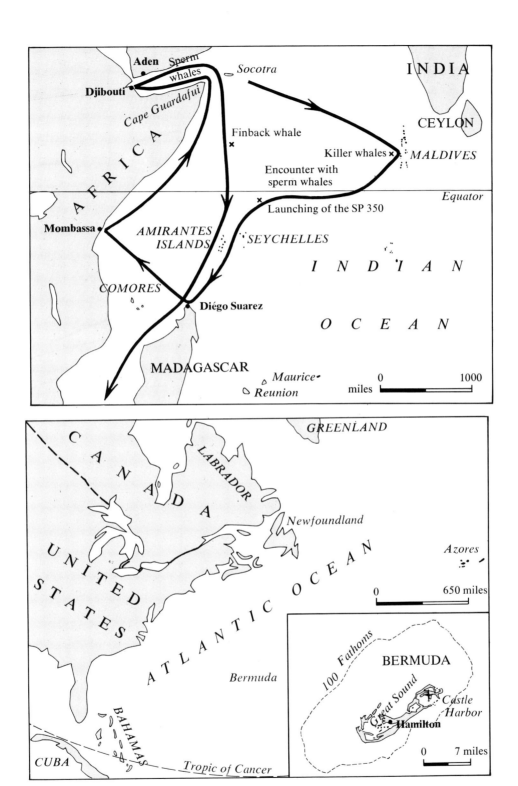

(Above) Encounters with cetaceans in the Indian Ocean.

(Below) Bermuda, where we undertook "Project Humpback Whale."

APPENDIX I

The Cetaceans

The Cetaceans

Cetaceans are marine mammals whose ancestors were probably land animals.* They are warm-blooded creatures; and, as Aristotle noted more than two thousand years ago, they breathe by means of lungs. Fertilization of the egg and gestation are internal, and they nurse their offspring.

* This appendix is based upon the works of Kenneth S. Norris, Dr. Harrison Matthews, Dr. F. C. Fraser, Ernest P. Walker, and upon the classification of the International Whaling Commission.

All cetaceans are characterized by tails that spread horizontally rather than, as in the case of fish, vertically. Also, they all have a blowhole or vent at the top of their heads, through which they breathe. The position and shape of this blowhole varies according to the species.

The cetaceans include approximately one hundred species and are divided into two orders: the *Mystacoceti* or toothless (or baleen or whalebone) cetaceans; and the *Odontoceti,* or toothed cetaceans.

The Mystacoceti

The *Mystacoceti,* or baleen whales, are characterized by the presence in the mouth of plates of whalebone (baleen), whose fringed edges act as a sieve through which water is strained to remove the small animals on which the whale feeds. The spacing of the fringe depends upon the size of the animals upon which a particular species normally preys. There are three families of Mystacoceti:

1.   The *Balaenidae,* which, in turn, is composed of three genera:

(a) *Balaena,* which includes only one species *Balaena mysticetus,* or the right whale.

The right whale grows to a length of 50 to 60 feet and has black skin, except for the throat and chin which are cream-colored. One third of its body length is taken up by the enormous mouth. It has no back or dorsal fin, and no ventral furrows. The right whale is able to suspend breathing for from ten to thirty minutes. Its gestation period lasts nine or ten months. Its principal food is krill.

Right whales were still abundant in arctic waters at the beginning of the nineteenth century. By the twentieth century, however, the species was almost extinct. At present, right whales are no longer found between Greenland and the Barents Sea. There are perhaps a thousand surviving specimen in the neighborhood of the Bering Straits, and these are protected by international agreement.

(b) *Eubalaena,* whose external characteristics are the same as those of the right whale, except for the mouth which is smaller and accounts for only one quarter of the total body length. *Eubalaena* includes the following species:

Eubalaena glacialis, which inhabits the North Atlantic and which, because of its modest size (40 to 55 feet) was hunted by the Basques as

(Right) The *Mystacoceti.*

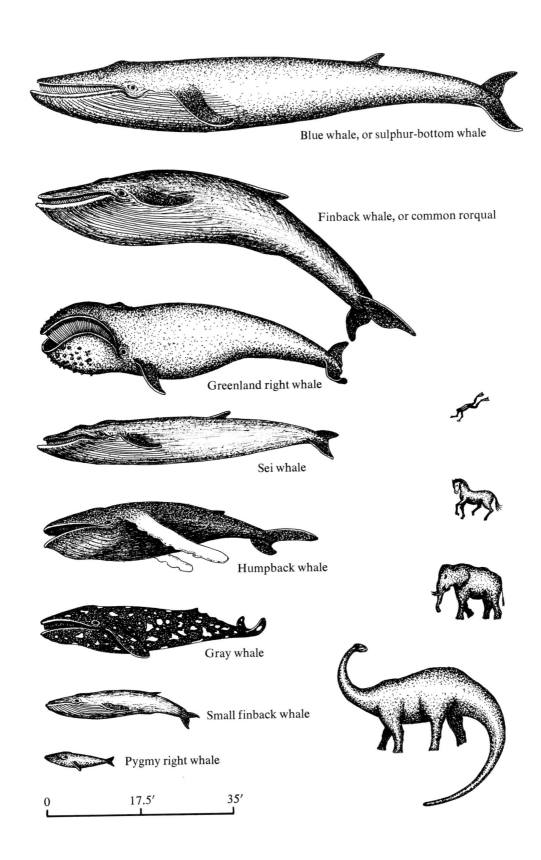

Blue whale, or sulphur-bottom whale

Finback whale, or common rorqual

Greenland right whale

Sei whale

Humpback whale

Gray whale

Small finback whale

Pygmy right whale

0   17.5'   35'

early as the ninth century. Specimens are extremely rare, and the species has been protected for the past thirty-five years.

Eubalaena australis, which lives in the waters of the Antarctic. Fifty years ago, this species counted its members in the hundreds of thousands. Whalers almost destroyed the species, however, and, at the present time, after thirty-five years of absolute protection, there are once again a few schools in the South Atlantic, in the vicinity of the Cape of Good Hope, and off South Georgia (an island of Antarctica).

(c) *Caperea,* to which only one species belongs: *Caperea marginata,* or the pygmy right whale, which has no economic importance.

2. The *Eschrichtidae,* which comprises only the *Eschrichtius glaucus* — our gray whale of Baja California, which is found near the American and Korean coasts. The gray whale has no dorsal fin. There are ventral furrows, numbering two or four.

The gray whale reaches a length of between 35 and 45 feet and weighs between 24 and 37 tons. Its baleen measures 11 to 13 feet. In color, it is black, or slate, and its skin is mottled with grayish patches of barnacles. Sexual maturity is attained at four and one half years, and gestation lasts between eleven and twelve months. A single calf is born every two years.

3. The *Balaenopteridae,* of which there are two genera:
   (a) *Balaenoptera,* comprising the following species:
      - *Balaenoptera borealis,* or Sei whale;
      - *Balaenoptera acutorostrata,* or lesser rorqual:
      - *Balaenoptera edeni,* or Bryde's whale; and
      - *Balaenoptera physalus,* or finback whale (also known as the common rorqual). It was the *Balaenoptera physalus* with which *Calypso*'s divers had several encounters. The finback whale measures 60 to 75 feet in length and weighs about fifty tons. Its back is grayish, and its white underside shows between 30 and 60 ventral furrows. There is a clearly distinguishable dorsal fin, rather high and triangular in shape.

      The finback whale travels in schools of 20 to 100 individuals. It feeds on plankton, crustaceans, and small fish.

      This species mates during the winter, and the period of gestation lasts between ten and twelve months. The male attains sexual maturity at five years; and the female, between three and eight years. Physical maturity, however, is not reached until the age of fifteen.

(Right) The odontoceti.

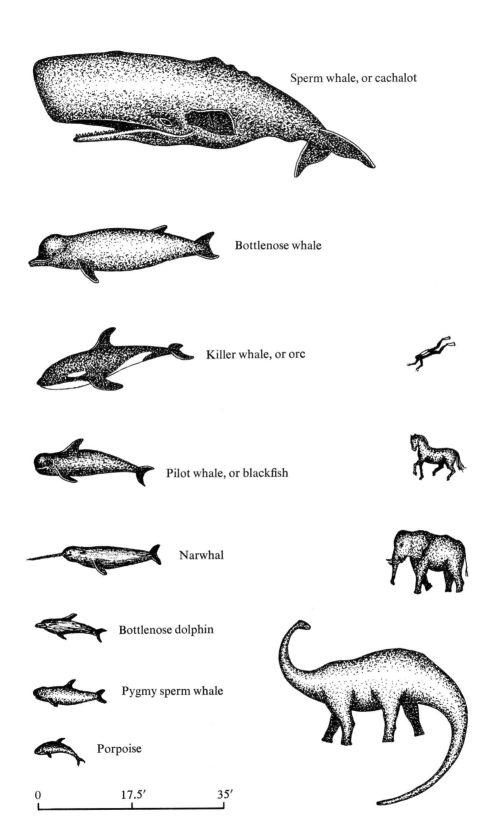

Sperm whale, or cachalot

Bottlenose whale

Killer whale, or orc

Pilot whale, or blackfish

Narwhal

Bottlenose dolphin

Pygmy sperm whale

Porpoise

0   17.5′   35′

Full-grown specimens may remain without breathing for from twenty to fifty minutes.

The finback whale has been one of the principal victims of whalers, and it is estimated that 90 percent of the species has been destroyed. In 1955, there were still approximately 110,000 specimens in the Atlantic; today, however, they probably number no more than 30,000.

Balaenoptera musculus, or blue whale (also known as the sulphur-bottomed whale), is the largest of the cetaceans and the largest animal that has ever existed on earth. It reaches lengths of between 80 and 100 feet, and the largest specimen known weighed 112.5 tons.

The blue whale winters in tropical waters, and spends its summers in polar seas. The skin is slate blue, and its throat is deeply pleated by approximately 100 furrows. Blue whales travel singly rather than in schools, and they are able to remain underwater for periods of ten to twenty minutes. Their basic food is krill.

They mate during May and June, and gestation lasts eleven months. One calf is born every two years. Sexual maturity is reached at the age of four and one half years.

The blue whale was the most avidly hunted of the great cetaceans because it yielded the greatest quantity of oil. In 1930, it was estimated that there were between 30 and 40 thousand blue whales in the Antarctic. Today, the most optimistic estimate sets the number at 2000, and perhaps fewer.

The blue whale is now a totally protected species.

(b) *Megaptera,* of which there is only one species: *Megaptera novaeangliae* — the humpback whale of our Bermuda expedition. The humpback whales and the gray whales are the only species to live in coastal waters.

The humpback's average length is 40 feet; its average weight: 29 tons. The upper part of the body is black, and the throat and chest are white. It is recognizable by its large white flippers, which measure a third of the length of the body. There are from 10 to 25 furrows on the neck and underside. Crustaceans are its staple diet.

Gestation lasts ten months. Sexual maturity is attained at the age of three; but full physical growth is not reached until the tenth year. A calf is born every two years.

During the 1930s, the Antarctic's humpback population was estimated at 22,000. At the present time, there are probably not more than 3000 specimens in the Antarctic. In the northern Pacific, however, there are an additional 5000 humpback whales.

Humpback whales are a protected species today.

The Odontoceti

The *Odontoceti* are toothed cetaceans. The number of teeth varies greatly by species, from the Goosebeak whale (or Cuvier's whale), which has two, to the dolphin with its 260 teeth. There are five families of *Odontoceti,* which include the majority of the species of cetaceans:

1. The *Monodontidae,* comprising two genera:
    - *Delphinapterus,* the beluga whale found especially in the arctic seas around North America (see Glossary); and
    - *Monodon,* the narwhal (see Glossary).

2. The *Delphinidae,* which contains nineteen genera:
    Steno, Sousa, Sotalia, Stenella, Delphinus (the common dolphin — see Glossary), *Grampus, Tursiops, Lagenorhynchus, Feresa, Cephalorhynchus, Orcaella, Lissodelphis, Lagenodelphis, Phocaena* (the common porpoise — see Glossary), *Phocaenoides* (Pacific Dall's Porpoise), *Neomeris* (Southeast Asian finless black porpoise), *Pseudorca, Orcinus* (killer whale), and *Globicephala* (the pilot whale, or blackfish, encountered by *Calypso*'s divers).
    Blackfish or pilot whales have rounded heads, the upper part of which projects over the upper jaw. They are between fourteen and twenty-five feet in length and are, as their common name indicates, wholly black. They have a dorsal fin, and between seven and eleven teeth in each jaw.
    Pilot whales travel in schools of several hundred individuals who follow a leader-whale blindly.
    Their main food is squid, which they pursue during their migrations. During the summer, they are found near the coasts of Newfoundland. They winter in warm waters, where they give birth to their young.
    Gestation lasts twelve months. The mating season is in the autumn. Males mature sexually at three years, and females at six years.
    Blackfish are the principal whale resource of Newfoundland, and between three and four thousand of these small whales are slaughtered there every year.
    The killer whale is another member of this genus to travel in schools. This mammal attains a length of about 20 feet and a weight of one ton. It is black, with white markings on its underside extending from the lower jaw to the middle of the stomach, and with another, smaller white spot above the eyes. The jaws each contain between 20 and 28 teeth. Killer whales prefer warm-blooded prey: seals, dolphins, and even baleen whales. They mate

between November and January, and gestation lasts between eleven and twelve months. The mother nurses her calf for a year following birth.

3.   The *Ziphiidae,* which characterized by a beak-shaped muzzle, include five genera:
   - *Mesoplodon* (beaked whales);
   - *Ziphius* (Cuvier's beaked whale, or the goose-beak whale);
   - *Tasmacetus* (Tasmanian beaked whale);
   - *Berardius* (giant bottlenose whale);
   - *Hyperoodon* (bottlenose whale — see Glossary).

4.   The *Physeteridae* contain two genera:
   - *Kogia* (pygmy sperm whale)
   - *Physeter,* the most common species of which is
   Physeter catodon — the cachalot, or sperm whale.

Of all the *Odontoceti,* the cachalot is instantly recognizable because of its oblique spout. It has two blowholes, but the left blowhole is the only working one. The cachalot is characterized especially by its massive head and squared snout. The head accounts for one third of the cachalot's body length. Only the lower jaw has teeth, but what teeth they are: each one ten inches long and weighing over two pounds.

The sperm whale has no dorsal fin, but does have a sort of "crest"; nor does it have ventral furrows.

It is usually dark in color, with spots that lighten as it grows older.

The white cachalot is a literary celebrity in the person of Moby Dick, immortalized by Herman Melville. A white or albino sperm whale has been seen in real life only once, in 1951. It measured fifty feet in length.

The largest cachalots — always males — reach a maximum length of sixty feet. They weigh between thirty-five and fifty tons. They feed principally on giant squid, which they seek out in the great depths of the sea.

Sperm whales live in family groups, or harems, of 20 to 50 individual whales. One calf is born every three years. Gestation lasts sixteen months, and the calf nurses for twelve months.

5.   The *Platanistidae* are the fresh-water dolphins generally found in the estuaries of large rivers. There are four genera:
   Platanista, the Ganges dolphin;
   - *Inia,* the Amazon dolphin;
   - *Lipotes,* found in China; and
   - *Stenodelphis,* the La Plata River dolphin.

APPENDIX II

Whaling

The hunting of whales is a very old human occupation, dating far back into recorded history. For men in wooded canoes, armed only with primitive harpoons, the whale must have been a frightening and deadly adversary. But when one remembers that paleolithic man earlier had hunted Mammoths with spears and weapons of flint, it should come as no surprise that man, the predator, later dared measure his strength against that of the great cetaceans. This is especially true when one recalls that, though the techniques of whale hunting changed and were improved through the centuries (as we shall see), the basic weapon by means of which man pitted his strength against that of the great whales remained essentially the same. It was always a harpoon, or spear, thrown by hand.

The Basques

The Middle Ages are the earliest period from which we know for certain the techniques and the extent of whaling. However, if we may believe Orosius' *Seven Books of History Against the Pagans,* written in the fifth century,* Norsemen were already whaling when Rome ruled the world. In any event, we know that the Basques were avid whalers before the twelfth century, and that they had very likely begun whaling as early as the ninth century. It was necessary for the Basques, as for any other whale hunters, to be as close as possible to their prey for them to be able to use their harpoons and lances effectively. But they had an advantage. Every year, the *Eubalaena glacialis,* or black right whale (which the Basques called *Sardako Balaena),* passed along their shores in migration. And this species was an ideal victim. Right whales are comparatively slow, timid and weak; and, unlike other species, they were relatively easy to hunt in small boats and not difficult to kill with the primitive weapons of the period. They also have another characteristic; after they are dead, they continue to float, while whales of other species sink. It was therefore possible for the Basques to tow their kill into shallow water, or even to shore.

The right whale brought wealth to the Basques. The hunters not only used the mammal's flesh for food, but melted its blubber and marketed it throughout Europe, where it became the principal fuel for lamps.

So courageous were the Basque whalers, and so proficient did they become, that, before long, there were few right whales remaining in the Bay of Biscay. (Indeed, today there are none at all.) The whalers therefore built larger boats and struck out into the Atlantic in search of the game that had deserted their own shores. The chase led them northward, through the terrors of storm and icebergs, to strange lands: Iceland and Greenland. They went as far as present-day Newfoundland and thus discovered the coasts of North America before the time of Columbus.† In the sixteenth century, they were hunting whales with such vigor in Greenland that, a century later, the right whale was no longer to be found in those waters.

The Basques not only risked the then unknown dangers of the North Atlantic in their ridiculously small boats for the sake of whale oil, but also

---

*The text describes the arctic voyages of Other, a Norse chieftan. The Histories were translated by King Alfred of England at the end of the ninth century.

†There is, in Newfoundland, a tombstone, bearing a Basque inscription, that dates from the end of the fourteenth century.

Navire Pêcheur à la voile et Depecement d'une Baleine.

Whaling ship: the cutting up of a whale. Engraving by Piquet (1791). *Bibliothèque Nationale.*

developed the process of flensing and boiling by which whale blubber is converted into oil aboard a whaling boat. The discoverer, it seems, was a mariner from St. Jean-de-Luz named Sopite, who invented the oven on which this process is based. Up until that time, it was necessary for the whalers to bring their catch ashore for it to be processed. And, in fact, Dutch whalers continued to do so until the end of the seventeenth century, and simply stored the blubber in barrels aboard their ships.

The Eskimos

We have less information about other people who, along with the Basques, were early whalers. And yet, we know that there were such peoples. In Scandinavia, for example, whale vertebrae were used as stools. And

Whalers attacking sperm whales. From Thomas Beale's *Histoire naturelle du cachalot*, London (1839). *Bibliothèque Nationale*.

Boat thrown into the air by a whale. Lithography of Saint Aulaire, from *Campagne d'un baleinier autour du monde:* (1840). *Bibliothè*que Nationale.

recently, in Greenland, some very old Eskimo villages were discovered in which the houses were built of whale bones. It is possible, of course, that these were the bones of whales that had gone aground. But we know for a fact that the ancient Eskimos developed a technique of getting as close to the whale as they could in their skin-covered canoes, and then of driving a spear into the animal's lungs — a mortal blow. As a buoy, they used an inflated sealskin, which would float if the whale sank or dived.

The Eskimo inhabitants of the Aleutians used to dip their harpoons in a poison that was very likely derived from aconite. And the natives of Greenland and of Spitsbergen used a bacterial poison that made any wound mortal. (In Norway today, in certain of the fjords, whalers use rusted arrows covered with the blood of dead whales, which induces blood poisoning in any whale that is shot with the arrow.)

The Dawn of Modern Whaling: The Eighteenth Century

At the beginning of the eighteenth century, the English, Dutch, and Danes, with the collaboration of the Basques, outfitted whalers who began hunting at Spitsbergen on a large scale. The English, Dutch, and Danes, along with their Basque tutors, had no more idea of the limitations of the natural resources of the sea than had primitive man — or, for that matter, the whalers of the nineteenth and twentieth centuries. They hunted relentlessly, competently, with a single purpose: to kill as many whales as possible in order to realize the greatest immediate profit. It seemed to matter not at all — even if they were aware of it — that such wholesale slaughter must necessarily impede, or perhaps even eliminate, breeding; or that their happy hunting ground at Spitsbergen might, in a few years, be empty of game. And so, the same thing happened for the second time in a century: the whales disappeared.

The French, too, and particularly the Normans, were whaling during this period, but on a relatively small scale. During the last quarter of the century, under Louis XVI, France had no more than forty whaling ships.

The Japanese were, as always, the whalers par excellence. They had the same advantage as the Basques: whales in migration passed near their shores. By the end of the seventeenth century, they had perfected a new technique: whaling with nets — and the nets, of course, were enormous, and equipped with many empty barrels to serve as floaters.

This technique required no fewer than thirty boats, some to round up an animal and the others to handle the nets. Once the whale was trapped within the nets, it was harpooned and speared until a man could, with relative impunity, climb on its head and attach a tow line.

The Dutch were no less assiduous. In the eighteenth century, there were 400 Dutch whaling ships, manned by 20,000 seamen. They hunted especially in Davis Strait, between Greenland and Baffin Island. They were followed by the English; and, in 1750, there were twenty whaling ships operating in this region. By 1788, there were 252. And again history repeated itself: there were no more whales to be found.

The Golden Age

It was at this time that the New England seafarers discovered the extraordinary abundance of whales along the eastern coast of North America. After the Revolutionary War, a whaling fleet was built in the United States; and this fleet was to be the basis for the sperm-whale hunting which was to provide a chapter in American economic history rich in color, courage, and marvelous legends, and also in misery.

As soon as the right whale became rare along the American coast because of excessive slaughter, American whalers began hunting everywhere on all the seas for cachalots. The cachalot, or sperm whale, was a much more fearsome adversary than the right whale. It was larger, stronger, and had a reputation for diabolical ferocity. Terrible stories were told of its monstrous intelligence, and of the fate of hapless fishermen who had become its victims.

Until the eighteenth century, no whaler had dared pit his weak weapons against this formidable animal. But now, Americans were demanding more and more whale oil; and this market justified, or at least resulted in, new feats of daring on the part of the whalers. Spermaceti, the wax contained in a chamber of the cachalot's huge head, was bringing a high price; and every sperm whale furnished a ton of it. It was on the cachalot's spermaceti that the fortunes of many of America's celebrated families were founded.

The whaling ships left from Nantucket, from New Bedford, from Mystic. The hunt continued through all seasons of the year; and young whales as well as old ones were the targets. It was a massacre, in every sense of the term; but a massacre with elements of drama. In 1778, Thomas Jefferson was writing to the French minister: "The Spermaceti whale discovered by the people of Nantucket is an aggressive and ferocious beast which requires of those who would hunt it as much skill as courage." Soon, they would be called "fighting cachalots."

Four-year Expeditions

The whalers had also discovered a new victim, far away in the Antarctic: the *Balaena australis,* or southern right whale. Between 1804 and 1817, 190,000 whales of this species were slaughtered, and they became more and more rare.

The whalers had, of necessity, to turn once more to the redoubtable sperm whale. Beginning in 1820, the Nantucket whaling fleet was growing. There were fewer and fewer small sailing boats with one or two hunting canoes (often manned by Indians), which had to return to port after taking five or six whales. And there were more and more large three-masters of 500 tons, carrying five, six or seven whaling boats, and a crew of forty men. These "South Seamen," as they were called, were perhaps the sturdiest sailing ships ever built.

In this Golden Age of sailing whalers, only extended expeditions were feasible; for only lengthy voyages could discover and kill a sufficient number of whales to justify the expense of the ship. When they sailed from their home ports, therefore, the South Seamen were often not seen there again for three or four years; for, in principle, they did not return without a full load of whale oil.

In the building of these ships, no attention was paid to comfort; and hardly more to sanitation. The crew was composed, for the most part, not of professional seamen, but the unemployed and the unemployable, the flotsam and jetsam of the whaling ports. Professor Paul Budker tells us that "in 1860, an ordinary seaman on an American whaler was paid twenty cents a day, while on land an unskilled laborer was paid ninety cents a day. In other words, in the United States the lowest category of worker on dry land was paid at least two or three times more than a seaman aboard a whaler."

Among the seamen, the harpooners occupied a privileged position. Their quarters were not in the forecastle, with the ordinary seamen, but amidships, with those of the officers.

Food and water were always scarce. Before leaving the ship's home port, the captain always took aboard as large a load of supplies as the vessel was able to carry. This practice had a reason: the captain did not dare visit ports of call in order to take on supplies, for, when a whaling ship did so, a good number of its crew usually deserted.

It has been said that today's sperm whales are not as large as those of the nineteenth century. Today, they reach a maximum length of 60 feet; but, we are told, in Moby Dick's time, they were often 90 feet long. And, in fact, the Jonathan Bourne Museum at New Bedford, Massachusetts, exhibits a cachalot's jawbone 23 feet long. And, it is reported that, in 1841, Owen Tilton of New Bedford killed a male cachalot 91 feet 8 inches in length.

What is certain is that, when measured against the size of the ships of that time, these whales must have seemed enormous. This is particularly true when it is recalled that whales were usually sighted from high up in a ship's rigging, from the crow's nest. From that vantage point, a man was on constant watch for the telltale spout, which he announced with the famous whaler's cry, "Thar she blows!" This ritual formula was, and remains, the only proper way to notify a ship's captain that a whale has been sighted.

The Battle

As soon as the alarm had been given, the whaling boats were lowered into the water. These craft were never more than 30 feet long, and were unusually light. They were carried suspended from the ship by davits, ready to be lowered instantly even in bad weather. A whaling boat's crew generally comprised a coxswain, an officer, and five seamen. Two of the seamen rowed to port, with oars fifteen feet long. On the starboard side, two others, and the harpooner, rowed with smaller oars. They were supposed to come as near as possible to the whale — which, given the swell and the small number of oars, must have been extremely difficult.

When the boat had drawn near to the whale, the coxswain gave a signal and the harpooner dropped his oar and picked up his weapon, turned, knelt on the gunwale, and threw his harpoon, aiming to hit the animal near the eyes.

The harpoon was attached to a line coiled in a basket. When the harpooner scored a hit, the whale usually began to swim away so rapidly that the line, as it uncoiled, had to be sprinkled with water to keep it from burning.

After the whale had been harpooned, a long and sometimes dramatic struggle followed. The whale dived but, slowed by the weight of the whaling boat that he had to tow, he could not go down very deep. And, of course, he had to rise to the surface in order to breathe. One can imagine how dangerous the situation was for the half-dozen men in the whaling boat, being towed along at 12 or 15 knots. But the real danger had hardly begun, for the next move was the most difficult of all. The coxswain and the harpooner now changed places, which meant that they both had to crawl along the entire length of the rolling, pitching craft, the coxswain toward the bow and the harpooner toward the stern. (The protocol of whaling required that it always be an officer — in this instance, the coxswain — who gave the coup de grace,

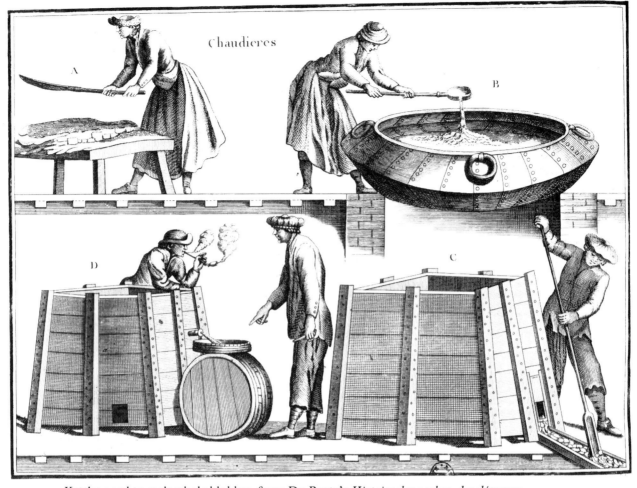

Kettles used to melt whale blubber, from Du Reste's *Histoire des pêches, des découvertes des établissements des Hollandais dans les mers du nord*. An IX de la République. *Bibliothèque Nationale.*

the deathblow.) When this had been done, and as soon as the whale surfaced, the craft was once more brought close in, and the coxswain took a five-foot spear — sharpened on all sides — and attempted to plunge it into the whale head, as near to the eye as possible. If he was successful, he then rotated the spear in the wound.

At this point, no one could tell what would happen. The whale might smash the boat and its crew with a stroke of its mighty tail; or, if it was a cachalot, it might attack with its mouth and splinter the craft with one snap.

Most often, however, the whale was now mortally wounded, and blood was running from its blowhole into the sea, turning the water red around the boat. Then the men cried, "Flurry! Flurry!" which meant that the whale was in its death agony.

The enormous cadaver had to be towed back to the mothership, which often was by now so far away as to be out of sight. (It happened frequently that a school of whales was sighted and several whaling boats lowered at the

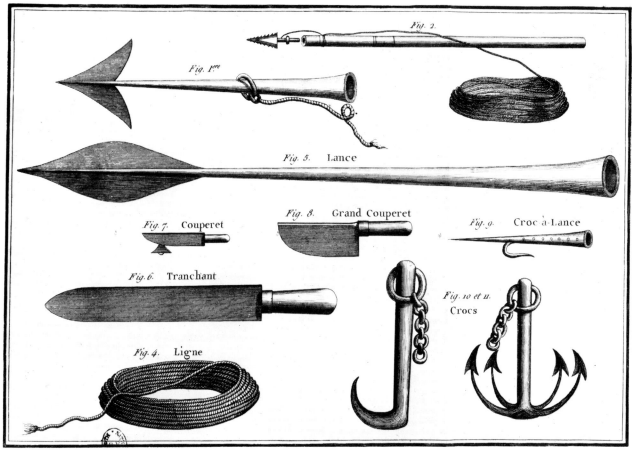

Harpoon, lance, and chopper. Du Reste, op. cit.

same time, so that it was not easy for all of them to make their way back to the ship with, or even without, their catch.) The whale was then tied to the ship's starboard, tail forward; and the butchery began. The men climbed onto the whale, despite the body's inevitable pitching and rolling, and began cutting away enormous slabs of blubber with their hooks. These slabs were passed onto the boat. As the men worked, the carcass was often surrounded by sharks, claiming a share in the spoils and ripping off pieces for themselves as they glared at the men working on the dead whale's back.

When the weather was good, this process lasted four or five hours. The flensing and boiling down of the blubber, however, took much longer. This was done on deck, in great kettles, into which the slabs of blubber were thrown. The blubber sometimes remained in the kettles for a day and a night, giving off an incredible stench and a suffocating smoke. No one slept until the job was done.

Occasionally, the whalers found an unexpected treasure: a ball-like substance, in the whale's entrails, that hardened on exposure to air. It was ambergris — a valuable substance used originally for medicinal purposes, and today in the manufacture of expensive perfumes. It is possible that the ambergris is a by-product of the sperm whale's diet of squid.

A Terrible Weapon

At this time, New Bedford, Massachusetts, was the undisputed whaling capital of the world. It happened, however, that the importance of whaling was already declining. Whales had been hunted so continuously that they were becoming harder and harder to find. Moreover, the commercial outlets for whaling products were slowly disappearing. Petroleum and electricity were replacing whale oil as the principal means of illumination.

Ironically, it was at the moment that whale oil was losing its importance that a new and terrible weapon was developed for use against whales: the harpoon cannon. Now, not only the right whales, the humpback whales, and the cachalots were in danger, but also the blue whales and the finbacks, whose size, up to then, had protected them.

Whales of sufficiently small size and sufficiently slow to be killed without great difficulty had become hard to find. In attacking larger and faster species, harpooners and whalers were now compelled either to face failure, or to take greater and greater risks. It was in the face of this dilemma that a Norwegian, Svend Foyn, marketed (1868) a harpoon designed to be shot out of cannon and containing an explosive head. This weapon had a pivoted crosspiece which was released upon discharge of the explosive, thus preventing withdrawal of the harpoon. The cannon also allowed a second line to be attached to the whale. Thus, the animal could be quickly brought back to the ship and secured to its side before it could sink. A later refinement was the pumping of compressed air into the whale after it had been harpooned in order to keep it afloat.

These new weapons allowed whalers to attack animals which, until then, had been considered too fast, or too powerful, to be hunted. Moreover, the advent of the steam engine made it possible for ships to approach to within 100 to 125 feet of whales — the ideal distance for a harpoon cannon. (A full-grown whale can swim at 14 knots; and, for a long time, motorized whaling boats' top speed was 10 to 12 knots.)

Svend Foyn's cannon quickly became indispensable, for whales — such as the right whale — that could be killed without it had more or less disap-

peared completely from the seas. What whalers now found on their expeditions into polar waters were, above all, finback whales. Even the most daring cachalot hunters had given up the chase late in the nineteenth century. But, in 1904, when a large number of them were discovered in the Antarctic, they began again — and this time, with the harpoon cannon and with more powerful and faster ships.

The End of an Age

At the beginning of the twentieth century, whale oil began to increase in value as certain manufacturers found uses for it. The whaling industry, now equipped with modern weapons and techniques, once more became profitable. New, fast whalers were commissioned, and factories were built in the Falkland Islands, at Newfoundland, etc. By 1904, the whalers were slaughtering the great schools of finback whales that had just been discovered in the Antarctic. Old cargo ships were anchored in protected bays, and to these were brought the carcasses for processing.

The resurgence of whaling, however, was short-lived. Little by little, the American whalers went out of business; and, one by one, the factories of New England closed their doors. In 1921, the American whaler *Charles W. Morgan* made its last expedition, and then was decommissioned. (The ship is preserved at Mystic, Connecticut.)

According to R. Clarke, the end of the sailing whalers came in 1925, when the *John R. Manta* and the *Margareth*, both schooners, were decommissioned at New Bedford.

But it was not yet over. In the mid-1920s, a group of Norwegians invented the factory ship — a ship equipped to take on board and completely process whales killed by smaller chasers. In 1925 and 1926, the factory ship *Lancing* was hoisting aboard, by means of an enormous ramp, the carcasses of the largest whales and flensing and boiling their blubber. This was the signal for a new massacre. In 1927-28, 13,775 whales were taken; and, in 1930-31, 40,201. By then, there were forty-one factory ships afloat. And the number of whales diminished accordingly.

The Antarctic was virtually empty of whales, and the Japanese and the

(Facing page above) Olaus, Magnus. Engraving from *Historia de gentibus septentrionalis* (1555). *Bibliothèque Nationale.*

(Facing page below) Olaus Magnus. Engraving from *Historia de gentibus septentrionalis* (1555). *Bibliothèque Nationale.*

Soviets turned once more to the North Pacific, where they found Sei and sperm whales. As the whalers of these two nations intensified their efforts, however, Americans, who had been among the most efficient hunters, gave up whaling altogether. Similarly, Great Britain, South Africa, Holland, and Norway were no longer maintaining a whaling industry.

Control

Beginning in 1931 and 1932, professional whalers, alarmed at the great decrease in the number of cetaceans, agreed to accept controls on the number of expeditions sent out each year. This was followed by agreement among whaling companies to limit the number of whales that each company was allowed to kill, the amount of whale oil that could be produced, and also the extent of the hunting season.

In 1937, the first international whaling agreement (called the London Convention) was signed by nine nations. Of rather limited value, it was in force until World War II. During the war years, however, whaling ceased almost entirely, and the various species of whales were thus enabled to increase their numbers somewhat. The whaling ships were either sunk or converted into tankers.

On February 7, 1944, a preliminary meeting repromulgated the provisions of the London Convention, and, in order to institute a standard unit of measure, established the Blue Whale Unit (BWU) — that is, a unit designating the quantity of oil furnished by one blue whale. This same meeting, on a purely arbitrary basis, lay down the following principle:

1 blue whale equals 2 finback whales equals 2 1/2 humpback whales equals 6 Sei whales. (These are the four species of baleen whale pursued by the whalers.)

In December 1946, the delegates of nineteen nations met in Washington, created the International Whaling Commission, and promulgated a new Convention. This agreement determines the dates of the opening and closing of the whaling season, prohibits the taking of a female accompanied by a calf, establishes minimum sizes of whale that may be taken (according to species), and, finally, sets up an annual "quota" (expressed in Blue Whale Units) of whales.

Certain species of whale were completely protected under the terms of the Convention; that is, they may not be hunted under any circumstances. These are the right whale, the gray whale of California, and the humpback whale. The International Whaling Commission decides which species are to be protected.

A whale hunt. Engraving by Piquet (1791). *Bibliothèque Nationale.*

In addition, a natural preserve was set up for whales, in which all whaling is forbidden. This is the largest preserve in the world: the arctic region between longitude 70 and 160 west.

Enforcement of the Commission's regulations is assured by the presence, aboard every factory ship and in every whaling station on land, of at least two inspectors.

"Since the end of the war," writes Professor Budker, "the whaling industry has subsisted above all on reserves of common rorquals. Blue whales and humpback whales complement these reserves, but the number of them taken is not large." At the present time, since blue whales and humpback whales are totally protected species in the Antarctic, the only species hunted in those regions by the Soviets and the Japanese are the finback and the Sei whales.

The End of the Massacre

An estimate reveals that, at the present time, there are approximately 220,000 large cetaceans in the sea; that is, whales belonging to the species that were most hunted. Of this number, 75 percent are finback whales; 15 percent, blue whales; and 10 percent, humpback whales.

For the past quarter-century, the International Whaling Commission has actively met its responsibilities. A scientific committee studies every aspect of the conservation of the various species. Of all the nations adhering to the Commission's rules and regulations, only three are still actively engaged in whaling: Norway (in a very small capacity), the Soviet Union, and Japan, who divide between themselves most of the annual quota of whales.

The twenty-third session of the International Whaling Commission, held in Washington during the summer of 1971, was of special importance. It was decided to abandon the Blue Whale Unit system since it was detrimental to certain species. Henceforth, quotas will be established for individual species — a system strongly urged for several years by the Commission's scientific committee. The last quota authorized was 2300 blue whale units, which was 400 units less than that of the preceding year.

Moreover, the United States has placed on its list of "endangered species" eight species of whales; which means that no whaling permits will be issued for any of these. This enlightened legislation has served to reinforce the fundamental determination of the International Whaling Commission to protect marine fauna with every means in its power. Similar legislation has recently been enacted which forbids the importation onto American territory of any product derived from an endangered species.

Illustrated Glossary

Amphipoda

An order of crustacean, subclass Malacostraca, division Peracarida. The carapace is always present, even though it may not always be distinct. The first thoracic segment, and occasionally also the second, is united to the head. Amphipoda are laterally compressed: *Gammarus, Talitrus, Caprella*. The *Cyamidae,* or whale fleas, are related to *Caprellidae.*

Apnea

Suspension of breathing of more or less long duration.

Aqua-Lung®

The Aqua-Lung,® or self-contained underwater breathing appartaus (SCUBA), was designed in 1943 by Jacques-Yves Cousteau and an engineer. Émile Gagnan

   The principal characteristic of this apparatus is that it is an "open-circuit" device; that is, the used air is expelled directly into the water, and fresh air is provided not in continuous fashion, but whenever the diver inhales.

   The air itself is stored in one or more air tanks (or "bottles" or "cylinders")

which are strapped onto the diver's back. Its flow is controlled by a regulator, which delivers air when the diver inhales and which assures that the pressure of the air corresponds to that of the water surrounding the diver. When the diver exhales, the used air is fed into the water by means of an exhaust located under the hood of the regulator. Two flexible tubes run from a mouthpiece to the regulator; one is for inhalation, the other for exhalation.

This simple and safe apparatus, entirely automatic and easily mastered, has, in effect, opened the doors of the sea to man and made it possible for a large segment of the public to experience the thrill of diving. The invention of the AQUA-LUNG,® therefore was a decisive step forward in man's conquest of the sea, and even in the history of human progress.

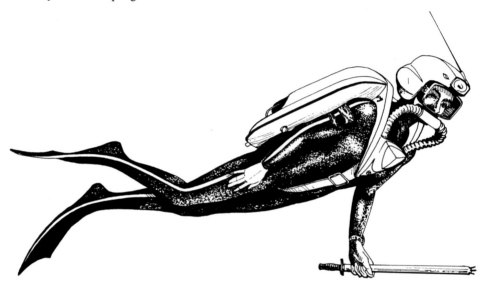

The Cousteau-Gagnan SCUBA.

The Cousteau-Gagnan independent diving unit was a revolutionary departure from the old "hard-hat" heavy diving rig, which most of us recall from the movies of the thirties. The hard-hat apparatus (so called because of the heavy copper helmet that it included) was complicated to use, uncomfortable, and dangerous. Moreover it required a long period of training, and it limited the diver to a small area of bottom. If, in the past twenty years, man has truly been able to go down into the sea, it is because of the independent diving gear — and its accessory equipment, such as the "fins" invented by Commandant de Corlieu, the mask, and the weight belt used to control buoyancy — which has proved its value as a means of exploration and scientific research even more than as a piece of sporting equipment.

Yet, even though man has now learned to operate autonomously in the sea, he is still susceptible to two of the dangers with which the hard-hat divers had always to contend: rapture of the depths, and decompression accidents. (See these two entries in the Glossary.)

Asdic

Acronym for Allied Submarine Detection Investigation Committee. It is an ul-trasonic detection device which enables a ship on the surface to locate a submerged submarine. Like radar, it was developed by the British on the eve of World War II.

Automatic Camera with Edgerton Flash

The automatic marine camera was developed by the Center of Advanced Marine Studies of Marseilles on the basis of a design by J.-Y. Cousteau. Essentially, it consists of a camera installed on a trailer which is towed along the ocean bottom by *Calypso.* It is automatic in the sense that it begins operating as soon as it touches bottom. The apparatus is equipped with an electronic flash designed specially for the "Troika," or trailer, by Professor Harold Edgerton of MIT. Both camera and flash are battery operated. The automatic camera and Edgerton flash permit us to take close-ups of the bottom.

Balanus or Barnacle

A fixed crustacean, division Entomostraca, subclass Cirripedia. They are usually known as barnacles, or acorn barnacles.

Barnacles live on the shores of every part of the globe. Another type of barnacle, the ship or goose barnacle, attaches itself to flotsam in the sea, and, especially in the days of wooden ships, to ships' bottoms. They feed on micro-organisms from the water, which they filter through their modified limbs. The larvae are free-floating.

Beluga

The Belugae, or white whale, is a toothed whale, which belongs to the family Mono-dontidae, genus *Delphinapterus.* It inhabits the arctic seas of North America, but it is also found occasionally in shallow coastal waters and in bays.

The Beluga is between 12 and 14 feet in length and weighs slightly less than a ton. It has no dorsal fin. A young Beluga is dark gray, but it becomes lighter as it matures until its skin is yellow-white.

Belugae travel in schools of about ten individuals. They feed in shallow water, on fish, squid, and crustaceans; and they themselves are an easy prey for killer whales.

The female matures sexually at three years, when she is about eight feet long. Gestation lasts fourteen months, and birth takes place between March and May. The young white whale is approximately five feet in length, and it grows at the rate of three feet a year for the first two years of its life.

The Beluga is protected by a layer of blubber four to eight inches thick. When melted, this blubber produces about 200 liters of oil for every animal.

The word "Beluga" is somewhat confusing, since it is also used to designate the white sturgeon which is the source of caviar. The name became current in the nineteenth century, and came from the Russian word *bieluha,* white.

Blowhole

The blowhole is the whale's nostril. There are, in fact, two blowholes, but, so far as the sperm whale is concerned, only one of them is a working nostril. This organ has no connection with the whale's mouth.

Within the blowhole (the opening of which is controlled by a powerful muscle), there are inflatable air pockets on either side of the opening. Two internal "lips" control exhalation and contribute to the modulation of sound. In addition, a fleshy lamella, shaped like a tongue, makes it possible for a whale to close the blowhole more or less tightly.

Bottlenose Whales

The bottlenose whale, *Hyperoodon*, is a toothed whale of the family *Ziphiidae*. It is found in the North Atlantic in summertime, and, in winter, it migrates southward, sometimes as far as the Mediterranean.

Adult males reach a length of about 30 feet, and females of 25 feet. A female 20 feet long weighs about 2.5 tons.

The color of the skin varies from black to gray, and becomes lighter with age. Bottlenose whales not yet fully mature are often spotted with yellow and white. Males have only two teeth, located at the tip of their snouts.

These mammals are able to remain under water from ten to twenty minutes when they are feeding; but, when they are harpooned, they are able to stay much longer than that without surfacing.

They travel in groups of four to twelve individuals, and feed chiefly on squid and cuttlefish.

The gestation period is approximately twelve months. A new-born bottlenose whale is about 10 feet.

An adult male 30 feet long and with a 20-foot circumference may yield as much as two tons of oil and over 200 pounds of spermaceti similar to the spermaceti of the cachalot.

Cachalot or Sperm Whale

The word *cachalot* was already in use in the mid-eighteenth century. It probably is derived from the Portuguese *cachalotte* ("big head"), or from the Spanish *cachalote*.

(See Appendix I, "The Cetaceans")

Cephalopoda

A class of the phylum Mollusca which includes four subclasses: Decapoda, Octopoda, Nautiloids, and Vampyromorphes.

The Decapoda have ten legs equipped with suctions cups, such as Spirules with internal shells, the cuttlefish, the Teuthoidae, and the squids (the commom edible squid, *Chiroteuthis* and *Architeuthis* — the giant squid which is the cachalot's favorite food).

The Octopoda have eight arms, all equipped with suction cups. This subclass includes the octopus which lives in coastal waters, the Eledon which lives farther out to sea, *Ocythoe* (the female of which weighs several pounds, while the male is tiny), and the Argonaut (or paper nautilus), the female of which secretes a shell-like enclosure which she uses as a nest.

The Nautiloids are found in the Indo-Pacific region. They have external shells, of which they occupy only the last section. This is the only subclass without suction cups.

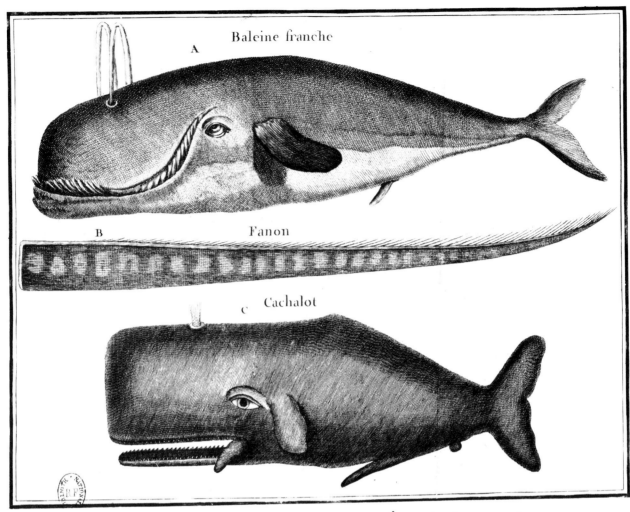

A **Baleine franche**

B **Fanon**

c **Cachalot**

Right whale and sperm whale. Du Reste, *Histoire des pêches, des découvertes des établissements des Hollandais dans les mers du nord*. An IX de la République. *Bibliothèque Nationale.*

The Vampyromorphes are fantastic beings with enormous eyes and luminous organs. They are veritable living fossils, only recently discovered.

Chiroptera

Chiroptera are bats, an order of mainly nocturnal animals highly specialized for flying. Their wings are formed of large membranous planes stretched between the elongated digits of the fore limbs.

In flight, the bat emits a constant series of ultrasonic cries which it uses to determine, by the amount of elapsed time before the echo returns, the direction and distance of the objects reflecting the sound. These sounds are also used to detect prey.

Clam

The common name of the *Venus mercenaria*, an edible bivalve or two-shelled mollusk that lives buried in sand or mud.

Coryphaena

There are two species of *Coryphaena: Coryphaena hippurus,* and *Coryphaena equisetis.* The first is commonly known as the dolphin fish, and the second as the pompano dolphin — confusing names, since *Coryphaena* are not related to the true (mammal) dolphins. Both are beautifully colored fishes of the open tropical oceans.

Decompression Accidents

Decompression accidents during dives are caused by the fact that gas from the diver's air tends to go into solution in the diver's blood. If the diver rises to the surface too quickly, this gas comes out of solution in the form of bubbles in the blood stream, which may impede circulation. The result is decompression sickness, (the bends), which is more or less serious depending upon the speed of the diver's ascent, the depth from which he began the ascent, and the amount of time spent at that depth.

Decompression sickness may be prevented by timing the ascent in such a way that the gas is diffused normally. And, for that purpose, tables have been worked out that indicate the number and duration of the pauses that a diver must make during his ascent, according to the depth that he has reached and the time spent at that depth.

Dolphin (Common)

The common dolphin is a member of the family *Delphinidae,* genus *Delphinus.* It is found in all warm and temperate seas, and occasionally in cold waters. The dolphin travels in schools of about twenty individuals.

The size of the dolphin varies from five feet to eight or nine feet, rarely more, and it normally weighs about 160 pounds.

The color of its skin runs from brown or black on its back to white on its underside. A darker streak runs from the periphery of the eye to the snout.

The common dolphin feeds in shallow water on fish and cephalapods.

The gestation period lasts about nine months, and the calves are born during the spring.

DSL

During World War II, sonar devices detected mysterious layers at various depths and in very diverse regions in the seas. These were labeled "Deep Scattering Layers."

Observation revealed that these layers rise toward the surface during the night, and sink during the daylight hours. It transpired that these layers were made up of marine fauna — animals that were photographed by Professor Harold Edgerton of MIT, from aboard *Calypso,* by means of a special flash apparatus developed by Professor Edgerton. The principal constituents of these layers are copepod crustaceans, jellyfish, and siphonophores.

Echo Location

A method of orientation used by several animals, including bats and birds as well as cetaceans. The animal directs itself according to the echo that it receives of a sound that it makes.

Flippers

Flippers are the pectoral fins of cetaceans. X-rays of these members show the bones of five "fingers" (except for finback whales), a "wrist," and an "arm." This is usually interpreted as evidence of the whales' land origins.

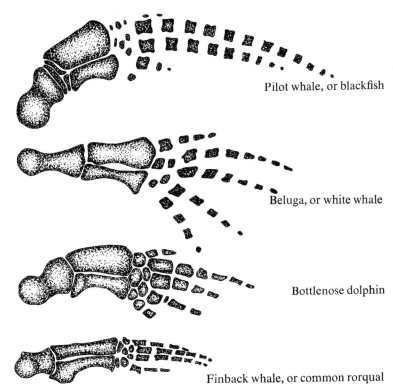

Pilot whale, or blackfish

Beluga, or white whale

Bottlenose dolphin

Finback whale, or common rorqual

X rays of the flippers of various cetaceans. Note that the finback whale has only four "fingers."

Harpoon

The harpoon has been used since the dawn of history for fishing and hunting. In primitive times, it was made of wood or bone, with one or two rows of barbs.

The *harpé,* as the Greeks called it (the word was derived from a Semitic term, hereb) is depicted on monuments dating from the third millenium before Christ. And in the language of the Basques, those intrepid hunters of whales, the word *arpoi,* taken from the Greek root, means "to capture alive."

The present form of the harpoon is described in a text dating from 1474.

An important modern development was the addition of a pivoted crosspiece to the head, which prevents a harpooned animal from shaking the weapon loose.

Jonah

The fifth of the "lesser prophets" of Israel, who lived in the eighth century before Christ. According to the Bible narrative, Jonah, in order to avoid fulfilling the Lord's command to predict to the inhabitants of Nineveh the destruction of their city, took passage on a ship. The ship was soon overtaken by a storm and was in imminent danger of sinking.

Jonah, convinced that the storm was a punishment for his disobedience, and wishing to avoid the loss of the ship and its crew, advised the seamen to throw him overboard. They did so, and, as soon as Jonah was in the water, he was swallowed by a whale.

The prophet spent three days in the stomach of the animal, where he took the opportunity to compose a canticle which is preserved to this day. At the end of the third day, he was vomited onto a beach.

Jonah had learned his lesson. He went immediately to Nineveh and carried out the Lord's orders.

The Book of Jonah, which forms part of the Old Testament, relates these adventures. The methods of modern biblical criticism, however, have revealed that the Book of Jonah was written, in all probability, long after the time of Jonah himself.

Krill

Krill *(Euphausia superba)* is a small crustacean Schizopod between two and three inches long. It is, in effect, a shrimp-like creature found in coastal waters, with an orange head and appendages and a green underside. This green color, which is visible through the thin stomach wall, is caused by the algae on which the krill feeds.

This crustacean, which produces a form of plankton, lives in cold water, and is much more common in the Antarctic than in the Arctic. It multiplies with extraordinary rapidity during the antarctic summer and covers the water with a reddish-brown layer — a layer which is usually about forty feet thick, but sometimes reaches a thickness of 3000 feet.

The krill matures at the age of two years.

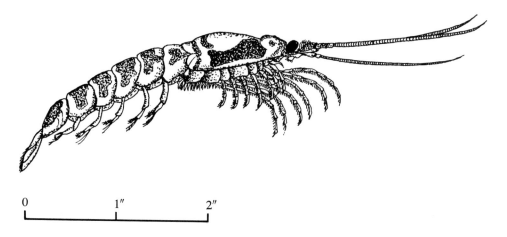

0   1"   2"

The krill (*Euphausia superba*), a small crustacean on which whales feed.

Level Reef

A level reef is a coral plateau, more or less long and unbroken, that extends along a shoreline or on top of another reef that is completely surrounded by water. Level reefs are found in shallow water in tropical seas.

Leviathan

The whale has always astounded man by its size and its monstrous appearance. The Leviathan, a sea monster, had its origin in Phoenician mythology, but it is commonly known through its place in the Bible.

Yahweh, in order to give Job an example of his power, describes the Leviathan: "From the depths of the sea came whales like islands, and the hideous Leviathans rising up on the sand with crocodiles twenty cubits in length. Man is before the sea like a child before a Leviathan's lair."

In the book of Isaiah, it is said "On that day the Lord, with his great and strong staff, will lay low Leviathan and slay the whale that is in the sea."

Some have thought, with good reason, that the biblical description of Leviathan referred to the cachalot. The spouting is described as "a smoke which rises from its nostrils as from a boiling kettle. In its neck, power has taken up its abode; and terror goes before him."

Not all commentators are agreed on the nature of the Leviathan, and some identify it with the crocodile rather than with the whale.

Here is the (negative) description given in the fortieth chapter of Job:

"Leviathan, too! Can you catch him with a fish-hook, or run a line around his tongue? Can you put a ring through his nose, or pierce his jaw with a hook? Riddle his hide with darts? Prod his head with a harpoon? You have only to lay a finger on him never to forget the struggle or risk it again. Any hopes you might have would prove vain, for the mere sight of him would stagger you."

And, in Isaiah, the Leviathan is a symbol for the powerful pagan nation that is to submit to Yahweh.

Minisub

There are several types of minisubs, or diving saucers, designed by Captain Cousteau and developed by the Center of Higher Marine Studies at Marseilles.

The *SP-350,* a two-passenger vehicle. It is equipped with a cinematographic camera, a still camera, a hydraulically operated pincer and lift, and a storage basket. The SP-350 has been used in more than 600 dives.

The *SP-1000,* or sea-flea, carries only one man but is designed to be used in conjunction with a second SP-1000. It has two exterior cameras (16mm. and 35mm.), both controlled from within, and tape recorders for recording underwater sounds. It has been used in over 100 dives.

The *SP-4000,* or Deepstar, is capable of diving to 4000 feet. It was built for Westinghouse and was launched in 1966. Since then, it has participated in over 500 dives. It is a two-passenger vehicle, with a speed of three knots.

The *SP-3000,* presently being tested at sea, was built for CNEXO. It is expected to attain a speed of three knots, and will carry three passengers.

Moby Dick

The most famous of the works of Herman Melville, *Moby Dick* is devoted to the subject of whaling as practiced by whaling ships of the nineteenth century.

The book is the story of the contest between Moby Dick, a great white sperm whale, and Captain Ahab, who has sworn to kill the whale. The work is also a poetic and symbolic representation of the eternal battle between man and evil incarnate as "the beast."

Ahab, who wishes to establish order in the world, finally is defeated and dies a victim of the monster. The forces of evil have won the victory. This pessimistic conception of human destiny is expressed in magnificent language that owes a good deal to the Bible, to Shakespeare, and to the English writers of the eighteenth century.

Moby Dick had no particular success during Melville's lifetime. It was only after World War I that its fame spread. In 1956, John Huston made a film of the book.

Herman Melville's own life was only slightly less an adventure than Captain Ahab's. He was born in 1819, in New York, of a family of eight children. At the age of thirteen his father died, and he was obliged to earn his living for the next years as a bank employee, a clerk, and a schoolmaster.

In January 1841, he signed onto the whaler *Acushnet,* whose destination was the South Pacific by way of Cape Horn. In July 1842, as the ship was taking on provisions at Nuku Hiva in the Marquise Islands, Melville deserted. A month later, he signed onto an Australian whaler, the Lucy Ann, the captain of which was wholly insane.

Life aboard the *Lucy Ann* was even worse that on the *Acushnet,* and Melville deserted once more, this time at Tahiti, along with a large part of the crew. Taken prisoner, he escaped to the neighboring island of Eimo. There, after two months, he became a seaman on a Nantucket whaler, the *Charles and Henry,* which took him to the Hawaiian Islands. In August 1843, he enlisted as a seaman aboard the U. S. naval frigate *United States,* which, fourteen months later, put into Boston.

Melville's seafaring life had lasted three years and nine months. With two desertions on his record, he certainly cannot be offered as the very model of a seaman or sailer. Nonetheless, he returned to the United States with his mind filled by an incomparable, though rapidly acquired, experience. He immediately began writing, and, a few years later, two works appeared simultaneously in New York and London: *Typee* (1846), and *Omoo* (1847). They were both successful.

His next book, *Tuesday,* was a total failure. He left New York in 1850 and went with his family to Arrowhead, near Pittsfield, Massachusetts. There, he wrote *Moby Dick,* his masterpiece which, when it was published, was almost completely ignored. His later books fared no better.

In 1866, Melville fell ill, and he accepted, in order to live, a job with the Port of New York Customs Bureau. After having two volumes of poetry published at his own expense, he died in 1891. He would be forgotten until thirty years had passed.

Narwhal

The narwhal is a toothed cetacean of the family *Monodontidae.* It inhabits the arctic seas, keeping to coastal waters and occasionally venturing into the mouths of rivers.

Its length varies from 10 feet to 16 or 17 feet — not counting its spirally twisted tusk, slightly to the right of the snout, which may grow to a length of 9 feet. The tusk is found only in the male.

The narwhal has no dorsal fin, but only a slight protrusion, or dorsal "crest."

Contrary to what is commonly believed, the narwhal's tusk is not used to break ice, nor as a weapon. It seems likely, in fact, that it serves no useful purpose at all.

In other times, the tusk was thought to be the "horn" of the unicorn, and was very highly regarded for the medicinal powers attributed to it. The purveyors of these "unicorn horns" were Norwegian fishermen who hunted the narwhal in Iceland and Greenland.

The narwhal travels in groups of six to ten individuals, with the females often being separated from the males. They eat cuttlefish, crustaceans, and fish.

The gestation period is unknown. The calf, at birth, measures four and one half feet in length, and remains with the mother for a time.

Observation Chamber

Calypso was originally a minesweeper, and it was necessary to modify her considerably for her new career as a marine research vessel. Among the other changes made, a "false nose" was added to the prow — that is, a metallic well that goes down to five feet below *Calypso*'s waterline and ends in an observation chamber. The chamber has eight portholes, through which we are able to observe and film anything in the water, even when *Calypso* is moving.

Observation Deck

What the text refers to occasionally as *Calypso*'s "crow's-nest" is not a crow's-nest in the classical sense. That is, it is not a platform atop a mainmast, but rather a raised metal platform built as far forward as possible so as to constitute an upper deck. It serves two purposes: it supports our radar antennae, and it provides an excellent vantage point for observation.

Observation Lumen

A research expedition by the Cousteau team, in the Mediterranean, the purpose of which was to determine the horizontal propagation of light at depths of 25, 50, 100, 150, 200, and 250 meters. The minisub SP-350 was used on this occasion.

Phototropism

Phototropism is a term used to describe a tendency of plants and animals to grow or move toward a light source. It is this response which causes newly germinated seedlings to grow upwards toward the light where their leaves and later their flowers will be in the best position for the life processes to continue.

Phytoplankton

Phytoplankton is a term used for the minute plant life which floats in the surface waters of the oceans. It is made up exclusively of unicellular forms: diatoms (which are plentiful in cold and temperate seas), dinoflagellates (in warm waters), coccolithophores, Cyanophycae (or blue algae), etc. Its development depends on the sun's light, which by photosynthesis builds up the organic matter in its tissues. Phytoplankton is essential to the life of the oceans, for it is the food source for the animal plankton (zooplankton) which in turn nourishes the larger animals, such as the blue whale.

Pinnipedia

An order of animals containing three families:
Otaridae: sea lions, furred seals;
Odobaenidae: walrus;
Phocidae: seals and sea elephants.

The Pinnipedia are mammals living partly on land at the edge of the sea, although they are beautifully adapted for life underwater. They feed on fish and crustaceans and are found in all seas except the Indian Ocean. They are most common in the polar seas.

Porpoise

The porpoise is a toothed cetacean of the family, *Delphinidae*, genus *Phocaena*. It is found from the Arctic Ocean to the west coast of Africa, and also on the west coast of Mexico. It varies in length from four feet to six feet, and its average weight is about 160 pounds.

The porpoise's skin is white on its underside, and almost black on its back. Its blade-like teeth number 54.

Porpoises travel in couples and also in schools of a hundred or so. They swim only a short distance beneath the surface, and rise to the surface to breathe every fifteen seconds. Their diet consists of small fishes that swim near the surface.

The porpoise's deadliest enemies are the shark and the killer whale.

Mating occurs at the end of spring and during the summer. The gestation period is eleven months. At birth, the baby porpoise is approximately half the length of its mother.

At certain epochs of history — at the time of Henry VIII, for instance — porpoise meat was regarded as a great delicacy.

Pygmy Sperm Whale, or Pygmy Cachalot

The pygmy sperm whale belongs to the family *Physteridae*, genus *Kogia*, and inhabits the Atlantic, Pacific, and Indian oceans.

It reaches a length of 9 to 13 feet. Its dorsal fin, situated in the middle of its back, is sickle-shaped. Its tail spread is about two feet. The average weight is between 400 and 700 pounds. Its head, which accounts for one sixth of the total body length, resembles that of the porpoise.

Little is known about the habits of these cetaceans. We know that they travel in schools, migrating to polar waters in summer and to temperate and warm areas in autumn and winter, where their females give birth. The mating season is quite long. The gestation period is about nine months. A 10-foot female's calf weighs approximately 175 pounds and is six feet long.

4

Rapture of the Depths

Rapture of the depths is a form of narcosis induced by the presence of nitrogen, and seriously impedes a diver's reasoning processes. The depth at which it affects a diver depends upon the individual. Some divers experience its symptoms at, say, 135 feet, while others are affected only at greater depths and later — sometimes too much later.

A diver's threshold of susceptibility can be raised considerably by replacing the nitrogen in his breathing mixture by a lighter gas, such as helium.

Siphonophores

Siphonophores are Cnidaria of the class Hydrozoa. They are exclusively marine animals and are able to float. They are fragile, transparent, and often magnificently hued in iridescent colors.

Siphonophores sometimes look like jellyfishes but are in fact hydrozoan colonies that are not fixed, but free-floating. The individuals of the colony therefore develop in such a way as to be capable of performing special and distinct functions. The axis of the colony is a stolon, at the end of which is an air-filled membrane (the pneumatophore) that serves as a floater.

Siphonophores feed on forms of marine life that they capture by means of venomous filaments — a weapon effective enought to be dangerous even to man.

Siphonophores reproduce by means of eggs, and also by budding in the form of medusae.

Sirenia

Sirenia are an order of aquatic mammals whose forward members have evolved into pectoral fins, and who lack hind legs. The tail is flattened horizontally.

There are two living families: the *Halicoridae,* or dugongs, and the *Manatidae,* or manatees; a third, the Rhytines (Steller's sea cow), was killed off by man in the eighteenth century.

The dugong lives in the Indo-Pacific region, in the Red Sea, and in Australian waters. It averages eight feet in length and weighs about 450 pounds.

Dugongs live alone or in small schools and feed on algae and on seaweed growing in shallow water.

The female has well-developed mammary glands.

The flesh, oil, and leather of the dugong is highly regarded in some parts of the world, and for this reason the animal has been hunted extensively. There are many places where their numbers have been greatly reduced.

Three species of manatee exist and are found on the West Coast of America, in the Tchad River basin, and on the coasts of Africa. They also enter rivers and their estuaries.

Manatees are somewhat larger than dugongs, reaching a length of about 14 feet and a weight of 1500 pounds. They are strictly vegetarians and feed on water plants that they pull out with their upper lip.

Manatees live in small groups, and are threatened with extinction, at least in certain areas, since they have neither defenses against man nor any natural timidity.

Sonar

Sonar (Sound Navigation Ranging) is an apparatus of underwater detection and communication. It is, in effect, the marine equivalent of radar, and is based upon the reflection of sound or supersonic waves.

Spermaceti (See Tank.)

Sperm Whale (See Cachalot. Also, Appendix I, "The Cetaceans.")

Spout

The whale's breath is the classic means man has of discovering a whale's location. When a cetacean rises to the surface to breathe, it gives off, through its one or two blowholes, a spout which is visible from a distance. It is, in fact, a whitish spray which acts as a marker for whaling ships. This spray cannot be attributed solely to the con-

Spouts of various whales.

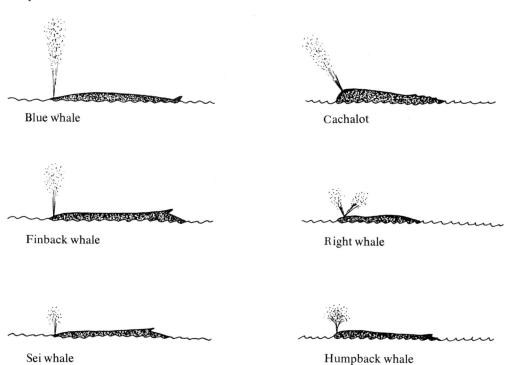

Blue whale

Cachalot

Finback whale

Right whale

Sei whale

Humpback whale

Gray whale

densation of water vapor in cold air, for it is visible even in tropical waters and climates.

As there is no passageway between its mouth and its blowhole, a cetacean cannot blow water out while exhaling.

Paul Portier, a French biologist, has offered the following hypothesis: the expansion in the open air of air which has been compressed in the thorax of a whale causes the condensation of the water vapor when the whale exhales.

F. C. Fraser and P. E. Purves have noted the presence, in the whale's lungs, of very small drops of oil and of mucus, which may explain the visibility of its spout. This oil in the whale's respiratory tract may also have a part in the absorption of nitrogen.

Each species of whale has a particular kind of spout. That of the blue whale and of the common rorqual is a single geyser that rises from 18 to 30 feet. The right whale's spout is double. That of the sperm whale is single, and emerges from the blowhole to the left of the whale and at a 45°angle.

Squid

The squid is a Cephalopod and a decapod — that is, it has ten arms, equipped with suction cups — and belongs to the family Teuthoidae.

The squid that forms the basis for several common dishes is only about eight inches long. It is this species that, at certain seasons of the year, group by the hundreds of thousands for their mating ritual — an event that was the subject of one of our films: *The Night of the Squid.*

Chiroteuthis, characterized by its extraordinarily long tentacles and slender body, is noted for its swimming ability.

Architeuthis, or giant squid, is the natural prey, and the natural adversary, of the cachalot. It is probably the basis in fact for many legends concerning marine monsters — sea serpents and, especially, the "Kraken" of the Norwegians. And, in fact, its size lends itself to this sort of interpretation, for its body may be twenty feet long, and its tentacles reach a length of perhaps forty feet.

Little is actually known about Architeuthis. It lives in the great depths of the oceans, at 10,000 to 12,000 feet, and rises to the surface only at night. Specimens are taken alive only rarely, and then with great difficulty.

Tank

A "tank" is a cavity in the forward part of the head of a cachalot (and of certain other toothed whales) which contains an oily substance, not unlike wax, called spermaceti. The biological function of this substance has not been clearly established.

The tank may hold as much as five tons of spermaceti, which is of a quality superior to ordinary whale oil.

Tegea

A lens which is installed on cameras in order to increase the size of the area that they may film. The apparatus has been adapted for use on a special camera, with a corrective lens, for underwater filming.

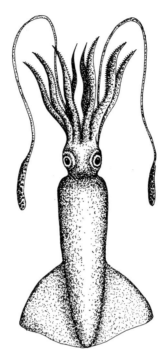

Giant squid.

Zooplankton (Animal Plankton)

Zooplankton is concentrated in the well-lit surface of the sea. (See DSL, Deep Scattering Layer). Herbivorous animals feed in that layer, as do carnivores.

Zooplankton make vertical migrations. At night, they occupy layers near the surface, and, during the day, sink deeper into the sea. In certain cases, light itself causes certain species to sink.

Among the zooplankton are the Radiolaria, Acantharia, Foraminifera, Cnidaria, Ctenaria, and a large number of crustaceans and mollusks.

Engraving from Rondelet's *Histoire complète des poissons* (1558). *Bibliothèque Nationale.*

Bibliography

Budker, Paul. *Baleines et baleiniers*. Paris, 1955.

Fitter, Richard. *Les animaux sauvages en voie de disparition dans le monde*. Paris, 1970.

Matthews, L. H. *The Whale*. London, 1968.

Norris, Kenneth S. *Whales, Dolphins and Porpoises*. Univ. of Calif., Los Angeles, 1966.

Riedman, Sarah R. and Elton T. Gustafson. *Home Is the Sea: For Whales*. New York, 1966.

Ruspoli, Mario. *A la recherche du cachalot*. Paris, 1955.

Slijper, E. J. *Whales*. London, 1962.

Walker, Ernest P. *Mammals of the World.*, Baltimore, 1968.

Walker, Theodore J. *Whale Primer*. New York, 1962.

Photo Credits

The documents reproduced in this volume are from the following sources:

*Bibliothè*que Nationale, Paris: 29, 247, 271, 272, 277, 278, 280, 283, 288, 300.

Roger-Viollet: 272.

Photographic Service, Embassy of the United States, Paris: 17.

Collection Jean-Horace Chambon: 197.

The photographs published in the present work were taken by Georges Barsky, Ron Church, Philippe Cousteau, François Dorado, Frédéric Dumas, Albert Falco, André Laban, Dr. Claude Millet, Yves Omer, Jacques Renoir, and Ludwig Sillner.

Several of the photographs taken on the surface of the water are from the private collections of members of *Calypso*'s team.

We should like to express our special thanks to M. Jean-Horace Chambon for his kindness in allowing us to photograph, and reproduce here, the two engraved whale's teeth from his personal collection.

Index

The Undersea Discoveries
of Jacques-Yves Cousteau

THE SHARK:
Splendid Savage of the Sea

The Undersea Discoveries
of Jacques-Yves Cousteau

THE SHARK:
Splendid Savage of the Sea

**Jacques-Yves Cousteau
and Philippe Cousteau**

ARROWOOD PRESS

Copyright © 1970 by Jacques-Yves Cousteau
Translated from the French by Francis Price

All rights reserved. No part of this work may be
reproduced or transmitted in any form or by any
means, electronic or mechanical, including photocopying,
recording, or any information storage and retrieval
system, without permission in writing from the
publisher.

Published in 1987 by

Arrowood Press
166 Fifth Avenue
New York, NY 10010

This edition published by arrangement with The Cousteau
Group, Inc., 38 Eleven O'Clock Road, Weston, CT 06883.

Library of Congress Catalog Card Number: 87-71044
ISBN: 0-88486-013-2

Printed in Spain

CONTENTS

INTRODUCTION
Jacques-Yves Cousteau

It has been more than two years since my ship, the *Calypso,* left Monaco to carry out its longest and most fascinating voyage. We have already dived, camera in hand, among the sharks of the Red Sea and the Indian Ocean. We have explored the archipelagoes and the lost isles of the Maldives; the Seychelles, Socotra, Aldabra, the Iles Glorieuses, the Europa Atoll.* We have rediscovered, on the banks of reefs, the prehistoric levels imposed on the sea by the cycle of glacial eras; we have danced with marine creatures who resembled the guests at a masked ball; we have clung to the fins of toothed whales and baleen whales and, for some of them, we have annotated the journal of their travels. We have uncovered marine fossils in the mountains of Malagasy; we have domesticated Pepito and Cristobal, two sea lions from the Cape of Good Hope, explored the wrecks of the island of St. Helena, sought the treasures of the Silver Bank shoal in the Bahamas, dived in our "saucer" to the bottom of Lake Titicaca, lived with the sea elephants of Guadalupe Island. And now we are preparing to cross the Pacific, diving and filming in the Galapagos and Society islands, at Noumea, on the Great Barrier Reef, and in the Sunda Islands between the Indian Ocean and the Pacific. I am translating this long and marvelous voyage into a vast and colorful cinematographic fresco, destined for the television screens of the

*The Maldive Islands, in the Indian Ocean, run north and south off the southwest coast of India. The Seychelles are in the Somali Basin, north-northeast of Madagascar (the Malagasy Republic), which is the great island lying off the east coast of Africa. Socotra is off the Gulf of Aden and the easternmost point of Africa. Aldabra is north of the Comoro Islands, which are to the west of Madagascar's northern tip. The Iles Glorieuses are northeast of the Comoro Islands. The Europa Atoll lies in the Mozambique Channel, between Africa's Mozambique coast and Madagascar.

entire world. I have put into it all the experience I have acquired in the course of thirty-three years of diving, all my love for nature and for the sea.

What is not apparent on the screen is the almost insurmountable difficulty of such an enterprise: the years of technical preparation, of research and documentation; the financial obstacles involving substantial personal sacrifices for a crew of one hundred and fifty men; the thousands of dives in conventional diving suits, the hundreds of dives in the saucer, the hours passed shivering in the cold water or in the decompression chamber, the nights spent repairing a piece of essential equipment or a flooded camera, the tempests of sand, the tropical cyclones, the accidents that occur in a ship in the middle of an ocean, the agonies we experience when we lose trace of a diver or a saucer — and lastly the most direct of all these risks, those of which Philippe is writing here — those which always accompany any meeting with sharks.

The Undersea Discoveries
of Jacques-Yves Cousteau

THE SHARK:
Splendid Savage of the Sea

ONE:

First Encounter

A meeting with a great blue shark. The story behind making the film on the behavior of sharks. Description of the *Calypso* and the team.

Philippe Cousteau's narrative

His entire form is fluid, weaving from side to side; his head moves slowly from left to right, right to left, timed to the rhythm of his motion through the water. Only the eye is fixed, focused on me, circling within the orbit of the head, in order not to lose sight for a fraction of a second of his prey or, perhaps, of his enemy.

His skin is creased with a thousand silky furrows at every movement of his body, emphasizing each pattern of incredible muscle. The crystalline water has ceased to exist; he is there in the unbelievable purity of the void and nothing separates us any longer.

There is no threat, no movement of aggression. Only a sort of nonchalant suspicion is apparent in the movements and attitudes of the shark, and yet he generates fear. Amazed and startled, filled with apprehension, circling with movements as slow and silent as possible, I try to keep him constantly in front of me.

There is something of the miraculous in the suddenness of his appearance as well as in his infinite grace; the surface of the water is far above and its absence contributes to the magical quality of the moment. He turns once more, and the sphere he encompasses expands or contracts, in accordance with his own primitive impulses or the subtle changes of the current. His silent

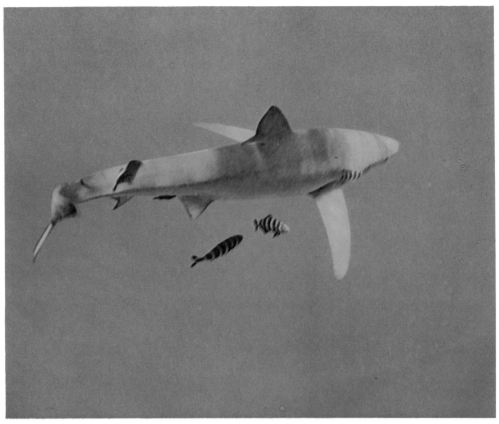

The most beautiful shark of all. This is a blue shark demonstrating one of his sinuous swimming movements. He is accompanied by three pilot fish. One of them is near the gills on the right side of his head. The blue shark appears out of nowhere in the middle of the ocean. He is definitely one of the dangerous sharks, one of the solitary species never running in packs.

circling is a ballet governed by untraceable mechanisms. The blue tranquillity of his form surrounds me with the sensation of a web of murderous and yet beautiful force. I have the feeling that I have accompanied his circular voyage since the beginning of time. His configuration is perfect. Suddenly, the idea that he deserves killing comes to me like a shock and instantly shatters the spell. Murder is the real function of this ideal form, of this icy-blue camouflage, and of that enormous, powerful tail. The water has returned to my consciousness, I can feel it again, gentle and flowing between my fingers, solid against my palms. I am one hundred and ten feet below the surface, in the clear, deep water of the Indian Ocean. With thirty minutes of air remaining and a camera in my hand, I am far from being an easy prey. Our circling has, in fact, gone

This is a side view of the blue shark under different lighting. You can see his wide black eye, his constantly open mouth engulfing the water that goes out through the gills. Underneath his mouth, attached by an overhead suction device, you can see a remora fish—the shark's traveling companion—eating the crumbs, leftovers from the shark's meals. The blue shark is by far the most majestic of all sharks. You can see the shape of his muscles in the back of his head and on the sides. The underside of his belly is snow white. You don't see his teeth now because they are retracted, lying flat on the inside of his mouth or palate.

on for only a few seconds and already I can hear the irregular snorting of the engine in the surveillance craft above me.

The great blue shark continues his approach toward me in the unchanging manner which has been that of his race throughout its existence. He is really a superb animal, almost seven feet in length, and I know, since I have often seen them before, that his jaw is lined with seven rows of teeth, as finely honed as the sharpest razor. I have already begun to ascend slowly toward the surface, simulating a few movements of attack whenever his orbit brings him sufficiently close. He perceives the slightest pressure wave from my smallest movement, analyzes every change in acidity or in the vaguest of odors, and he will never allow himself to be surprised by an abrupt movement. He can swim at a speed of more than thirty knots and his attack would probably be impossible to parry. But he is still circling slowly around me, making use of the cautiousness that has protected his species since its first appearance on this planet more than one hundred million years ago. I know that the circles are growing inexorably smaller and that I will probably succeed in repelling his first attack, but I also know that this will not discourage him. Startled for a moment, he will resume the circle of hunger, his attacks will become more and more frequent, and in the end he will break through my feeble defense and his jaws will close on the first bite of my flesh. Drawn by invisible signals, other sharks of the open sea will appear, climbing from the lowest depths or slicing the surface with the knife of their dorsal fins. And then it will be the scramble for the spoils, a frenzy of hunger, of bloody and irresistible strength and horror. For this is the way of the great sharks of the open sea.

I climb back into our surveillance boat, the *Zodiac,* after a last glance at that flawless silhouette and the great staring eye, already regretting the impression of unconquerable power and exalting confrontation, cursing my weakness and being grateful for my fear. I look at the others, companions in dives like this one; burned by the sun, wrinkled by the sea, they look at me and understand: there is a shark beneath us.

Stretched out on the burning rubber of the *Zodiac's* seats, already numbed by the heat and the sun, I think back to all the events that have brought us here to the middle of the Indian Ocean. It is an effort — an enjoyable effort — to recall the beginnings of our adventure.

In the spring of 1966 I was in Hollywood, completing work on a film on the subject of the Precontinent III experiment. I had made this film for the National Geographic Society in Washington, during the thirty days that I and five other divers had spent in our "home" on a ledge three hundred feet below the surface of the Mediterranean. It was a fifty-eight-minute color documentary, expressly produced for television use. As it happened, the company that produces films for the National Geographic Society is Wolper Productions, Inc., whose home offices are on Sunset Boulevard in Los Angeles. It was because of this that my father and I made the acquaintance of the man whose faith and enthusiasm would later permit us to set out on a series of unforgettable adventures: David Wolper. For a long time past, my father had been thinking of a series of films on the sea, designed for television, but the project had come up against the ingrained habits of Madison Avenue and had never been realized. Then, suddenly, David Wolper suggested that we make twelve films of one hour each on subjects of our own choice, and with financial backing sufficient to assure us of more than adequate equipment. Obviously, it was going to be necessary to secure even more financial support, but, having completed three or four films as a result of the agreement reached with David, we were confident that we could fill out our budget from the funds obtained through release of these films in other parts of the world.

The discussions on the terms of our contract took place in New York, and I remember the many evenings spent in conference with lawyers and technicians, dragging on far into the night, and followed by lengthy discussions between my father and myself in our hotel room, as we elaborated on the fantastic projects we had in mind. There was nothing to stop us now: we were going to visit all the seas of the world, equipped with completely new and up-to-date matériel; we would find and film the coelacanth in his hidden depths, dive with the giant calamary squid of the Humboldt Current, and rediscover the galleons of Christopher Columbus. Thanks to David's enthusiasm, and then to his successor, Bud Rifkin's, we would be able to do everything that fascinated us, and above all we would be able to do it with a camera, to fix on film everything we loved and found marvelous in the sea.

The first film of the series was scheduled to be the one most likely to intrigue and attract the attention of viewers, and what maritime subject is more fascinating to everyone than the shark? It is a legendary animal, known to all, even to those who live far from the sea.

It was for this reason that we were now aboard the *Zodiac,* on our way back to the *Calypso* after this magnificent dive. The *Calypso,* a 130-foot converted minesweeper, was the ship on which we had carried out many past experiments, but until this time our work had been of a far more scientific nature. Hydrology, biology, geology — all the sciences of the sea, and all kinds of serious, dedicated scientists had been the *raison d'être* of the *Calypso.* Now, for her cinematographic mission, she had been entirely modified and refitted. The scientific winches and scoops had made way for one-man submarines, and the research laboratories had become photographic darkrooms. (A sketch of the *Calypso* on page 246 shows how she was organized and fitted.)

Each of the two 500-horsepower engines had been completely reconditioned before we set out, in preparation for a voyage that would last for five years. The crew's quarters in the forward section of the hull had been arranged to provide space for six more men — film technicians or additional divers. In

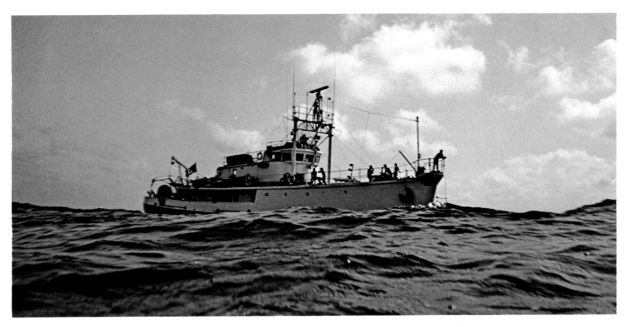

The *Calypso* sailing the Indian Ocean, mounting the swells that forewarn of the coming monsoon.

Captain Bougaran, skipper of the *Calypso* during the greater part of the shark trip.

Albert Falco, one of the older members of the crew. A renowned diver, Falco has been Jacques-Yves Cousteau's companion for many years and his right arm on many projects. He is the pilot of all our deep-sea vehicles, and has brought much valuable knowledge back from his numerous trips underwater.

Jean-Paul Bassaget. He was the first lieutenant on the shark expedition, and is now the skipper of the *Calypso*. He is tough, always ready and willing.

The moments before a dive are always exciting. We never know what we are up against or what we are about to discover. Philippe Cousteau is standing in the center, and Canoë Kientzy is sitting to the right. Bernard Delemotte has his back to the camera. We are aboard one of our launches in very flat, calm water. One of the islands is visible in the far background. Hazy days such as this are unusual.

Bernard Mestre. He is our intellectual sailor. He holds a bachelor's degree in literature, yet he is a simple sailor on board the *Calypso,* having spent most of his life on board ships. He enjoys working on deck, as well as diving, and he usually keeps the ship's logbook.

the aft hold there were two one-man submarines, capable of reaching depths of more than 1500 feet, while just above them, on the rear deck, a hydraulic crane was installed to lift them from the hold and set them in the water, without manual effort and without fear of the swell of the sea. On the main deck, the "diving center," which also served as a working post for the electricians, was filled with entirely new diving equipment. The wardroom, the kitchen, and all the other interiors had been refitted.

On the upper deck, a new stateroom had been added to the captain's bridge, and a television control room had been fitted out next to the radio shack. A new radar, larger windows, and two chest-high map tables had completely altered the aspect of the bridge itself. Everywhere, including the observation chamber set beneath the prow, closed-circuit television cameras kept the bridge abreast of whatever was happening, either on board ship or beneath the surface of the water ahead of the hull. All in all, the ship was a tool perfectly adapted to its mission. Her fast small boats could carry a camera man to the locale of any event at any time. In the hold, there was a hot-air balloon that would make it possible for me to film all the operations from above, or even to discover some things that might escape a lookout on the deck. In addition to the indispensable smaller equipment — lenses and several light cameras — the equipment for filming included two 35-millimeter and two 16-millimeter Arriflex cameras, two 16-millimeter Eclair cameras, and three quartz-synchronized Perfectone sound recorders, which permit the camera and the recorder to be separated.

The undersea equipment included twelve cameras manufactured in our own workshops in Marseilles. Of these, four were for filming in 35-millimeter and the rest for 16-millimeter. For lighting, in both the open air and the water, we used quartz lamps of either 1000, 750, or 250 watts, in autonomous battery-powered units or powered by a 110-volt source on board the *Calypso*.

Our diving gear was now completely streamlined by a plastic shell that

Michel Deloire, a close friend of Philippe Cousteau's for many years. Deloire was a stand-by oceanaut on the Conshelf Three experiment in 1965, to replace Philippe if anything happened to him before down date. He is an extremely skilled and talented cameraman-photographer. Deloire was with us from the beginning of this expedition, and shot some of the most beautiful footage ever taken in the water. Also he is an excellent diver, and most of his work takes place under the sea. We also have topside cameramen, like Jacques Renoir, but Michel is our chief cameraman and often handles the camera topside too.

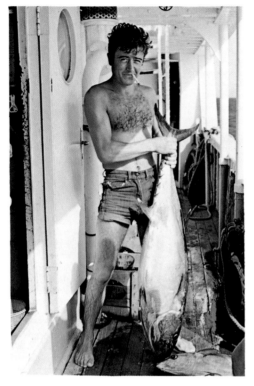

This is Canoë Kientzy. His real name is Raymond Kientzy, but we've always known him as Canoë. He is one of our chief divers on the *Calypso*. He was with us during a good part of the shark trip. His enthusiasm and perfect knowledge of the sea made our expedition easier and more successful.

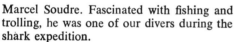

Marcel Soudre. Fascinated with fishing and trolling, he was one of our divers during the shark expedition.

Bernard Delemotte, also an old friend of Philippe Cousteau's, and a diver on the *Calypso* for many years. He is now ranked as chief diver, supervising the diving crew and all the equipment. His insight into the behavior of the animals of the sea is remarkable.

Paul Zuéna. He was first mate on board the *Calypso* during the trip. He knows the business of running a ship and keeping it fit, inside and out. He keeps the equipment in top shape, and seamanship holds no mystery for him. He would be worthy of a much larger ship—something like the four- or five-masted Cape Horn-type clipper of former days.

Serge Foulon is a young diver who was with us for a time but left. Very much at ease in the water, Serge is a witty fellow, always graceful in the water during filming. He also served as our cook during land expeditions.

Bernard Chauvellin. Bernard was second lieutenant on the shark expedition, and is now the first lieutenant on board.

enclosed not only the four bottles of air compressed into tanks of specially welded steel, but also an ultrasonic telephone for communication with the other divers. A radio for use on the surface and the batteries for our lamps were mounted on the helmet. This helmet, which was also made of plastic, contained receivers for the two communications systems and a highly directional quartz tube governed by a switch placed to one side. A single-piece insulating coverall completed the diving suit. Thus equipped, a diver gains almost 30 per cent in freedom of movement and swims more rapidly with less effort. Designed and manufactured by the engineers of the Centre d'Etudes Marines Avancées (CEMA) in Marseilles, this equipment was the realization of my father's old dream of increasing the efficiency of, and adding an overall completeness to, traditional diving gear. And despite the lack of enthusiasm of our "old" divers, too-long accustomed to their traditional equipment, the new autonomous units represented the first notable progress in the matter of self-contained diving equipment since the invention of the Cousteau-Gagnan aqualung.

In October 1966, we were ready to get underway on a voyage to check out both our new matériel and our techniques. For this, we had decided to use a smaller ship, the *Espadon,* a converted trawler equipped with prototypes of all the equipment to be used on the *Calypso.* We also planned to test our 16-millimeter cameras and two completely new types of film, Ektachrome 7241 and 7242, which had just been put on the market by the Eastman Kodak Company. The expedition was to last three months. It was made up of ten men under the command of Albert Falco, and had as its goal a study of the sharks of the Red Sea.

In February 1967, enriched by the experience acquired on the *Espadon* and having modified our equipment to eliminate its defects, we embarked on the *Calypso.* As we left the port of Monaco, crowds on the wharves showered us with flowers and confetti. The Prince of Monaco and Princess Grace had made a point of paying a personal visit to the ship and, as testimony of their good wishes, had left with us a magnificent St. Hubert dog,* whom we christened Zoom.

---

*The St. Hubert race was bred by the monks of St. Hubert in France in the middle ages. Because of their qualities as hunting dogs and of their power as well as their gentleness, the ownership of such dogs soon became the sole privilege of the kings of France and of the monks of St. Hubert. From the St. Hubert dog a more popular breed was created and became more successful, i.e., the bloodhound.

Any departure on a sea voyage is a glorious moment, but that one was the most splendid of all. A kind of miracle had just taken place. In the age of efficiency, of the scientific imperative, and the law of profitable return, we were leaving with no precise goals, no Draconian demands on our time, no accounts to render to anyone, free to journey wherever our fancy led us. Our only task, our profession, was to see. In a time of superspecialization, we became the farseeing eyes of all those who could not or would not journey themselves. We were akin to those knights-errant who traveled across the world and returned to tell the king the news of the Holy Land or of Mauretania. We were different in the sense that we would bring the story of our adventures not to a solitary king, but to millions of people. When one thinks of it, however, the task becomes enormous. We could imagine each of our future viewers, and know he would be hoping that we brought back accounts of things that were beautiful, true, and intellectually rewarding. Each of them was investing some degree of confidence in us, and this implied a heavy responsibility. We could no more deceive this confidence, this patience, this need for information on the marvels of the deep than we could have abandoned a blind man we might have been guiding across a busy street. Although we had no timetable to respect, no itinerary to follow, we nonetheless had a mission, and we were determined to carry out this mission to the fullest extent of our strength and our enthusiasm.

In a very short time we were out of sight of the rock of Monaco and of the Museum of the Sea which crowns it. Everyone on board shared in my joy and excitement. They were all companions of many years' standing — some had been with my father since 1951; all of them knew their work to perfection and the majority were capable of successfully carrying out three or four different functions. The captain of the *Calypso,* Roger Maritano, had occupied this post for several years, as had Captain Bougaran, who succeeded him. Their first and second lieutenants — Jean-Paul Bassaget and Bernard Chauvellin respectively — were young and competent, in addition to being excellent divers. In charge of our engines was the oldest member of the crew, René Robino, who had been with us ever since our first voyage. With implacable energy and precision, Maurice Léandri directed the team that kept the ship seaworthy. Our two chief divers were Raymond Kientzy and Albert Falco, whom we had nicknamed Canoë and Bébert. They had both joined the *Calypso* at the exciting time of our salvage of the wreck of a Greek galley just outside the harbor of Marseilles. I shared the underwater camerawork with my friends

Jean Morgan, the cook. He can make fish taste like rabbit, and he can vary a menu of tuna about twenty-five ways. He is worthy of the best restaurants, and makes life on board a constant state of euphoria with his distinctive cooking. Morgan is a native of Brittany.

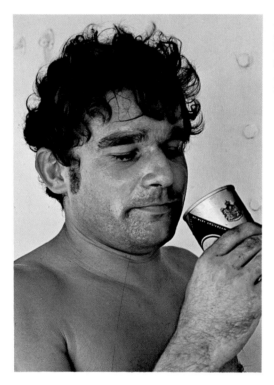

Jean-Marie France, one of our mechanics. A soft-spoken, discreet, gentle person, he has never been heard to say anything that was unnecessary. France can fix anything from an outboard motor to one of the main engines of the *Calypso* in less time than it takes a team of ten other mechanics.

Raymond Amaddio, the *Calypso's* maître d'hôtel. Interested in everything that goes on aboard ship, besides his own work, Raymond directs his efforts toward keeping the spirit of the crew at its highest level. He gives constant attention to the needs and requests of the crew.

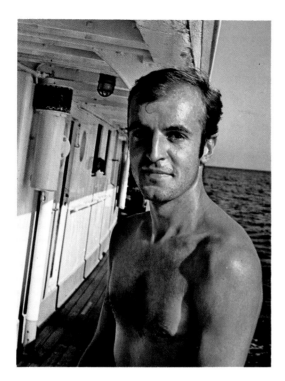

Jacques Renoir, topside cameraman and sometime diver. He is one of the most talented topside photographers to have set foot on board the *Calypso*. His excellent photography made the film very attractive, and recorded all the team's topside actions faithfully.

Philippe Cousteau, September 1967.

Eugène Lagorio. He is the sound engineer for films. Responsible for the synchronized sound sequences of most specials, Eugène also records the sounds of underwater animals. In addition, he is the radio technician on board and handles all electronic-maintenance problems. He is an extremely talented electronician, and his duties also encompass the care of the radar and the operation of all deep-echo-sounding equipment. Eugène is a bright and humorous fellow, a very good companion.

Michel Deloire and Yves Omer, and the on-board tasks with Jacques Renoir. From Eugène Lagorio, our radioman and sound engineer (nicknamed Gégène), to Jean Morgan, our cook, every man on board knew and respected his shipmates. It was a totally solid crew, marked by perfect professional excellence. Frédéric Dumas, who had assisted my father from the very beginning, has become a world authority on undersea archeology, and he is still the counselor whose vast experience of the sea and the creatures that live in it greatly enhanced our chances of success.

In 1951, when I was only ten years old, we had explored the Red Sea with Dumas and Robino. I had dived in the undersea forests of Alboran with Kientzy, and descended into the submerged craters of the Azores with Falco. Fifteen years later, Deloire was my assistant and would be eventually, in case of accident, my replacement in the thirty days of the Precontinent III experiment in survival at three hundred feet beneath the surface. With us also were

René Haon is a sailor aboard the *Calypso,* and was second to Paul Zuéna. He has since been promoted to first mate.

Jean Servelo is our electrician. He is constantly busy with the underwater-lighting equipment and with the ship's own electrical circuits.

Omer and four others, among them André Laban, who directed the work of the little group of oceanauts. We had all, at one time or another, needed or helped the others; we had all confronted the same problems or experienced the same emotions. It was a unified team, formed by my father and molded by his spirit of adventure and his respect for life.

Now, the night of our departure, I joined my father on the captain's bridge and we stood there for a long time, contemplating our world and rediscovering the movement of a ship, which our bodies had forgotten during the months of preparation in Paris and New York. My head was filled with thoughts of that fabulous animal, the redoubtable man-eater, and of the metallic beauty and invincible strength of that incomprehensible monster — the shark.

In six days, we would be at work in the Red Sea, and then the adventure would really have begun.

Roger Chopian is a mechanic, and he can work with machine tools like a musician with his favorite instrument. He can engineer and tool for us the most delicate part of a camera or tape recorder, or the radar, or any engine part that must be replaced. He remains cool under all circumstances.

Joseph François. Doctor François was the medical doctor on the shark trip. His practice has taken him all over the world. He is a fine physician, with an understanding for people and an ability to put them at their ease that makes it pleasanter for his patients to follow his advice or take his medicine. Doctor François was quite successful, during this trip, with all the illnesses that usually plague a ship under tropical conditions. His contribution to the good cheer on board was substantial.

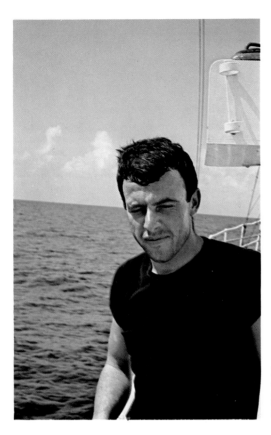

José Ruiz, one of the divers. José made his debut with the *Calypso* team and remained with it. He had his first experience with sharks on this expedition.

Roger Dufrêche, our chief mechanic. Mechanical objects hold no secrets from him, and he can build anything aboard ship that may be requested —from a hot-air-balloon inflater to a new spear for tagging guns.

TWO:
Why Tell of Sharks?
Past experiences.
Encounter in the open sea
with the great *longimanus.*
Threats to modern divers.

Philippe Cousteau's narrative continues

One afternoon in the summer of 1945, on the rocks of a little cove between Sanary and Bandol on the Mediterranean coast of France, my father adjusted two miniature self-contained underwater-breathing units on the shoulders of my brother, Jean-Michel, and myself. Then, holding each of us by the hand, he led us out into a few feet of water at the edge of the rocks. My brother was six and a half years old at the time, and I was four. I remember nothing of this first dive, but I have often been told about it. In our astonishment at the underwater world, we both described aloud everything we saw, with the result that we swallowed quantities of salt water.

Since that day, no creatures of the sea that I have chanced upon have inspired irrational fear in me: none, that is, except the shark. I have, however, been stung or bitten by a certain number of them — moray eels, jellyfish, and even by the lowly sea urchin. I have encountered other species of foreboding aspect, such as sting rays and Manta rays, sea elephants, and both the grampus or killer whale and the sperm whale. But each bite or sting was caused by my own clumsiness in regard to these animals, and not to any malignant aggressiveness on their part. The same thing is true of the shark, which I also do not regard as being a killer without a cause, but I cannot prevent myself from thinking that he is the only animal in the sea who possesses the strength, the tools, and the motivation necessary to inflict on me an irreparable mutilation or even death. He is not, of course, the only animal capable of killing a man; the list of those is a long one. I could cite some few of the most widely known, but such an enumeration would be in no sense exhaustive. Only a biologist could draw up such a list, and a volume titled *Dangerous and Venomous Animals of the Sea* does seem to cover the subject exhaustively, at least as of the present state of our scientific knowledge. In the Persian Gulf and in the waters around Indonesia there exist sea serpents of from one and a half to three feet in length whose venom is fatal, but they avoid man whenever they can. The bite of certain small octopuses of Australia or the burns caused by the tentacles of the Physalia jellyfish can be fatal. A sperm whale or a killer whale can cut a man in two, and the other cetaceans are perfectly capable of breaking the spinal column with a blow of their tail. Even a peaceful dolphin could kill a swimmer, in the same manner in which he disposes of sharks. There also exist sea crocodiles, which haunt the coasts of Indonesia and are greatly feared by the local populations. But none of these animals constitutes a real menace to divers. The majority live either far out at sea or in the greath depths — as, for instance, is the case of the giant squid of the Humboldt Current.

Sharks, however, are everywhere in tropical or temperate waters, and some species, such as the Greenland shark, even live in glacial oceans. They are found at great depths as well as on the surface and even in the estuaries of rivers and in some fresh-water lakes in Latin America. It is, therefore, possible to encounter a shark wherever man ventures on or under the sea, and the encounter can be fatal.

Man has succeeded in eliminating from the surface of the earth the majority of animals and a large number of the insects that could imperil his life. When the race has not been entirely destroyed, what remains of it is generally herded into a reserve, as is the case with the great wild beasts of Africa and India. But in many cases, intensive hunting has so reduced the species as to render any threat from it practically nonexistent.

I do not wish to philosophize on human attitudes, and I can only express my sorrow at the often unjustified destruction of so much richness and beauty. I am ashamed of the out-and-out hypocrisy of some measures, supposedly for the protection of the species, which amount to nothing more than the sale of so many pounds of lion or elephant — at an exorbitant price per pound — to a privileged and wealthy few who would be more at home in a psychiatric clinic than in their "sporting clubs." And I cannot help but express the poignant sense of regret experienced by both my father and myself when we are

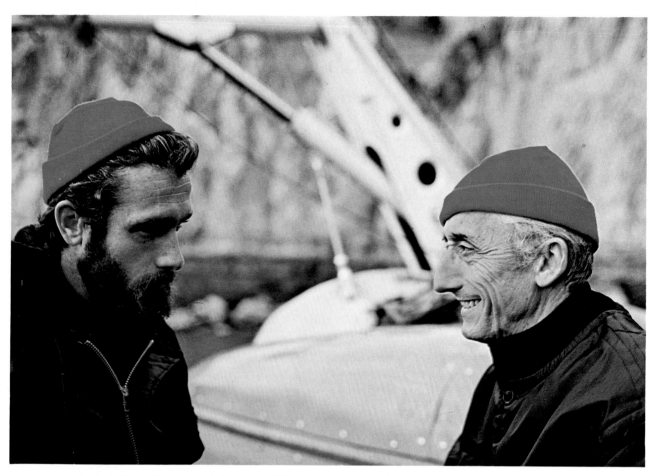

Jacques-Yves Cousteau (right) and Philippe Cousteau on the rear deck of the *Calypso*, discussing the order of the day. The background is supplied by a hydraulic crane and one of our one-man submarines.

forced to stand by helplessly and watch the destruction of cetaceans such as the great blue whale, the largest living creature of all time and one that will soon be no more than a memory.

The shark need have no fear of such a fate. The majority of the races of squali, to which sharks belong, are perfectly adapted to their mode of life and their enormous number makes their extermination extremely difficult, if not impossible. This, in turn, makes the shark one of the last of the animals dangerous to man and still uncontrolled. There are squali practically everywhere; almost all of them can be dangerous or deadly, and there still exists no effective form of protection that is easily transportable by one man. This, added to the fact that civilization is at last turning back toward the sea and thereby considerably augmenting the possibility of encounters between man and shark, has lent urgency to the need for a more complete knowledge of shark habits. Several nations have already established laboratories devoted entirely to this task.

There is a mystery attached to the relations between man and shark, and the stranger attitude is perhaps not that of the animal. For a very long period, man was ignorant of the existence of sharks, and until the middle of the sixteenth century there was not even an English word to designate this species: the Spanish word *tiburon* was currently used. To fill out this linguistic note, it might be remarked that the French word for shark — *requin* — stems from "Requiem," the Mass for the dead; reflecting sailors' fear of the appearance of this beast in the waters around them. Some even feared that sighting a shark presaged the death of a member of the crew. In antiquity, there is mention of sharks only in the writings of Herodotus, Aristotle, and Pliny. Pliny, in particular, went so far as to distinguish among four different species of sharks. Before these Greek writers, no precise mention of sharks is to be found, and yet it may be that the first legend relating to the squalus is in the Bible. Linnaeus, the eminent eighteenth-century Swedish naturalist, was convinced that the monster that swallowed Jonah was a great white shark and not a whale. And ever since the Bible many, many other stories have been told of this fantastic animal — most of them horrible. These stories, true or false, have contributed toward creating a psychosis of the shark in all the sailors of the world and even in men who are simply interested in the sea, without the slightest intention of even going near it.

Second in violence only to the monstrous fury of hungry sharks is the blind hatred of man for this species. I have watched and filmed scenes of carnage of implacable cruelty, in which normally quiet and reasonable men used axes to hack at the bodies of sharks they had caught, and then plunged their hands and arms into the blood streaming from the entrails, to extract their hooks and their bait. Floundering about among the gutted carcasses for hours on end, pushing hook and bait back and up to within inches of the quivering jaws they would normally never have gone near, these men were gratifying some obscure form of vengeance.

This psychological factor, this almost automatic loss of self-control on the part of the most hardened man when he finds himself confronted with a shark, is probably responsible for many cases of fatal attack.

Whether it be through the study of human reactions or through a study of the habits of the squalus, our civilization now must establish an effective method of protection against sharks. Unless we do this, our invasion of the oceans will be delayed or made difficult of accomplishment, because the great mass of nonprofessional divers will be afraid and will hesitate to venture into the sea.

Moreover, the shark presents us, on a scientific level, with a very particular case. It has been estimated from the study of fossils that the first sharks made their appearance in the oceans around the beginning of the Cretaceous period of the Mesozoic epoch — approximately a hundred and forty million

Two divers equipped with their new gear—streamlined backpacks, and helmets with individual lights. They are examining a white Gorgonia. Gorgonias are colonies of very tiny animals eating the plankton of the water, and they look like the white hair of an undersea beast.

years ago. And since their first appearance the squali have undergone only insignificant changes. They have survived changes in temperature, in salinity and in types of nourishment, as well as in the level of the waters. They are a living contradiction in the sense that their cartilaginous skeleton is relatively primitive while their reproductive system is complex and developed beyond that of other fish.

Sharks belong to the elasmobranch, or cartilaginous, class of fish, as opposed to the various classes of bony fish. The elasmobranch, in turn, are divided into two subclasses, the holocephalian and the selachian; and it is to this latter subclass that sharks belong. Other cartilaginous fish belonging to this same classification include the small sharks known as dogfish and various species of rays, including the numbfish and the guitar fish.

Jacques-Yves Cousteau's narrative

The reactions of a man confronted by a shark are of an impassioned nature. They are rooted in legend and influenced by tales deserving no credence whatever. The search for objectivity is a discouraging enterprise. I have met several men who have been bitten by sharks and survived serious wounds; their scars had a sinister appearance, particularly to me, since, as a diver, I inevitably identified myself with the victim. Each time this has happened, dozens of questions have flashed through my mind and I have listened avidly to the answers, as if they would at last reveal the truth to me. But this has never eventuated. The majority of the victims were unable to describe what had actually taken place, and others had more or less consciously elaborated their stories. So today, I am reduced to taking into consideration only my own memories, knowing very well that the same mechanism that caused my own reaction to such stories will undoubtedly provoke skepticism on the part of other divers.

With or without special means of protection, alone or in groups, in warm waters as well as cold, it is now thirty-three years that I have been diving, and often in the company of sharks: all kinds of sharks, sharks of every disposition, sharks reputed to be harmless, and sharks known to be deadly. I and my diving companions fear them, laugh at them, admire them, but are forced to resign ourselves to sharing the waters with them. The latent menace

The incredibly blue color of the blue shark's back explains his name. One can see the elegant silhouette of this animal, with his long pectoral fins and his very thin fins on back and underside. He has a keenly pointed snout. He is one of the fastest sharks in the sea. He has remora suckerfish on the right side of his dorsal fin; on the other side swims a pilot fish close by. The unusual size of his pectoral fins gives him great agility in the water. His gills are flared, for he is moving rapidly at this moment, and the water is rushing through them at high speed.

they embody has always been our diving companion, and they have some-times — rarely — chased us from the sea.

But after an experience of three decades, might it not now be time to sum up, to shift through all these personal memories and allot to emotions and indisputable facts their proper places?

In the Mediterranean, sharks are rare and cause few accidents. But their very rarity confers a peculiar solemnity on each encounter. My "first" sharks, at Djerba, were Mediterranean and impressed me unduly, because I had not expected to see them. On the other hand, in the Red Sea, where it is practically impossible to dive among the reefs of the open sea without being surrounded by sharks, coexistence was inevitable and my companions and I very soon became imprudent, almost unaware of their presence. I even sensed in our team the beginnings of a certain affectation of disdain for these inoffensive prowlers, a tendency to feign ignorance of them, to speak of them only in jest. I argued against this form of snobbishness because it could become dangerous, but I was vulnerable to it myself. It is intoxicating for an awkward and vulnerable creature, such as a diver becomes the instant he drops beneath the surface of the water, to imagine himself stronger than a creature far better armed than he. It was in this climate of excessive vanity and confidence in the early years that I dived myself and allowed others to dive, without protection,

This hammerhead shark is one of the rare forms seen on the Red Sea venture. Although its mouth is relatively small compared to its body size, the shark is considered dangerous. It is an awkward creature, and the sight of it generates fear. The strange shape of the head is one of the mysteries of the shark world. Some scientists suggest that it gives better vision, although that has not been proved with any certainty. Others suggest that because the nostrils are separated and located at each end of the hammer-shaped head, the shark has a better directional sense of smell. Hammerhead sharks often congregate and hunt in packs.

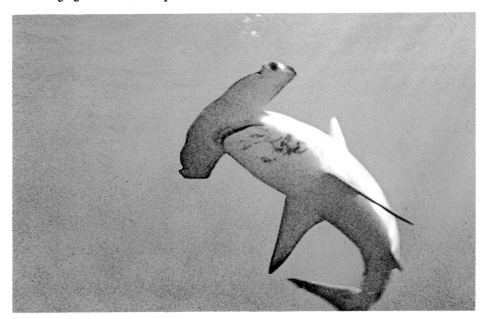

in the most dangerous waters. On the reef of João Valente, in the Cape Verde Islands, we jostled or pulled on the tails of animals over twelve feet in length, incomparably more powerful and competent than we awkward intruders with steel bottles on our backs, our field of vision limited by the masks we wore, and caricatures of fins on our feet. The day at João Valente when Dumas and I glimpsed in the distance the pale silhouette of a great white shark (the species that all specialists qualify as a man-eater), we were frozen with terror and instinctively drew closer together. We had seen him before he saw us. But as soon as he became aware of our presence, it was he who was seized with panic; emptying out his intestines, he disappeared with a single flick of his tail. Later, in the Indian Ocean, the same incident occurred on two separate occasions. And each time, the violent emotion brought on in us by the appearance of the great white shark gave way to an unjustified sensation of triumph when he fled at the mere sight of us. Each of these unusual encounters provoked great excitement among us, and with it an excessive confidence in ourselves and a consequent relaxation of security measures.

Deep-sea diving with self-contained breathing equipment brings with it a kind of narcosis, which we christened "intoxication of the depths": it becomes evident anywhere around a depth of a hundred and thirty feet and becomes annoying and even dangerous at depths below two hundred feet. The "intoxication" manifests itself in a sort of euphoria, then in a quickening of some of the senses — the hearing in particular. The sense of reality is reduced, and consequently the instinct of self-preservation. All these symptoms disappear, as if by magic, during the period of return to the surface. It is therefore logical that the depth to which one dives, since it can bring about such psychic upheavals, can also influence the reactions of a diver confronted with sharks. Once, in mid-Atlantic, on board the *Elie Monnier,* we encountered large schools of dolphins, so we brought the ship to a halt while we dived among them, as far down as a hundred to a hundred and fifty feet. The dolphins disappeared within a matter of minutes, but we could still see schools of yellow-finned tuna and great ocean sharks, a hundred or so feet below us. I can remember now the eerie sensations of these insane dives. At about one hundred and fifty feet the surface had practically disappeared and the area of water surrounding me was strangely somber, a blue that was almost black; the intoxication of the depths was there, flooding my entire being, but it seemed to me to be controllable, like the first puff of opium. Mad with liberty, weightless, and completely removed from the world, listening to the beating of my heart in this pelagic silence, I was ready to commit any kind of imprudence. And today I realize that I committed all of them.

Far from the surface, where the sun perhaps was shining, but still more than two miles from the bottom of the sea, lost in water which was black as ink and yet incredibly transparent, because light passed through it without interference, I lost all notion of horizontal and vertical. I could no longer distinguish between up and down. I had only one reference with which to orient myself: the bubbles of air escaping from the pressure tanks on my back. What I felt in the course of these giddy dives was perhaps stranger, even more disconcerting than the impressions felt by the first "space walkers." The astronauts, leaving their capsule, can clearly see the familiar stars and planets, while I felt myself lost in immensity, with no landmarks to guide me. The only reassuring existence in my realm was a somewhat remote one; the boat which I knew — or thought — to be above me, carefully following the traces left on the surface by my air bubbles. It was in this extraordinary atmosphere that sharks made their most dramatic appearance. I still knew little of these sharks of the high seas and I was fascinated by their majesty. They were generally much larger than those of the reefs. There were species of them, at that time, which I was unable to identify. The majority had sharper noses and more clearly defined silhouettes than, for example, the tiger shark. They seemed to be following the schools of dolphins, but maintaining a certain distance from them. When they appeared out of nowhere they made no effort to approach me, but instead changed their course when they were about fifty feet away, as if to keep me in sight. The first time I found myself in this situation, the sighting of the first shark was a violent emotional shock. Framed in light in the darkness of the water, he stood out clearly, in an unreal, terrifying manner. And, certainly as a result of the intoxication caused by the one-hundred-fifty-foot depth at which I was swimming, the admiration and fear I experienced were abruptly transformed into an unreasoning sense of exultation. I swam straight toward the great shark, armed only with my camera, but he drew away from me, keeping the same distance between us. I went on swimming through the blue-black depths, pursuing a silhouette which finally disappeared, diving far down below me; I was alone now, breathing hard, lost, my temples throbbing, my mind disturbed, realizing confusedly that my conduct had been idiotic, but proud of thinking myself capable of putting such a formidable creature to flight. In an element which was not naturally mine, which put out traps for me at every flick of my rubber fins, I felt the vanity of having conducted myself as a conqueror, a master. I had put — we had put — the great ocean sharks to flight; man was invincible, beneath the water as well as on earth. The legend of man-eating sharks collapsed around me.

Alas, this senseless pride survived in me for only a few weeks. It was dissipated by our first encounter with *Carcharhinus longimanus,* the shark that is the undisputed lord of the tropical oceans. In an earlier book I have recounted in detail the circumstances of this first meeting, which came close to being the last for Frédéric Dumas and myself. On board the *Elie Monnier,* we had harpooned a whale, a *globicephalus,* in the tropical Atlantic, off the coasts of the Cape Verde Islands. Our victim, a toothed cetacean weighing almost a ton, was still struggling at the end of a three-hundred-foot line and the other *globicephali* were swimming around the ship, reluctant to abandon their still-living comrade. And of course, some large sharks began to appear. Our ship was stopped, linked to the whale. Dumas and I went into the water, carrying three-bottle tanks on our backs. I also carried a camera, to film the activity of the whales which still surrounded us. The drama began almost at once.

A scientist has just opened the belly of this mother sand shark, finding it full of almost mature babies. A shark can have twenty or more babies at one time. In spite of their primitive internal organization, sharks have a superior reproduction organism, and it was surprising to learn they also have feelings for their offspring—at least there is built-in protection for the young. The mother shark, after giving birth, will not eat for days in the area where she gave birth, so as not to eat her babies by mistake.

Philippe Cousteau's wife, Jan, pictured here, was an assistant to Doctor Walker when he made this Caesarian operation. She devoted much time to these little babies, and she actually saved them by placing them in a tank where they all survived and were studied for a long time.

On a sandy bottom in the Red Sea, this reef shark with black tips swims in the foreground while Michel Deloire, obviously shooting another shark, holds the camera in the background. The reef shark is a very nervous and excitable type, which we found on several occasions to be quite dangerous.

We had scarcely entered the water and were only fifteen or twenty feet below the surface when we saw Lord Longimanus — or, as we came to call him, the Lord of the Long Arms. He resembled none of the sharks we had met before. His squat, gray-brown silhouette was sharply etched against the clear blue of the water. His head was very round and very large, his pectoral fins enormous and his dorsal fin rounded at its extremities. Both fins and tail were marked at the extremity with a large round white spot. He was preceded by a tiny pilot fish poised just in front of his snout and probably propelled by a pressure wave. Confident — too confident — in ourselves, we dropped the line that still linked us with the ship and swam straight toward him. It was some time — much too long a time — before we realized that the Lord of the Long Arms was drawing us with him into the distance, but was not in the least afraid of our approach. As soon as we realized this, we were seized with an almost paralytic fear and wanted nothing more than to return to our ship. But it was too late. The *Elie Monnier,* still attached to the dying whale, had not been able to follow us and had lost sight of our air bubbles in the general commotion of the sea. She was drifting, far from us. We were out of sight of land and I knew that in this area the sea was almost two miles deep. Two blue sharks, very large but classic in form, came to join our *longimanus* and then the three squali began to dance around us, in a gradually narrowing circle. For twenty seemingly interminable minutes, the three sharks, prudently but resolutely, attempted a bite at us each time we turned our back on them or each time one of us went up to the surface to signal — in vain — to our far-off ship. Miraculously, the gig which the captain of the *Elie Monnier* had put overboard to look for us found us and saved us from imminent death. Shortly before we were hauled from the water I had arrived at the point of smashing my camera against the head of the *longimanus,* in the forlorn hope of warding off his attack and gaining a little time.

This misadventure, which I would judge very severely today, was a result of the excessive confidence in ourselves acquired during the preceding weeks. It was also due to the temperament of the Lord of the Long Arms. Since that time we have encountered hundreds of these roundish sharks with round fins and round spots: they are the only member of their species that is never really afraid of divers.

On several other occasions we have also experienced difficulties with sharks. On the east coast of the volcanic island of Djebel Taïr in the Red Sea, for example, Falco and Dumas were forced to take refuge in a coral grotto to protect themselves from a pack of sharks that seemed to be in the throes of an extraordinary mass frenzy. And in the waters south of this same island of Djebel Taïr, Dumas and I found ourselves in the midst of several dozen small sharks, about three feet in length, who were highly agitated about something and behaved rather like a pack of young wolves. We were forced to leave the water at once. We have discovered, as a matter of fact, that very young sharks are often more disturbing than larger ones. Sometimes they will be seized with a collective panic and flee, but at other times, on the contrary, it is impossible to get rid of them.

In this connection, I remember an incident that took place near the island of Boa Vista in the South Atlantic. We had captured a female tiger shark that was on the point of giving birth. Doctor Longet performed a Caesarean operation on the dying animal and twenty or so perfectly proportioned little tiger sharks were put back in the water. I was in the water at the time myself, carrying a wooden stick I used to scatter the sea urchins from the area where I was working. Without hesitation, one of the newborn sharks seized the stick in its jaws and shook it vigorously, flinging the whole weight of his body into the attack, in perfect imitation of the movement of adults when they are biting off portions of the flesh of wounded dolphins or whales.

It was while thinking of this baby shark biting on a stick and of the camera I had used to ward off the attacks of the *Carcharhinus longimanus* that I decided to provide our divers with what we later termed a "shark billy." This is a simple three-foot shaft of wood, equipped with blunt, non-slip points at one end. Along with the antishark cage, it is still the only protective device of some effectiveness.

Among our collections in the Oceanographic Museum in Monaco, we have some fossilized teeth of a species of shark that has now disappeared — the *Carcharodon megalodon*. These razor-sharp triangular teeth resemble the teeth of the great white "man-eating" shark, the *Carcharodon carcharias,* but they are enormous — ten times larger than those of its contemporary descendant. They suggest a race of super "man-eaters," more than sixty feet in length, which luckily lived in an era long before the appearance of man. Unfortunately, the teeth of this titanic ancestor are all we possess, since the skeletons of sharks, being entirely cartilaginous, leave no trace. It was therefore necessary for our taxidermists to observe the strictest scientific caution in constructing a life-size model of this vanished giant. In his open jaws, he could have swallowed a small truck!

THREE:

The Perfect Killer

**The wounded sperm whale
and the fury of the
open-sea sharks
in the Indian Ocean.
The shark's perception of
pressure waves.
The shark's sense of smell.
Shark and spearfisherman.
The shark's acute sense
of vision.**

Jacques-Yves Cousteau's narrative continues

Putting men in cages to protect them from sharks is what we have been doing for the past twenty years, since we could not carry out such an operation in reverse, which would have been much more logical. These human zoos, cages of steel or aluminum, are hung beneath the *Calypso,* or even beneath one of the smaller boats, to provide our divers with a shelter in case of need. If all goes well, they do not use them. If relations between men and sharks become strained, the divers retreat toward a cage. If the situation becomes untenable, they enter the cage and give the signal to be brought up to the surface. It is because of these cages that we have been able to observe and film sharks during their most savage orgies of feeding.

The "perfect killer" is equipped with an enormous jaw set with incredibly sharp teeth, with a powerful and efficient means of propulsion, and with very sensitive devices of perception. However, this block of muscles is supported only by the relatively weak cartilaginous skeleton, the jaw is withdrawn be-

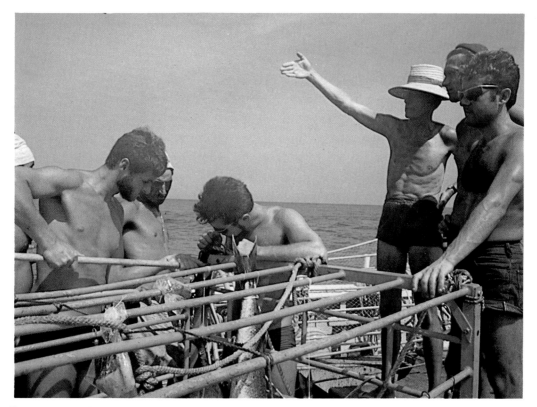

Jacques-Yves Cousteau, wearing a funny hat, is directing the reinforcement of a shark cage. From left to right: Serge Foulon, Paul Zuéna, Claude Templier, Jacques-Yves Cousteau, Philippe Cousteau, and Marcel Soudre. Inside the cage can be seen the fish that will serve as bait.

neath the head, the jawbone is lacking in rigidity, and the teeth do not really form a part of it. Can these contradictory characteristics be compatible?

It was not until fifteen years ago, when the *Calypso* became involved in a drama of the high seas, that I was able to observe closely the actual functioning of the killing machine that is a shark. One hundred miles north of the equator, in the middle of the Indian Ocean, the *Calypso* encountered a large number of sperm whales, dispersed in little groups of from three to seven each and moving quite slowly, probably because of the presence of numerous baby whales. We followed them all morning, sometimes very closely, so closely, in fact, that at a speed of only eight knots, we were unable to avoid a collision between the prow of the ship and a large female, probably weighing about twenty tons. Our precious underwater observation chamber was badly dented by the shock, and Louis Malle, who was in the chamber filming the whales, got a rude jolt. We had just gotten under way again when a very young whale, about twelve feet in length and doubtless no more than a few weeks old, crashed into our port propeller. The sharp blades of the propeller sliced into the body of the unfortunate whale like a machine for slicing ham, and he began to bleed profusely. In spite of his wounds he swam off to rejoin his parents, and for some time the group of adults surrounded the little victim of the accident, trying to help and protect him. Then a very large male, probably the leader of the herd, lifted himself vertically out of the water, supporting himself on the violent lashing of his tail, and for several seconds held more than a third of his body above the level of the waves. In this position, he half-turned toward us and we were sure we could read fury in his glittering little eye. The *Calypso* had seriously wounded two of his charges and he seemed to be studying us carefully, weighing the possibility of revenge. But he apparently decided the danger was too great and plunged back into the ocean. The rest of the herd followed him almost at once, disappearing into the depths, leaving the mortally wounded baby behind. We cut short its suffering with a bullet in its head, and then secured it to the line from the crane on the quarterdeck.

It was not very long before the first shark was sighted, then there were two, ten, twenty. They were all *Carcharhinus longimanus,* the long-finned lords of the deep. They ranged in size from eight to twelve feet. They were joined very shortly by a superb blue shark, about fifteen feet in length, with a long, pointed snout, a slender silhouette, and enormous, expressionless eyes. He was a "blue whaler." Just behind their mouths, almost all the sharks carried a half dozen or so remoras, or sucking fish, oddly resembling decorations on the chest of a general, and they were all escorted by a cloud of pilot fish. While the protective cages and the diving and filming material were being prepared, I observed the behavior of the horde of sharks that now surrounded the bleeding whale. Where had these marauders come from, surging out of the immensity of the sea, a hundred and fifty miles from the nearest island, and with almost three miles of water beneath our keel? They had undoubtedly all been satellites of the school of sperm whales, remaining prudently in their wake, respectful of their power, but ready to take advantage of the slightest weakening, and living on the scraps of their meals.

The attitude of the sharks in their first approach was perfectly clear-cut. Carrying prudence to its extremes, they circled around the still-warm carcass of the baby whale, maintaining a constant, almost lazy, speed. But even so, they seemed very sure of themselves. They quite obviously had no fear of us. If we chased one of them away with boat hooks, he returned a moment later. Time was working for them, and they knew it. The prey could not escape them.

For an entire hour these maneuvers continued, and still not a single shark had ventured too close to the little whale. Then they began to touch him with their snouts, barely grazing him, one by one and hundreds of times, but making no attempt to bite. They behaved the same way with our protective cage.

Suddenly, the blue shark lunged and bit. With a single blow, as if from some giant razor, pounds of skin, of flesh, and of fat were sliced away. It was the signal; the orgy was about to begin.

With no apparent transition, the calm of the preliminary round gave way to the frenzy of sharing in the spoils. Each mouthful snatched by each passing shark dug a hole the size of a bucket in the body of the dead whale. I could not believe my eyes. Instinctively, and horrified, I thought of similar scenes which must have taken place after a shipwreck or the crash of a plane into the sea.

Because of the safety afforded by our cage — although it was constantly bumped and jostled by these ravenous beasts — we were able to film their saturnalia in close-up, at a distance of only a few feet. It was as a result of this experience that I learned the mechanism by which a shark bites into his prey.

The shark's jaw is located far back beneath his long snout, but this does not prevent him from biting directly into the flesh. When he opens the jaw, the lower jawbone is thrust forward while the snout is drawn back and up, until it makes almost a right angle with the axis of his body. At this moment, the mouth is located forward of the head and no longer beneath it. It resembles a large wolftrap, equipped with innumerable sharp and gleaming teeth. The shark plants this mechanism in the body of his victim and uses the weight of his own body in a series of frenzied convulsions, transforming the teeth of the jawbones into saws. The force of this sawing effect is such that it requires no more than an instant for a shark to tear off a splendid morsel of flesh. When the shark swims off, he has left a deep and perfectly outlined hole in the body of his victim. It is terrifying and nauseating to watch.

Philippe Cousteau's narrative

One of the mysteries of nature that most highly stimulate the imagination is that of communications. On the surface of the earth, the presence of a predator in a forest is known immediately to all the forest's inhabitants. Vultures and other carrion-eaters appear in the vicinity before an ill or wounded animal

A great blue shark with two pilot fish and remora under his mouth. The shark swims close to the diving ladder at the rear of the *Calypso*. The photographer was hidden between the rudders of the ship to shoot this picture.

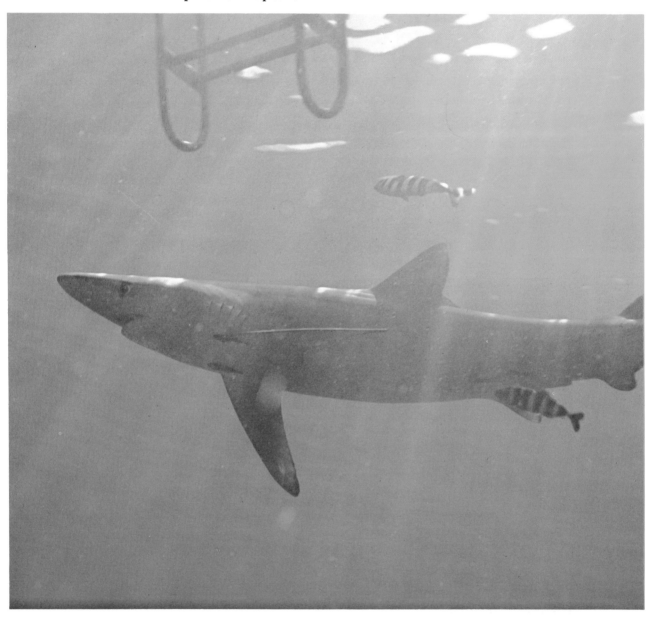

has had time to die. In our world of air and light, warnings are provided by sight, scent, and sound, not only to animals but to ourselves. For underwater animals, sight and the sense of smell play simple roles and function more or less as they do on the surface. The same thing is true of the sense of hearing, but in the aquatic world one factor has changed. I think I may say that all marine animals resemble their cousins on the surface of the earth in that they can emit sounds, but they have the unique capability of moving within their liquid element without producing any audible sound. It is this that creates a "silent world." And yet, marine animals, like land animals, have the faculty of foreseeing the arrival, the passing, the absolutely silent attack of one of their own kind. It is this faculty, which I believe to be common to all fish, that I have termed the "comprehension" or the "sensation" of water. Bodies — either more or less solid — moving through a liquid element create what has come to be known as a pressure wave. A pressure wave is similar to the puff of wind felt by a man standing on the street when an automobile passes at high speed. In liquids of feeble density, these pressure waves or zones do not travel very far, just as the wave of air from the automobile is not felt if the man moves a few steps away from its path. On the other hand, the more dense the element the more easily the waves are spread, the greater the distance they travel, and the greater their speed. In the sea, each moving body is surrounded by its own network of pressure waves which vary in relation to every characteristic of this particular body and its movement — its speed, the nature of its flesh, its size, its form, or whatever might serve to identify it. Obviously, the means of detection and interpretation of pressure waves vary greatly with each species of animal and even a highly developed marine mammal such as the dolphin is incapable of determining the origin and cause of the pressure wave he feels on his sensitive skin. Bony fish, on the other hand, can derive from pressure waves all the information necessary to their survival. Although a different system is at work, the same thing is true of the cartilaginous fishes — among them, the shark.

In the case of squali, it is generally admitted that the sensorial system most specifically adapted to detection and interpretation of pressure waves is concentrated in a narrow band which runs along each side of the animal, from the region surrounding the eye to the slender section at the beginning of the tail. This is the "lateral" system, made up of canals running beneath the skin and linked to the outside by minute tubes opening, through the pores, onto the water itself. These canals are filled with a mucous substance which transmits and perhaps even amplifies vibrations, and they are also strewn with finely lidded nerve cells. The movement of the lids on these cells, relative to their normal position of rest, releases a nervous influx which is instantly communicated to the brain. The information thus gathered is then analyzed and determines the reaction of the shark. I have seen sharks appear from behind a bank of rock or coral, moving swiftly, and obviously attracted by violent clapping of the hands, done in an effort to send out strong pressure waves.

Some biologists think that the shark's perception of vibrations, such as pressure waves, is limited to a maximum distance of one hundred feet from their source. The auditory sense, on the other hand, is thought to be far more highly developed and would permit reception of information coming from a much greater distance. I shall return to this subject in chapter 12.

One of the senses of marine animals that most astonish me is that of smell. I have difficulty imagining that odors can be distinguished in water, which is certainly the most neutral of elements. And yet, sharks are capable of following a scent across miles of ocean and arriving precisely at its source. It was probably this faculty which made it possible for them to locate our poor little whale, since the wounds in his body released vast quantities of blood into the sea.

The shark's nostrils are formed in such a manner that his movement through the water creates a continuous current passing over his sensory cells. The nostrils form a kind of furrow in the head, generally running lengthwise or even diagonally to the body, in order to increase the surface of contact between the mucous membrane and the current of water. In those species of sharks that remain motionless at the bottom for long periods of time, the current created by breathing through the mouth is sufficient to cause a circulation of water in the nostrils. Although it is infinitely more sensitive, the olfactory system of squali is based on the same principles as our own. In air, odors are created by suspended particles which are diluted in solution with the mucous matter that covers the interior surface of the nose. It is this chemical solution that excites the olfactory cells. In the marine world, the water itself forms the base of the solution and transports the chemical agents to the cells of the olfactory organ. The fundamental difference and the remarkable particularity of the shark's olfactory system, as compared with ours, lies in the extreme directivity of his response to odors. In most cases, the nostrils of sharks are set very wide apart and can detect differences in the concentration of an odor, causing the shark to turn in the direction of that nostril which has perceived the strongest scent. Moreover, the natural lateral movement of his head while he is swimming permits the nostrils to explore a fairly considerable arc and thus to indicate more precisely the location of the source of the odor. Obviously, the more widely spaced the nostrils the greater the sense of directivity in the olfactory organ; and this has been advanced as one of the possible causes of the strange evolution of the shape of the head of hammerhead sharks *(Sphyrnidae)*. In this particular species, the nostrils are located at the extremity of the lateral protuberances of the head, which in the case of some adult animals can mean a distance of two feet apart.

On board the *Calypso,* we carried out an experiment to study the shark's faculty of directivity and the extreme sensitivity of the olfactory system of squali. We poured a coloring solution of fluorite green onto the flat sand floor of a sixty-foot-deep reef in the Red Sea and followed its course for about a thousand feet. The course of the liquid did not follow a straight line, because of the little eddies and whirlpools formed by the current as it flowed around the obstacles of coral. We marked it with reference points planted in the sand. Then a plastic bag containing the almost colorless liquid extracted from pressed fish was planted at the exact point at which we had poured in the dye marker.

Our wait was of short duration. Two sharks appeared at almost the same time, separated from each other by only a few feet. They were swimming rapidly, seeming impatient, and moving their heads swiftly from left to right. They were followed almost immediately by four others, none of them very large, averaging about three feet in length. All of them skimmed along close to the bottom of clear sand, whose wavelike conformations caused their shadows to vibrate strangely; all were intent on their own pursuit and totally ignored our presence. In the sea, as everywhere else in the natural world, the business of hunger is second in importance only to that of love. As they passed each limb of coral, they seemed a little disoriented and their excitement increased, probably because of the eddies of water which momentarily obscured their trail. In all, however, their search was completed within a distance of less than ten feet from the marked trail and in a time of not more than eight minutes. Seeing these sharks behaving exactly like the dogs of a hunting pack, I remembered the name the Greeks had given them: hounds of the sea.

We conducted this experiment, under simulated conditions, in order to recreate a natural and extremely dangerous situation. When an undersea hunter has caught a fish with his spear gun, he generally removes it from the

The speed capabilities of the porpoise are amazing. This one is breaking surface at high speed, trying to catch up with our ship. Porpoises are capable of maintaining this speed for long periods of time, while the shark can swim as rapidly but only in short bursts.

spear, attaches it to his belt, and goes on with the hunt. In doing so, he leaves behind him a trail of blood and scent emanating from the wounded or dead fish he is carrying at his waistline. If there are any sharks in the area, they will arrive on the scene almost immediately, attracted primarily by the pressure waves set up by the frantic movement of the dying fish. After this, they will pick up the scent of dead fish and trace it to the foolhardy swimmer, thus bringing about another "shark attack," although I know of no fatalities, so far, among Scuba divers.

When one reads through the reports of attacks on imprudent undersea hunters throughout the world, it becomes apparent that all, or almost all of the wounds inflicted by sharks are at the level of the waist, precisely where any dead fish are attached. What renders matters so inevitable under these circumstances is the fact that while a normal diver remains a problem to the shark and incites him to prudence, because of the shark's lack of positive information, an undersea hunter surrounded by the scent of his catch becomes a natural prey to the unhesitating shark. In full consciousness of the risk they are taking, certain devotees of the aquatic massacre they term sport attach their captives to a length of cord which they then trail at a distance of fifteen to twenty feet behind them. And, as a rule, they survive unhurt from the attacks of sharks.

In his fine book, *Shark Attack,* V. M. Coppleson writes: "Most injuries to skin divers have been caused by sharks robbing them of fish. Spearfishermen holding fish should never be surprised to find they have a shark for a companion." Among our crew, of course, there is no question of such imprudence, and if by chance we have decided to spear a fish for study purposes or to give a change to our menu, the hunter surfaces as soon as the fish is speared, and passes the entire gun to the companion in the small boat which has accompanied him. If he sees any sign of sharks in the area, he leaves the water at once.

One of the most tenacious of the legends circulated with regard to sharks is the one which claims that he has poor eyesight. Like all such information with no basis in truth, this legend is dangerous, since the unwarned diver may allow a shark to approach, in the hope of going unobserved. Our experience on the *Calypso* has been considerably different. One day, for example, when I went into the water on a shallow reef off the coast of Africa, near the Cape Verde Islands, I sighted a shark at a considerable distance from me. I could scarcely make him out, and was only able to do so because his grayish color was silhouetted very clearly against the dazzling whiteness of the sand. At that particular moment, I was floating at a very shallow depth, without making any movement, so that the sound of bubbles from my aqualung would be confused with the light splashing of the water. I turned my eyes away for a few seconds, to study the symmetrical design of a giant ray just beneath me, which had half-covered itself with sand, as rays often do in an effort to make themselves invisible. I am not sure now whether it was simple instinct or a perception of movement, but I turned back abruptly toward the location of the shark. And immediately, every muscle of my body tensed. He was no more than thirty feet away and was launched toward me as hard and swift as a missile. My hands held no protective device and I was alone. The sight of a shark coming at you head-on is very strange, and obviously it is from that angle that he seems most formidable. The eyes are almost invisible, because of their lateral positioning, while the slit in the half-opened mouth, and the three regularly spaced fins give him the appearance of a malignant and terrifying symbol imagined by some Aztec sorcerer. When he had approached to within two feet of the rubber fins I had hurled at him as a futile gesture of protection, the shark turned suddenly and swam back toward the depths.

From a full-face angle, you can see that the shark has lost most of his grace and beauty. He is just a mean-looking, dangerous killer.

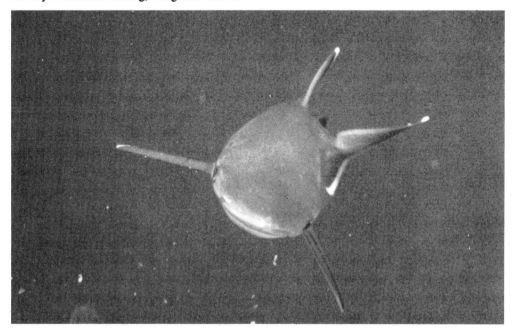

I must admit that I did not think to identify his species, but he must have measured seven to ten feet in length.

There had been no sound, no scent, and it appears certain that sight was the sense responsible for this attack. Professor Perry W. Gilbert, after having studied the visual processes of twenty or so sharks, arrived at the following conclusions: the retina of the shark's eye is extremely rich in rods and relatively poor in cones, which would imply a great sensitivity to light but a relatively small power of resolution and perception of colors. To increase the sensitivity of the system, silvery plates, or tapetum, placed behind the retina, reflect light back through the retina, allowing it to be stimulated twice by the same ray of light. To protect the eye from an extremely bright light, a membraneous surface of pigmented cells can extend to cover the silvery plates and render them inoperative. The pupil is highly mobile and can be closed to an extreme degree, so that it no longer forms anything more than a tiny point or a slit, according to the different species of shark. The crystalline lens, which is almost spherical and cannot change shape, has a high refractive index, and in its rest position, provides a sharp image of objects in the far distance. To focus on nearer objects, the muscles attached to the lens thrust it forward, without altering its shape. The shark is thus perfectly equipped to see at a distance and to distinguish among forms, especially if they produce a contrast in luminous intensity with the light surrounding them. The high degree of sensitivity of the shark's eye also makes it an excellent organ of perception in very feeble light.

In the experience I have mentioned, the shark was beneath me and my body was clearly silhouetted against the harsh light of the surface, so all conditions were favorable to him.

All these attributes, these unique characteristics, and still others, which I will describe in the course of our accounts of later confrontations, make of the shark a terribly efficient predator. In his own kingdom, he seems invincible and, in fact, he very nearly is — or rather, he was, for a period of millions of years, until his universe was invaded by warm-blooded animals, the cetaceans. It was only these superior beings that brought about the defeat of the shark. On the surface of the earth, great reptiles weighing tens of tons were exterminated by relatively tiny mammals. In the marine world, there was no extermination, but simply the appearance of a superior intelligence and a greater power of adaptation. And with this, the shark was despoiled of his invincibility.

FOUR:
Warm Blood and
Cold Blood
**What happened to a wounded
dolphin out in the sea.
The shark follows dolphins
or other herds
of sea mammals.
A shark killed by dolphins
in an aquarium.
How sharks feed on whales.**

Philippe Cousteau's narrative continues

A sunrise, the changing pattern of waves on a beach, a snowfall, a star-studded sky — these are daily spectacles, and yet I never tire of them. For me, dreams emerge as much from contemplation as from the most decisive form of action, and the magnificent disorder of a universe governed by chance and through the medium of ephemeral and changing laws becomes a familiar thing. In the course of these marvelous wanderings of the mind, the vain desire to understand it all vanishes, leaving behind only an instinctive exaltation and joy. And there is no vision which draws me toward these carefree reveries quite so strongly as the sight of a group of dolphins playing in the waters at the prow of a ship.

When the group is numerous, they seem to arrive from every direction at once. Those who come from behind swim with all their strength and speed, following the line of waves tossed up and out by the prow. They spring up almost horizontally from the outermost flank of the wave and plunge back, just beneath the surface, at the precise spot where the displacement of water is most favorable to them. When they arrive forward of the ship their movement is slower and they will circle about in an impeccable pirouette, waiting for the proper moment to place themselves within a few inches of the prow, where the pressure wave created by the ship assures them of a maximum of thrust. Then the game really begins. They swim simply, their sihouettes slightly blurred by the streaming flow of water, skimming its surface in quest of a few rapid breaths of air. Like the best competitive swimmers, they limit their breathing periods as much as possible, exhaling beneath the water and creating a string of silvery bubbles spurting up from time to time from the blowhole in their heads. These underwater exhalations are also signs of excited conversations among the playful dolphins, as the air forced through the more or less tightly closed blowholes produces vibrations that the animal modulates and uses to communicate with the others. The best places for their game, in the hollow of the wave just in front of the prow, are scarce, so each member of the team takes his turn at occupying one of them. From the observation chamber beneath the forward section of the *Calypso's* hull, the spectacle seems unreal. In conjunction with the displacement of water by the ship, they appear almost motionless, propelled by some magical force. All the movements of acrobatics form a part of their repertoire: spins and somersaults, vertical plunges or leaps above the water. Sometimes they allow themselves to be pushed along by the vessel, almost matching their tail to the roundness of the bow; they will remain absolutely motionless, conforming perfectly to the axis of the ship's movement, driven through the water by the thousand horsepower of our diesel engines and expending no effort to propel themselves but only to hold on. The youngest among them are permitted only very brief periods at this game, always accompanied by their mother, swimming close beside them, either from simple caution or because the strength of the children does not allow them the effort of maintaining the precarious and tiring position for any length of time. I have never seen a baby dolphin join the play by himself; it would seem that this is forbidden. All of them watch us closely through the screen of water and glass, and their laughing eyes seem to be waiting for encouragement or applause. It is the warmth and gaiety of their regard that attracts me most. I have seen the ship's doctor perform an "autopsy" on a female found ill and dying off the coast of the island of Stromboli in the Mediterranean. Since he had not succeeded in curing her, he decided to study the body, in an attempt to discover the reasons for her illness — which turned out to be a ruptured intestine. During the whole of the operation he did not speak a word, and his face wore an expression of gravity which revealed his emotions. The anatomy of the dolphin is so close to our own that the analogy was haunting him.

Dolphins are mammals, just as we are, and like us their blood is warm. The size, the weight, and the number of convolutions of their brain are closely related to ours, and the same thing is true of their other organs. Because of their internal system, dolphins are fragile animals, far more so than fish or squali. But their adaptation to the sea has been no less complete or efficient. Like the sharks, they have attained a hydrodynamic state of near-perfection. Both are capable of almost the same speed in short sprints and both are widely represented in all the seas of the globe. Their nourishment is the same, based on fish, but there is one difference: the dolphin does not eat meat, while the shark occasionally does. And this is what has made them enemies. Two rival lords cannot share the same domain, and inevitably one must dominate the other. Here, the fundamental difference lies in the fact that the shark, feeding on meat, represents a natural threat to the dolphin, while the latter represents none to the squalus, whose flesh does not interest him. Once, for the first time, certainly millions of years before man, a hungry shark must have attacked a dolphin. We can imagine that the shark was the victor in this original combat, and as occurred in biblical history, he became the marine incarnation of evil. The analogy with the biblical story of creation ends here, since the shark, although he remains the Cain of the aquatic world in the minds of most men, has not been so fortunate in his feudal realm as the descendants of Abel's brother have been in ours.

Paradoxically, the transformations undergone by the dolphin in successfully adapting himself to marine life have in no way weakened or bothered him. On the contrary, the vertebral column of a land animal has given him a more efficient vertical swimming movement, especially for an animal that breathes on the surface. His smooth skin, distended by fat, facilitates and even controls the flow of water around him (the laminar stream), and reduces resistance to his forward movement to a minimum. And lastly, the fact of being a warm-blooded animal makes possible a far more prolonged muscular effort than that of any fish, including the shark. In mammals, the blood circulates more rapidly and under greater pressure than in cold-blooded fish. Consequently, since the quantity of oxygenated blood which reaches the muscles of warm-blooded animals is greater, so too the effectiveness of the

The porpoise in the foreground is racing with
our launch, the *Zodiac*. The *Zodiac* has a
forty-horsepower engine, and it is here traveling at a speed in excess of twenty knots. The
porpoise, by the mere fact that he is jumping
high out of the water, shows that he is just
playing and not really giving his all.

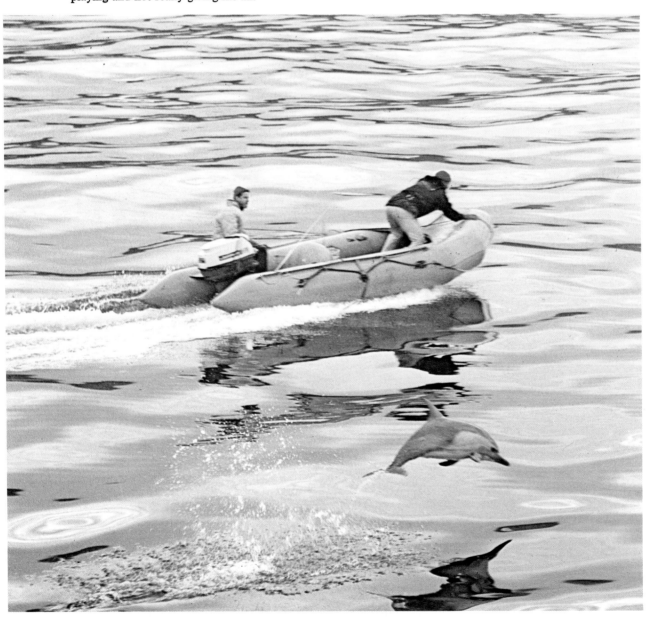

muscular tissues is greater. In sum, although the dolphin and the shark are capable of comparable bursts of speed over a short distance, the dolphin can maintain this speed for a considerably longer period of time. In passing, I might mention that the greatest speed measured for a dolphin is close to thirty knots but this might not be his maximum speed in the event of danger. Moreover, this speed may vary according to species and there are a dozen different species of dolphins.

Another fundamental difference — and this one to the shark's advantage — is the disproportion between their jaws. The jaw of the shark is formidably equipped with teeth which are both sharp and pointed, capable of cutting across the bone as well as into the flesh, and opening into a mouth of impressive size. The dolphin's mouth, on the other hand, carries only small, pointed teeth, inclined to the rear, adapted to catch and hold on to a fish, but not to cut or to tear apart. And yet, it is this jaw of the dolphin which constitutes his principal weapon of both attack and defense against the shark. We shall discuss the mechanics of this on pages 53-56.

Finally, the principal advantage of the dolphin is his superior intelligence and the ability he has developed of communicating with his fellows. The shark is a solitary beast, resembling in this sense some Alaskan wolves. His association with others of his own race is only occasional and never planned. When it does occur, it is primarily at moments of a division of spoils. The dolphin, on the contrary, lives in very highly organized groups, capable of inventing and applying a single strategy for the entire group. I have often noticed, however, that the groups of dolphins cruising the high seas are always followed, a few hours later, by several large sharks. We must, therefore, imagine that the squali find what they are looking for; but how? I doubt that anyone really knows, but perhaps things happen thus:

Twilight on the ocean is always a mystical ballet, grave and true as no other spectacle can be. It is a changing of values so profound, so complete that everyone, man or beast, experiences it in the very depths of his being. In the vast liquid space, threaded with changing vibrations, the troop of dolphins slows down and gathers more closely together, as does every band of nomads when night approaches. On the long flat swell, the crests of waves take on a roseate color, a bloody presage for the troop, since the night often assumes the countenance of death. Little cries and warnings are called back and forth in the sharp rhythm of trills and chatterings proper to their language. The ranks close up, and the young take their place near the dorsal fin of their mother. A trifle farther out, the males form the protective circle. And a mile away, the sharks also change formation. Forewarned by the waning of the light and by their obscure millenary instinct, they too move more closely together. The purplish rippling of the last rays of sun mingles with the thin, steely furrows plowed by the tail and the triangular fins. Night is now complete, and the dolphins are sleeping. A few inches beneath the surface, they return to it every half minute, still sleeping, to breathe its cold and humid air. The young regulate their breathing on that of their mother, jealously guarding the favored position just to the rear of the dorsal fin. All of the troop frequently opens its eyes to the silver-studded velvet of night at sea.

At night, because of the evaporation caused by the rays of the sun during the day, the air on the surface of the sea seems colder while the water, in contrast, seems tepid and restful. A solitary dolphin has allowed himself to drift from the immediate proximity of the group. His sleep, which is generally interrupted every few minutes, is deeper than normal. And yet, those moments of wakefulness required to resume his place in the formation are often vital. Is he an old soldier more fatigued by the long day's journey than he has ever been before? Or a carefree youth lingering for a last frolic among the slopes of the evening swell? Or perhaps just a sick dolphin, whose sleep is already eternal?

The silvery eye of a great blue shark picks out the still, black form, and when it is a matter of the pursuit of a solitary prey there is no hesitancy in his reaction; he attacks.

From the shattered chest of the dolphin, a great black bubble of air carries away his own life and, with it, the last warning he will ever convey to his fellows. The rest of the troop, instantly alert but blinded by the night, can only listen to the sounds of the pack of sharks which now accompanies the dead dolphin as he sinks toward the abyss in an apotheosis of pale phosphorescence. The sea resounds with sharp, short cries. These are the signals sent out by the other dolphins, and in listening for their echo they learn the location of the enemy, the prey, or the friend. Thanks to this echo-sounding apparatus, which pierces the darkness around them, they now know that the danger is past, the pack is far beneath them and probably satiated. The night again is calm, disturbed only by the frenetic ballet of the luminous micro-organisms constantly tracing out their web of ephemeral light.

I do not think that every night brings such tragic consequences for the dolphins. In fact, sharks follow the troop primarily to secure food from the bodies of ill or wounded animals left behind, from babies born dead, and even from morsels of the umbilical cord or the matrix rejected after a birth. Accidents such as those I have described above must be rare, and I have myself seen sharks flee from dolphins.

It was in the Red Sea, along a coral barrier on the western edge of the Farasan Islands off lower Saudi Arabia. In the crystal-clear water, dotted with busy fish, my attention was suddenly drawn to an abrupt and unexpected movement. A shark of respectable size shot by me like an arrow, clearly in bewildered flight and closely followed by two dolphins. Just as they were about to disappear in the distance, I could distinguish two other forms arriving from the opposite direction and forcing the shark to turn ninety degrees to his left. He vanished in the direction of the open sea, still followed by the now-united group of four dolphins. I had the impression of witnessing one of the cruel games of the sea, and this time it was the shark who was its scapegoat. I do not know how this particular hunting party ended, but if I am to go by the studies made at Marineland of the Pacific, the big California aquarium, I can only conclude that it was not in a victory for the shark.

The events I am about to relate took place in several aquariums in the United States, and form the basis of my contention that the shark, although he represents a constant threat to the dolphin, can nonetheless be defeated and held at bay. In one large tank containing several female and some male dolphins, a shark had been living for weeks in seemingly peaceful co-existence. The shark spent all his time swimming along the bottom and eating regularly the food given to him by the aquarium personnel. The dolphins played among themselves and occupied the entire space of the tank, paying no attention to the shark. Then, when one of the female dolphins arrived at the end of her time of pregnancy and was about to give birth, this well-established routine changed abruptly. Either the dolphins had suddenly had enough of the presence of a stranger in their midst or — and this is more likely — they were aware of the danger of giving birth to an infant while this ancestral enemy, so highly sensitive to the smell of blood, was still about. In any event, they decided to rid themselves of him.

Taking their point of departure at the far end of the tank and moving with all the speed of which they were capable, the dolphins took turns at smashing the point of their muzzle against the abdominal cavity of the panicky shark.

This porpoise is breaking the water so rapidly that even with our camera's very high shutter speed he is slightly blurred. He is gaining on the ship, with his back way out of the water, showing here, too, that he is not really giving all he can. It is partly because of their speed that porpoises can do away with sharks with relative ease.

After a few minutes of this performance, the shark was dead. His body bore no visible wounds, but his entrails had been ruptured as thoroughly as if he had been struck with a battering ram.

On another occasion, dolphins rid themselves of a shark, which had been placed in their tank, with such violence that his body was found the next morning at a distance of almost thirty feet from the pool. He had been "thrown overboard," so to speak, and no one could tell whether he was already dead at the time or had died later of asphyxiation.

Making use of their echo-sounding apparatus, their speed, their pointed "beak," and especially of their intelligence, dolphins can hold sharks at bay most of the time, but this is not the case with all cetaceans. Whalers returning from their hunting trips have often brought back horrible tales of enormous packs of sharks attacking whales and tearing them to pieces. These must, however, be relatively rare cases, since the strength of the larger cetaceans is sufficient to crush any form of squali. They may perhaps have been instances of ill or weakened solitary whales, or even of animals mortally wounded by the whalers themselves, or by their natural enemy, the killer whale.

There is no real evidence of any such concerted action on the part of sharks, and it is only the smell of food, blood, or debris which can unleash a massive attack. Obviously, if such an attack does occur, there are very few things capable of resisting it. But, generally, everything takes place as if nature, frightened by the weapons she has herself furnished to sharks, attempts to counterbalance them through a deficient sense of aggression and the absence of a collective intelligence.

Every year, however, sharks mass in large numbers at the entrance to the lagoons of Lower California, to await the migration of the gray whales. In December, regularly, the gray whales migrate from the Arctic to the coasts of Mexico. There, the mothers give birth and raise their young, until the month of March, when they return to the Arctic Ocean. As is true of all wild species, there is a mortality rate of approximately 30 per cent, either at birth or in the weeks that follow. The gray whale, a small species of baleen whale, reaches a size of sixty to sixty-five feet at a maximum. The females give birth, in remote branches of the lagoons, to a single infant (or, rarely, two), weighing about a ton. They then nurse the baby for three to four months.

During one expedition in this area, our research team was guided by Professor Theodore Walker of the Scripps Institute in San Diego. The preceding year he had seen many sharks, one of which had been identified as a white shark (*Carcharodon carcharias*) from a photograph the professor had taken. From our own observations, we had believed that sharks do not penetrate very far into the disturbed and relatively shallow waters of lagoons, and in all my dives in this area I never saw one. One day, however, as Michel Deloire, Professor Walker, and I were exploring one of the interior creeks of Scammon's Lagoon, we found evidence of their presence. A young, dead whale had been left stranded on a beach by the receding tide. I was overcome by a feeling of sadness and melancholy at the sight of this animal who had died without ever having lived, lying there now, an easy prey to the sea birds, in the midst of this landscape of dunes stretching off as far as the eye could see, engulfed in silence, a powerful marine creature destined to be nothing more than carrion. He had probably died of some illness, but on his flanks he bore the sharp, oval marks of the jaws of sharks.

What is astonishing in the case of the gray whales is the fact that the sharks know at what time of year they migrate, and consequently gather together to await them. I do not believe, however, that whale flesh, any more than that of dolphins, forms a regular part of the shark's food. It seems to me more likely that it is simply the expectation of some debris, the remains of a birth, perhaps, borne out by the tide, which causes them to linger around the passages leading into the lagoons. In a sense, it is something like a famished dog waiting for the moment when the cook will bring the garbage through the door of the kitchen.

One species of cetacean combines all the advantages of the dolphin and is also armed with a jaw even more formidable than that of the shark. This is the killer whale, whose power and ability to combine his actions with those of other members of his race are so great that he can defeat even the largest whales of other species — although the adult killer whale measures only between fifteen and twenty-five feet in length. This superiority is amply demonstrated in an account of a spectacle witnessed by Professor Walker. As he was surveying the migration of gray whales from a Coast Guard helicopter, he saw a group of killer whales, along the coast of Lower California, apparently just playing on the surface of the water. A half mile away, a nine- or ten-foot shark was also swimming lazily on the surface. Suddenly, Professor Walker saw one of the whales plunge vertically into the sea and disappear. About three minutes later, the whale shot up just beneath the shark and leaped clear of the water, holding the shark crosswise in his mouth. The two forms seemed suspended in air for a fraction of a second, and then dis-

The *Calypso* at night, sailing the very calm Red Sea.

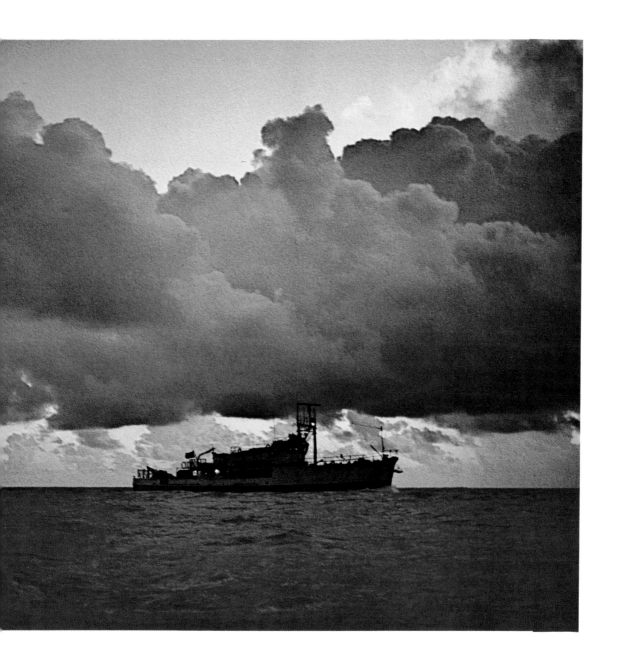

appeared in a shower of spray. The explanation Professor Walker gives to this extraordinary sequence of events is that the killer whale (*Orcinus orca*) had detected the presence of the shark through its echo-sounding apparatus, despite the distance that separated them. Plunging vertically, he had made his approach at a great depth and then raced to the surface, again vertically, thus taking his prey completely by surprise. A vertical attack from the depths is the last thing a shark might expect.

Thus, the shark is not infallible and in the marine world, as in our own, intelligence and subtlety can win over brute force — if not always, at least quite often. And in the battle between warm blood and cold, it is the mammal that triumphs over the fish. The shark is not the uncontested lord of the deep, but he is certainly the most widely prevalent and most dangerous creature of the sea to another race of warm-blooded mammals: man.

FIVE:

The Squaloscope

Abu Marina.

Operation "la Balue."

The capture and study
of sharks.

Study of anesthetics: cognac,
MS-222.

The respiratory system.

Philippe Cousteau's narrative continues

Canoë (Raymond Kientzy, one of our two chief divers) woke me very early this morning. We were in the Red Sea, in sight of the reefs of Abu Marina.* Together we climbed to the very top of the mast on the upper deck to select the best possible anchorage for the *Calypso*. The spectacle of the vast labyrinth of reefs (most of them barely at the level of the water), of deep channels, and little islands of white sand, made us oddly quiet and thoughtful. It resembled a giant artist's palette, covered with every variation of blues and greens. In these waters we were about to carry out all kinds of experiments and observations on sharks in captivity.

The succession of coral peaks and deep-water inlets extends over an area of several square miles. The average depth of the water within this area is about 200 feet. Our past experiences had shown us that it is often on the exterior borders of these reefs that one finds the most life. Over where the last reef plunged vertically to a depth of 2500 feet, the wild animals of the open sea came in to swell the life surrounding the reef itself. The hunting is better there; it is the privileged domain of the great predators. Sharks cruise

*In the Suakin group, off the coast of Sudan.

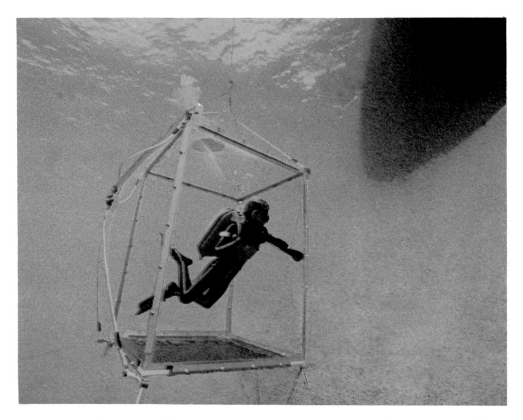

Inside the plastic cage called la Balue, Marcel Soudre is floating as if in a bubble. Of course, because of their transparency, the plastic domes that protrude at every side except the bottom of this cage are barely visible, but they are extremely resistant.

here constantly, accompanied by barracuda, great tunas, and schools of silvery fish of the caranx species. It is along this ledge between the open sea and the small, highly colored world of the reef that life becomes more active, and also more violent.

We decided to anchor the *Calypso* very close to the reef, on the eastern side of its outer border, toward the sea. The sonar showed us a bank of sand about sixty-five feet wide and slanting down in a gentle slope. Its depth was about forty-five feet at its highest point against the coral wall, and reached eighty-five feet at the edge of the deep-water area.

As soon as the motors were stopped, a diving team — Canoë and Serge Foulon — went into the water to explore the reef and find the most favorable spot for our installations. A few minutes later they returned and directed us toward a kind of passageway between two coral peaks. On either side, magnificent clumps of multi-colored coral rose to the surface, surrounded by clouds of gleaming, busy little fish. And on every side, the slope inclined gently toward the blue depths. Large species of caranx and schools of surgeonfish seemed to flow in an uninterrupted stream through this miniature Gibraltar.

Is was a perfect spot and our first mate, Paul Zuéna, brought the *Calypso* broadside to the axis of the passage at a distance of about sixty feet from the reefs. The device we planned to use here was a cage six and a half feet tall and four feet wide, with sides formed of domes of transparent plexiglass, highly resistant to shocks. The entire cage was pierced with small openings, designed to allow water to flow into the interior, where the diver was situated. The occupant of this strange apparatus — in this first experiment, it was Marcel Soudre — could either film what was happening outside through the

The structure seen in the background is called a squaloscope—a cage used to house sharks. It was designed by Philippe Cousteau's brother, Jean-Michel, as a means of trapping sharks in order to study their behavior in a confined environment. The roof of the cage is made out of the same kind of domes used in la Balue. In the foreground swims a black-tip reef shark. You can see about five sharks in the picture, but fifty more are swimming around.

transparent walls, move outside himself through a trap door cut into the flooring, or simply observe the behavior of the sharks from a place of complete security. Moreover, this cage, which was designed by my brother, Jean-Michel, and named by him "la Balue" in honor of the unfortunate Cardinal la Balue who was rumored to have been imprisoned in an oversized bird cage by Louis XI, also allowed us to determine whether a diver might be subject to direct attack by sharks. Lastly, when it was turned on its side and the door left open, it made an excellent trap for the capture and study of medium-sized sharks.

With my camera focused toward the surface, I filmed la Balue as it was lowered into the water, which was so clear that I could easily make out the 130-foot length of the *Calypso's* hull. No sooner was la Balue completely submerged than Marcel swam down and into it and released the cable linking it to the ship. It floated gently down, like some majestic soap bubble, visible primarily because of its aluminum uprights and frame. The current was running in toward the passage and lifted the cage slowly toward the summit of the slope. A few small sharks with black-tipped fins had already left the vicinity of the bottom and were mounting toward the cage. They were no more than three feet long and seemed extremely prudent. They circled once or twice around la Balue and then went back down to their lazy evolutions close to the sandbank. It is a rare thing to see these sharks leave the immediate proximity of the bottom or that of a bank of coral, but they can also become dangerous because they are often less cautious than other species and more easily excited. They are the only sharks I have ever seen bite at a prey on first passing it. Marcel, in his plexiglass bubble, was also well aware of this, so he had stopped watching me and was now attentively surveying the sharks.

At last, la Balue touched bottom and I began the descent toward her, filming a long traveling shot. I had emptied my lungs, and I sank down in a completely motionless state, headfirst, and with the camera forming a prolongation of my body. Sucking in air in little mouthfuls, I was experiencing once again the pure joy of movement in three dimensions. When I arrived at the level of the cage, Marcel had already turned it over, so that it was resting horizontally on one of its convex sides. The trap door was open and Marcel had opened a sack containing pieces of fresh fish. I propped myself against a bank of coral and watched, preparing to film. Almost immediately, one of the little sharks snatched the head of a caranx and fled. He was followed instantly by two others and there was a short struggle for possession of the bit of fish. The matter was settled abruptly when the first shark took it on himself to swallow the entire piece at one gulp. The others turned away and the first swam off into the distance, his mouth still open and his head jerking back and forth in a series of brutal convulsions. Then began the race to divide up whatever other spoils there might be. The first incident had brought an additional fifteen or more sharks to the scene, all of the same species and none much longer than about four feet. I pulled back a trifle farther into my coral hiding place and Marcel was forced to close the trap door more and more often, as the sharks' circling became more frequent and more rapid. I noticed that if a shark snatched up a tender bit of the fish flesh and bit into it, there was no consequent frenzy of jealousy and pursuit; but if, on the other hand, it was a bony fragment or a head, the tumult began at once. The sound of teeth grating against bone or even the crunching sound when a shark bites into and crushes a fish head probably constitutes a clear call to any other sharks in the area. Now, the action surrounding the cage had become violent and disordered. Several times I saw a shark crash into the transparent plexiglass and turn away in bewilderment. I do not think they were attempting to get at the diver inside, but only to reach the sack of fish. Every time this happened, I saw Marcel automatically react defensively, holding out his hands and moving toward the back of the cage. It was comical, but perfectly natural. If the shark could not see the obstacle between him and his prey, so too the diver had to become accustomed to not seeing the plastic that protected him.

These mad onslaughts of hordes of sharks toward the precise point where one of their own kind has devoured a bit of fish are terrifying things to watch. They give the impression of being completely unstoppable and fatal. Once, when I was diving with Canoë on the sunny slope of a little reef in the Red Sea, we came very close to becoming victims of this same phenomenon. We had speared a caranx, but since the wound was not mortal, he was struggling fiercely at the end of the line. A long shark with white fins appeared almost at once and began cruising around just outside the little fault in the rock in which we were partially sheltered. It became a matter of urgency to finish off our fish before his movement attracted the shark too close. Canoë therefore pulled out his diver's knife and plunged it into the caranx's head, piercing the bone and destroying the nerve centers. I saw the big shark turn, so quickly that his movement was no more than a blur. He covered the few feet separating him from us at fantastic speed and hurled himself violently against the air tanks on my partner's back. Then, apparently stunned a little, he turned again and swam away as fast as he had arrived. Neither Canoë nor I had had time to make a move, but fortunately my friend, protected by his aqualung, was uninjured. I think that what brought on this lightning attack was a combination of the sound of the knife piercing bone and a last jerking movement of our poor victim. There can be no doubt that sharks hear perfectly, and experience has shown that they react to the sound of blows under water, to the sound of a bell, or to the noises made by a diver at work. In general, their reaction is one of intense interest, and bits of advice in the manner of: "If you see a shark approaching, beat the water with your hands," or the famous warning given to beginning divers, "If you want to drive a shark away, cry out in the water," are little short of criminal. I have often tried the two methods I have just mentioned and at best they have shown no results other than giving me a severe case of laryngitis or sorely bruised hands. In the majority of cases, the immediate consequence of a blow of the palm against the water or a shout was an immediate attack. Often, during dives made for the purpose of studying or filming sharks, we have used the method of calling out beneath the water, not to drive them away, but precisely to attract them into the range of the camera.

Another of our instruments is the "squaloscope," conceived and designed by my brother, Jean-Michel, to serve as an enclosure for the observation and study of sharks in a confined area. It is a rectangular box, twelve feet by nine, and three feet high, with sides formed of vertical bars placed about six inches apart. The roof is composed of four transparent plastic domes, making it possible to observe the sharks that are inside the squaloscope. There is no bottom to it, and one of the sides is divided into two sections and provided with a plastic slab which moves in slots to form the door.

We had put it in place that same morning, and a large distribution of fish from the ship contributed to attracting sharks to the area where we were working. Paul Zuéna, our first mate, had dropped the squaloscope to the level of the water, alongside the hull. Since the air imprisoned in the plastic domes sufficed to keep the whole thing afloat, it was a very simple matter to tow it into position directly above any site we had chosen to work in. When we "uncorked" the aperture in the peak of each dome, the air escaped, water flowed in, and the squaloscope fell as gracefully as an autumn leaf, to come to rest on the sandbank sixty feet below.

We had adopted the technique of "bodyguards," which meant that we dived in teams of two men each, and one of these was responsible only for protecting the back of the other. The first group was made up of Canoë and José Ruiz. I was in charge of the camera, with Serge Foulon as my bodyguard. At the very first glance, I could make out a good twenty or more sharks. Many of them were reef sharks, with black fins and measuring about four feet at most, but among them were several larger sharks with fins bordered in white. These were *Albimarginatus,* definitely more disquieting than the others. They made me think of tigers in the midst of a brood of domestic cats.

They had already begun their lazy circling, studying the squaloscope with their expressionless eyes. Some of them swam up, as if to meet us, but

A shark is following a sliver of fish that is being pulled into the squaloscope. The diver in the background will immediately close the door, rendering the shark captive. Amazingly enough, when the shark entered the cage, although he was about to get the prey he instantaneously forgot his goal and busied himself only with a means of getting out. He started circling excitedly. The other sharks around show the first signs of frenzy, which can become dangerous, especially with the one at the left coming straight at the camera.

This is back-to-back protection, employed when there are several sharks in open water. This white-tip reef shark is kept away by the diver facing us, with the help of the short stick in his right hand pointing at the shark. The back-to-back position is applied when there is no reef nearby or vertical cliffs, or anything, to protect the 180 degrees your sight cannot cover; the back is, of course, almost as vulnerable as the front. By this means, the divers can protect each other very efficiently.

when they had come only halfway they turned abruptly and went back down toward the bottom. Sometimes this procedure can become dangerous to divers. It seems that if one shark is swimming a trifle fast, the others sense his haste and rush to move ahead of him. Although it never occurs with the larger sharks, one often sees four or five small ones approaching at fantastic speed, ready to bite without hesitation.

Canoë set to work putting in place the apparatus we had devised for capturing the sharks. Through the bars of the side of the squaloscope opposite the door, he passed a hemp rope bearing at one end an unbarbed fishhook planted in a morsel of fresh fish. This rope extended across the cage and through the door, with the bait left just outside. When a shark found the piece of fish and lunged for it, Canoë would quickly withdraw the rope, and if the shark followed the bait inside the squaloscope, the door would close behind him. It is an extremely simple process when applied to rabbits or mice, but when it is carried out by four divers sixty feet beneath the surface on a reef in the Red Sea and surrounded by a pack of more than twenty-five sharks, it is quite a different matter.

Things became confused very quickly, and the rhythm of events accelerated. Canoë and José succeeded in getting two sharks into the squaloscope at once, but by this time the scent of fresh fish was acting on all the others like smoke on a beehive. While José was putting the bait back in place, I saw two fairly small sharks crash against the framework of the cage and rebound like ricocheting bullets. The water around us was streaked with gray silhouettes flashing by in every direction. It became difficult to see everything that was happening. A six-foot shark bit into the bait and so fiercely battled Canoë's attempts to pull him into the squaloscope that the whole cage trembled. The man on one end of the rope and the shark at the other pulled with all their strength, until the shark succeeded in wedging himself against a corner of the squaloscope and broke the rope. Out of the corner of my eye I saw José ridding himself of the sack of fish he was carrying in his hands; a small shark opened an enormous mouth and swallowed the whole thing, sack and all. Canoë beat off one of the big *Albimarginatus* with blows of his fists and started toward the surface. At this moment I felt a shock against my left leg and saw a four-foot shark sweep by. He had brushed me with his snout, but fortunately he had not taken a bite. Gathering together in a tight little group, each of us surveying one sector of the area around us and lashing out with shark billies and cameras, we swam back up to the boat, still surrounded by a carrousel of gray arrows, enormously powerful but completely unorganized.

I think it is the irrationality in this frenzy of sharks that strikes me most. It gives me a feeling of complete impotence, such as I never experience in any other circumstances. The shark is the most mechanical animal I know, and his attacks are totally senseless. Sometimes he will flee from a naked and unarmed diver, and at other times he will hurl himself against a steel cage and bite furiously at the bars.

With any other animal, I know that my actions or reactions have a direct influence on its behavior. A crow will fly away if I walk through the fields carrying a stick, since he knows that it might be a rifle. A dog reacts if he senses that someone is afraid of him, and even the fish along the coasts of France are more tame when a diver is not carrying a spear gun. The shark moves through my universe like a marionette whose strings are controlled by someone other than the power manipulating mine; he seems to come from another planet, and in fact he does come from another time. He has not evolved since his beginning, more than a hundred million years ago; he is still in his original state of disorganization. His actions have no logic and are not even natural, and yet he is perfectly adapted to his life. Or perhaps the reverse is true and his order, his logic, are simply not the same as mine. There do, after all, exist intelligences just as different from ours quite near to us — those of insects, for example.

We climbed back on board the *Calypso* still dazed, silent, imbued with an emotion that was neither fear nor apprehension for the future. We felt no sense of relief at having — all of us — escaped from imminent peril, and yet we were exhausted, vaguely conscious of having passed through an exceptional experience. I remembered the shock I had felt against my left knee and could not help but wonder by what chance I had not been bitten.

This habit sharks have of bumping against strange objects floating on the waters has been the subject of intensive study. Professor Budker, in particular, has concluded that squali can taste objects through the use of "sensorial crypts" dissimulated beneath the peculiar scales of the shark's skin. These sensorial crypts are constituted in a manner similar to that of the gustatory papillae, and although they do not react to the same chemical substances, they are linked by their nerve fibers to the same nerve as that which controls the papillae of the mouth and the pharynx. Thus, sharks can obtain information on the taste of a potential prey by rubbing their skin against it. Either because the water in the immediate vicinity of the prey is charged with revealing chemical substances, or because the abrasive skin of the shark detaches a sufficient number of particles of matter to cause a reaction in the nerve terminals of the crypts, the hunter is immediately informed as to the nature of the object he has rubbed against. It was probably the disagreeable flavor of my neoprene-rubber diving suit to which I owe the fact that I still have two legs.

That afternoon we went down again, but this time the big steel cage went with us. Now, in case of necessity, we would not have to fear the dangerous moments of a slow climb to the surface, when we would be deprived of the protection offered by the floor of the sea and an attack could come from

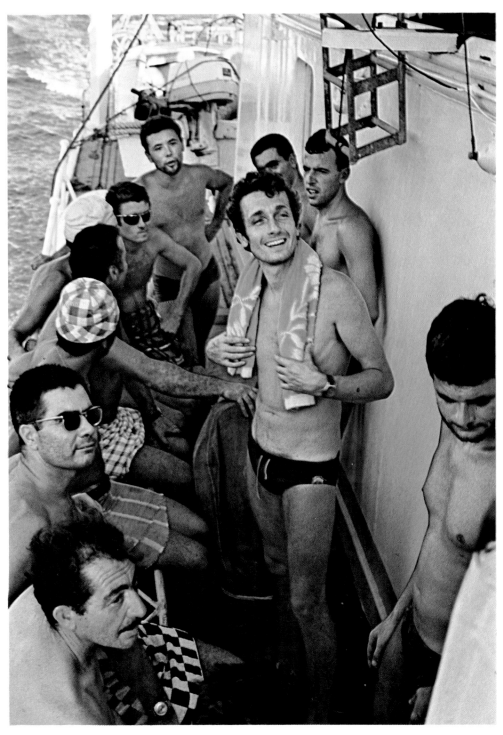

Back on board is usually a very happy time. The first order is the customary informal conference, each one relating his adventures. Here we are seeking some shade from the heat of the sun and perhaps a little cooling breeze.

any direction. In addition to this, proximity to the surface seems to excite sharks and makes the actual moment of leaving the water dangerous.

The squaloscope was empty. The two captured sharks had twisted the light aluminum bars out of shape at their centers and succeeded in escaping. Even twisted in this fashion, the spacing between the bars was inconsiderable and it must have been necessary for the sharks to pass through them on their sides; I marveled at the strength that made this possible. Bernard Mestre, who was accompanying Canoë, made a ligature joining together all the bars at their center and thus reinforcing the squaloscope. This time we did not use any hook; the morsels of fish were simply tied to the rope held by Canoë. In this way, we hoped to prevent any captured sharks from demolishing the squaloscope, as the one he had hooked that morning had almost done. Bernard Chauvellin, who was my bodyguard, stayed close behind me, ready to protect me from the rear and to assist either of the two others.

There were more sharks than there had been in the morning, but the *ambiance* was even more mistrustful. I speak of ambiance because, to an experienced diver, there is a different ambiance connected with every dive. And with sharks, ambiance is of fundamental importance. Sometimes we sense that we can caress them or ignore them, and at other times we are immediately conscious of danger. I have known dives in which, although the sharks showed no change of attitude and continued circling at the same speed, we all felt and shared a spontaneous nervousness. At such times we become wary, ready for action. The warning is never ignored, even though it may be vague and inexplicable. And at other times, although nothing may have changed in appearance, we sense that we are secure and know instinctively that we can approach the animals with impunity.

Thirty or so of the "black fins" — the reef sharks — and ten to fifteen of the *Albimarginatus* with the white-bordered fins were circling slowly around the squaloscope. A small grouper had now made it his residence and remained undisturbed as we went about our work on the sand floor surrounding his improvised shelter. This time, our operations had been meticulously programed in advance and we were able to carry them out more efficiently. In a short space of time, four of the black-finned sharks were captured and we began our experiments. We planned to try out several different anesthetics, with the object of tranquillizing the sharks and thereby permitting us to carry out further research. Among other things, we hoped to be able to cover their eyes, both to test their sense of smell and to facilitate the placement of electrodes for an encephalogram.

To begin with, we tried out a whitish liquid known as product MS-222, which is well known to biologists, who use it in the capture of live specimens of fish. We administered it to the sharks through a giant syringe whose piston or plunger is operated by a compressed-air cyclinder. Since the pressure of air contained in the cylinder is greater than that of the surrounding pressure, the product is expelled in a great cloud of white liquid when a valve is opened.

Bernard Mestre caught hold of a pectoral fin on one of our captive sharks and pulled the animal up against the bars of the squaloscope. Despite his frenzied struggling, Canoë plunged the tube of the syringe into the shark's mouth and released the valve. The syringe emptied itself and the water grew cloudy everywhere around the shark's head, in front of his mouth as well as behind his gills. When the syringe was entirely empty, Bernard released him, and the animal immediately resumed his circling within the squaloscope, ramming his snout against its sides, just as he had been doing before. We waited in vain for some sign of weakening, but he seemed absolutely impervious to the product and went on swimming, with no sign of tiring.

We have tried all kinds of products and methods, with varying but seldom satisfactory results. As a last resort, we considered a highly French technique: the injection of cognac. Doctor Eugenie Clark had advised us to try hypodermic shots of alcohol, but since we had no alcohol on board and the concentration of it in cognac was sufficient, we decided to use it as a substitute. I remember Doctor François standing on the afterdeck, with his graduated receptacles and his big veterinary's syringe, waiting for my father, who came on deck carrying an unopened bottle of three-star cognac. Obviously, before the syringe could be filled, the cognac had to be tested and that could not be done without obtaining the opinion of all the divers. At last, however, the syringe was full and we went down the diving ladder. It was a joyful experiment, and everyone seemed hopeful that it would succeed. The level of cognac remaining in the bottle bore witness to the numerous trial runs we had thought necessary before applying the theories of scientific authority. This time, the ambiance of the dive was one of pronounced optimism. Unfortunately, when we reached the bottom, we found only dead sharks in the squaloscope. Our subconscious awareness of a serious situation returned at once. The waters around us were deserted, and of all the sharks

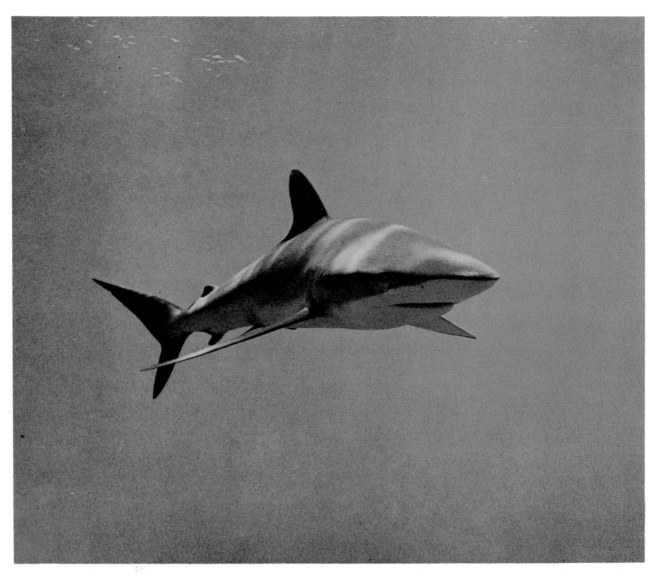

A typical aspect of the shark in open sea with the sun playing through the surface on his back.

that had been here earlier, only the four motionless forms in the squaloscope remained.

Canoë set down the now-useless syringe and reached through the bars of the cage to catch hold of the tail of one of the sharks. He was indeed dead, and so were all three of the others. Far off, at the very limit of our vision, I could make out several slowly circling forms. They were sharks, but they had suddenly become cautious and remained at a considerable distance from us. The cognac was forgotten as we tried in vain to coax these vague and faraway silhouettes to return. Our pieces of fresh fish attracted only the little grouper, and it was not until after we had removed the dead sharks that we were able to continue with our experiments. What could it have been that caused this signal of mistrust to carry across the water?

Other experiments, carried out in Florida and in the Pacific, have shown that the odor of dead sharks effectively repels other squali. One of my father's close friends, Conrad Limbaugh (who has since been the victim of a diving accident while visiting an undersea cavern), has described one of these experiments. While he was with a group of ichthyologists studying the shark populations surrounding Clipperton Island in the Pacific, several dead sharks were left on the beach one day. Two days later, their carcasses, which had been cut open for dissection, began to rot and the liquids produced by decomposition ran down the sloping sands in long rust-colored rivulets. Shortly thereafter, the sharks, which had been extremely abundant in these waters, abandoned the area completely.

Intrigued by this fact, our friend then carried out systematic experiments with meat in varying stages of decomposition, using it as bait on his lines. Sharks did not even approach it. These interesting results did not, however, lead to more extensive experimentation, for a very simple reason. The system, however effective it might have been, had disastrous effects on the experimenters, since the smell of the putrid meat caused violent attacks of seasickness.

Among the professional shark fishermen of South Africa or Florida, it is a well-known fact that it is useless to leave a sharkline in the water for more than a few days. These men use as many as two hundred hooks to a line, and they know that sharks caught on the first day will die within a few hours. After the third day, no living shark will approach the bait.

On board the *Calypso,* we verified this fact many times: if a dead shark was left on the bottom, the others disappeared within a matters of hours.

It is possible that a more detailed study of these facts would lead to the discovery of an effective product for repelling sharks and protecting swimmers. Since Mr. Limbaugh utilized not only shark meat but also the meat of other fish, the widespread belief that squali eat only spoiled flesh was proven false. In cases of extreme famine, some sharks may accept a bait of putrid meat, but such cases are rare.

Our sharks in the squaloscope were dead simply because it was too small. They had died of asphyxiation. The majority of sharks, such as the great white shark *(Carcharodon carcharias),* the blue shark *(Isurus glaucus),* the black-finned reef shark *(Carcharhinus maculipinnis),* and the hammerhead *(Sphyrna lewini),* among many other species, swim unceasingly, day and night. There are two reasons for this, one being that sharks do not possess a "swimming bladder" — that organ which can be inflated at will and permits fish to stabilize themselves at different depths; if sharks stop swimming they will sink. The other reason for this continuous movement is the fact that sharks, with the exception of some species, have no mechanism for pumping water so that it will pass over their gills and the oxygen will be transferred to the blood stream. In other species of fish, the mouth is constantly in action, to create a continuous current of water over the gills, even in the absence of any actual movement on the part of the fish. The common goldfish, for example, can remain perfectly still in his glass tank and breathe easily. The majority of sharks, however, depend for their respiration on their movement through the water. Our squaloscope was too confined in its dimensions and condemned the sharks it contained to asphyxiation, because it prevented them from swimming continuously and fast enough.

Since our own experience with the death of the sharks, Doctor Clark has given us several other examples of the same problem. Sharks on which experiments have been carried out can be revived by forcing them to swim in their tanks; divers push or pull them through the water until they have regained consciousness. And in a reverse example of the same situation, sharks employed for the filming of such adventure spectacles as *Thunderball* were tranquillized by being towed backward or simply immobilized for a certain period of time.

We have adopted other, more effective methods of capture, but I shall always remember that big metal-and-plastic structure resting on the sands of Abu Marina. The reef sharks that surrounded it taught us a valuable lesson. At a time when we were becoming too sure of ourselves and relaxing our security provisions, they showed us to what extent nature and the sea are perverse and changeable. That precarious return to the surface was a warning that went home to each of us and reinforced the security precautions of the whole team.

The sum total of these experiments was, however, far from being negative. In addition to valuable information on the behavior of sharks, we had arrived at a more complete understanding of the techniques to be used in the study of sharks in captivity. But such a study, in an enclosed area, presented logistical problems of transportation and preparation. Therefore, it seemed clear that the next phase of our operations should be directed toward the study of sharks at liberty.

SIX:

Bullfight in the Deep
We tag sharks with darts.
The nine-foot *longimanus.*
Territorial claims of sharks.

Philippe Cousteau's narrative continues

My camera is pointed toward Raymond Coll, who has just left the big steel cage and is swimming slowly, holding his spear ready for use. From the corner of my eye I can see a blue shark more than nine feet long, moving on a course that will converge with Raymond's. The shark seems indifferent to the diver, who is now describing a gentle curve that brings him closer to the animal with every movement of his arms or his rubber fins. As he approaches the point of contact, Raymond accelerates slightly, stepping up the rhythm of his swimming just a trifle. The shark's round eye does not leave him for a second. They are now less than six feet apart, and still approaching each other. I release the shutter of the camera, and its clicking sound seems to act as a signal. Raymond's arm reaches out and the tip of the spear penetrates the flesh at the base of the dorsal fin. With a single flick of his enormous tail, the blue shark streaks off to a distance of about sixty feet and then resumes his lazy course. The turbulence he has caused in the water has almost upended the diver, who is now prudently retreating to the cage, followed by two gray sharks with white fins. Raymond glances at me and lifts a thumb in triumph. His normally impassive eyes are glittering behind his mask; he has succeeded.

I turn back toward the shark and can see that, although still some distance away, he is coming back toward us, but slowly and apparently indifferent to us. When he passes in front of me, I can make out the swirling movement of the little yellow plaque attached to the short banderilla Raymond has just planted beside his dorsal fin. This is the fourteenth animal we have

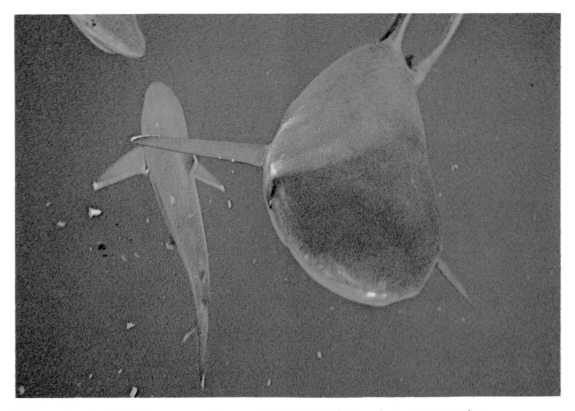

He is coming straight at the camera. Those small white dots that can be seen are crumbs of fish, which are not enough of a mouthful for the shark. They are not even bite-size, but the smell they generate in the water excites the sharks immensely. These sharks are called *Albimarginatus,* the white-tip reef sharks found in the Red Sea.

marked today, and he will also be the last. I give the signal for return to the surface and the ship.

This is a much less simple sport than it might appear to be. Not all sharks are as good subjects as the big *Galeocerdo cuvieri;* most of them react more rapidly and their reactions are dangerous. To "mark" an animal, Raymond must approach to within less than four feet of him, then plant the point of the spear as close as possible to the dorsal fin and quickly withdraw the shaft. This leaves a banderilla of treated stainless steel planted in a region in which the shark's flesh is most firm and where it will in no way irritate him. Attached to the banderilla by a thread of plaited nylon is a plaquette of orange plastic, bearing a number and the address of the Oceanographic Museum of Monaco.

On two separate occasions today, a shark has turned back on our im-

The shark cage in action. Two movie lights are attached to the upper side of the cage, while one diver is pointing to a shark, ready to set out to tag him. In his left hand he is holding a spear, which will serve as a tagging device.

BULLFIGHT IN THE DEEP 81

promptu matador, jaws wickedly open, and Raymond has had to beat a quick retreat to the cage. Fortunately, the animals had not pressed their attack, and after a time they had gone away. I have been watching this undersea *corrida* with a feeling of unreality bordering on the miraculous. Even the bright colors are there, the yellow-gold, the red, and the royal blue, while the trumpet and trombone sounds from our regulators and our air bubbles provide music for the *fiesta brava*. All the divers wanted to try their hands at this new sport, but it is unquestionably Raymond Coll who has had the greatest success at it — perhaps because of his Spanish ancestry. Nonetheless, I am still a trifle uneasy about it. This is not a single bull that he must face, but an entire herd, with a whole realm of space in which to retreat and attack again. It is a three-dimensional *corrida* which has been taking place before my eyes.

We began this experiment with the goal of studying the mode of life of the Red Sea sharks. My father had noticed that, quite often, one reef might have a considerable population of sharks while the adjoining reef, just a few miles away, had none. Moreover, because it was often possible to recognize sharks by their distinctive scars (almost all of them bore scars), it seemed that the same population of sharks always frequented the same corner of the sea Very little is known about the migrations of sharks; at the very most we do know that, at certain times of the year, large gatherings of some species have been seen in areas of shallow water or in the estuaries of large rivers. Numerous research centers throughout the world, notably in South Africa and Australia, are devoting themselves to the study of the possibility of large-scale shark migrations. To this day, however, no real light has been shed on the subject; we do not even know if sharks do, in fact, migrate from one region to another. The problem of a suitable material for marking the animals is certainly one of the most important restraining factors in such a study. The majority of marking devices are rejected in a relatively short period by the shark's organic system. This was the case with ours; but they may also be bitten or torn off by another animal or scraped off by contact with rocks or sunken wrecks.

Our program was less ambitious than any such detailed study. We wanted simply to learn whether the shark known as a "reef shark" was a sedentary animal or moved from one reef to another in search of food. And we knew that the plaquettes we used for marking would probably remain in place no more than a few months. Another of our goals was to establish whether, in the event that the sharks are sedentary, they maintain a territory exclusive

The diver is going out now. Having shifted his spear to the right hand, he is diving straight toward the shark.

Now he is letting the shark go by and will swim as quickly as possible to place himself along the shark's side.

With cameraman Michel Deloire in the right-hand corner, the diver, Raymond Coll, is swimming straight for the shark. Not unlike a bullfighter handling his *banderillas,* the diver must anticipate all movements of the shark and react accordingly.

to themselves, as do a great many reef- or shore-living species. Obviously, if the sharks turned out to be sedentary, any further experiments we might attempt would be facilitated, since they would learn to accept our presence among them.

In the course of a week we marked more than one hundred and ten sharks in the vicinity of eight reefs or islets of the Suakin group, in the Red Sea. Aside from the great blue shark of that first day, we had encountered only some *Albimarginatus* and a few of the *Carcharhinus obscurus* which inhabit these coral reefs. Then we left the region for three weeks, to carry out some other work in the south and outside of Djibouti.

On Friday the twenty-ninth of September, the day after our return, Paul Zuéna tossed into the water a two-pound bait of meat, along with the large hook on which it hung. I was in the water, and Paul's movements, deformed by the refracted light from the surface just above me, seemed somehow monstrous. As he manipulated his line, his silhouette danced against a background of blue sky, resembling a pygmy with gigantic arms sowing seed across the waters. The shark climbed straight from the depths, emerging from the shadows on an absolutely vertical course toward the bait, which now floated at the center of a circle of concentric ripplings. He resembled nothing so much as a projectile perfectly adjusted on its target. Again, it was a large *Albimarginatus,* about seven or eight feet long, but his rounded belly bore witness to recent feeding and, in fact, he hesitated for a long time before biting. After he had circled for a quarter of an hour, some other sharks entered into the circle and showed signs of attacking the bait. This was all that was needed. One last time, the big shark turned in front of my cage, clearly displaying the yellow plaque at the base of his dorsal fin, and then swallowed the hook.

A shark's manner of eating is extraordinarily supple. He neither speeds toward the prey nor does he slow down; he seems simply to breathe in the portion he has chosen, which disappears into his still-opened mouth as he passes on. But should that portion contain a hook, the mouth and the entire body is seized with a violent convulsion as it penetrates the flesh, and he hurls himself forward with all his strength, thus pushing the hook further into his flesh.

I could guess that Paul would be watching his line as it streaked out, accompanied by the shrill whistling of his carefully soaped reel. Encountering no resistance, the shark slowed down and Paul took the line in hand, beginning to draw it in, slowly, gently, but ceaselessly. Now the shark began to fight back furiously, beating against the surface of the water with his tail, or plunging desperately toward the bottom. The others, watching him, had drawn back a little but were still not far away. One of them, in fact, had swallowed the portion of meat our captive had coughed up in his efforts to regurgitate the hook. Now, they were circling like vultures, ready to profit from anything that might develop. The captive shark lost strength very quickly and his defensive actions became weaker — this brute of an animal was a fragile prey. For one thing, the line on which he was hooked immobilized him, hindering the continuous flow of water through his gills, and thus asphyxiating him; and for another, his internal constitution also contributed to this weakness. There is no sustaining ligament, no muscle to hold a shark's intestines in place; the natural intestinal support is the water outside the fine abdominal wall. As soon as a shark is taken from the water and no longer has this support beneath his abdomen, his thin skin distends and his internal organs are torn apart by the effect of weight. Once removed from the water, even if he is immediately returned to it and swims off quite normally, a shark is almost certainly condemned to death, since the chaos created in his intestines will no longer permit them to function normally. But even if his struggle for life is short — and this is not true of all species — the shark does not die easily.

When I returned to the deck of the *Calypso,* I watched, with no joy in my heart, as our old enemy died. All his beauty had vanished; he lay there, limp, dirty, pathetic, his scarred and tortured tail beating the rhythm of a final swim. This sort of thing may go on for an hour or more with a dying shark, and many men have suffered a nasty wound because they imprudently ventured too close to the animal. The great mouth of our shark still snapped at the void and his soiled body quivered and trembled for a long time. Canoë removed the marking plaque and went off with it to my father's cabin. After a final glance at the expiring shark, I followed him. When we consulted our marking records — the books which told us where and on what date each shark had been marked — we found that this particular animal had been marked in exactly this same place a month before.

Of some sixty-five recovered plaques, the same result occurred in fifty-seven cases. The species of shark we had marked was obviously sedentary, at least during a part of the year. This observation, however, was extremely inconclusive, since there was nothing to inform us of the habits of these same sharks at other times of the year. The laboratories or scientific institutions

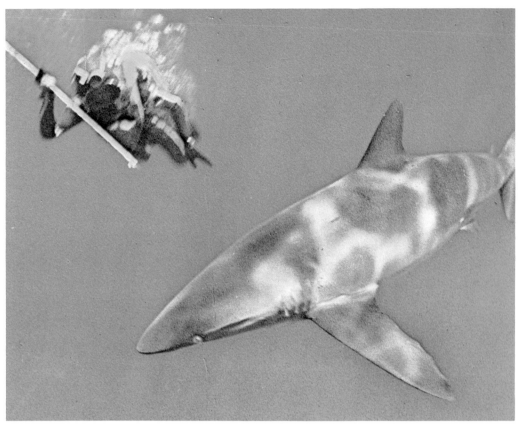

The diver is now in position and has raised his arm, to plant the small tag in the shark's skin.

There you see the spear being withdrawn, in the upper left-hand corner, and leaving the little tag on the shark's back on the right of the dorsal fin.

There it is. The shark is marked, and the diver accompanies him for a few seconds.
(Note: Vertical lines are scratches in the original motion picture negative.)

that concentrate on this matter have set up systematic specifications for marking. But the difficulties in such a process are enormous and we had neither the time nor the means to overcome them.

Shortly after we had established the first principle of the sedentary character of these sharks, we recognized a second — territoriality. When it is said that a shark possesses a territory, it would seem to indicate that a portion of the reef is reserved to him. Every day, when we dived in the same spot, we saw the same sharks, recognizing them most often by their scars. This is not, however, an absolute rule, since the same shark may be seen elsewhere on the reef, while other sharks are patrolling his territory. They are tolerated there; the possession of a territory does not mean that the shark expels all others from it. He contents himself with the knowledge that he is master of it. We have verified this same principle with many other species of fish — groupers, trigger fish, some varieties of lion fish, moray eels. A large shark will admit other sharks to his territory, on condition that they do not pose a problem of direct competition. They are reduced to seeking their food on a catch-as-catch-can basis, far from the eyes of the master, and they eat in his presence only when he leaves them the remains or when his prey is so large that he is occupied with eating on one side and cannot immediately attend to them. If these rules are not respected, there is instant warfare, testified to by the scars left on one shark's skin by the bite of another. But even these rules, which may be set for one corner of a reef, are often upset by the appearance of a foreign and stronger animal. Like a duke descending on some petty baron, the great ocean shark occasionally descends on his less hardy or more fearful vassals.

Shortly after our second stay on the Suakin reefs, we returned to the reef surrounding Dahl Ghab Island (near the western edge of the Red Sea, off Sudan), to continue with our marking program. At the same time, we inaugurated a communications system which permitted me to speak directly by telephone to my father or to anyone else on the bridge of the *Calypso*.

In the larger cage, Marcel Soudre was in charge of the long marking spear and drew sharks toward him by throwing out a morsel of fish from time to time. I was in a smaller, individual cage, facing Marcel's, with my camera ready to film. Fifteen or so sharks of two separate species were circling around us. There were several large *Albimarginatus,* and the others were very supple gray sharks. I recognized the lord of the manor immediately; he was an old *Albimarginatus* whose mouth had been torn apart at one side, leaving a scarred and gaping hole when it healed. He was swimming peacefully, and it was perfectly clear that the others were avoiding him. He was a frequent visitor in these parts, almost an old friend. He had come to watch us in every one of our dives in this spot. We had marked him several days before, and he had turned on us, seeking to bite. He gave us the impression of a tough old warrior, wary and precise. Whenever another shark sped toward a piece of our fish, he struck at him as hard and swift as a missile, and the other abandoned his prey. It sometimes happened, however, that the smaller shark was able to eat and get away before he was caught, and in this case the big *Albimarginatus* ceased his pursuit and resumed his circling, wasting no time on useless anger.

It was in this atmosphere of well-established order that we set out to mark the last sharks of the group. I had exhausted the magazine of one camera, so I telephoned to the surface and asked that another be sent down. When it arrived, loaded with four hundred feet of new film, I was preparing to adjust the F-stop and focus when I glimpsed a dark mass just at the limits of my vision — about a hundred and fifty feet away. Then I began to notice that the sharks, which had been coming up to us more and more readily for the past half hour, were now nervous and wary. At first, I did not understand what had happened, since I did not associate the vague form I had seen with this new attitude of the sharks surrounding me. This situation went on for several minutes, and then, at last, I understood everything. The cause of the sudden agitation was approaching.

I recognized it as one of the most formidable of the deep-sea sharks, a great *longimanus,* well known to my father and all of us, more than nine feet in length and accompanied by at least eighteen pilot fish, each of them a good-sized animal. It was because of this moving cloud that I had not at first recognized the shark in the somewhat cloudy water.

While the brute strength of other sharks is tempered by their beauty and the elegance of their form and movement, this species is absolutely hideous. His yellow-brown color is not uniform, but streaked with irregular markings resembling a bad job of military camouflage. His body is rounder than that of other sharks and the extremities of his enormous pectoral fins and his rounded dorsal fin look as if they had been dyed a dirty gray. He swims in a jerky, irregular manner, swinging his shortened, broad snout from side to side. His tiny eyes are hard and cruel-looking. The cloud of pilot fish changes shape, sometimes scattering and then drawing closer together in an uncertain, nervous rhythm. From time to time, one fish will detach itself from the group and go off to inspect an object of some kind, then hastily return and take up its former place. Two large remoras and one smaller one form dark spots on the shark's belly.

I had a vague consciousness of sudden silence, and when I became more fully aware of it I realized that I myself had been breathing more slowly, almost as though I was attempting to hide. A few feet in front of me, Marcel too had forgotten his work and was watching the intruder. The big white-finned shark had disappeared, and the others were swimming rapidly, furtively, keeping well away from the newcomer. Sharks accompanied by pilot fish have already been compared with great Flying Fortresses surrounded by a squadron of fighter planes, and it is an image which gives a clear impression of the destructive force embodied in this vision.

This particular shark was swimming in lazy circles, about fifty feet from

The shark is gulping the lure, a piece of fish meat which we put on the hook of Paul's line. After a period of time, we fished the sharks to withdraw the tags, in order to learn of their migrating habits. This one is a white-tip shark about eight feet long.

The shark has swallowed the whole lure and is about to be hooked.

He is now pulling at the line. We can barely discern the red tag he is wearing just behind the dorsal fin. He is a good catch.

The shark is pulled out and the tag will be removed, to be logged in the book for subsequent study.

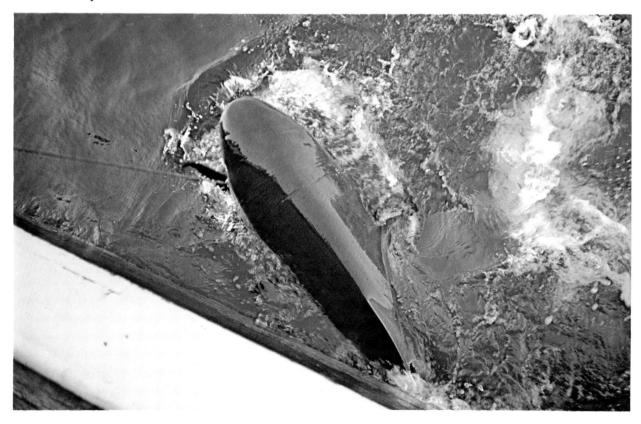

our cages, but his mere presence had brought the scent of fear to this little corner of the ocean. A few more minutes passed, and then I reacted at last. I was not going to permit this animal to ruin our dive, so I signaled to Marcel to go on with his work. A morsel of fish was waved about outside the cage, and when a small shark darted forward to seize it, Marcel managed to mark him perfectly. While I was checking my camera to see how much film remained, I saw the *longimanus* again. He seemed to be paying no attention to us and had even moved a trifle farther away. Marcel had no more fish with which to attract the other sharks within range of his spear, so I used up the rest of my film on random shots of the sharks remaining in the area. I was on the point of signaling for us to be brought to the surface when I was suddenly surrounded by a rustling flight of black-and-white pilot fish. They had left the shark, as if at some mysterious signal, and were circling about me like a swarm of moths around a flame. About fifty feet from my cage, the great ocean shark turned suddenly and hurled himself forward at incredible speed. In a fraction of a second he was beneath the stern of the *Calypso* and had snatched at the gleaming casing of the transmitter-receiver of the undersea telephone, which was hanging just below the surface. The cable was sliced in two as cleanly as if by a giant pair of scissors. The shark turned violently back on himself and furiously coughed up the metal box, which promptly sank to the bottom. Without a moment's pause, the shark arrowed his huge body toward Marcel, who had just time enough to close the door of his cage. The shark ricocheted away like a bullet, and turned straight toward me, seizing the bars of the cage in his jaw — a scant six inches from my face — and shaking it like a madman. I had a vision of the rope to the surface being cut and the cage drifting down, leaving me no alternative but to try and get back to the ship on my own, exposing myself to this frenzied attack. And then, abandoning the twisted bars of the cage, he turned again and disappeared as swiftly as he had attacked, followed by his straining escort of pilot fish.

It seemed to me that I remained there for an eternity, motionless, almost without breathing. I had not had time to be afraid before. Marcel was watching me, and I was dimly aware of a great plume of air bubbles around his head. At last, I could feel the cage going up, and I emerged in the blinding sunlight. I climbed out of the cage, feeling curiously calm and preoccupied with insignificant things like the seam of my diving suit or the position of a length of rope. My father's appearance brought me back to reality. He had

This is the great *longimanus* during daytime. He is accompanied by one pilot fish, in the foreground, and several more above him, swimming just below the surface. His gray-brown markings are quite irregular, and he has more of a dirty appearance than the painted look of other sharks. His extremely wide fins provide him with good control over his movements in water. Pilot fish do not steer the shark. They merely accompany him for the leftovers from his meals.

Emerging from a long dive is a good moment, as the sun hits your face and warms your skin; and you know you have some good material inside the camera.

seen everything on the undersea television screen which watches all our operations, and his laughter was a little more hearty than usual. . . .

Later that day I made another dive under the same working conditions. The great ocean shark did not show himself this time, and I thought of him with a kind of secret jealousy. This solitary hunter — a minuscule but formidable figure in the immensity of the sea — had returned to his own domain. The other sharks seemed smaller to me now, reduced to their own petty quarrels, to their own little hierarchy. The old *Albimarginatus* had reappeared, but far from being the lord of the manor, he now seemed nothing more than a country squire, marked with our plaque as dutifully as a domestic animal wearing a license.

In the course of all our studies of sharks, we have often verified this idea of distinct territories. Not only have we determined the existence of local hierarchies, by which a shark who is master of the southern area of a reef may be just tolerated in the north, where another is the ruler, but we have also verified the fact that few or no sharks change territories. Intrigued by stories of shark fisheries that have selected a particular location because of the abundance of its shark population, and then gone bankrupt two or three years later, we decided to try the same system. We spent two days fishing for sharks near the island of Gharb Myun in the Farasan Islands. At the end of this period, the only sharks remaining in the area were some small *Albimarginatus,* measuring no more than three or four feet. Thanks to Paul Zuéna's skill as a fisherman, we had caught all the larger sharks of that territory. The tiny island surrounded by the reef of Gharb Myun is located at a distance of only one or two miles from the other reefs and islands of the group. And yet, in all of our dives there, we encountered only those sharks we had spared and marked during our previous stay. This does not mean that the reef had not been visited by other sharks; it certainly had been, but they had probably returned to their own territories. We feel quite sure that the small sharks of this region will grow rapidly and take complete possession of it, now that our fishing experiments have provided them with a more abundant source of nourishment and less competition.

In the course of these active weeks, we had tried to pierce the mystery surrounding the daily lives of the squali of this area, and our knowledge had greatly increased. But now, prodded on by the passage of time, we abandoned this study and set out to shed some light on another aspect of the existence of sharks — their reactions when faced with man.

SEVEN:
Arthur's Experience
with the *Albimarginatus*

Arthur's frightful ordeal.
The feeding habits
of sharks.
Best means of protection.
Experiments
with antishark
products.

Philippe Cousteau's narrative continues

Today, I was diving with Arthur, to study the behavior of sharks when confronted with an undefended diver. A few sharks, their fins and tail bordered with white, could be seen swimming in the clear water surrounding the *Calypso*. They seemed lazy, even indolent, almost as though they were attempting to conceal their strength behind the façade of a peaceful appearance. I went down the ladder first and swam immediately to the antishark cage suspended about thirty feet beneath the keel of the ship. The *Calypso* was anchored about one hundred feet off the reef of Dahl Ghab, in the southwest portion of the Red Sea; the water below the keel was approximately five hundred feet in depth. It was a day of torrid heat, without a breath of wind, and I was far more comfortable in the water than I had felt on deck. A few feet away, Arthur had just entered the water and was beginning his somewhat awkward evolutions back and forth in front of the cage. Although the only result of my entrance into the water had been to focus the attention of the few sharks in the immediate vicinity, Arthur's more clumsy arrival had attracted other animals and their lazy swimming had abruptly become rapid.

I kept my camera pointed toward Arthur, whose face mask was now reflecting the sunlight in blinding rays. What a perfect prey he was, completely without defense. His jerky movements could doubtless be heard at a considerable distance by the sensitive hearing system of the shark, and the rays of the sun glittering from his mask constituted a virtual call to murder. The atmosphere had changed almost at once; the slightly obscene swaying motion of sharks when they are swimming without any definite goal had given way to the supple, precise movements of the animal in a state of alert. There were

The great shark coming at the diver is an *Albimarginatus,* a white-tip reef shark. The "diver" here is fortunately a dummy we used to test the reaction of sharks to the fully dressed diver. The shark circled for a fairly long time, the usual period. It was a huge shark, probably well fed, judging from the roundness of his belly. Hunger was not a driving force in him. He tore one leg off the dummy, which we dubbed Arthur, and came back for more. At that point we knew enough and pulled the dummy out. This experiment proved that whether or not a diver is covered by a layer of foam rubber, he is vulnerable to sharks.

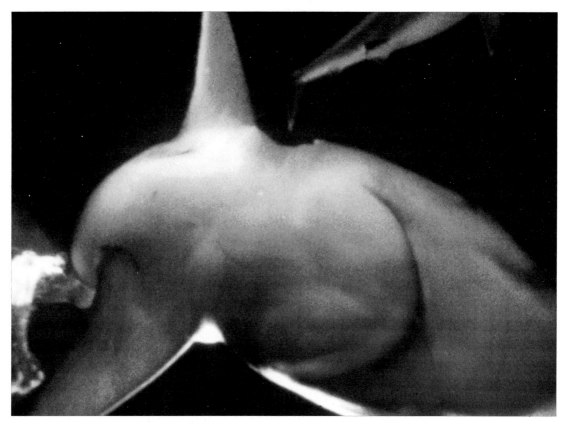

The shark confronts the camera before disappearing in the dark.

now seven or eight sharks swimming around us. I recognized two large *Albimarginatus,* more than six feet in length, among some very slender gray sharks with extremely small pectoral fins, but I was unable to identify these. Suddenly, something in their attitude changed, and I noticed at once that they were now swimming abreast of each other, straight toward us. One of the big *Albimarginatus* swerved, very rapidly, and swept up toward Arthur. At the last moment, he turned away and sped off into the distance, followed by all the others. It was several seconds before I realized that my camera was still running. I had been so startled by the suddenness of the attack that I had forgotten I was holding it. Arthur was still moving impassively in the sun, just above and in front of me. Off in the distance, the big shark turned gracefully in the water and came back, straight toward us again. This time, he seemed to be aiming for Arthur's back, but his mouth brushed against the right leg instead. He turned again, his mouth open, and I could hear across the water the terrible sound of the monster's teeth closing on — steel. The shark shook his head furiously and tore off the dummy's leg, leaving only the steel armature sticking out of the rubber diving suit like a broken tibia.

I shut off my camera and returned quickly to the cage, since all the sharks were now hurling themselves indiscriminately at anything in the water. One of them smashed against the cage, and then darted off in the direction of Arthur, who was being hauled out of the water by the men on the deck above us. I signaled for my cage to be brought up too. After what I had just seen, I felt reluctant to leave it and swim the short distance to the diving ladder.

When I set foot on the deck, the faces around me were grave. My companions were standing in a little group surrounding the mutilated form of the dummy lying on the stretcher we had used for carrying it. I knew what they were thinking. Each one of them was imagining a face behind the empty mask, his own, perhaps, or that of any one of us. I tried to shake off the macabre atmosphere by suggesting, in a somewhat nervous voice, that what remained of the dummy should be thrown back in the water. But my remark had no effect on the general gloom of the scene; I had come close to using the word "corpse" in speaking of the dummy, and throwing it back in the water would have had too much resemblance to the burial of a sailor at sea. Someone jokingly suggested that we might read a prayer for Arthur, but the pleasantry was met with glacial silence. All through the rest of the day we were moody and morose, and my sleep that night was peopled with frightful visions. For several weeks after that, everyone redoubled his security measures and displayed new respect for any sharks we encountered.

The idea behind the construction of Arthur was to discover whether the rubber diving suit and the aspect of a diver under water were sufficient to drive off sharks. It had, in fact, been our settled belief in the past that attacks on fully suited and equipped scuba divers by sharks had never had tragic consequences. We had, therefore, fabricated Arthur from an armature of steel bars, dressed him in one of Yves Omer's diving suits, and stuffed him with foam rubber. A small, round watermelon was placed in a helmet to represent the head, and a plastic facsimile of one of our aqualungs completed the silhouette. Outwardly, Arthur was an exact duplicate of our own appearance undersea.

The first experiments we carried out with him had had no results. We were not particularly surprised by this, since it would have been rather strange if an object of steel, plastic, and rubber had attracted the interest of an eater of meat and fish. We performed these experiments only when the sharks were

The great *longimanus* surrounded by his court, or cloud of pilot fish, is interested in the dead carcass in the foreground. The *Carcharhinus longimanus* is certainly one of the most dangerous species. Individuals are only found in high seas and very seldom come close to shore, but they are very determined. They will attack in spite of all the means of defense we employ, and they will not get discouraged as would many other species of shark. They are ugly but also quite powerful.

It is the same shark, the *longimanus,* bearing our tag on the left side of his dorsal fin. The *longimanus* is fairly squat and his fins are not pointed; they are rounded at the edge. His head is large and round. His color here appears to be metallic gray, but it is more on the brown side during daylight. This one has a bellyful of food and is not so aggressive any more.

This is his head, mouth opened. The teeth are not clearly visible because they are embedded in the flesh of his mouth. They become erect only when the shark is taking a bite. His eye, as you can see, looks cruel and cold.

calm, since we knew that if we tossed Arthur into the water in the midst of one of their frenzies, he would immediately be torn apart, as would any other object in the water at such a moment. The experiment could not, however, be considered perfect because of the impossibility of giving life to the dummy; and no one will contest the fact that animals, even sharks, know the difference between the quick and the dead. We decided, therefore, to provide Arthur with an enticing scent.

To accomplish this, we had tried all kinds of products, from beef bouillon, in which we had soaked the foam rubber that padded the steel frame of the dummy, to bits of fish hidden in the diving suit itself. We had just seen the results obtained from the experiment with bits of fresh fish inserted in the dummy. We had, however, noticed that the attack was not nearly so immediate as it would have been had the same portions of fish been thrown directly into the sea. We think the rubber suit is a form of protection that is not to be

This picture shows the size of one bite by a shark of eight or nine feet—average length. The bites are round and clean-cut, due to the sawing lateral movement of the head and the shape of the teeth, with their sharp, serrated edges.

neglected, even though it is in no sense sufficient. Moreover, it is possible that the scent of the human body is not particularly enticing to sharks. And lastly, there is also the possibility that our shape and size, as well as the color of our diving suits, cause us to bear some resemblance to dolphins — and the shark never attacks a dolphin unless he knows him to be injured, weakened by illness, or in some other way disabled.

One of the many widespread legends on the subject of sharks, and one of the hardest to dispel, is to the effect that the shark is a carrion-eater and appreciates more than anything else meat that is spoiled or in the process of decomposition. There are no facts whatever to support this theory. I think that a famished shark will bite into anything at all: according to the extent of his hunger, this might be a wooden plank or a corpse in decomposition, but neither the former — obviously — nor the latter forms part of his preferred diet. I have seen sharks bite into hooks baited with beef, but their movements have always been lacking in real desire, and when they did eventually bite, it was only after a long period of hesitation. I remember that, during an earlier cruise, we had been obliged to rid ourselves of an entire side of beef because a breakdown in the cold-storage system had made our supply of meat unfit for consumption. The enormous package had been wrapped in sackcloth, heavily ballasted, and sunk on a corner of sand just at the edge of the coral shelf of the reef where we were anchored. For several days thereafter, the side of beef remained intact, even though there were many sharks in the area. It was not until after a week had passed that the meat disappeared, and when a tiger shark, which we had noticed in the preceding days because of his size and his lean and hungry look, appeared with swollen and distended abdomen, we realized what had happened. The shark's lack of enthusiasm for this particular prey had been conquered by his hunger. We were also struck by the fact that a shark only about ten feet in length could have swallowed an entire side of beef.

To be sure, deep-sea sharks follow schools of mammals, and sometimes follow ships, to feed from their leavings, but this means nothing in itself, since these castoffs are always fresh food. Moreover, it is our belief that the energy requirements of sharks are very small; they are inclined to swim in open, unobstructed waters in which the slightest movement on their part propels them over a considerable distance. They do not suffer from cold, and their calorie loss must be minimal, so that one good meal should permit them to exist for a very long time.

Here he is passing behind the cage to get to the food. With open mouth, he closes in for the attack very, very rapidly.

He first rubs the piece of food lightly with his nose, and then he will take a bite.

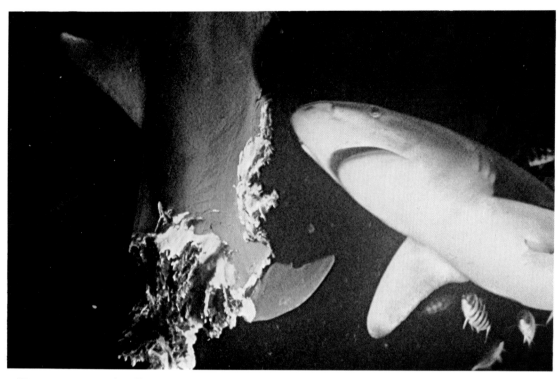

Here you can see the pilot fish under his belly coming in with him to eat the crumbs.

Mouth open, he goes in for a twenty-pound mouthful.

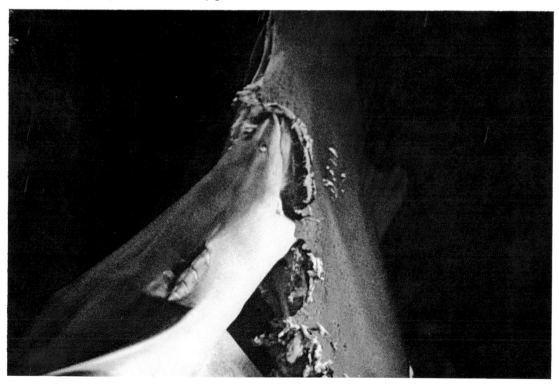

The study of the shark's digestive system provides some support for this theory. Shark's intestines, as compared with those of mammals, are extremely short: an adult man has intestines approximately thirty feet in length, while a nine-foot shark has a maximum of about seven feet. Moreover, sharks seem to have the incredible ability to digest only certain portions of their stomach contents, while other portions remain almost intact for long periods. This may be a form of natural reserve which permits the sharks to live for some time by storing and preserving a single meal. Sir Edward Allstrom, director of the Taranga Zoo, near Sydney, Australia, has recounted the case of a fifteen-foot tiger shark housed in one of the zoo's tanks. Over a period of twenty-one days, the shark rejected the horse meat it was fed, first swallowing it and then vomiting it a few days later. The shark died, and an examination of the contents of his stomach revealed two perfectly preserved dolphins. They had probably been devoured a few hours before the capture of the shark. But how he had been able to preserve the dolphins intact while rejecting other food remains an enigma.

It is in this same zoo that studies have been made on the quantity of nourishment absorbed by sharks. In his book, *Shark Attack,* V. M. Coppleson cites the cases of two sharks, one of them eleven and a half feet in length, the other just about ten feet, and each weighing approximately three hundred and fifty pounds. In one year, the first shark consumed one hundred and ninety pounds of fish, while the other consumed two hundred and twenty. He also noted a very sharp decline in the sharks' food requirements during the winter months — from May to August, in Australia. It would seem, therefore, that the nutritional needs of sharks are well below those of insatiable voracity, for which they have acquired a reputation.

Over the years, we aboard *Calypso* have been impressed by the briefness of elapsed time in a shark frenzy, even more than by its violence, however incredible that may be. During one night dive, I saw four sharks attack a wounded dolphin and tear him to bits, within a matter of minutes, despite all our feeble efforts with spears and shark billies. Nothing could have resisted these demons incarnate. They bit into the dolphin's flesh, tearing away a mouthful of anything from sixteen to twenty pounds, then turned back and bit again, with a horrible wriggling movement of their entire body, and constantly surrounded by a cloud of pilot fish speeding about in every direction. The rays of light from our projectors, reddened with blood, the silvery flashing of the pilot fish, the sound of teeth scissoring into flesh, and the movements of these great gray and white forms, created a kind of horrible fantasia which seemed to go on forever. And yet, it was only a matter of five minutes and then everything was calm again. Even though the body of the dolphin was only half-devoured, his attackers had gone away and resumed their prudent circling. Some of them had even left the scene of the feast altogether, disappearing silently into the blackness of the sea. Only one remained behind, cautiously nibbling at his dead victim, taking bites that would have seemed insignificant a few moments before.

Their appetite is very quickly satiated, and a meal such as I have just described probably permits them to live for several weeks. But, for most sharks, this would be an exceptional repast. For those sharks that follow the great schools of cetaceans, it must be the habitual means of survival; once or twice a month, an ill or dead dolphin, and the rest of the time just the residue from births or other leavings. For those sharks that haunt the reefs and therefore do not have such a source of nourishment, there can be no precise answer to the question of their normal feeding habits. I have seen some fish attack others and fail to kill the intended victim, leaving him still swimming and trailing blood. And in every such case, a shark has appeared immediately and swallowed up whatever was left of the wounded animal. This occurs relatively frequently, since it is rare for a reef fish to pursue another if it escapes his first attack. In fact, the majority of such fish hunt in much the same way as a man hunting ducks; they simply lie in wait, protected by their blind of coral, until an imprudent visitor comes within reach. But if they fail in their initial assault, they are reluctant to follow the quarry into deeper waters, far from the protection of their coral hiding place. It is this moment of hesitation which provides opportunity for sharks or other predators from the open sea. It would certainly seem, therefore, that the favorite food and primary nourishment of sharks is fresh fish, and that sharks are capable of hunting for themselves.

After all, the occasions for seizing the would-be prey of another fish are not too frequent, sharks are comparatively numerous, and consequently they must go hunting. That their basic fare is fish might seem to contradict theories derived from the incredible list of objects found in the stomachs of captured sharks — objects ranging from canned goods to the remains of human arms and legs and other parts. Certain species of small sharks, with jaws particularly well adapted to this specific task, apparently feed on shellfish and crustaceans, which they crush between the flattened teeth lining both

The shark, *longimanus,* surrounded by his pilot fish eager for crumbs, takes a firm grip on the already torn flesh of the dead porpoise.

With the shark cage and the head of the diver in the right foreground, the shark now shakes his head from left to right with incredible violence to saw the piece of meat he is going to gulp.

You can see the teeth, now erect, inside the mouth of the shark, tearing away at the carcass.

The diver is attempting to set out to tag the shark, which, needless to say, in this frenzied moment can be extremely dangerous. The diver is wearing his black-rubber light helmet. This complete sequence was shot at night about thirty feet below the Red Sea.

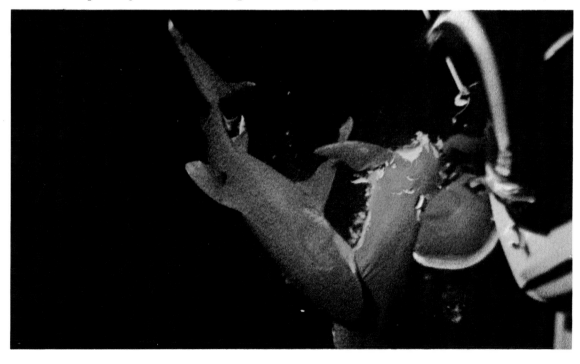

sides of their jaw. The majority of large sharks are extremely active predators, who survive on the leavings of the great schools of cetaceans or from a hunt of their own which may lead them to attack schools of very small fish. Such is the case with the thresher shark. What might be termed "terrestrial" flesh, such as that of a steer or a man, is doubtless not their favorite food, but they will eat it whenever they find it necessary.

In any case, few species of sharks, in comparison with their total numbers, are capable of seriously harassing man. In addition to the other sources of nourishment I have mentioned, sharks are known to feed on seals, turtles, and some sea birds. The largest species, the whale shark and the basking shark, feed exclusively on plankton, small fish, or small crustaceans, such as crayfish and red crabs. (There are some theories to the effect that these two last-named species of shark come to the surface only occasionally, which would explain the rarity of their sightings by seamen or fishermen.)

One of the most disagreeable experiences I have known in my years of diving was that of seeing a shark appear at a time when I had no means of protection in my hands. And yet, when I look back through the journals I kept on board ship, I constantly come across the notes I have made of such encounters: "Wednesday, December 7, — This morning, on a preliminary exploration, we dived on a little reef just north of the island of Malathu [in the Farasan Islands]. The coral here is small and stunted, somewhat resembling a heath or moor in the south of France. Many small, apparently timid, sharks haunted the beginning of the dive. Suddenly, from out of the depths beyond us, I saw three large *Albimarginatus* — seven to nine feet, I would guess — climbing toward us, swiftly and determinedly. They were far too large for me to contend with, especially on a free dive and with empty hands. I hastily signaled to the doctor, who was accompanying me, to get back to the *Zodiac,* and followed him as rapidly as I could. I managed to get aboard just as the sharks decided to launch their first attack."

It was episodes such as this that led us to devise our number one tool of protection — the "shark billy." In order to keep the shark at a distance without wounding and thereby angering him, we now always carry a staff of wood or aluminum, about three feet long and equipped at one end with a circle of small nails that grip the shark's skin and prevent him from simply slipping by it. The handle at the other end of the billy is provided with a loop, rather like that on a ski pole, so that it will not be wrenched from our hand by the shock of the attack. It is not in the least cumbersome to use, and although it is certainly not very impressive to look at, the billy is nonetheless very effective. It would be false to say that this device alone is adequate protection, since a shark thus turned away will almost invariably resume his patient circling and wait for another opportunity to attack. It is an exception to the rule if he allows himself to be so easily discouraged and simply swims away.

For this reason, and also because the most dangerous time in any encounter with a shark is the brief period in which the diver is attempting to leave the water and is temporarily blind, we almost never go down without the added protection of an antishark cage. Most of the time, it serves only as an elevator back to the surface, but in the event of danger it provides a shelter against any attack. We designed and built cages of all sizes and shapes before finally settling on two models. One type, capable of holding four divers, is approximately cubical in form, measuring seven feet in height by six and a half in width. The door opens in two sections, either from the top or the bottom, or both ways at once, if the work we are doing should require this. The other type of cage is almost spherical, with a trap door at the bottom and semicircles closing the top. It was designed for a single diver and can be used on the bottom, suspended from the ship, or by a diver propelling himself through the water by the movement of his legs, which project through the opened trap door. On many occasions we have been forced to make precipitous retreats to our cages, in order to avoid serious accidents. They also provide us with our only means of studying and filming the great shark frenzies while remaining in complete security ourselves. It was primarily for purposes of filming that we built la Balue, the plexiglass cage already mentioned, but although this type of cage is ideal for cinema use, it offers too great a resistance to water currents and tides and is too fragile for general use.

During the Second World War, the general staffs of all the world's armed forces evinced a growing interest in the study of sharks. Hundreds of sailors on torpedoed ships, as well as the pilots and crews of planes shot down over water, died horrible deaths because of sharks. This state of affairs caused great concern among the various military specialists and technicians, and there was good reason for it. As a single example, I might cite the following story:

At nine-fifteen on the morning of November 28, 1942, the British transport ship *Nova Scotia* was sunk by the torpedoes of a German submarine. The ship went down thirty miles off Cape St. Lucia, a promontory of the coast of Natal in South Africa. In addition to her crew, the *Nova Scotia* was carrying

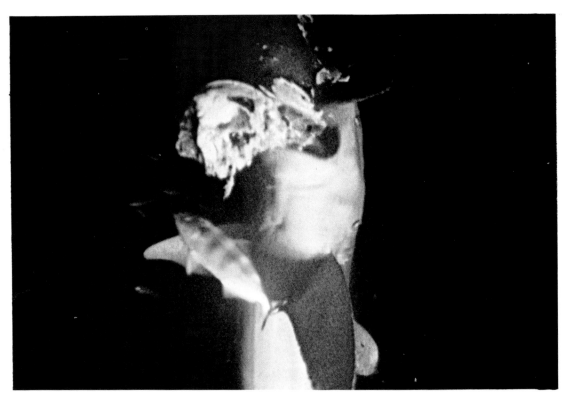

Now the shark has his mouth full of meat, tearing it to shreds.

He goes down, gulping his meat.

Another shark comes out, straight at the photographer. In the foreground you can see the hand of the diver, Serge Foulon, with his short tagging dagger in hand.

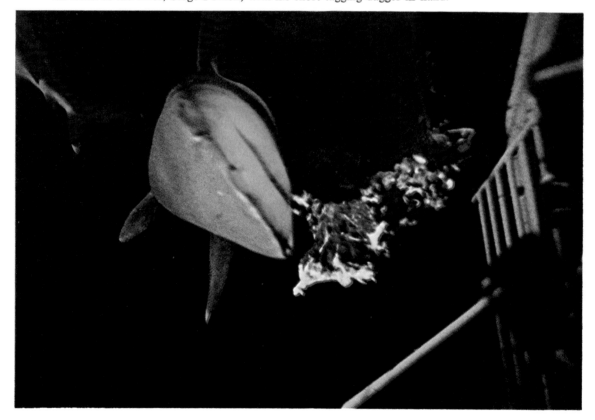

765 Italian prisoners of war and 134 South African soldiers, returning to Durban after having served in the Near East. Most of the lifeboats were destroyed in the explosion of the torpedoes, and hundreds of survivors were left with only their life belts or rafts of wood or rubber. One of the ultimate survivors of the disaster gave this account: "Suddenly, the ship was rocked by two terrible explosions, and we knew that we had been hit by torpedoes. I tried to reach my life belt, but the ship was already listing badly and I slipped in the oil and gasoline that covered the deck. I fell into the sea, wearing only a pair of swimming trunks. The water was covered with oil, but I swam until I found a floating spar and clung to that. Hundreds of men were swimming around me, clutching at rafts and other pieces of wreckage. Another soldier from my own regiment swam up and caught hold of the other end of the spar. He was wearing a life belt. We drifted all night. By dawn the next morning, the current had carried away the oil on the water, but we were still surrounded by other survivors. A little later, my companion told me that he thought it was better to die than to go on clinging to a piece of wood, with no hope of rescue. He said that he was going to let go, and refused to listen to me when I tried to change his mind. When I finally realized that my efforts were useless, I asked him to leave me his life belt. As he was unfastening the straps, he suddenly let out a horrible scream and the whole upper part of his body was lifted out of the water. When he fell back, the sea was red with blood and I could see that his lower leg had been cut off. At the same moment I saw the gray form of a shark swimming rapidly around him, and I got away from these as fast as I could. Then some sharks began to gather around me. They looked to be about six or seven feet long, and from time to time one of them would swim directly toward me. I clapped my hands in the water with all my strength, and that seemed to send them away. At last, I was able to reach one of the rafts and climb into it." Sixty hours after the submarine attack, the survivors were picked up by a Portuguese ship. A total of 192 persons were saved, but many of those who died were killed by sharks.

The effect of such stories on the morale of the men who fought in the air or on the sea was, understandably, disastrous. It was for this reason that many military laboratories in all parts of the world set to work to discover some effective means of protection against sharks. The final result, a discovery of the United States Naval Research Laboratory, was a small rectangular tablet containing a mixture of 20 per cent copper acetate and 80 per cent of a powerful deep-purple coloring substance. These ingredients were mixed with a wax which dissolved in water. The tablets were distributed to all personnel involved in operations on or above the water, and doubtless provided them with great moral support.

We tried out these "shark chaser" tablets during a series of dives in a depth of about one hundred feet, just off the Shab Arab Reef in the Gulf of Tadjoura, where the Red Sea and the Gulf of Aden come together. We lowered an installation made up of two cages facing each other, so that the cameraman in one cage could follow the movements and experiments of the two divers in the other. There were few sharks the first morning; the water was a trifle cloudy and carried along by a current of about a quarter of a knot. Serge Foulon opened a sack of fresh fish and released a few pieces to drift with the current. Almost at once, several silhouettes appeared in the milky depths. They were *Carcharhinus obscurus,* sharks with black-tipped fins, and averaging three to four feet in length. As soon as they were within easy range, José Ruiz opened his sack and freed the "shark chaser" tablet. It drifted four or five feet to the end of the attached ribbon and floated in the current, leaving behind it a thick, blackish smoke screen. As it dissolved, the dye expanded into swirling clouds, carried gently away from us by the movement of the water. A few minutes later, I saw six long and flexible forms tracking the path of dye and copper acetate just as dogs will track the source of a scent of roasting meat. They were large sand sharks, which weave through the water like serpents. One of them was more than fifteen feet in length — the largest sand shark I had ever seen. Although I knew them to be completely harmless, I instinctively recoiled at the sight of them. Serge, for his part, did not flinch and simply held out the tail of a barracuda to our new guests. The largest of the sand sharks scented first to the right and then to the left and at last came to nibble gently at the morsel of fish Serge was still holding. None of them seemed in the least bit disturbed by the "shark chaser," which still surrounded us in a thick, blue-black fog. We did not consider this first experiment satisfactory, so we set up another.

Before I went into the water, I watched Canoë Kientzy preparing what he called a "sandwich." He was slitting open some fresh fish and slipping into each of them a "shark chaser" tablet, stripped of its outer wrapping. When he had tied the whole sandwich back together, he attached it to the end of a long cord. I went down the ladder and into the water extremely cautiously, because we had sighted two *Albimarginatus,* more than six feet long and circling the ship in an apparent state of excitement. The moment I entered the water they turned in my direction. I have already mentioned the unbelievable appearance of the shark when he is seen from directly in front. Nothing remains of his beauty or his somewhat awkward grace. I could see only the pointed snout and two wide-spaced eyes, the disturbing, faintly ridiculous swaying movement of his body, the symmetrical pectoral fins, and the black line of his mouth against the lighter gray of his belly.

Turning, and swimming rapidly into the protection afforded by the two propellers of the ship, I entered the waiting cage and half-closed its door. When I signaled to Canoë, he tossed out the "sandwich," which came to rest just about ten feet away from me. The moment it entered the water, the tablet released its cloud of blue-black ink and the fish in which it was inclosed was hidden from my view. The smaller of the two sharks began to move a trifle more rapidly, turned brusquely away from the cloud of dye, then turned again, swam back toward it and passed through it from one end to the other. When he appeared, he had the sandwich in his mouth but was having trouble swallowing it — doubtless because Canoë was still holding on to its length of cord. Great, violet clouds were expelled from his gills with each of the convulsive movements of his mouth and head, as he tried to rid himself of the fish. At last, he succeeded in biting through the cord and swam away, leaving behind him two separate clouds of purple dye. I could not prevent myself from laughing hysterically, and the camera in my hands jumped up and down. We would have to start all over. I knew this, but it was simply too funny — seeing clouds of a product, which was supposed to repel a shark and discourage him from biting, expelled from his gills like smoke from a badly tuned motor.

We tried again. Second "sandwich," same result. In spite of the failure of these experiments, however, I feel sure that copper acetate does nothing to improve the digestion of the shark.

In many laboratories, and on the *Calypso,* all kinds of chemical products have been tried, and all with the same lack of real success. They may work with certain species of sharks, at certain times, but it is impossible to draw any definite conclusions from these experiments. As for the American "shark chaser" itself, we have tried it often, during all our voyages and under extremely varying situations, but it has never yet been successful. The only chemical substances which have a definite effect on sharks are so caustic that they are dangerous to all organisms, including the human body.

Thus far, two types of barriers have been tested as protection for bathers

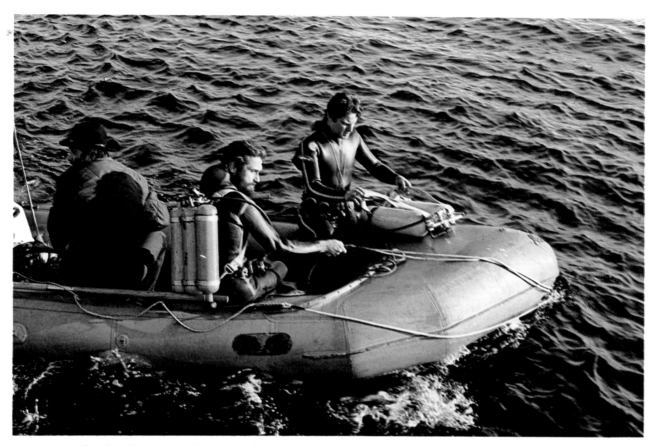

Our favorite means of transportation. The *Zodiac* allows us to go anywhere, jump into the water, climb back on board; this little boat carries as many as eight or nine people.

on beaches. One such system, which was tested by Australian authorities, consists of an electric screen in which two wires, one suspended from buoys close to the surface, and the other held on the bottom by weights, are maintained at a differing polarity. This system has seemed to be reasonably effective; several sharks have been observed to be either paralyzed or turned away. The Australian Government, however, has not felt that it was satisfactory. The price of installation was prohibitive and the infallibility of the system far from certain.

Another kind of barrier, made up of fine bubbles of air, also has had a temporary success. For several years, in fact, it was thought that man had found the ultimate weapon. Experiments conducted by Doctor Perry Gilbert have, however, demonstrated the uncertainties of this procedure. Experiments of more or less the same nature have also been carried out in South Africa. A tank twenty feet long, eight feet wide, and six feet deep was divided into

A different species of shark — the dusky shark, out in the open sea. This is the kind of shark we had when we tried the Johnson shark screen.

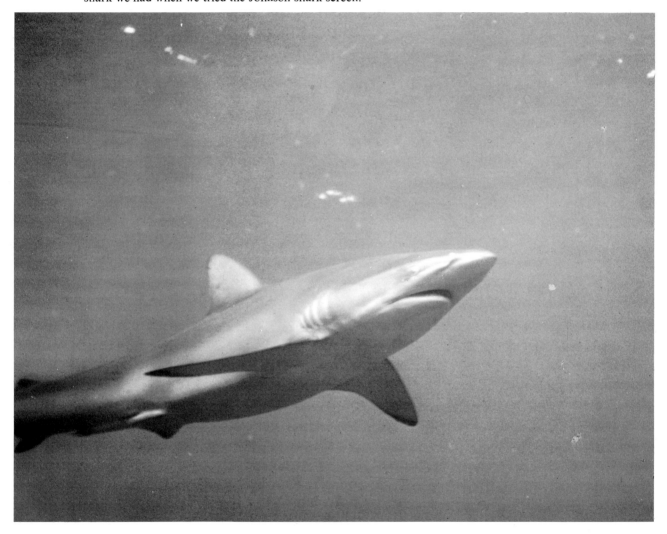

two sections by a pipe which was pierced with small openings and placed on the bottom. A compressor fed air into the pipe, so that it escaped through the holes and formed a curtain of fine bubbles, completely separating the two parts of the tank. Two series of experiments were then conducted, with a seven-foot *Carcharias taurus* and a six-foot *Carcharhinus obscurus*. In both series of tests, the barrier was formed while the sharks were at one end of the tank, and although the *Carcharhinus obscurus* remained on that side, the other shark began swimming very rapidly and passed through the barrier several times. In another series, when a wounded but still living fish was placed in the water on the side of the tank separated from the sharks, both animals crossed through the barrier within a matter of seconds and attacked the other fish.

Some divers claim that exhaling a large breath of air in the direction of an approaching shark will cause him to flee. The procedure will succeed with the majority of inoffensive sharks, but these species tend to avoid any encounter with a diver, so the efficacy of the system is, at least, open to question. I have employed it myself, with sharks of the dangerous species — tiger sharks and blue sharks, for example — without ever finding it successful. Moreover, in the course of our many dives, I have seen sharks pass with complete indifference through the large clouds of air bubbles emanating from my companions' breathing equipment.

The procedures for the self-protection of the diver that have been tried out at one time or another are numerous and varied, ranging from cartridges of dynamite to compressed-air-driven harpoons and including such devices as ultrasonic generators, extracts of spoiled meats, and electrical discharges. We have tested many of them, and found that the majority are ineffective, some extremely doubtful, and others too cumbersome for the diver. There is, however, one that merits attention, the Johnson "shark screen," which we termed "Johnson's bucket," because of its peculiar shape. We experimented with it near the reef surrounding Dahl Ghab island.

At first, the device seemed ridiculous to us. It is a kind of buoy, formed of three superimposed inflatable rings, to which is attached a large pouch of waterproof plastic about six and a half feet deep. When the upper part has been inflated, the shipwrecked individual (or the experimenter, in our case) settles himself into the "bucket" thus formed and fills it with water until it attains its full size. In this manner, he is floating in a waterproof, cylindrical enclosure, which isolates him from the water around him. It is a far more

The most familiar aspect of the shark: seen through the surface—the very sinuous shape coming toward the boat, searching lazily, with the dorsal fin and the caudal fin skimming the surface. This is the sight that has frightened generations of sailors and so many bathers. This is the sight for which guards scan the waters from the lookout towers of Australia and South Africa so that they can warn bathers and divers of the perilous sharks' whereabouts. It is a characteristic shape, but people often mistake this shape for that of a dolphin or a large fish.

rational device than it might seem at first glance. For one thing, when the whole "shark screen" is deflated and folded, it is not at all cumbersome; and for another, perhaps more important, no scent can filter through to the shark, and he does not have a visual sighting of arms and legs beating at the water.

Several sharks were swimming around the motionless *Calypso* when I first descended cautiously into the orange circle of the buoy. I filled the dark-green pouch immediately, and clung with one hand to the hook of our hydraulic crane. By following this procedure, I could be lifted rapidly from the water in case of attack. It was a new impression for me, and not at all agreeable, to be situated with my head just out of the water and unable to follow the movements of the sharks on the choppy surface. I no longer felt any desire to laugh at sharks snapping up fish baited with tablets of copper acetate.

The shark nearest to me was no more than a grayish blur of changing shape, slipping in and out of focus. He turned, very close to me, quite obviously interested in the shark screen and its occupant. I raised my head and tried to lift my neck and shoulders above the surface, hoping that I could then see more clearly. Once, I felt the rasp of his body against the plastic of the pouch, followed almost immediately by the shock of his flicking tail. Several times, he passed so close to me that I could have reached out and touched his fin. My left hand was still gripping the hook of the crane so tightly that the knuckles were white with strain.

Canoë Kientzy was watching the experiment from one of our small boats nearby. He was armed with a high-powered rifle, but that reassured no one. The plastic material of which the cockpit was made — as thin and fine as paper — swung back and forth to the movement of the waves, and I found it difficult not to interrupt this natural movement with inconsidered kicking of my feet.

To complete the experiment, I decided now to try to attract the shark toward me. I slapped at the water with the palm of my hand, and at the same time some fresh fish bait was thrown into the water from the ship. At last, the big shark started straight toward me, moving fast and determinedly, and I promptly gave the signal to be hauled aboard. Still clinging to the cable of the crane, I looked down and saw him pass, six feet below my dangling legs but well away from the empty shark screen. A false alarm — he was attacking the bait, not me.

In a later experiment, we put a whole flotilla of these Johnson buckets in the water. Doctor Millet, Jacques Renoir, Serge Foulon, Claude Templier, and Marcel Soudre each occupied one, while René Aaron manned a rifle in the *Zodiac* to assure their security. Canoë and I planned to film the reactions of the sharks from beneath. There were two large, gray sharks, about seven feet in length and with small pectoral fins, thinly bordered with black on their lower surface. Their manner of swimming was supple, slow, and sinuous; and their hollow bellies attested to the degree of their hunger. Another pair of sharks was scarcely visible, very far below. I lifted my head above water and listened for a moment to the slightly caustic pleasantries being exchanged by our guinea pigs. Then I dived again.

Beneath the surface, I was again confronted with an unimaginable spectacle. In the universe of the unreal, where the silver light of the sun cleaves the deep blue of the sea, the two sharks above me seemed to be swimming at the center of the green pockets. They lazed through and among these lifeless, odorless objects, and then, with no hesitation, they both turned and launched themselves directly at Canoë, who repelled them with great sweeps of his shark billy. Returning at once to their earlier state of indolence, they abandoned my "bodyguard" and turned on me, hoping, perhaps, that I might prove an easier prey. When I had climbed back into the *Zodiac,* I repictured the scene in my mind and came to the conclusion that Mr. Johnson's shark screens have a good future.

I do not believe that these screens could be effective against a shark in a frenzy of hunger, but the chances are not large that a shipwrecked person, or a man or woman landing in the ocean from a disabled plane, would encounter such a situation. For my part, I think that Mr. Johnson's buoys can very definitely increase the possibility of survival of anyone alone on the high seas. One point, however, should be made: the plastic material is extremely fragile, and anything can tear it open, so due caution should be observed with such things as belt buckles, shoes, and watches.

Confronted with the ineffectiveness of traditional methods of self-protection employed by divers, we have settled on a technique that has often saved us in tricky situations. Instead of crying out under water or blowing clouds of air bubbles or plunging straight toward any shark of menacing appearance — methods which have no practical effect — we practice what we call back-to-back defense. Since we had already arrived at the principle of never diving alone, there is always a minimum of two, and in case of danger, far from a protective cage, we place ourselves back-to-back, with each man using one hand to hold on to the diving suit of the other. In this position, each man can effectively defend a sector that does not exceed his angle of vision. And of course we never dive without having a protective instrument of some kind in our hands. In waters in which we are likely to encounter sharks, we carry either a shark billy or a camera.

The one thing of importance that emerges from this brief summary of the various means of protection against sharks is that none of those actually in use, with the exception of the cumbersome steel antishark cage, is absolutely sure. The further we advance in our knowledge of sharks, the more evident becomes the futility of any attempt to understand them completely. Their reactions are unpredictable, and ordinary statistics are of no value. I have seen hundreds of sharks follow the same technique in approaching to attack and bite, and yet, on some occasions, they have surprised me by attacking in a completely different manner. It goes without saying that the greatest prudence is always necessary, but it should be prudence based on respect and not on contempt.

EIGHT:
The Island of Derraka
The narrow escape
of Dr. François.
Individual cages.
Battling a swarm
of little sharks.

Philippe Cousteau's narrative continues

A catastrophic week passed by. Every afternoon, the haboob, that violent storm of burning sand, beat down on the ship and prevented us from working. At about two o'clock, the sky above the western horizon would turn a reddish-gold and the sea would cease to live, its surface becoming absolutely motionless, seeming almost solid. The already stifling temperature became intolerable; our bodies ran with sweat and every movement was torture, aggravated by the rash of prickly heat with which we were all afflicted. Then the storm was on us and the howling wind raised little spouts of water that mingled with the sand and covered everything with a coating of yellowish, destructive mud. Since we had gotten under way at the first signs of the approaching storm, we were usually anchored in the shelter of some small island when it actually struck. As soon as it became possible to work again, we were forced to put in what seemed interminable hours of meticulous cleaning, in order to protect our delicate and valuable equipment. Our eyes red and swollen, we moved about like automatons in a sandy, unbearable universe.

These difficult days undermined the morale of the crew, caused deterioration of matériel, and finally made it necessary for us to put in at Massawa, the capital of Eritrea, for a premature overhaul. My father decided to take the *Calypso* in, without losing any more time in these waters. Canoë and I succeeded in persuading him to leave us on a deserted island farther out at sea, with enough supplies for a week, and with equipment making it possible for us to get some work accomplished. The time remaining to us to complete our film and our study of sharks seemed very short to me, and I was eager to try to make up for all the days lost to us by the wretched sandstorms.

After a rapid exploration of a half-dozen isolated scraps of sand, we selected the island of Derraka in the Suakin group. We decided on the location of our camp and then set to work at once to open a more or less navigable passage for our small boats through the belt of water-level coral that surrounded that Red Sea island. The team to be left behind was made up of Canoë, Doctor François, Serge Foulon, and Raymond Deloire. Raymond was a still photographer and the brother of our excellent chief operator, Michel Deloire. I accompanied them, of course, to do the filming.

When we had brought our equipment ashore and set up the tent, we returned to the *Calypso* for a little "farewell" dinner prepared for us by Jean Morgan. In the course of this dinner, we worked out a precise program of what

This is our camp on Derraka Island. Despite the brightness, it is approximately four o'clock in the morning. The photographer is Raymond Deloire. Pictured in the foreground, sleeping on the red-and-blue mattress, is Canoë. Next to him, still wrapped in his sheet, is Foulon. Standing is our doctor, and Philippe is reading a book, or trying to catch a few more minutes of sleep, on the low cot next to the tent.

This is the island's lagoon just in front of the camp. The photographer is positioned in front of our tent for this shot. On the left you can see our compressors. They are air compressors used to recharge our tanks. The equipment right in front of us, with a can of oil and gasoline, is used for the outboard motor. One of the launches on the beach is the security launch, the one we will use only in case of emergency—for example, in the event the *Zodiac* encounters engine trouble outside the lagoon area; the strong currents could make it impossible for the *Zodiac* to return, forcing it to drift for miles and miles. Possibly a light wind could haul it way out of reach. Radioing the always ready security launch would bring help instantaneously, and the situation would be under control within a short while.

The birds along the shore are feeding on remnants of the fish we cleaned in that area for dinner. Two people are spending this exasperatingly hot hour of the day in the cooler water of the lagoon. That is the place where Doctor François was endangered by a sand shark. Every day from 10 A.M. to 2 P.M., or even longer, the water provided us with relief from the unbearable heat of the sun.

we wanted to accomplish during our stay on the island. First of all, a study of the small sharks of the sand flats, then a continuous surveillance of a portion of the coral cliffs, with the idea of forming a kind of census of the visitors from the open sea who came here in search of nourishment. And, of course, we also planned to ignore no aspect of the life existing on this desolate strip of sand itself.

At last we said goodby to the others, with a handshake that may have been a trifle more formal than was our custom. Although, in theory, we were running no particular risk, the stay of a group as small as ours on an isolated island in the Red Sea is not exactly a picnic. In case of an accident, we were far from any surgical equipment; and in the unlikely case of a visit from any mainland natives, we would have been at their mercy. I promised myself to allow no one to risk anything that seemed in the least uncertain, especially where sharks were concerned. The *Calypso* drew away from the shore and was rapidly lost to sight in the gathering darkness. In what seemed just a moment, only the sound of her engines still came to us across the becalmed sea.

That first night, I was the only one that seemed interested in anything but rest. The *Calypso* had scarcely disappeared before my companions wrapped themselves in sheets and slept, exhausted by this day of excitement and activity. Left alone, I walked slowly down to the water. I had the curious impression of approaching some secret rendezvous with my dreams. There was no moon, and yet everything shone with a mysterious light that seemed to emanate from the landscape itself, rather than being simply reflected by the objects it struck. I had no tendency even toward thinking or meditation; I just watched and listened, without understanding, perhaps somewhat as an animal does. The water of the lagoon was warm and alive, rustling with the sound of thousands of claws and tiny legs, of microbattles, and of scurryings back and forth. As is true in most tropical seas, a fluorescent stream of light flashed across the water at the sudden move of a fish. On the beach, every wave traced a drawing different from all the others and then was erased a moment later, leaving not even a memory. At the water's edge, innumerable armies of hermit crabs maneuvered to the rhythm of some incomprehensible logic. Since I was standing motionless, everything took place very close around me. A crab went by, trailing a live and feeble chick, doubtless stolen from one of the sea-swallow's nests which covered the island. They passed within inches of my foot, and disappeared into a hole in the sand I had not seen. A little ten- or twelve-inch sand shark was swimming at the very limits of the water, searching for small shellfish or for crabs, whose exit from the water he would block with his own body.

I was torn away from my silent communion with nature by the sound of voices coming from the camp, and hurried back there as rapidly as possible. Millions of hermit crabs had invaded the camp area and were climbing across the bodies of the sleepers they had so unexpectedly awakened. For the next hour, we stood and watched as this multitude of tiny creatures emerged from the edges of the scraggy bush behind us and passed by on their way to the sea. It was a journey of almost two hundred feet which, for them, might require an hour or more. They climbed over or detoured around every obstacle they

Some distance away from the *Calypso,* visible at the right, are the two launches; one of them is moored and the other is going to be docked with it. We are about to drop the cages overboard into the little cove where sharks had been spotted that morning. It is a small bay, set between two coral heads bearing the whitest sand at the bottom. This is to be a tagging operation.

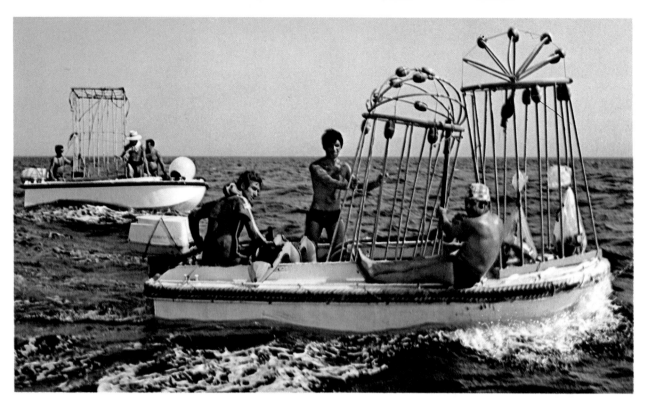

Some of our shark cages are portable aluminum cages. The small round shapes on top are floats. A cage is floating on the water when the diver enters. The diver brings with him a lead weight, which causes the cage slowly to submerge. While submerging, the diver attaches the weight to the bottom of the cage, thus enabling him to free both hands for his work. One of the prime advantages of the portable cage is the fact that it is neutral in water, enabling the diver to steer it by opening the rear door, sticking his legs out, and swimming with it in the direction of his choice. In order to surface, all the diver has to do is dump the weight, thus causing the contraption to rise slowly to the surface.

In this picture Doctor François is on the right, with Jean-Paul Bassaget, center, holding a cage. Philippe Cousteau is driving the launch. The second launch is occupied by Canoë Kientzy, Jacques-Yves Cousteau (a towel in his hand), and Marcel Soudre in the rear.

It is now time to get into the water after a last reading of the available light topside proves favorable. The reading will be rechecked underwater for filming.

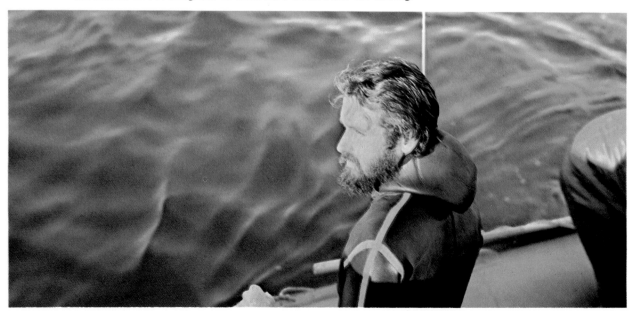

came to, and there were obstacles everywhere. This gigantic nightly migration was not the exclusive property of our campsite; it took place along the whole length of the beach on this side of the island. The tidal wave of scurrying little animals eventually disappearing into the water was an extraordinary spectacle — and I never saw them carry out the same mass procedure in reverse.

In the days that followed, we acquired the habit of not retiring until after the passage of this clicking, clattering wave. I think, personally, that all the hermit crabs awaited a certain degree of obscurity, toward the end of the afternoon, before beginning their descent to the sea. I would see them gathering along the edges of the thorny bushes which cover the central part of the island. In compact clusters, they would wait for dusk, the shock of their shells forming a continuous rustling sound as they brushed against each other. On their return, they must have come back at differing times, in accordance with whatever luck they had had in accomplishing whatever need it was that took them to the water — reproduction or simply feeding. Thus, when they returned across the beach, one by one, they went unnoticed.

On the day after our first experience with the crabs, we explored the island from one end to the other, setting out very early, before the heat of the sun made such movement impossible. The island is elongated and a trifle narrower at its center than it is at either end. It is oriented roughly from northeast to southwest, and surrounded by a sandbank forming a lagoon several times larger than the island itself. It is covered with a thorny vegetation having very small dark-green leaves, and its center forms a shallow and slightly less arid valley, which we christened The Happy Valley. Obviously, there is not a drop of fresh water on the entire island, and yet life abounds on it. We have visited dozens of islands like this and my companions are bored with them. But it is always a source of wonder to me that these shelves of arid sand, lost in the saline furnace of the Red Sea, could form a refuge for a secret, but dense and bustling form of life. It is primarily the birds which dominate the life of the island, peopling it with their cries and movement, and sometimes also with the brilliance of their colors. And in this universe, the sea eagles reign as unquestioned masters. Using twigs and bits of driftwood, they construct mounds which may rise anywhere from three to ten feet in height. The nests which crown these artificial hillocks are always filled with feathers, bones, and, especially, the remains of dead fish. I once saw a sea eagle fishing on the sandbank of the island of Marmar in the northern Farasan group. The bird hovers motionless above the water and then, like all other birds of prey, he drops like a stone, claws stretched out toward his intended victim. In the case of the sea eagle, the prey may be protected by as much as two feet of water and the bird will vanish into it completely for a fraction of a second before laboriously rising again. Through strength alone, he frees himself of the water and climbs slowly to a height of a hundred or so feet, where he seems to pause to shake out his plumage, forming a shower of tiny rainbows, and then flies on to rest on the sand. The body and legs of this bird are completely inadapted to swimming, and the force by which he succeeds in lifting himself free of the water, simply through the power of his wings, is a magnificent thing to see. His island domain provides him with everything he needs to feed himself and his young, until the day arrives when he chases them off, to preserve the balance of the realm and his own supremacy.

The sea eagle is not the only bird of prey in this territory, however. There also exists a species of small blue-gray hawks, which I saw for the first time on Derraka and have never seen on the islands on the other side of the Red Sea. I think this is due to the presence on the islands of the Suakin group of many small rodents, which provide nourishment for the hawks. They bear a strong resemblance to large martins, having the same elongated wings and the same acrobatic manner of flight.

In the springtime, the sea swallows come to lay their eggs and hatch their young, while the solan geese (perhaps more commonly known as the booby gannet) take possession of the island in November and December, for the same reasons. In both cases, the island is literally covered with eggs and then with the grayish forms of baby chicks; the air vibrates constantly with their strident cries, and countless battles take place. Some red-beaked gulls survey these immense nurseries attentively, hoping to snatch up a helpless chick or an egg; they will break the egg by dropping it on the rocks, and then consume its contents.

It was on Derraka that I saw to what extent man's intrusion destroys the fragile equilibrium of natural life. Our arrival on the island had disturbed the swallows around the campsite, so they had left their nests temporarily and had probably not been able to find them again in the darkness. As a result, a swarm of ocypode crabs had descended on the nests in a murderous raid and carried off many of the chicks, which were still too weak to defend themselves. As I had seen on that same night, the dawn surprised a great many crabs hastily dragging off the newborn birds.

On another occasion, as I was walking very cautiously between the eggs of a nursery of baby swallows, I noticed that the sea swallows feared my presence more than a few gulls that followed close behind me. As a result of this, a circle formed around me in which the young were no longer protected by their parents. The gulls, knowing more of the situation than I, profited from it to steal several chicks, despite the furious cries of the swallows circling in the sky not far away. I could not help but wonder why the gulls had waited for such a unique opportunity. They were much larger and stronger than the little swallows, so it seemed to me that they could have helped themselves to what they wanted at any time they chose. The explanation lies in the fact that the gulls are not at all numerous in this region, and each time one of them approaches a nest a swarm of swallows attacks him and forces him to retreat. By frightening the swallows more than the gulls, my presence had upset this balance of forces. But even so, the gulls had great difficulty in leaving the involuntary protective circle I had created for them, and most of them could only escape the confines of this menacing circumference at the price of losing their prey.

I have never attempted to protect one animal against another, and our arrival in this microcosm of a world was no less natural than would have been a cataclysm of any other kind. When, on occasion, I have caught myself in the act of qualifying one animal as "good" and another as "bad," I have been tempted to laugh. I have seen storms reduce the population of entire islands to nothing, sweeping off all life in a few hours. Our sole ambition, on the *Calypso,* is to maintain the natural sequence of events, in the presence of humans. In other words, not to indulge in the useless, gratuitous massacre which is termed hunting for sport. Our needs in fresh fish for nourishment are generally satisfied by fishing, and only rarely by underwater hunting. And hunting as a land sport is almost unknown among the members of our crew.

At the northern end of the island, we came across an accumulation of empty shells and red madrepore, gathered together in an unusual shape. It was a Moslem tomb, oriented to the northeast, in the direction of Mecca and the tomb of the Prophet. The mound seemed to have been built in the form of a ship, with two large pieces of coral planted vertically at either end, to represent the prow and the stern. The comrades of the man who was guiding this ship on its longest journey had adorned it with all the flowers of the sea. All the care of the gravediggers could be read in the area surrounding this final resting place. They had dug up and flattened out a mound of fine sand, bordered with tufts of dried coral, now white as bones. Shells, possibly left as offerings, had been piled more than three feet high and decorated with fragments of multicolored bottles, with here and there a red splash of Tubipora coral. The man had probably been a pilgrim, herded with others from the African coast into

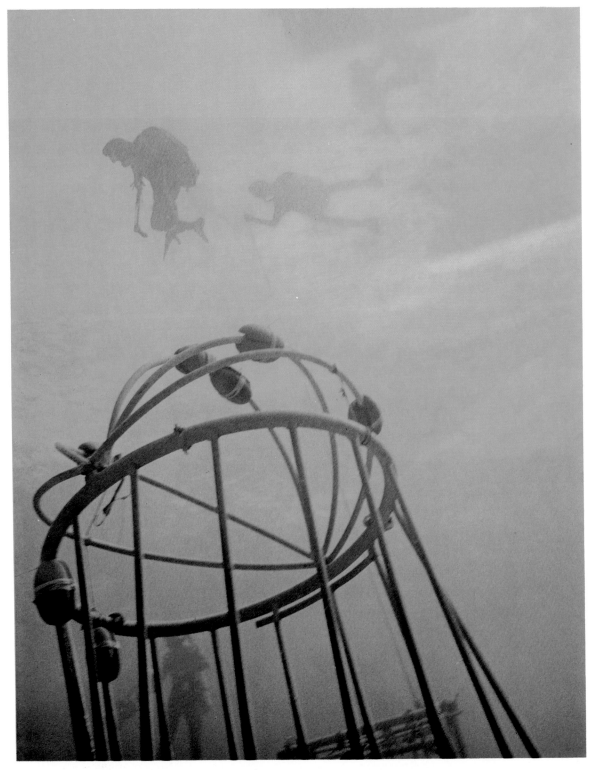

Below the anchored launches, divers are swimming down to their respective cages. One of the one-man cages is in the foreground. The photographer's cage is sitting in the background. The figures at the surface are observers swimming. We must get the cages positioned before we enter.

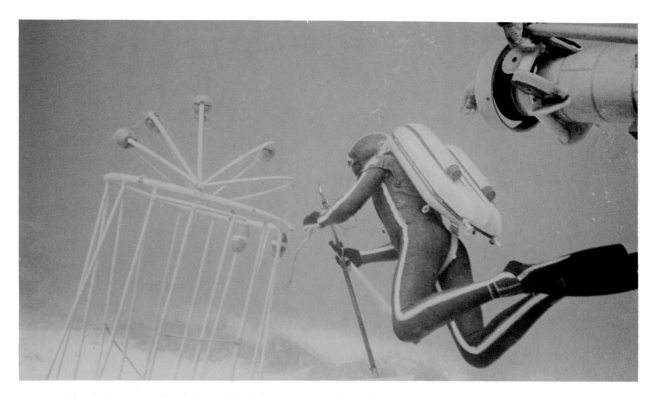

No sharks are yet in sight as this picture is taken. When they finally appeared, however, there were many. Michel Deloire was filming.

The look on Serge's face shows the state of mind we experienced during those dives; anything could happen and we had to be extremely cautious.

a small sailing vessel and succumbing later to the terrible conditions of the voyage. Or perhaps he was one of those old nakhodas who presided over the destinies of these coastal vessels, seated motionless at the center of their ship until they died. They commanded the young fishermen who gathered shells for mother-of-pearl and caught a few fish for their food.

Everywhere we went, the land seemed pock-marked, riddled with subterranean galleries which collapsed beneath our feet, revealing burrows no larger than a man's thumb. At first, it seemed that this might be one of the effects of the infernal heat, but we later discovered the real nature of this underground network. One night, after the regular migration of the hermit crabs, we were invaded by the mice. They were scarcely more than an inch in length, but their numbers were incredible and they attacked everything in sight. Their sudden presence stunned us for a moment, but then we immediately began looking for some means of shelter for all our perishable goods, either by hanging them from poles or enclosing them in waterproof cases. It was this invasion that supplied me with the answer to the presence on Derraka of the blue-gray hawks. I still do not know whether the leaves on the bushes provide water to quench the thirst of the tiny rodents themselves, but the next morning we found all our water bottles filled with their dead bodies. They had been able to enter through the necks of the bottles, but once inside they had drowned, because they were incapable of climbing out of their glass prison. For our own needs, we now had only one keg of water, containing less than twenty gallons.

Our exploration of the island had taken up the entire morning, and at about eleven o'clock, when the heat and the sun became unbearable, we hastily consumed a slice of grilled tuna and then went into the water. We stayed there, paddling idly about, until three-thirty, by which time it was again possible to support the furnacelike heat.

Every day thereafter, we spent the hottest hours comfortably immersed in the lagoon, wearing wide-brimmed hats to protect our faces. Doctor François regaled us with interminable and very funny stories, and the early afternoon hours passed in an atmosphere of gaiety and enforced idleness. Outside the water, the temperature would have read ninety-eight degrees in the shade — if there had been any shade. But there was nothing but the dazzling white sand, whose reflection, added to the sunlight, would have burned our bodies to a crisp in a few hours.

It was during one of these required bathing periods that Doctor Francois was attacked by a shark. Our work usually began at four o'clock in the morning, and after we had finished and had a rapid meal we went to an area just at the edge of the beach where the water averaged only two to three feet in depth. The water here in the lagoon was refreshing enough, although quite warm, but as one drew closer to the outer reef surrounding the island, the water became agreeably cool. On the second day, Jo — as we all called the doctor — began walking through the water toward the outer side of the lagoon. Suddenly, he disappeared from our sight and there was a great splashing of water, in the midst of which we could clearly make out the tail of a large shark. We were racing across the lagoon when Jo reappeared, very calmly, and a shadowy form flitted across the length of the outer reef and vanished in the distance. Jo explained what had happened, in fewer words than he normally used for one of his stories: he had been walking along slowly when the sand beneath his feet had suddenly erupted, much as if a rug had been pulled out from under him. In spite of his surprise and the confusion in the water, he had then made out the shape of a shark, which had turned back toward him and then, for no apparent reason, turned again and gone away.

This is by no means an unusual story, and many people have been surprised by sand sharks in the same conditions. Some have even been seriously bitten. A sand shark only three to four feet in length possesses a jaw that is quite sufficient to bite off a respectable piece of anything it attacks, and although its teeth may be small they are no less sharp for that.

That same evening we made a night dive, to try out our underwater floodlights and, if possible, to gather enough lobsters for a meal. Along the reefs of the Red Sea and the Indian Ocean, lobsters come out only at night. Invisible during the day, they hide in deep holes in the protective coral, to escape their enemies. Night, by depriving these predators of their normal resources, becomes day for the lobsters, who emerge from their shelters and hunt through the sand and coral in search of food. On the island of Abu Latt, in the Farasan group, I have even seen some who came completely out of the water to cross an obstructing coral peak.

Six feet beneath the surface, the beam of our lights brushed across tufts of coral bursting with unsuspected color. Fish with great, staring eyes remained frozen in place, as if paralyzed by the ray of some science-fiction weapon. They drew away slowly, and it was even possible to reach out and caress the iridescent scales. (These nocturnal adventures always give me the feeling of being a slightly mad magician. My light is a magic wand, capable both of creating fantasies and of destroying them. When I flick the switch, I am still dazzled and find myself back in the darkness of a void. Flick it again, and I am in the midst of a fantasia of anarchic creations, independent of me.

This one is a white-tip reef shark moving in the night. Its shape is disquieting in those dark hours. François's projector provided the lighting.

A night shot of a shark as it appears in the distance. The diver in the foreground has his eye on the killer and will try not to lose sight of him, or he would really be in trouble. Chances are, however, the diver will retreat to the reef and stay hidden among the coral heads.

Sometimes I swim very fast, sometimes slowly, often lying on my back, looking up into the mirror of the surface as my visions appear, explode, and vanish in the thin shaft of my light.) A short distance away, Jo seemed bathed in the aura of his projector, as if he were caught in a multicolored spider's web. Like myself, he was reaching out to the motionless fish, his movements reflecting his astonishment at this artificial familiarity with animals who normally fled at the sight of us. We were the St. Francis of the fish.

Suddenly, it was over. My magic beam had lost its power, and irradiated nothing but the void. We had arrived at the edge of the outer reef, where an absolutely vertical cliff plunged down to a depth of over six hundred feet. The water in front of us now was black and empty. Clinging to the last tufts of coral, we tried to search the depths with our fast-weakening projectors.

It was the beam from my light that picked up the reef shark. He was a very large reef shark, about twelve feet long, and he was slowly swimming up the river of light. When he arrived at what he apparently considered a reasonable distance from its source, he swerved lazily and began gliding toward me. The reflections of light on his body were almost silvery, and his eyes, with their contracted pupils, seemed tiny spots of black. The narrow shaft of my light threw all his scars into sharp relief, like some sinister form of tattoo. Little threads of flesh dangled from a recent cut at the corner of his mouth. But, somehow, there was an astonishing impression of purity in his movements and in his form, etched as it was in silver against the total blackness of the night. For a moment or two, he patrolled the edge of the cliff, then plunged straight down and disappeared.

I was frightened now, certain that he had not really gone, that he was swimming somewhere around us, his unmoving little eye still fixed on us. The night was filled with disturbing shapes, and in our efforts to see in every direction, the fading beams of our lamps danced an incoherent ballet. I was invaded by a feeling of total impotence; the water which a moment before had been so gentle had now become an enemy, armed with an unknown and hostile life. Our projectors, and all the technical progress they represented, were no more than futile playthings that we vainly brandished like arrogant Prometheuses. We had thought ourselves capable of chasing off the night with our tiny sparks. But the night remained, immense and solid. In a night dive on a reef such as this, as soon as one moves about too much, becomes uneasy, and loses absolute self-control, one's movements may precipitate one against the fiery, razoredged peaks of coral that inflict thousands of small but painful scratches and wounds. At last, my light picked up another slender form. It was a shark, not the one we had seen before, smaller, but seeming no less formidable. But now I had escaped the hypnotic sorcery of the night and was aware of our danger. Jo and I, watching each other closely, began to swim back toward the beach. When we were halfway there, we came across the *Zodiac*. Canoë had thought it wise to follow us, and assure us of an immediate exit from the water in case of danger. We collapsed in the bottom of the boat, not speaking, listening to the murmurs of the night.

The silvery image of that great shark haunted me through the rest of the night, even though I knew that the constant, vigilant patrol did not cease with darkness. I have said before that sharks, unlike most other fish, do not possess a swimming bladder that would permit them to float in equilibrium at any level of water. If a shark ceases to swim, he sinks slowly to the bottom. He is thus forced to live in a state of constant movement. Some fishermen, in regions where sharks are particularly abundant, have tried to capture them with explosions of dynamite. It is a completely impracticable system, since a shark killed in this manner will never rise to the surface. This factor, added to the absence of respiratory muscles in their systems, forces sharks to swim unceasingly, day and night, in search not only of food but of vital oxygen. It is a searching that may last for more than thirty years.

I went to sleep at last on the sand of the beach, thinking of this creature condemned to eternal journeying, to the incessant caress of water against his body, to an implacable, unending love affair with the sea.

Before we left our island, the *Calypso* rejoined us, to take part in a last experiment. With the help of Paul Zuéna, our first mate, we installed a complicated marking setup in a passage through the reef. We placed the large cage, to be used by the film cameraman, on a floor of white sand at the bottom of a wide fault. On either side of the entrance to this cage and at a slightly greater depth, there were two smaller cages for the banderilleros, the divers with the marking devices. At the center of the stage thus set, we placed transparent spherical plastic traps containing bits of fresh fish. In addition to this, each of the two smaller cages carried a sack containing more small pieces of fish. On the surface, my father was in one of the small boats, from which he could direct the entire operation, and Raymond Deloire was in another, prepared to photograph events from this angle.

At about two o'clock, the whole setup was in place and the program began, with a large distribution of fish. Serge Foulon was in the small cage to the left of the entrance and I was in the one to the right. Michel Deloire, with the film camera, was in the large cage, protected by Canoë, who was armed with a long, solid shark billy. A reconnaissance team we had sent out in the morning had reported a considerable number of fairly large sand and reef sharks in the area, so I expected to see them appear momentarily in the turning from the cliff, attracted by the sounds we had made and by the scent of fresh fish. I was somewhat deceived when I saw only one, then two, and then two more very small sharks, no longer than my arm, swimming rapidly and apparently nervous. But this deception did not last long. One after another, more than fifteen sharks suddenly appeared, excited, scenting the atmosphere like a pack of wolves.

Many divers ridicule these small sharks, considering them easily frightened and not worthy of concern. They are generally right in this opinion, but only if the sharks are alone or in very small groups. These same divers are likely to reckon that a man faced with a vicious dog is in far greater danger. Personally, I prefer dogs; there is almost always some way to outmaneuver them — unless they have been trained by man to attack. A shark less than three feet long can quite easily tear a foot or a hand from an overconfident diver. Its jaws are larger than those of any dog, its teeth much sharper and perfectly adapted to slice a limb in two.

I glanced toward Michel, in the large cage. He seemed as disappointed as I had been, and ready to return to the surface, so I signaled to him to wait. Serge, as impassive as ever, was preparing his spear for marking. Within a few minutes, the pack that had now gathered had burst the plastic traps and the fish inside had been completely devoured. I recognized some small black-finned sharks and a few of the sinuous sand sharks. Our little arena was filled with them. They were all swimming very fast, and seemed to rebound from the walls of multicolored coral like bullets from a rifle. I realized that the scent of fish must by now have penetrated the whole of this relatively enclosed space, making any detection of its source of origin almost impossible and thereby exciting them even further.

It occurred to me suddenly that sharks as small as these could pass between the bars of our cages, and this is precisely what happened. Two of the little demons slipped into my cage and thrashed about between my legs, attempting to reach the sack of fish, which they had finally found. For several seconds, I kicked at them like a jackass, trying to force them out, and when I had succeeded in this I set to work to rid myself of the sack. Even as I fought off new attempts at entrance with great slaps of my open hands against the bars, I tried to detach the plastic bag, but I could not do it. Cursing at José, who had thought he was doing a good job in attaching it so solidly, I unsheathed the little dagger that formed the handle of my shark billy, but it had not been sharpened and would not cut well enough to sever the nylon cords of the fastening. All around me now, a carrousel of little sharks was engaged in a frenzied saraband. They bit at everything within reach, including the bars of the cage, shaking them between their teeth like mad dogs. Serge seemed to be having the same problems, but out of the corner of my eye I caught a glimpse of Michel, calmly registering it all on film.

A shark succeeded in penetrating the roof of the cage, and while I battled with him, a blow of his tail displaced my face mask, depriving me of vision. Now I was beginning to be overwhelmed by a feeling of frustrated rage. I was not going to be torn to pieces in this idiotic cage by these little brutes. I managed to readjust my face mask, emptying it of water with a great blast of air, and then opened the upper door of the cage. Kicking with my feet and lashing out with my hands, I got out at last and reached the shelter of the big cage, standing with my back to it and facing out toward the enemy. But as soon as I left the little cage, the sharks abandoned me and became entirely concerned with the sack of fish. In this moment of calm, I watched as they tore it apart and swallowed its contents. Serge, who had succeeded in ridding himself of his sack almost at the beginning, had remained in his cage and even managed to carry out several fine markings.

At the entrance to the bottleneck of our passage through the reef, several large forms cruised back and forth, but made no attempt to enter. The great sharks had refused the invitation to our party; we had underestimated their reluctance to enter enclosed areas. On the surface above us, my father was swimming slowly around his boat. It was he who had made possible my flight by tossing out bits of fish not far from my cage, attracting the majority of the little sharks toward an easier prey.

When I came up, I was furious about the way the experiment had developed, but all the others laughed about it so heartily that I soon found myself joining with them. For a long time thereafter, the men of the ship would ask me to explain how it came about that I had grown so fond of sharks that I carried one under each arm inside my cage.

It was the first time that sharks of such small size had been a real danger, but it was not to be the last, as I was able to testify at the time of the terrible frenzy at Shab Arab.

NINE:

Frenzy at Shab Arab

**Arrival at
Shab Arab Reef.
A terrible mass frenzy.
The killing of a shark
and its effects.**

Philippe Cousteau's narrative continues

The bottom appeared as a black line on the sensitized paper of the powerful echo sounder. Several of us were gathered around my father, watching the delicate tracing as it sloped gently upward. The total silence which reigned on the *Calypso's* bridge was broken only by the calm voice of JYC* giving his orders, and the voice of the helmsman as he repeated them.

Jean-Paul Bassaget, our first lieutenant, was transcribing the meanderings of our route onto the chart before him. It was night, and Canoë's face, as he leaned over my father's shoulder, reflected the slightly reddish glow of the instruments on the control panel.

"Right one five."

"The helm is right one five."

I was aware of a slight vibration as the ship veered a trifle to starboard. We were about to open up a new sector of the reef of Shab Arab.

"Hold her steady."

"Steady as she goes, Commandant."

"What is our heading?"

"One three zero, Commandant."

"Keep her at one three zero."

"Yes, Commandant."

*My father was always referred to by his initials — JYC — in a name that would sound rather like "Jeek" in English.

In the moment of renewed silence, my father changed the scale of sensitivity of the echo sounder to increase the precision of the graph, and the recorder began to turn more rapidly, giving out an almost imperceptible rasping sound. I knew that, inside the earphones, the slight tapping of the departing beams and the echo from the reflection on the bottom were mingled with the sounds of water against the hull. The graph on the paper showed that the bottom was no more than twenty-five feet beneath our keel.

"Come down to plot five, Jean-Paul."

"Plot five, Commandant."

Another vibration, this time more pronounced. The ship was slowing down. The line showing the depth of the bottom was still climbing.

"Stop engines. Prepare to anchor."

Jean-Paul's reply was almost simultaneous with the voice of the first mate.

"Engines stopped."

"The anchor is cleared, Commandant."

For a few moments longer, the *Calypso* continued on her course. The bottom was now no more than fifteen feet beneath her keel, and the graph was recording a series of dark clouds just above it. They were schools of fish, directly beneath us. The atmosphere on the bridge was a trifle strained.

"Drop anchor!"

The sound of the anchor chain rattling through the hawse seemed to break the hpynotic spell which had claimed all of us. Suddenly, the air was filled with sound and conversation, lights were switched on, questions and answers were exchanged. When the engines stopped, the rest of the ship seemed to come alive, breathing a new, even more intense form of activity.

As I did on every such occasion, I had observed with an admiration tinged with pride as my father demonstrated yet again his perfect knowledge of the sea and of everything connected with it. I have known highly skilled seamen who make use of echo-sounding equipment as they would of a precise and impersonal instrument, but I feel sure that, to my father, it is something much more than this. He had guided us precisely to the spot we were searching for, with as much sureness as if he were actually walking on the sea floor, with no hesitation whatever, using the ship and the elements themselves as a virtuoso might use his favorite instrument. I could not help but think of it in these terms; a perfect and reassuring harmony. We were moored just at the edge of the plateau of coral, and while the anchor rested at a chain's length of about thirty feet, the prevailing current was such that the stern of the ship remained exactly above a depth of ninety to one hundred feet — the depths most propitious to our work.

On a map of East Africa, forty miles north-northwest of Djibouti, in the Gulf of Tadjoura, there is the shadowy area marked "Shab Arab Reef,"* but this is slightly redundant, since the word "Shab" means "reef" in Arabic. As is true of all such reefs lost in the high seas, Shab Arab is a refuge for marine life. It is not difficult, therefore, to understand that by protecting and nourishing the smaller species, the reefs become a sort of food warehouse for the hunters from the deep. In choosing Shab Arab as our anchorage, we hoped to find an abundance of all forms of life, and especially of sharks.

Now the motors were completely silent, all motion had ceased, and the entire crew gathered in the wardroom to hear my father define the goals of the next day's work. When he had concluded, I took on the task of translating his intentions into the language of cinematography and specifying each individual's role.

Arrival at a new location, particularly if it takes place at night, always arouses in me a childlike, impatient enthusiasm. The smooth black water against the hull trembles with feverish activity. From time to time a very small fish will leap desperately into the air, attempting to escape an invisible pursuer whose dorsal fin traces a momentary furrow in the water, straight and sharp as an arrow. At the fierce flick of a tail, tiny galaxies of luminescent particles are born and die in an instant, bearing witness to the life or death of some tiny animal. Sometimes, perhaps, a louder splash will cause me to lift my eyes from the water just below, but I can see nothing but a network of ever-shortening waves, coruscating in the luminous path of moonlight. At such times, I long for an understanding as inscrutable and all-seeing as that of the gods.

At four o'clock in the morning, we began setting up our first operation of this day's work. We wanted to make an underwater film of a shark attacking a fish hooked on a line. As a beginning to our experiments with sharks, we catch a great many fish for use as bait, and on many occasions our victims have come to us reduced to nothing more than the head, the rest of the body having been cleanly bitten off. There have been times when it was impossible to bring in even a single fish, and I have seen a small boat commanded by

*The site of the experiments mentioned on page 117.

The presence of the small-fry fish of the reef guarantees that large predators are about.

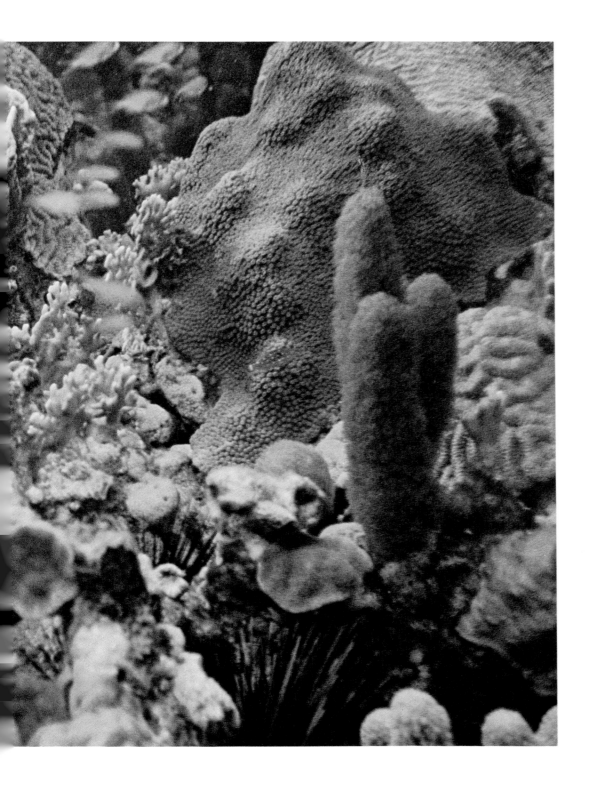

Paul Zuéna, our first mate and master fisherman, return to the *Calypso* bearing only the remains of fish mutilated by barracudas or sharks.

Therefore, in order to bring our present task to a successful conclusion, one of our small, flat-bottom aluminum boats was equipped with two cameras, hung over the stern and just below water level. Between these two film cameras, a television camera covering the same field was linked to a receiver in the boat. Thus, Michel Deloire could watch the action on the television screen a few feet away and start his film cameras at the exact moment of his choice. Since any system of propulsion on the aluminum boat would have made the whole experiment impossible, it was towed behind another boat equipped with a forty-horsepower Johnson outboard motor. The towline was maintained at a length sufficient to keep the photographic boat well clear of either the wake or the turbulence caused by the propeller of the tow boat. A silvery decoy, or "spoon," was trailed just within the range of the cameras, about ten to twelve feet behind the aluminum boat.

It was dawn when we put these two boats in the water, and two hours later we were ready to begin. The delay was caused by the necessity of adjusting the angle of filming on the cameras, and covering the forward part of the photographic boat with a canvas, in order to screen the light of the blazing sun and thus improve Michel's view of the television screen. The system for mounting the cameras on the stern of the photographic boat was conceived and made on board the *Calypso* by our chief mechanic, Roger Dufrêche, and we soon discovered that it worked perfectly — holding the cameras securely in place and transmitting no vibration.

In the first few minutes of fishing, Paul Zuéna experienced no difficulty in bringing on board more than a hundred pounds of fish, including a tuna, some barracuda, and several amberfish. Michel filmed the fish as they chased the decoy and bit into it, and then the struggle that took place before they were finally captured. When the first shark attacked, it was not at all in the manner we had looked for as a result of our other experiences in fishing for bait. A caranx weighing between sixteen and twenty pounds had been fighting the line for two or three minutes when Michel first saw the shark, following in the wake of the desperately battling fish. At almost the same moment as he appeared on the television screen, Paul saw the triangular fin break the surface just behind their boat. Michel's fingers were already gripping the trigger that would start the cameras, but the shark seemed in no hurry. He simply followed behind, effortlessly it seemed, and keeping a distance of exactly three feet

The smaller cage, on the right, was to prove that we had been overconfident in reckoning with the danger from small sharks, for the bars were not closely enough spaced to keep them out.

between himself and the caranx. It was only when Paul began to haul in our captive that the attack took place. The shark accelerated as swiftly as if he had been launched from a bow, seemed to pass the caranx without having touched it, momentarily blotted out the television screen and then vanished. The whole thing had been so sudden that, despite the tension of the moment, no one had reacted. Only the bleeding head Paul finally hauled into the boat attested to the reality of the attack. The caranx had been cut in two just behind the gills. The semicircle that marked its death was perfectly clean and sharp, and yet it had required no more than a fraction of a second for the shark to accomplish it.

All through that morning, Michel filmed attacks of varying kinds, sometimes slow and calculated, sometimes instant and terrifying. In one case, the

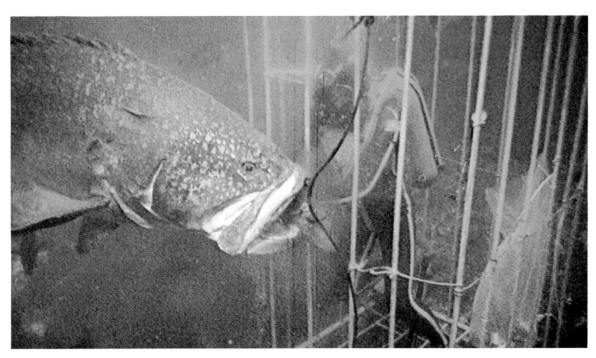

This is the type of encounter that really makes the day. It is rare to see a fish of that size. It is a grouper. His mouth open, he plans on devouring a fish that Serge had harpooned earlier for shark bait.

Serge, trying to retrieve the fish for his original shark-baiting purpose; we are not in the business of tagging groupers, and it would have been a wasted effort to forego the bait, but this grouper was so beautiful that we finally consented to let him have his dinner. The photograph was shot at one fiftieth of a second and the jaw of the fish is blurred. This demonstrates the incredible speed at which groupers project their mouths open, absorbing an extreme quantity of water, thus sucking in their prey.

His gills are opened wide to eject this tremendous amount of water, while his eye is rolled back by the effort. He has the fish completely in his mouth and he is about to withdraw.

Serge is still holding on. Having gained some ground, he has succeeded in liberating more of the fish. But the grouper did not submit, and the bait was still stuck inside the mouth of the gigantic fish.

shark had swallowed the entire fish and found himself caught on the same decoy his prey had swallowed. Obviously, however, the line was not strong enough for his weight and he broke it almost at once. At about noon, Michel, Paul, and their helpers returned to the *Calypso,* exhausted by the heat and nervous tension, but happy with the success of the mission. They also brought back enough fish to furnish bait for the dives we planned that afternoon.

As the objective of our first dive, we had planned that Serge would mark as many sharks as possible, and also spear a fish in the midst of the shark pack, so that we might observe the results. Serge was to occupy the big steel cage, while I would be in a small aluminum cage held on a horizontal level about six feet from the bottom by cast-iron weights made fast to lengths of rope. Two television cameras — one in each cage — would record the scene for my father and Doctor Eugenie Clark on the bridge of the *Calypso.* I carried two cameras, to film whatever happened around Serge and the big cage.

The water was the color of a translucent opal, so clear that I could make out the bottom, some seventy-five feet below, almost as soon as I entered. There were at least a dozen sharks cruising slowly back and forth along the length of the *Calypso's* red hull. They did not seem either very large or very aggressive, but their number foretold the possibility of some problems. Just above the level of the sand bottom, I could make out the forms of still other sharks, but it was difficult to estimate their size or number, since their grayish silhouettes were confused with the shadows they cast on the parallel ridges dug in the sand by the current. Seen from above, they were incredibly supple in their movements and seemed to be wandering aimlessly around the elongated silhouette of the *Calypso* projected on the bottom by the sun.

Serge's cage came gently to rest, raising a fine cloud of sand which dissipated almost at once. From where I lay watching, the environment of water made his movements seem as graceful as those of a dancer as he opened the door, slipped outside, and turned the cage around so that it was facing into the sunlight. Indifferent to the sharks, a large turtle paddled slowly toward the cage and proceeded to examine it at close hand, rather like a nearsighted old man. Serge offered it a piece of fish, which it ignored, and then it turned and swam away, with long, untroubled sweeps of its paddlelike front legs. For some reason, it reminded me of those old men who sit in the sun along the streets of Spanish villages and occasionally walk a few steps to visit with friends.

The sharks were becoming more and more numerous. There must have been at least fifty around us now, but they were still slow and indifferent in movement.

I had not noticed the arrival of an enormous grouper, which passed to my right and planted itself on the sand not more than three feet away from Serge. It was a bluish-black color, at least six feet long and seeming almost as big around. Its mouth opened and closed to the rhythm of its breathing. There was a terrible white scar across the top of its head, and one pectoral fin had been almost completely torn away. The grouper is a fish of rather terrifying appearance, giving an impression of brutal strength. Its alert little eyes seem extremely wary, and I know that it is capable of starting to move with incredible rapidity. Serge tossed it the piece of fish the turtle had refused. It drifted onto the sand a foot or so in front of the grouper, which simply opened its mouth a trifle wider, but made no other movement. The piece of fish disappeared, sucked in by the displacement of water. It was a fascinating spectacle, so fascinating indeed that I forgot about the sharks, although they were beginning to grow a trifle restless. With each tidbit Serge tossed to it, the enormous fish inhaled a little water and the morsel of our bait seemed to fly into its mouth, where it was instantly swallowed up. (Later on, I was to remember this moment, when Canoë and I found ourselves face to face with a fish of the same species but twice as large.) As a final offering, Serge flung out a barracuda weighing twenty pounds. It was absorbed as swiftly and easily as the other, smaller pieces, and then the grouper bestirred itself and swam away, as indifferently as it had arrived.

The sharks were now passing back and forth between our cages, almost with familiarity, seeming only slightly more nervous, a trifle more swift. Serge began scattering little crumbs of fish, so that their scent would permeate the water and attract our targets within reach of his marking spear. The circle began to close in immediately and the usual carrousel began. Sharks were arriving from every side, and I had the impression that there must be hundreds of them. They were of all sizes, ranging from quite small to more than six feet, and at least four different species were represented. In the space of the nine feet or so that separated our cages, I counted seven at one moment. They practically blocked my view of Serge. They swept by rapidly and sometimes turned on their own tails to snatch at a few crumbs of fish. Serge's spear was kept constantly in action, planting the little banderillas next to the dorsal fin,

Having abandoned the fish to the grouper, Serge proceeds to bait sharks with a barracuda caught that morning.

The frenzy starts when all those fish crumbs begin to surround the cages. The scent from them agitates the sharks' nerves.

Serge successfully tags a shark that is snapping at the barracuda he is holding in his left hand.

Another successful tagging.

and the general excitement grew to such a point that I saw one shark hurl himself in pursuit of another and tear away the little orange plaque with which he had been marked.

The sea itself seemed to have gone mad, filled with hurtling forms crossing each other's paths in meaningless, disordered trajectories. I retreated to the farthest corner of my cage, since it was open at the front and I could not close it. Serge tossed out the head of a caranx as large as a football, and the frenzy surrounding us reached a fever pitch. Ten sharks came down on it at once, and then attacked each other ferociously in the attempt to gain possession of the prize. In order to film this, I had to lift my head and shoulders out of the cage, and a shark managed to squeeze himself halfway in. I dropped the camera and used both hands to force him back through the bars. In doing so, I got several cuts on my fingers from the rough skin along his jaw, but fortunately for me he did not close it on them. Profiting from an instant of relative calm, I recovered the camera, but just as I was drawing back into the cage another shark smashed the reflector on its light attachment.

The situation now was becoming untenable. They were biting furiously at everything and shaking their heads in a kind of demented fury as they fought among themselves to tear apart whatever morsel of fish they had obtained. One shark succeeded in getting into Serge's cage, and Serge was forced to beat him off with the point of his marking spear. In the meantime, another had found and snatched up the whole sack of fish in the cage. He fled at once, followed by all the rest of the pack. In a sense, it was a stroke of luck for us, since the period of calm that followed gave us time to regain our composure and set things to right in our cages. The water was cloudy now and visibility had greatly decreased. I glanced at the counter on my camera, to be sure that I still had sufficient film, and decided to continue. The light was still functioning and I managed to get the reflector back into something resembling its original shape. At the same time, Serge was busily repairing his twisted marking spear.

When he had finished, he glanced over at me, and when he saw me nod, he took the spear gun from its bracket in the cage and fired a spear into a small shark, piercing its body from one side to the other. I prepared myself for a rush from all the rest of the pack, but it was exactly the reverse that occurred. The movement of all the other sharks immediately became more deliberate, and they withdrew to some distance from the cages. I was really taken completely by surprise. After having heard so many stories concerning cannibalism in sharks, this sudden timidity and mistrust confused me. One might actually have thought they now realized we were dangerous and were keeping their distance. Serge pulled sharply on his line to withdraw the spear, and the wounded shark swam off, trailing a cloud of blood. The others moved out of his path, but they nonetheless followed him discreetly. Perhaps they were waiting until he was farther from the source of danger before devouring him — I don't know — but I did notice that, as soon as he had disappeared, the sharks remaining in the area were again on the alert and the carrousel started up again.

This time, rather than aiming at another shark, Serge speared a red snapper. He was a large, strong fish and his desperate battle for survival brought on a renewal of the frenzy of a few moments earlier. In one violent leap, the unfortunate snapper freed himself from the spear, but at the same moment a shark tore away a portion of his back. In his dying flight, he somehow swam between the bars of my cage and I clung to its sides with all my strength, attempting to beat off his enraged pursuers. I could feel the cage resounding, seeming to crack into pieces around me beneath the sledge-hammer blows of these maddened animals. At last, the snapper found a way out — and was instantly devoured. The water surrounding me was filled with twisting, tearing bodies, insensate with fury and almost hidden in trails of a dark-green blood. I thought of my father, hunched over the television screens above, watching this maniacal battle.

Jacques-Yves Cousteau's narrative

It was, in fact, because of the television equipment (two cameras below, one in each cage, and two closed-circuit receivers in the *Calypso's* chart room) that we on board were enabled to follow everything that happened to Philippe and Serge, or to Canoë and José Ruiz. It was a very popular program . . . The mechanics, the cook, the doctor, the crewmen — everyone invaded the bridge and clustered behind me, staring wide-eyed at the two screens which brought us simultaneous images of two aspects of the same occurrence. When I glanced behind me, I could see the gleam in the eyes of my companions and evaluate, from the tension reflected here, the fascination sharks hold for men. This electric atmosphere, which is inevitably created around the television screens when we are diving in a shark-infested area, is exactly the same as the atmos-

Now one shark has successfully retrieved the barracuda from Serge's grip, tearing it apart, while another is aggressively rushing to get a piece of the action.

A sliver of fish floating toward the cameraman's cage as a shark shoots for it like a torpedo. A diver is looking on in the background. In the upper-left corner, other sharks have also spotted this piece of fish and they, too, are rushing for it.

Serge has speared an innocent little fish that had passed by to witness the action. The sharks' reaction is instantaneous, as they make their dash for the poor fish.

Sharks have begun showing their excitement, shooting between the cages, four and five at a time, rushing past us in frustration, with quick nervous turns, biting at anything they find.

phere that fills a bull ring at the moment of truth. No other undersea adventure or experiment would release so much pent-up feeling in the members of our crew, and they have been dealing with sharks for more than fifteen years.

For me, television screens are an incomparable tool of observation. Pen clutched in hand, I am totally absorbed in these two jerky, glittering pictures, from beginning to end of each descent of the cages; hoping to note down the smallest point which might permit us to understand a little more of the motives of shark behavior. The undersea cameraman is provided with a radiotelephone, and so am I. I remain in constant communication with the team in the cages. Messages go through quite clearly from the surface to the bottom, but from the cages to the surface they are often quite difficult to understand. The diver's speech becomes nasal because of the increase in density of the air breathed in at a depth of sixty or seventy feet, and also because the sound of air bubbles escaping from the breathing apparatus obscures some words. I have, in fact, recommended that no conversation be carried on unless it was necessary to ask for a change in the placement of the cages or to interrupt the operation for reasons of safety.

Each time the cages are brought back to the ship, the divers come to me and share their personal observations. It is these men, the direct witnesses to what has taken place, who are the most sensitive element in all our experiments. It is they who, in *living* these experiments, are at the very sources of the information we are seeking. They may remark an entire sequence of indices which sometimes seem of no significance, but which I carefully note down. Undersea television is totally incapable of replacing direct human observation, but through it I am assured of constant contact with the various teams, as they replace each other in the water. And this, in turn, makes it possible for me to form a synthesis of the reports of all the divers.

Dives involving the use of the cages require lengthy preparation, and are difficult to set in operation. In the course of this expedition, we carried out a total of twenty-three such dives, averaging thirty-five minutes in length and anywhere between twenty-five and ninety feet in depth, at varying hours of both night and day. In the course of her stay on board the *Calypso,* Doctor Eugenie Clark often came into the chart room to watch the television screens with me and was essential in interpreting the events taking place below.

Shab Arab, which Philippe has described so graphically, is teeming with life. Netting more than two hundred pounds of fish (which we pass out to the sharks every day) is a formality requiring no more than half an hour. In addition to this, sharks themselves are extremely abundant in the vicinity of the reef, but since they cannot always be found, I have been led to the belief that they travel in bands, like wolves. Our numerous markings have, however, confirmed the fact that the sharks of Shab Arab are of a relatively sedentary nature. There are all sizes of them, some very large ones included, but the average size — which is a reflection of their average age — is smaller than that of the sharks to be found on the reefs in the Suakin region of the Red Sea. They became accustomed to our presence very rapidly, and seemed to have understood that we brought them food. Several times, we watched as they entered the divers' cages, and, each time, we on the surface were doubtless more frightened than the divers themselves; but on such occasions they never made any attempt to bite, only desperately trying to escape from the confined enclosure. Their period of excitement goes on for as long as there is food to be had. As soon as our sacks are empty, our sharks turn away and swim off into the distance. A large shark does not like the idea of a good piece of our fish being taken away by a smaller shark; he will race at him, seeming almost as though he were growling, bare his teeth and appear prepared for a kill, but he will not bite. The big nurse sharks will come and eat from the hand of the divers, but if they should be given a good fat piece of fish, one of the smaller white-finned sharks will approach and literally snatch it from their mouths. They would never dare do this sort of thing with a larger shark of their own species. They all prefer fresh fish to our refrigerated supplies, but they will grow sulky if the fish has been caught even so recently as the day before.

All these seemingly reassuring remarks have no significance whatever when one of the "frenzies" described by Philippe takes place. On such occasions, as we watch from the safety of the ship, we are overcome first by anxiety and then by terror. Twice, I have felt compelled to intervene and cut short the experiment by having the cages recalled to the surface.

Philippe Cousteau's narrative

I always remember the foregoing episode with surprise, since I had seen at least one case in which the outcome was very different: a wounded shark inspired not fear or caution but cannibalistic fury in the others. At a time when we were anchored near a reef in the Red Sea, we had decided to blast a passage

The sharks have now seized the fish.

It takes about five seconds for them to really take a bite and swallow it.

After that, their excitement is generated to the point of rushing on anything they can devour, and anything that happens to be in their path.

This one passing right in front of our camera is tagged. The small red tag following his dorsal fin floats like a little *banderilla* planted on his back on the near side. The tail of another shark underneath is moving by, much closer.

This photograph was shot with a very wide-angle lens, meaning that the sharks are as close as four feet — even closer — to the camera.

through the barrier with dynamite, so that our small boats might enter the lagoon. During the first tryouts of the electric detonators, Eugène Lagorio, who was in charge of setting up the necessary equipment, tossed one of them overboard, after having linked it with the plunger on the ship. He did this for two reasons: to avoid any possibility of someone's being hurt and to test the waterproof qualities of the detonator itself. At the precise moment at which Eugène pressed down on the plunger, a small shark none of us had seen swallowed the detonator. He had probably been attracted to it by its casing of brilliant copper. Before any of us had had a chance to move, we heard a muted detonation and then watched as the little shark began to sink to the bottom, trailing blood. Almost immediately, a large *Albimarginatus* appeared from out of nowhere, lunged at our unfortunate victim and sliced him in two with a single movement of his jaw. Then he turned on himself, swallowed the remainder of the little shark and went on his way, his belly swollen with food. Once again, we had been given a demonstration of the irregularity of the reactions of sharks. Their attitude is probably a function of circumstances which our atrophied senses cannot detect.

In this context, one other matter comes to mind; a fact related to the personality of sharks — because they do have a personality, despite their primitive appearance. In the first stages of a dive in a new territory, it is simple to mark a certain number of sharks almost immediately. But then we notice that all those that present themselves for our food have already been marked. In a short time, the divers are surrounded with sharks bearing a little banderilla, and it becomes impossible to learn anything about those that continue to remain aside. This is not a question of species, since the same thing occurs with all species. The only explanation that seems reasonable to me is that some sharks are more courageous than others of like size and species. This discovery had considerable importance in my mind, since it led me to observe

This is a shot of the same area, recounting the same type of frenzy much later at night. It is even more strange and frightening in the dark.

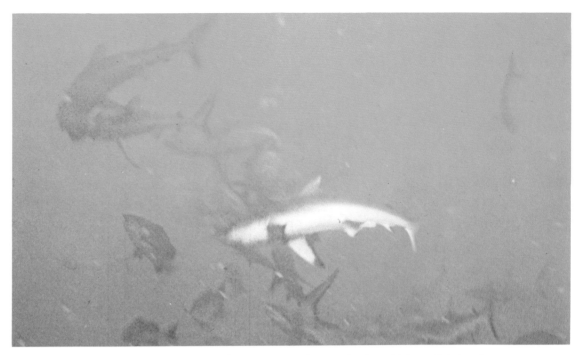

The bait in the upper-left-hand corner is being sought by two sharks, which are fighting for it as a herd of others are desperately trying to find the food by sense of smell. Since fish-bait scent permeates the area (we started distributing it two hours earlier), they are not very definite as to its location.

A typical daytime frenzy. An incredible disarray of twisting and turning bodies, tearing at the same piece of fish.

Finally, one shark snatches the food and absconds, pursued by all the others.

The chaos is now compounded. That shark exiting from Serge's cage had entered it by bending the cage bars out of shape on the other side. Serge is now pushing him out. We were very lucky that no harm befell any of us.

and marvel at the life of sharks, rather than regarding them simply as beautiful but potentially dangerous objects.

Since these earlier experiences, it has become possible for us — at least, in the majority of cases — to estimate the atmosphere of a dive in an area of sharks. From the moment of entrance into the water, we could foresee the probable tempo of the *corrida* and decide the need for strong protection or none at all. The trap, however, lies in trusting too much in this sense of perception, since, as we have observed so many times, the reactions of sharks are always unpredictable and often seem to reach the point of folly.

On the same evening as the great frenzy at Shab Arab, we decided to carry out a night dive. This time, we set the cages one above the other, instead of side by side. In this manner, the diver filming the experiment was situated above and could obtain a close-up view of the entire operation.

The instant the lower of the two cages had touched water, a pack of sharks struck at it as if they had been propelled by rockets. They tore at the steel of the bars, bit through the electric cables, and demolished several waterproof lights. The flat-bottomed aluminum boat, returning alongside after an exploratory trip, was violently attacked by sharks attempting to bite into the propeller of the outboard motor. But this larger and more powerful dentist's drill must have cut through several jaws, since blood began to spread in great, swirling clouds. The sharks, however, succeeded in stalling the forty-horsepower motor and breaking the cotter pin on the propeller. Canoë, wisely, ordered the cages brought up immediately, and the experiment was put off until another day.

On the next morning, there was only a single, small shark near the ship, and no others came throughout the day. What mysterious reason had caused them to flee we will know only when we have learned how to analyze the infinity of pressure waves, the new scents and sounds, those secret messengers of the sea.

We had recorded some interesting encounters with sharks during our Conshelf Two experience in the Red Sea, and we now turn to these for the light they throw on shark behavior.

TEN:
Sharks and Settlers
The Story of Conshelf Two
and the sharks.
In the saucer we meet the
Abyssal Shark.
The settlers.

Philippe Cousteau's narrative continues

I tightened the slipknot around my father's ankles, tapped lightly on his shoulder, and took my position six feet behind him, putting a little tension in the rope. He yanked his legs and I felt a tug on the rope; it was the "go" signal. At the same instant I heard the hushed noise of the camera starting to run. I began swimming straight ahead, slowly increasing speed until I reached the maximum I could do. Glancing rapidly above my shoulder, I could see the brilliantly lit twin windows right behind me, and clearly defined on them the silhouette of my father, whom I was towing backward straight out into the night. The dark water was warm and full of phosphorescent particles streaking the obscurity like innumerable shooting stars. I was breathing fast and hard, swimming as rapidly as I could, and when I glanced back again, the windows of the undersea house were far behind. Yet, I could still see shapes moving across the lighted frames. I felt another tug on my line and stopped, beads of sweat running down my forehead and along my nose behind the face plate. Turning around, I quickly freed my father's legs from the rope and we started back toward the Conshelf Two village.

From a distance, at night, the station looked like a science-fiction outerspace base. Multicolored rotating beacons marked the shape of the saucer hangar on the right, of the big "Starfish" main station in the center with the

This is a typical Red Sea or Indian Ocean reef, falling straight from the surface as far down as 2600 feet. The diver is using a low ledge for protection against a pack of sharks that were right in front of him. These cliffs of coral growth are an awesome sight.

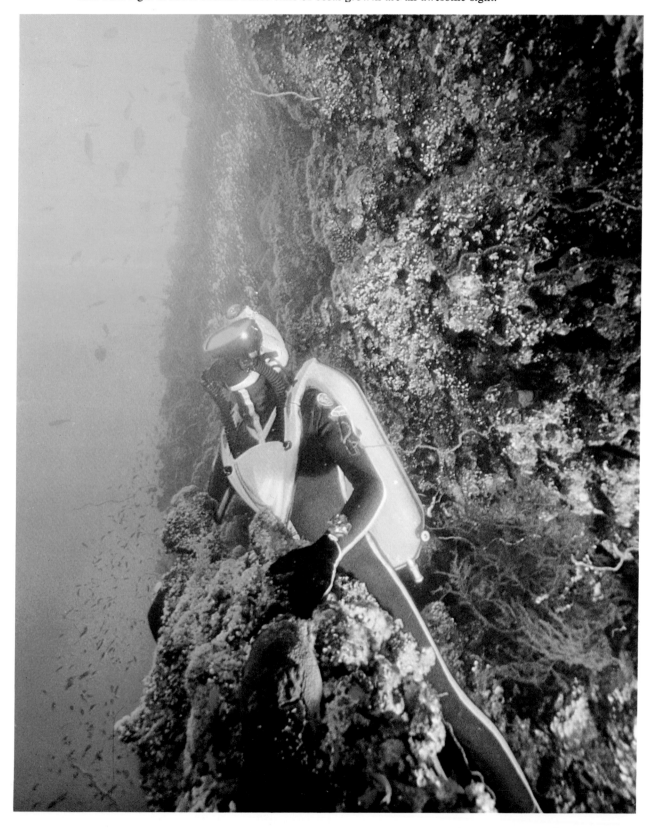

Some moments in the water prove poetic and magnificent, devoid of all false excitement, and filled with joy and beauty. This is the crevice between rocks and coral heads where the diver delights in swimming between the rocks and on into the overhang.

two picture windows, and farther below, of the deep cabin. Scattered around were several shacks, which housed equipment for everyday work. The upper station was resting on a sandy ledge thirty-six feet below the surface against the coral wall of the outer reef of the Shab Rumi (Roman Reef) atoll in the southern Red Sea. Fifty feet below the main-station level was the deep cabin, which was hung along the vertical coral cliff that formed the base of the whole reef. Up above our heads the elongated shape of the *Calypso's* hull reflected the green and red flashes of the beacons. We hurried back to the safety of the main habitat.

The Conshelf Two experiment had been planned to demonstrate the feasibility of manned undersea stations. The year was 1963. The location had been chosen so as to be away from all our bases of supplies and because of the extreme weather conditions. If it succeeded there on the desolate coast of Sudan, it would be possible to achieve the same thing anywhere on the globe. A team of six divers lived in the main station for a month, and two oceanauts occupied the deep cabin for two weeks. Chosen from professional and nonprofessional divers, the team experimented with new gas mixtures and worked all day at underwater chores. In the main habitat, "Starfish House," a complete biology laboratory supervised by Professor Vaissière studied reef ecology as well as microorganisms. One of the studies conducted during the Conshelf Two adventure was the intereffect of a human colony and its natural undersea surroundings.

During the experiment, everything had been recorded on film, and a movie entitled *World Without Sun* was made from the footage. It was for the purpose of shooting one of the sequences of this film that my father and I had been in the water that night. It was a long pullback from close to the habitat windows, and far into the darkness. My father held the camera and I pulled him backward for a distance of about a hundred yards. The result was such an unreal effect that many people believed, when seeing the shot on screen, that it had been faked in a studio. It had not been faked, and I remember my feelings as I swam in total darkness in waters where, as my father will recount, many sharks were lurking.

In fact, these four weeks of work on the bottom of the sea helped us to realize better what the relationship between future undersea settlers and their environment will be when man decides to colonize the sea floor. Understandably, we were most concerned with the problem of "sharks versus settlers."

Jacques-Yves Cousteau's narrative

The problem of sharks had been a major factor in all our preparations, and as is always the case when it comes to sharks, nothing had turned out as foreseen. At Shab Rumi, sharks were one of the favorite topics of conversation on board the two ships as well as in the houses beneath the sea.

"What has happened to all the sharks at Shab Rumi?" Albert (Bébert) Falco asked during one of our undersea dinners in Starfish House. "I explored the reefs along the Sudanese coast for more than eighty miles, and I found sharks everywhere; particularly here, at Shab Rumi. I hesitated to advise this location for the experiment, just because of them. And during the first weeks of work, when we were just setting up the village, they worried us constantly. What has happened to them now?"

"They are still here, Bébert," I said. "You saw some yourself, yesterday, at South Point. Kientzy reports having seen them every time he makes a dive from the Deep Cabin. And when I stand in the launch on the surface and there is a night dive going on down there, I am always worried, because I can see their fins, just a couple of hundred feet from the diver's lights."

"It's the same story with all the shark fisheries," Dumas remarked. "Everyone who thought he was going to make a fortune catching sharks, whether it was in South Africa or Australia, in the Gulf of Tadjoura or at Dakar, has eventually been forced to give it up. They may have a few months of miraculous catches, but then they find the sharks have gone. The same thing happened at Djibouti. In 1930 it was infested with sharks, but once the development of the port began, they went somewhere else. . . ."

I had personally met the most famous shark hunters, Captain Young, who wrote a classic book on sharks, and two remarkable women, Anita Conti and her associate, Paquerette, who had organized and directed a large shark fishery in Conakry. They all were of the opinion that sharks were smart enough to emigrate from fishing areas.

Here at Shab Rumi, however, since the first stages of our operations, we had disturbed the natural life of the reef as little as possible. I had forbidden

This is a mere example of the beauties of the reef, with its fan-coral background. The incredible shapes and colors of the fishes do not always seem to have a functional reason for being.

underwater spearfishing, and even fishing from the surface had been almost completely avoided. When we needed fish, we sent our small boats to hunt for them at a distance of more than five miles from our reef. We often distributed food to the moray eels, the snappers, the triggerfish, even to the barracudas. The moray eels came and ate from our hands. The triggerfish laid their eggs at the very doors of our undersea houses. One of them had actually been tamed by our diver-cook, Pierre Guilbert. In spite of our comings and goings, the savage bumpfish continued to sleep every night in the crevices no more than thirty feet from our village. We had even been adopted by an enormous barracuda we named Jules. We had hoped that the sharks, too, would remain, and we were equipped to study their habits without risk to ourselves or danger to them.

But they remained impervious to our lures. The live fish stocked in the fragile plastic enclosure constituted a form of provocation for them, but it had no effect. They had chosen to remain at a distance. Oh, we knew they were not very far away; they had simply enlarged the circumference of their circle around our installations. They came into the area only furtively, and at night.

A quarter of a mile or so from our village, at the southernmost tip of the atoll of Shab Rumi, there were still many open-ocean fish and sharks. One of these, a large tiger shark, was an old inhabitant of the region. He acted like a very sedentary Shab Rumi citizen. He circled around us every time we made an exploratory dive in those waters. (Philippe has told earlier how this brute hesitated for days before swallowing a spoiled carcass of beef that we had sunk right in the middle of his territory.)

In the third week of the Conshelf Two experiment, we wanted to collect geological samples from the reef at various depths. The oceanauts from Starfish House were in charge of gathering such samples in their authorized diving range, from thirty of eighty-five feet of depth. But deeper, such activity had not been planned for the two "black-mask oceanauts" living in the deep cabin. Accordingly, I organized a geological dive from the surface. Armand Davso was equipped with hammer and chisel. I took an underwater camera to film the action and Philippe accompanied us, carrying two spare cameras. We submerged. We rarely had gone down so fast as we did in trying to keep up with Davso, who was drawn down like a piece of lead by his sledge-hammer. We passed swiftly along Starfish House on the left, then along the deep cabin on the right. At one hundred and fifty feet, the vertical coral cliff ended abruptly and a grayish sandy beach sloped down to the "second cliff" a hun-

SHARKS AND SETTLERS 177

dred feet away. There, on the edge of the new drop-off, stood one of our five small antishark cages, a shelter for oceanauts, connected to the undersea headquarters of Starfish House by special alarm signals. We had carefully installed and tested all this shark-proof emergency equipment, but had never had an opportunity to use it.

We sank deeper, reached 230 feet, stopped. I selected a big block of coral rock and triggered my camera; Davso started hammering heavily on the block. The loud, muffled clangs disrupted the silence of the deep. Almost at once, I saw in the field of my camera two large white-tip sharks emerging from the blue and rushing to the scene, straight toward Davso's back. I shouted in my mouthpiece. Davso did not hear and kept on hammering. Philippe then acted as a bodyguard and swam directly at them. They slowly altered their course, passed alongside Davso, circled close around us for a while, and vanished as they had come. We had had no time to retreat to the shark cage. . . . The loud hammering had attracted sharks as explosions do, and Philippe's decisive attitude had discouraged them.

We went back with the desired samples, watching the ponderous Davso climb the cliffs as a mountain climber would. Back on board, we told Davso the experience he had missed by being so conscientious in his work.

It does seem probable that sharks remain away from any center of human activity in the sea, more or less as tigers remain at a distance from the towns and villages of India. Inhabited undersea stations, which are certain to multiply in number in the future, will therefore have little to fear from sharks. But why should sharks withdraw thus, when they have had no experience with man, that newcomer to the ocean? I cannot help but relate this fact to observations we have often made on the high seas — primarily of scores of formidable deep-sea sharks remaining at a respectful distance from schools of dolphins or whales. It is possible that sharks vaguely identify us with these marine mammals. In that event, they would not hesitate to attack us if we were alone or in difficulty, but they will remain at a prudent distance from any of our collective installations.

It was now nine o'clock in the evening — time to call an end to our exchange of views on the subject of sharks, to take leave of our hosts, the oceanauts, to leave Starfish House, and to return to the *Calypso*. Dumas, Falco, and I got into our diving gear in the ready room. I suggested to my two comrades that we might make a short tour of the undersea village before going back to the surface.

The water slapped back and forth in the entrance hatch just as it would

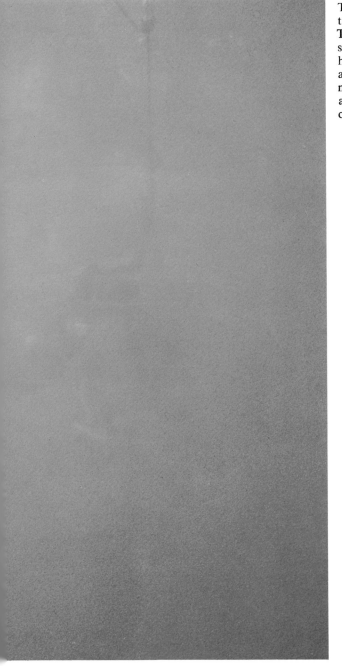

The shark cages had been lowered out at sea. A tiger shark of considerable size is passing by. This is a fairly rare species. We consider tiger sharks extremely dangerous. Although we haven't had much experience with them, they are capable of grave damage. Their jaws are massive, teeth razor-sharp, muscles powerful, and their mouth is out of proportion to the size of their bodies.

in a very small swimming pool. One after the other, we slipped down through this horizontal doorway and found ourselves floating free in the darkness of night, behind the steel bars of the antishark vestibule. We lit our waterproof guide lights and left this big cage, which now appeared to have been a useless protection, since the sharks had left the area.

At first, we swam slowly over to the saucer hangar, and I lifted my head out of water in the interior of this strange garage beneath the sea. Our little submarine was there. A red light on the electric panel indicated that the batteries were being charged. After a brief look around, we returned to open water. The coral shelf dropped away sheer beneath us, and a moment or two later we could make out the vertical cylinder of the deep cabin. When we reached it, eighty-five feet beneath the surface, I glanced through the portholes. Kientzy and Portelatine had turned out all the lights and were doubtless seeking a period of sleep made difficult by the heat and humidity inside.

I hesitated to go down farther. At this time of night, the narrow beam of our lights was of little help, and the black void beneath us was a realm of fear. We pushed on to the base of the cliff and then swam along its embankment, one hundred and fifty feet below the surface. We came to a clump of black coral where, standing before us like some giant lobster trap, was our antishark cage Number One. It seemed to me that I had caught a glimpse of a long silhouette and the glittering reflection of a greenish eye. We turned and began the ascent of the cliffside. A swarm of brightly colored fish hovered around our four cubic enclosures as we passed. We could make out a dim light above us and a little farther out. That would be the *Calypso*. Beneath her stern, near the ladder we would use to climb aboard, hung a thirty-foot length of rope, weighted down with iron. In order to effect the indispensable breathing period that would protect us from accidents of decompression, we were forced to remain here for forty minutes, clinging to the rope in the darkness, accompanied rather disturbingly by our barracuda, Jules.

The *Calypso* was anchored just southwest of the island of Socotra, in the northern part of the Indian Ocean near the Gulf of Aden, where the bottom is about three hundred feet in depth. Henri Plé, who was on duty on the bridge, came to tell me that the saucer was ready. In spite of the overpowering heat, I pulled on a wool slipover: it would be cold below. The saucer was resting on its cradle on the afterdeck. Albert Falco and I weighed ourselves on a bathroom scale, and our respective weights were inscribed in chalk on a small blackboard. Armand Davso calculated the total and decided to add a little more water to the ballast inside the saucer. This correction should insure, roughly at least, the equilibrium of the little submarine.

Falco and I squeezed into the saucer, and as he carefully closed and screwed down the hatch, I regulated the oxygen supply, opened the ventilator of the air-purification system, checked the batteries, the oil pressure, and the heading indicated on the gyroscopic compass. I synchronized our timepieces and Falco turned on the tape recorder. He then signaled by telephone to Jacques Roux, the saucer's maintenance engineer, that everything was in working order. We stretched out on our stomachs on the foam-rubber mattresses, which had been designed so that our heads would be close to individual viewing portholes. Inside the saucer, there was a quiet but resonant ambiance resembling that of a factory. Some of the engines turned constantly, others started and stopped automatically, and contact elements snapped periodically. Maurice Léandri maneuvered the hydraulic crane that lifted the saucer from its cradle on the *Calypso's* deck, and for a few seconds we swung gently in the air. Then, with Maurice's habitual mastery of this operation, the saucer slipped gently into the sea, creating no more sound than the crumpling of a piece of silk.

Almost at once I saw two sharks cruising at some distance from us. Christian Bonnici, the diver in charge of getting the saucer safely away, did not lose sight of them for a moment, even though he was also carrying out his routine tasks. First, he scrubbed off the plexiglass portholes, and then, at a signal from Falco, climbed to the upper surface of the saucer, disconnected the telephone, and unhooked the last nylon rope linking us with the world outside. Slowly, the saucer began to go down. Our echo sounder clearly indicated the edge of the reef, three hundred feet below. We settled on it just a few minutes later. It was a grayish plain consisting of mud and fragments of stone. Falco dropped the seventy-five-pound outside ballast, which had helped to carry us down, and regulated our ability to descend or ascend by pumping out several liters of water. Next, he switched on our primary motive power, twin pusher jets, coughing out powerful streams of water to our stern, and we headed to the south, along the line of sharpest descent.

At a depth of 325 feet, we reached the sharply defined line that separated the plateau from the cliff. And here, as in the Red Sea, we came across an overhanging "sidewalk" that ran along the upper edge of the cliff. Until this time, no instrument, no echo sounder, however precise, had ever detected the presence of this ledge. It is a perfectly horizontal *corniche,* from six to

The beam of our lamps detects a blue shark swimming close by, his mouth open for breathing, and his wide eyes adapted for night vision. His reflection on the flat, calm surface appears almost as worrisome and perilous as he actually is.

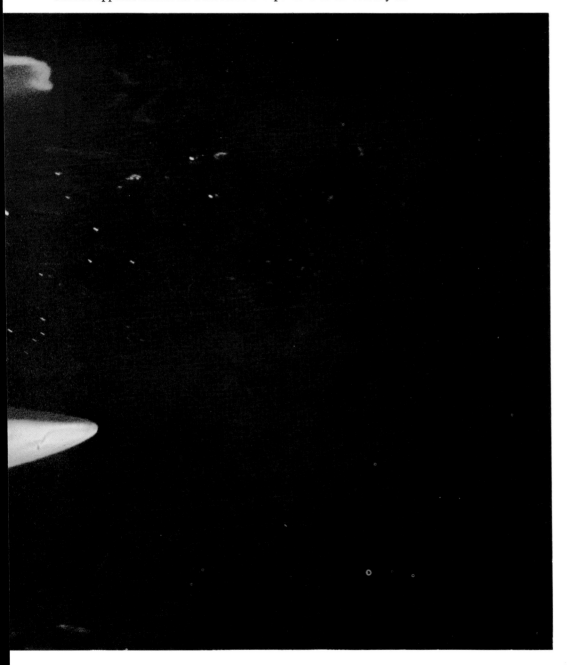

thirty feet wide, running continuously along the crests of the ridges, through all the reefs, the islands, and the buried volcanic peaks — always at a depth of 330 to 350 feet. This discovery, which we could have made only from the saucer, suggests that the surface of the sea in this area was at this level during one of the great glacial epochs thousands of years ago.

The two sharks had followed us as far as this, but they deserted us when we began drifting slowly down along the cliff. On this wall of naked rock, life forms became progressively rare. Occasionally we would sight some gorgonians, which are also known as fan coral, some Bryozoa and small crustaceans, but very few fish of any kind.

At about 450 feet, the saucer stopped sinking and came to rest between two levels of water, as if it were poised on a sea floor. "It's the thermocline," Falco said. We had reached the frontier between the warm surface water and the cold water of the depths, and were floating on a layer of fluid that was denser because it was colder. We could have continued our descent at once by letting a few quarts of water into our internal ballast, but we preferred to let nature make the necessary correction herself, by chilling the outer shell of the saucer. The thermometer fell from 32° to 25° Centigrade. Falco put on a sweater. In a few moments, our gravitational descent resumed.

At a depth of more than 850 feet, we reached the end of the vertical desert. The cliff here was riddled with large crevices, teeming with fat red fish weighing as much as five or six pounds, and also some large groupers. We settled on a kind of step about thirty feet wide and paused to examine the animated world around us. The rocks were studded with strange little crustaceans, eight inches long and waving claws almost as large as themselves; the cliff walls were almost hidden by clouds of shrimp. Fish we had never seen before were emerging from holes everywhere, as if they were eager to inspect us: some of them were bright red, while others were a motley design of mauve and yellow; still others were marked with vertical stripes of brown and white. As far as the eye could see across the mud and pebbly-sand expanse of the flat bottom, there were thousands, millions of crabs.

We started the jets again, heading east and skirting the base of the cliff. Everywhere we looked, the ground was masked by a tide of tangled, marching, kicking crabs, most of them about the size of a man's fist. This gigantic congress of crabs must certainly have been brought about by the fact that it was their mating time. Falco and I spent almost an hour gliding over this living carpet, occasionally pausing for a few moments to observe the behavior of the crabs.

Suddenly, Falco cried out, "Look, Commandant, to your left, in the distance!" I squinted my eyes against the porthole, trying to see as far as possible. A form that was still not clear to me was climbing slowly toward us. It was a shark, but an enormous, unbelievable shark. He was swimming straight toward the saucer, as though he were blinded by our lights. I did not at first recognize the species; it was the monster's size that impressed me most. He must have been twice as long as our little submarine, and weighed easily three thousand pounds. He swept around the saucer in a majestic arc and miscalculated his course; a powerful sweep of his tail shook us up considerably. Obviously, we were in no danger inside our steel armor, but it is a rather strange experience to feel yourself being knocked about by a creature of this size, almost nine hundred feet below the surface of the sea.

The enormous beast made several turns in front of us, while still caught in the glare of our lights. I could not help but admire his power and grace — the strength of a bull, the supple movement of a serpent. He had six branchial clefts on either side of his head, and this helped me to identify him. He was a *Hexanchus griseus,* sometimes called a cow shark. He is very rarely encountered, presumably because he inhabits areas of great depth and comes to the surface only on very rare occasions. The way our giant "six-clefts" friend behaved, I could not help but associate him with two other giants, even larger than he, the whale shark and the basking shark. They all make only rare or seasonal appearances at the surface. The rest of the time they vanish to untold depths and provinces; practically nothing is known of their lives in the depths. Maybe some of them are responsible for these mysterious large excavations in the mud that we have often photographed with automatic deep cameras lowered to the bottom of the Mediterranean, eight thousand feet down.

Our cow shark swam around us long enough for us to film him, and then bumped into the saucer again, apparently by accident. In any event, he was suddenly seized with panic, gave another violent flick of his tail, and disappeared into the depths of his own kingdom. And this kingdom, alas, was still inaccessible to the diving saucer. Poised at the edge of the second cliff, Falco and I swept the void into which the giant had disappeared with the saucer's headlights, hoping to attract him back toward us. After half an hour

Blue shark in the night.

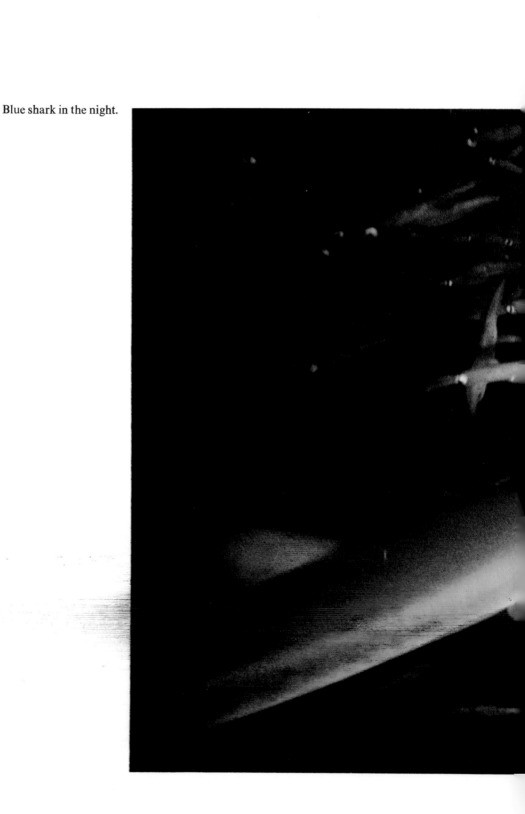

of waiting in vain, Falco jettisoned a fifty-five-pound ballast weight, so that we could return to the surface. Twenty minutes later, we were picked out of the water by the *Calypso*. For many weeks after that, both Falco and I talked and dreamed of the extraordinary dive and of our meeting with the cow shark, the lord of depths that are still beyond our reach.

Coexistence between sharks and settlers is not always entirely peaceful. We had a dramatic demonstration of this near the reef of Shab Arab, in the Gulf of Aden. The *Calypso* was anchored at the extreme northern edge of the reef, above an area of vertical cliffs, which, here too, dropped straight down to a depth of nearly nine hundred feet.

Falco and I decided to make a night dive along these cliffs in the diving saucer. As soon as it had been put in the water, we saw several large sharks in the beams from our headlights. Their number increased rapidly as we went down, and in a short time we estimated that there were at least three dozen of them surrounding us. They seemed much more active than was normal. We set down the saucer on a little mud slope at a depth of about 350 feet, to carry out the usual instrument check and adjust our buoyancy before continuing our exploration. Through the portholes, perfectly safe inside our metal shell, we could see all those sinister silhouettes, now circling very close around us. The spectacle was unique and magnificent. Unfortunately, the saucer's cameras were able to film only a very small part of the mad round dance. We decided to return to the surface and set up a dive with an anti-shark cage, so that our cinematographer could film our divers and this exceptional horde of sharks at the same time.

Half an hour later, after we had attached powerful floodlights to the cage, it was put into the water, empty, as usual, and dropped to a depth of one hundred feet. The cameraman, Pierre Goupil, his assistant, Pierre Duhalde, and two divers, Christian Bonnici and Raymond Coll, followed it into the water, carrying their cameras and shark billies. The brilliantly lit cage provided them with a perfect point of reference, and they went down rapidly, experiencing no particular fear. When they were halfway to the cage, they could see the green glitter of the eyes of a dozen or so sharks reflected in the beam from their own flood lamps. They set to work calmly to film them, but the pack of sharks at once began circling around our crew, and as the circles drew tighter the number of sharks increased. Within a few moments, there were about seventy of them in the immediate vicinity. Suddenly the divers realized that there was no longer a question of filming but of self-protection.

Goupil was confronted with a difficult decision. The antishark cage could hold only three men, which would leave the fourth alone and at the mercy of the vast pack of predators. Goupil rang several times on the alarm, to have the cage pulled back to the *Calypso's* deck, and then seized his assistant, who was the least experienced of the divers, and pushed him inside. Then Goupil, Bonnici, and Coll installed themselves as well as they could on top of the cage, sitting back to back and facing out toward every possible angle of attack.

The sharks immediately broke their circling formation and launched themselves forward like wolves, directly toward the men, obviously aware of their crushing superiority in numbers. The divers fought back with shark billies, cameras, lights, anything they had in their hands. On the deck of the *Calypso,* no one had yet grasped the gravity of the situation. Following Goupil's signal, one of the divers who was operating the winch thought it best to bring up the cage very slowly, to facilitate the process of decompression for the men below. The closer it came to the surface, the more fiercely the sharks attacked, but somehow the three men on top of the cage managed to beat them off. When it broke water at last and was hauled aboard, they were all unhurt. The frustrated killers thrashed the surface into a miniature storm.

Goupil had scarcely recovered from the shock of this attack when he suggested going down again, but with just two men, this time locked inside the cage before it was lowered into the water. Since the diving saucer would be in no danger, he wanted to film it with this horde of sharks, rather than risk the lives of other divers. The idea seemed a good one, so we altered the floodlight arrays on the cage and Pierre Goupil and Daniel Tomasi took their places inside, where they, too, would be perfectly safe. Falco and I piloted the saucer to a depth of about eighty feet, in the midst of the shark pack. All this, of course, required a certain amount of time. When the saucer finally drew close to the cage, Falco and I were astonished by the sight of Goupil and Tomasi, having dropped their cameras, performing a crazy kind of dance inside the cage. They were leaping about in every direction possible and slapping constantly at their ankles. Thousands of little white dots were swirling around them, picked out clearly in the brilliant light of the projectors, and reminding us of mosquitoes or gnats caught in the lights of a garden on a summer night. The human silhouettes inside the cage were twisting into every imaginable shape, as if seized by some sudden madness. The cameras and the sharks had been forgotten. Neither Falco nor I could understand what had happened, but a moment later, we saw the cage start up toward the

This blue shark leaves the standard wake at the surface; he is about to pursue the large group of squid on the other side.

surface, doubtless as a result of the second sounding of the alarm that night.

Half an hour later the saucer was back in its cradle on the deck of the *Calypso*, and we climbed out. The after deck was deserted, but it was also covered with blood stains. I raced to the officers' mess and found Goupil and Tomasi stretched out on tables there, with bandages around their ankles and their features still drawn with lines of pain. There were spots of blood on the floor, on the tables, and even on the partitions. The doctor was perplexed and anxious. Our friends had been attacked, as soon as they entered the water, by thousands of "sea mosquitoes," which are tiny isopods, a form of planktonic crustacean almost invisible to the eye but as ferocious for its size as the famous piranhas of the Amazon. The claws of these isopods tear off a minute portion of flesh every time they bite. Each of our two victims had lost at least a pint of blood.

Goupil and Tomasi had been completely protected against them by their neoprene diving suits — except for the small area of their ankles between the rubber fins and the bottom of the tight-fitting pants. As the cage was being hauled to the surface, they had been battling these mini-monsters and were almost unaware of the sharks encircling them. Maurice Léandri, who was operating the crane, had stopped it for five minutes, while the cage was still several feet below the surface, to allow for the obligatory decompression period.

Goupil said to me: "During that halt, I was suffering such torture from the mosquitoes that I was tempted to open the door and go out and join the sharks...."

When the *Calypso* came back to home port from the Conshelf Two experiment in the Red Sea, we had gained considerable experience with sharks and with manned undersea stations. We began thinking about the future of human settlements on the bottom of the oceans and about the relationship that would develop between sharks and settlers.

We started at once to prepare for Conshelf Three — twenty-seven days at 330 feet in the Mediterranean. The experiment was to take place two years later, but without delay we drafted long-term programs in the fields of engineering, of physiology, and of practical applications.

In Marseilles, facilities were built to carry tank dives to a theoretical depth of five thousand feet; in such chambers, it would be possible to determine the reasonable limits of helium-oxygen "saturation dives," as well as to test the intricate instrumentation needed in the very deep Conshelf station of the future.

Plans were made for a three-hundred-ton, ten-man submarine completely self-supported and capable of becoming a mobile "home under the sea" for four oceanauts diving and working extensively at depths down to two thousand feet. This independent mobile settlement, called "l'Argyronète," is now under construction.

An international training center for scientist-oceanauts was proposed to UNESCO and recommended by the Intergovernmental Oceanographic Conference.

Projects were studied to carry the activity of undersea settlers into various fields such as undersea farming, mining, drilling for oil, oil exploitation, geological and biological observations and studies, and entertainment centers.

A long-range program was outlined to develop an amphibious man: *Homo aquaticus.*

The future of human settlements on and beyond the continental shelf is almost unlimited. Of course, I do not believe that human colonies will ever emigrate to the sea floor forever: we are too much dependent on our natural environment, and there would be no serious reason to abandon all those things we love: sunshine, fresh air, country, landscapes . . .

But there will be, more and more, important tasks in science and industry that will require temporary but extended settlements of large groups of human beings working on the bottom of the sea for several months at a time. Locked there by decompression problems, they will need medical and recreational facilities, very much in the same way as oil specialists settle in the desert for periods of — say — five months. These requirements mean huge constructions and investments. Such schemes will be possible only when a quantity of problems are solved. Among these problems is protection against sharks.

Today we think that sharks retreat from an area where settlements are constructed. But we are sure that they do not retreat very far; they stay in the vicinity. They may be attracted back to the inhabited area by explosions or by a variety of noises like bangs or clangs. And we do not know if, after a longer period, they would not overcome their fear and come back in packs to attack isolated small groups of workers. A lot more research is necessary. A good working theory would be that the world of fish in general and of sharks in particular is less of a visual world than it is a world of acoustic and pressure waves. Sound and pressure waves of yet little-known frequencies may be able to attract sharks or to repel them from the settlements.

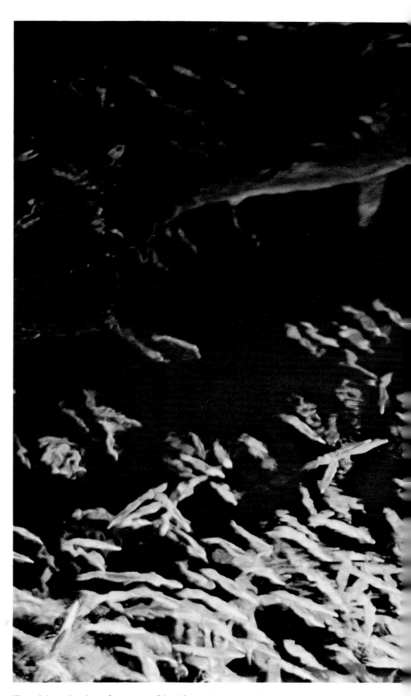

Two blue sharks of respectable dimensions, eating.

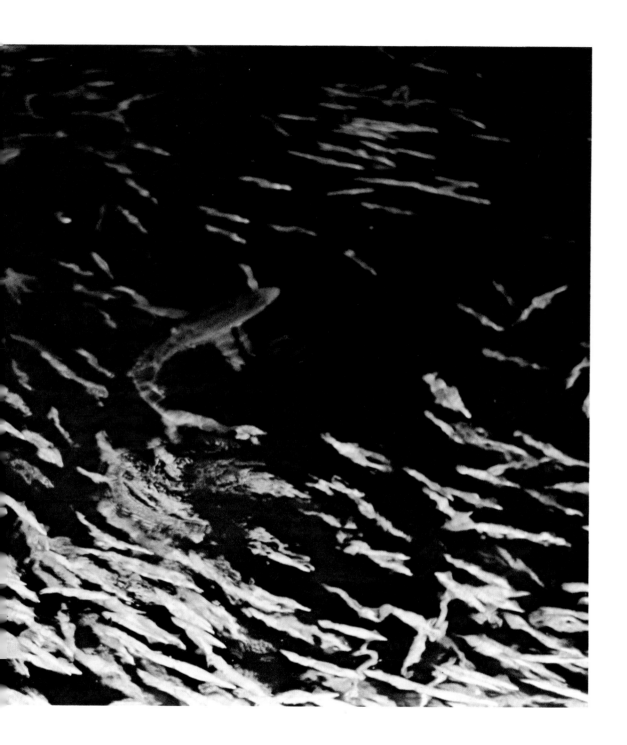

ELEVEN:
Peaceful Giant
Our encounter
with a whale shark.
Shark legends.

Philippe Cousteau's narrative

It was not until May of 1967 that we finally encountered a whale shark. For a week the *Calypso* had been sailing a north-northwest course in the Indian Ocean, from Diego-Suarez toward the Gulf of Tadjoura. The stopover in Diego-Suarez had been our first important port of call since February and, as it always was, our reception in this great port of the Malagasy Republic had been charming. The *Calypso* was placed in the hands of the workers in the naval shipyard, and for the next week they labored to remove the marks of almost four months of constant navigation and hard work.

The long evenings spent in conversation on the terrace of the hotel, dreaming of future projects and listening to the whispered sounds of the forest, far from the constant movement of the deck beneath our feet and the continuous murmuring of the ship and all its mechanical equipment, had revived our thirst for a new departure, new scenes of action. Beneath the apparent nostalgia we felt as we watched the land drop below the horizon, far behind us, we sensed the quiet enthusiasm which always accompanies a new beginning. During this week when we had been sailing north, we had imagined and prepared all sorts of traps we had never used before, and made our plans for new experiments, which would allow us, perhaps, to arrive at a better understanding of sharks.

But nothing had prepared us for this splendid meeting. The whale shark is certainly the largest fish in the world. He may reach a length of sixty-five feet, and a size of thirty or more feet is quite common. Encounters with this giant are rare, and no one knows precisely whether he follows a strange pat-

The whale shark is certainly the largest fish in the world. It is a shark, albeit totally harmless. This shark very seldom appears at the ocean's surface; it is fairly curious about divers and will not swim away at great speeds, of which it is capable. It usually swims leisurely in areas where vast quantities of plankton may be found. Although their shape is monstrous, the whale sharks are not likely to harm a diver with their mouth, but a stroke of their powerful tail would bear disastrous consequences.

tern of migration or is sedentary. He feeds on plankton and small fish, as do whales, and probably passes his life following the deep-sea currents which carry his nourishment from one ocean to another. My father, in all his long career as a navigator, has encountered this enormous animal only twice.

The whale shark is a squalus with five branchial clefts, bearing the scientific name *Rhineodon typus.** He is gray-brown on the back and sides, with round white or yellow spots spaced throughout the body and the tail, becoming smaller and more closely grouped on the head. Sinuous bands of color, yellow or white, and very narrow, mark his back with transverse stripings. The belly is white or yellow. The mouth is almost always open, forming a gap as much as six feet in width and from twelve to twenty inches in height. It is lined with a surface of rough platings, probably intended to crush any prey which might be a trifle too large.

In spite of his colossal size, the whale shark is considered harmless to man. He swims lazily, at a speed not exceeding three knots. He is often covered with a large number of remoras and surrounded by a myriad of pilot fish of all sizes, from the thickness of a man's thumb to that of a tennis racquet handle. We had all heard a great deal of talk about this giant of the seas, but no one on board had yet been close to one.

As was customary on board the *Calypso* in periods of normal navigation, two men were permanently assigned to lookout duty and charged with reporting any form of activity that might call for investigation. Whether it was the air spout of a whale or a simple piece of floating wood, nothing was too small or too insignificant for us. My father's insatiable curiosity about everything concerning the sea had communicated itself to the entire crew, and the smallest unidentified spot on the surface was sufficient to warrant a detour.

Jacques-Yves Cousteau's narrative

Sunday, May 7. 11:30 A.M. The *Calypso* was cruising at ten knots, between Mombasa and Djibouti. At this time of year, the Indian Ocean, where it borders the coast of Africa, is still calm. The famous southwest monsoon is already assembling its forces, but has not yet attacked. The surface of the water reflects disturbing tropical clouds, but there has been no indication of life to attract our attention since the day before. Not the smallest school of bonito, not a single flying fish, and no sign of the blowing of a whale.

*The name is sometimes given as *Rhincodon typus.*

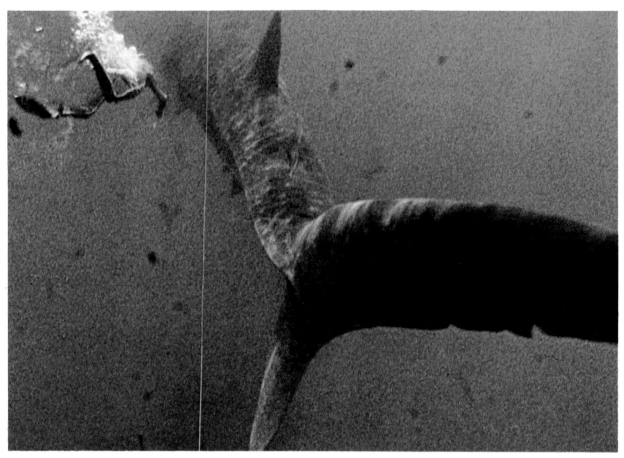

This is another view. The diver is swimming extremely
fast to catch up with the whale shark, although the
animal itself is moving very slowly.

The diver had been released from our launch some distance back. When
the shark finally outdistanced him substantially, we picked the diver up
and gained speed to catch up with the shark. After the shark outdistanced him again, the diver climbed back on board the *Zodiac* and we
set out to catch up with the shark once more.

The sea resembles a desert, and yet the water is not very clear. The surface is laden with plankton large enough to be seen when we look out over the deck rails. This morning, we had spent a long time studying the passage of this stream of minute, erratic creatures, through the portholes of the observation chamber beneath the prow. They were simply white dots, or filaments, or little cups of crystal; a whole world of Copepoda, of jellyfish, of salpa. And all this population, of course, struggles for its own survival, obeying the same simple and cruel laws as the fish of the reefs and the beasts of the jungle. But their destiny depends on themselves to only a very small degree. They are carried about at the whim of the currents. They proliferate or die in mass, according to the caprice of temperature or salinity. This morning, the tropical sea was so thickened by the quantity of suspended living matter it contained that it resembled nothing so much as a gigantic bowl of hot soup, served for some unknown Gargantua. This ridiculous idea, which we had at first exchanged as a joke, was suddenly to find an unexpected confirmation.

At eleven thirty-five, Pierre Li on the port watch noticed something in the water and called it to the attention of the bridge. A few moments later Captain Roger Maritano ordered the helm to port, and the *Calypso* was on her way to track down the object. At first, we could make out only two large fins, separated from each other by a distance of many feet, but there could be no doubt that this was a very large animal. Soon, it became evident that it was not a species of marine mammal. It appeared, in fact, to be an enormous shark, half asleep on the surface. A pilgrim shark or a whale shark? We knew very little of either. The pilgrim shark is an impressive specimen, sometimes attaining a length of thirty feet. He makes an appearance in the Mediterranean during the spring (generally in April), traveling in little groups and swimming lazily on the surface. Then he disappears, and no one knows exactly where or how he lives during the rest of the year. But the whale shark is by far the largest and heaviest living fish of our time — if one bears in mind that the whale itself is not a fish, but a mammal. The whale shark is a pure shark, and only his size justifies his descriptive name. This giant likes warm and very deep waters, and comes to the surface very, very seldom. An encounter with him is a rare event indeed...

Excitement aboard the ship was intense. The *Zodiac* was put into the water within a few minutes, and the cameramen, Barsky and Deloire, and the divers, Falco and Coll, leaped into it. They made a noiseless approach to the somnolent animal, and the divers slipped into the water. The shark's tail was very tall and very long, the dorsal fin massive and rounded — it was actually a whale shark! He seemed interested by the *Zodiac,* and began to swim very slowly around it. He was about thirty-five feet long. Deloire swam closer, trying to film him with an undersea camera provided with a wide-angle lens. The enormous animal presented his profile first, and then came straight toward the camera. His open jaw resembled the forward end of a jet engine on an airliner. When he was no more than five feet away from Deloire, he suddenly submerged, just enough to pass beneath the diver. Coll, for his part, had equipped himself with his famous banderilla, with which he had already marked so many other sharks. He dived with the monster, and dived again; each time he was outdistanced he would climb back on board the *Zodiac.* When the little boat caught up with the shark, Coll dived once more. When he emerged from the water for the last time, he described what had happened, in his usual laconic terms:

"The caudal fin is six and a half feet, from end to end. The dorsal is a little over four feet at its base and almost four feet in height. The eyes are round, slightly slanted, and very alert. He sees very well. Twice, he came back for another look at the *Zodiac,* and each time that we approached him from in front, he lowered his head a little and passed beneath us. We saw him dive several times: he begins by inclining gently toward the bottom and goes deeper, in the manner of a submarine, but when he does this he comes back to the surface a few minutes later and just a little farther away. But when he had had enough of playing with us, he just swung over to a vertical axis and disappeared, straight down, like a sounding whale. I held on to his tail several times, and he did not react at all — either to attack or to defend himself. His skin is rough and covered with round spots, hard to see. There were remoras clinging to his skin almost everywhere, especially behind the branchial clefts. There is a cavity there, where they go in and come out. There was only one pilot fish with him, a striped one. I had trouble planting a plaque near his dorsal fin; the skin is very hard to pierce and I twisted the point of the spear."

A few minutes later, a second specimen of the same species appeared, an even larger one than the first. This one measured forty to fifty feet. Number Two, as we christened him, did not stay with us as long as his predecessor, but Coll succeeded in marking him and then, clinging to his dorsal fin, was dragged down with him as he plunged into the depths. Coll stayed with him to a depth of almost a hundred and fifty feet.

"At no time," he told me later, "did he even attempt to escape or to get rid of me. His only reaction occurred when we came into his line of vision, and the reaction was curiosity . . ."

Meeting with and filming the two whale sharks was a considerable stroke of luck. Why is it that they are so seldom observed? Undoubtedly because they come to the surface only under very particular and very rare circumstances — perhaps when, in especially fine weather, a certain admixture of plankton of which they happen to be fond is carried to the surface by the current. In fact, when we were able to study them underwater, our two prize specimens seemed to be swallowing enormous quantities of plankton in their gaping jaws. Baleen whales also feed exclusively on plankton and very small marine animals, and they are equipped to gorge themselves on this form of nourishment at a depth of up to eighty feet during the night and, sometimes, at a depth of as much as seventeen hundred feet during the day. The depth of the plankton varies with the light. The whales come to the surface only sufficiently often to breathe. Whale sharks, which are not subject to this need, come to the surface far more rarely, almost inadvertently.

Perhaps because of the similarity of their feeding habits, there exists another resemblance in the behavior patterns of whale sharks (cold-blooded fishes) and whales (warm-blooded mammals): we had just had an opportunity to observe with our own eyes the fact that whale sharks do not submerge by swimming toward the bottom on an oblique line. They *sound,* going straight down on a vertical line. No other shark does the same thing.

The divers had been particularly impressed by the enormous opening of the jaw, likening it, as I have mentioned, to the forward opening of a jet engine. The whale shark's teeth are very small, but they can be dangerous. Our American friend, Conrad Limbaugh, was once seriously hurt when his forearm was accidentally caught in this gigantic mouth. Although the shark, obviously, did not bite, Conrad nonetheless suffered extensive bruises and lost considerable portions of skin.

Philippe Cousteau's narrative

It seems natural that animals as fabulous as sharks should have inspired all sorts of legends and customs among the primitive peoples inhabiting the shores of the sea. What seems less natural is the fact that, in the majority of

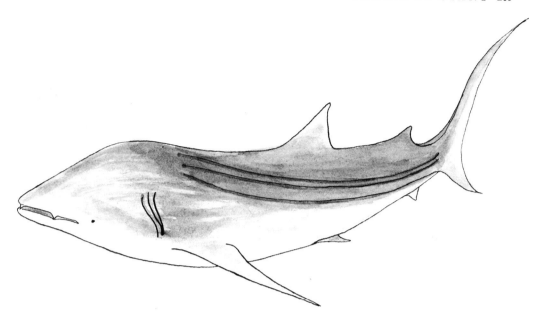

such tales, the shark assumes the personality of a benefactor. He may be Kama-Hoa-Lii, the reincarnation of a well-loved ancestor, or the god of plenty, or even the protector of fishermen lost at sea. Never, in the course of all of my visits to out-of-the-way seafaring communities such as these, have I heard the shark spoken of as traditionally an evil animal. This attitude is all the more surprising when it is considered that relatively inoffensive animals such as whales are generally considered malefactors by most primitive populations. And other species, which are totally incapable of the slightest harm except in the event of an improbable accident, have a reputation as bad as it is completely unjustified. The manta rays, which are frequently called "devil-fish," are a good example of this. In his book, *Sharks Are Fished at Night,* François Poli speaks of the superstitious fear in which the giant ray is held by fishermen along the coast of Cuba. Some of these men even claim to have been hypnotized by the manta, and there are stories to the effect that boats have been dragged down into the depths with their entire crew aboard, or that the monster has been seen to leap to a prodigious height and then fall back on a fishing boat, crushing it relentlessly beneath his fantastic weight.

All the books of discoveries and the tales of journeys across the seas in the Middle Ages speak of marine monsters enveloping ships in their tentacles and breaking them up like nutshells. Such imagery certainly contributed to giving the sailors of the time a reputation for bravery, which is well justified, in fact, when one thinks of the ships of that day and of their incredible fragility. It may very well have been a thirst for local renown that led these men of the sea to spread such stories. Although it is true that the giant squid actually does reach more than fifty feet in size, the appearance of such monstrous animals is extremely rare. During their crossing of the Humboldt Current, the members of the *Kon-Tiki* expedition saw many of them, several nights running, but fortunately they caused no damage. To my knowledge, the best example of an unjustified reputation for evil is that of the giant clam. According to legend, this warm-water bivalve mollusk is capable of closing on the arm or leg of a diver and holding him prisoner until he drowns or until the man himself amputates the imprisoned limb. Although this creature really does attain proportions of as much as two hundred and fifty pounds, the space between the edges of its shells, in an open position, is proportionately so small that it would require the abilities of a contortionist to slip even the wrist between them.

The shark, on the contrary, is an actual menace, and is present in practically all the waters of the world. However, perhaps in an attempt to reassure himself, man has made him into a beneficent deity in the majority of the regions in which he abounds.

Captain Young and several other writers tell that in the Hawaiian Islands, the shark was one of the most powerful of divinities. The shark king, Kama-Hoa-Lii, who ruled all other sharks, could assume human form whenever he wished. The legend states that he lived in a cavern large enough to shelter his enormous body, somewhere in the waters outside Honolulu. With the help of the powerful shark Kalahiki, he was thought to be the protector of fishermen in danger. He foresaw all the hazards of the sea, and therefore was prepared to come to the help of ships and crews threatened by tempests, contrary winds, or periods of calm. If they were threatened with such perils, the natives lighted a great fire on their ships and poured into the sea the juice of a plant called the awa. As soon as he received their appeal, Kama-Hoa-Lii dispatched one of his shark subjects — he never revealed himself — to act as a guide and lead the threatened boat back to its home port.

If the incantations were correctly formulated and the offerings pleasing to him, he could also become the protector of the oppressed and avenge the injustices of a tyrant or of a jealous husband.

The special ability of the shark gods to assume human form was, quite naturally, the basis for many fantastic stories. Some of these all-powerful beings made use of their unique power to seduce and marry the young virgins and beauties of the archipelago. Male children born of such a mating were all endowed with their father's powers, and the only sign of their divine status was a shark's jaw marked across the back, between the shoulder blades. The child's relatives were carefully instructed by the father never to allow the young god to taste of flesh, since he then would acquire a liking for it and cause horrible damage. It goes without saying that sometimes an overindulgent grandfather would break the law, and the child, in turn, would follow the villagers as they made their daily trips to the edge of the sea. There, he would leap into the water, reassume the form of a shark, and satisfy his insatiable appetite by devouring his comrades. If it was discovered that he had lost the cloak or "kapa" which covered the menacing jaw on his back, the young god must then throw himself into the sea and swim to a nearby island; there he might continue his murderous activities in a new hunting ground, where his identity was unknown.

In spite of such tales, the signal honor of being reincarnated as sharks in their next life was conferred on the wisest of all the wise men of the Hawaiian tribes. Those so honored were highly respected in their present existence, and a shark's jaw was tattooed on their back by the seer of the island. These gods-to-be were supplied with food by the villagers and lived away from the other settlements, in cabins built for them close to the sea, on the frontier of their future kingdom.

But it was not only in the legends of these islands that the shark was a very important personage. Archeology has revealed traces of ancient customs that were very real. Not far from Pearl Harbor, vestiges of marine arenas have been found, formed from blocks of stone set in the form of a circle and with a gateway left open to the sea. In this kind of theater, which is reminiscent of the Roman Empire, gladiatorial combats were held between sharks and men. Under the critical gaze of the kings and the people, naked men, armed only with short daggers, confronted deep-sea sharks. These weapons, specially designed for such occasions, consisted simply of a wooden handle bearing a shark's tooth as a point. It was, in fact, very ingenious since the skin of sharks is extremely tough and a razor-sharp tooth is one of the rare instruments capable of piercing it. Moreover, Hawaii at that time still knew nothing of the uses of hard metals. The archeologists cannot tell us how such combats usually turned out — whether it was the man or the animal who was most often the victor, or what sort of festivities crowned the games in honor of the all-powerful and generous Kama-Hoa-Lii, the great shark god.

But if the archeologists are incapable of satisfying our curiosity as to

This is a nurse shark, technically called *Genglymos-toma cirratum*. Nurse sharks, closely related to sand sharks, are extremely supple and swim almost like snakes. They seem to be nearsighted, and they hide in crevices for long periods of time. One method of getting them out of those crevices—tugging at their tail—has been employed, but it can prove quite harmful. It was a shark of this type that we encountered on Shab Arab, but that one was much bigger.

the outcome of these Hawaiian aquatic *corridas,* we can find an answer to the question at another point of the globe. The peoples of the West Indies, like those of the Pacific Islands, are in constant contact with the sea and have always had many excellent sailors and fishermen. Sharks are abundant and active in this region, too, and although they are not the object of such passionate cults, they are the subject of a great many tales. On the island of Santo Domingo, I have been told the story of two Negroes who regularly did battle with sharks. There was no special arena, but just a shallow lagoon linked to the sea by a canal which could be closed with stones and branches of trees. No dagger with a shark-tooth point was used, but a solid blade of the best steel. Once a large shark had been trapped in the lagoon and a predetermined sum of money paid over, the gladiator, armed only with this blade, entered the water, and a fight to the death began. More often than not, it went on for only a few seconds before the man succeeded in planting his weapon in the animal's side. Since these two men made their living from this dangerous sport, it would seem that they fought frequently and were generally the winners. Regardless of this, confronting a man-eating shark in the muddy waters of a lagoon demonstrates either a quality of courage that is extremely rare or a phenomenal inability to recognize danger.

In Central America, we again come across the belief that the shark is a beneficent animal, and more or less taboo. François Poli, in the book I have already mentioned, *Sharks Are Fished at Night,* tells of the almost ritual fear of the natives living along the shores of Lake Nicaragua, when they are asked to go fishing for sharks. These lake sharks are fresh-water sharks, remote descendants of sea sharks who have gradually become acclimatized to their new condition. There are some theories to the effect that when the mountain chain which shelters the lake was formed, a pocket of sea water was separated from the rest of the ocean. Over the course of centuries, this water became fresh water and the sharks it contained adapted themselves to it. This acclimatization is not surprising when one remembers certain species of South African sharks who pass a portion of their lives in the brackish waters at the mouths of rivers. Some have even mounted the Zambezi River to a distance of three hundred and forty miles from the coast, where the water, quite obviously, is perfectly fresh. The sharks of Lake Nicaragua have been definitely established as being related to these "Zambezi sharks."

François Poli also recounts how the Indians of this lake region, in accordance with ancient custom, would adorn the bodies of the dead with all their jewelry and then consign the body to the sharks. Hearing of this custom, a Dutch adventurer decided to put the primitive beliefs of the natives to his own use. He set himself up in a house situated near the spot where these burial-sacrifice ceremonies were held, and went shark hunting immediately after each one. It was said that he accumulated a considerable fortune before his activities were discovered by the Indians, but then he was murdered and his house burned to the ground.

The only occasion on which the Indians enter into conflict with the lake sharks occurs when, through misfortune, one of them is bitten by a shark and loses an arm or a leg. Then the hunt for the guilty animal is relentless, until the amputated limb is recovered and can be buried beside the victim, so that he may obtain entrance to paradise.

In the winter of 1967, my brother, Jean-Michel, preceded the *Calypso* into the port of Tuléar, on the southern coast of the Malagasy Republic, in order to make the necessary preparations for our stopover there. While waiting for us to arrive, he had many conversations with people living in the region and was told by a little girl that the members of her tribe had absolutely no fear of sharks, since they believed them to be the reincarnation of their ancestors. "And," the little girl said, "grandfather would not hurt me, would he?" These people are also among those who are convinced that in the event of a shipwreck, sharks will appear and guide their descendants safely back to shore. Obviously, no one in all this region hunts for sharks, with the exception of a few "vasa," white foreigners, who are considered sacrilegious.

On the sand beach of a tiny island in the Mozambique Channel, north-

west of Madagascar, there exists the only shark fishery of the entire island continent. Here, an old Arab who does not share the beliefs of the Malagasy natives stretches out lines from the edge of the shore and catches an appreciable number of sharks every night. As recently as a few years ago, he also gathered in the remoras — the extremely powerful sucking fish that attach themselves to sharks — and sold them, alive, to the tribes of fishermen in the other islands of the channel. The new owners of these fish attached them by the tail to a solid length of fishing cord and then set them free in the waters along the barrier of the reefs. Once liberated in this fashion, the remoras often attached themselves to others of the large fish or to the turtles in which these waters abound, and the hosts they had selected were then hauled in and sold. This delightful custom has now practically disappeared, and with it has gone a tidy source of income for the shark fisherman. Now, he tans the skins of his victims and presses their livers. These occupations, although considerably less romantic, provide him with a peaceful and happy existence, despite the foul odor of the tannery and the mistrust of his neighbors, who regard him as little less than a sorcerer.

In the marvelous islands of Polynesia, the attitude of the people toward sharks varies greatly, from one island, even from one tribe, to another. They certainly are not always considered gods, and sometimes they are simply ignored. In some tribes, the only precaution taken by parents and relatives is to capture a certain number of the monsters and close them up in vast, shallow lagoons where their children go to play every day. In this manner, the young people, who will depend on the sea for more than half their food, learn from their earliest days to understand and to control the sharks. Later in life, if they encounter sharks in the course of their fishing, they will know what attitude to assume and will not give in to panic. I know, from experience, that a shark confined in very shallow water moves with difficulty, and that the agility of Polynesian children is incredible to see; so the risk of accidents in these lagoons is reduced to a minimum. The wisdom of the idea is, therefore, quite striking, since this ancient custom eliminates the factor of panic and uncontrolled reactions which are so common in encounters of men with sharks. An American scientist, William Murphy, is intending to engage in extensive study of the psychological factors which intervene when a man is attacked by a shark, with the goal of augmenting the safety of swimmers and divers. He thinks — and, I believe, rightly so — that the unreasoning fear which takes hold of men confronted with sharks transforms swimmers from worthy opponents into easy prey. His research, if it leads to a better understanding of the psychological relationship between men and sharks, could be the basis for truly effective methods of defense.

In the Philippines, a combination of animism and a belief in the transmutation of souls into the bodies of animals forms the basis of many local religions; animals that could be used as much-needed food sources are, on the contrary, tamed and abundantly fed. These practices transform wild animals ranging from birds to river eels into family pets. All are considered to be the reincarnation of ancestors.

Happily, the taboo applies in a Filipino family to only one or two species. Some families respect serpents, others hogs, and still others parrots, and a family has no compunction whatever about killing and eating the sacred animals held in veneration by its neighbor. It is quite normal, therefore, to make a feast of the reincarnation of ancestors — provided they are not your own.

I have already noted some of the roles accorded to the shark-god in the Hawaiian Islands — at a time when they were still known as the Sandwich Islands — but there is one that is perhaps most important. In all the villages, each family selected a totem of its own, and one of the most respected was that of the shark. If a stillborn child was born to a man who worshiped the shark-god, he would attempt, by means of magic, to transfer the soul of the

This is the dusky shark dashing in front of the camera out in the open sea. Another beautiful sight in the underwater world.

unfortunate baby into the body of a shark. To perform such an operation successfully, the father wrapped offerings of fruits and sacred roots in a ritual matting of straw, and placed the body of the child with these. Then, after many prayers and incantations, he confided the precious package to the sea, hoping that it would be favorably received by the god. If the divinity accepted the sacrifice, he would, in turn, protect all the other members of the family against attacks from his servants.

In a temple dedicated to the shark-god in the mountains behind the sea, priests, whose skin was constantly bathed in rock salt and water, so that it eventually seemed to be covered with scales, predicted the exact moment at which the god accepted the offering and transformed the little body into a shark. The moment of this announcement was accompanied by rejoicing on the part of the family, and a banquet was offered in honor of the priests.

Many of the customs and beliefs of primitive peoples reflect their fear and impotence in the face of natural phenomena and dangerous animals. Almost everywhere in the world, volcanoes, earthquakes, tigers, or serpents are honored and feared — or rather, they are honored because they are feared. In most cases, however, these invincible forces were, or still are, represented by malignant deities. In the case of the shark, one of the most dangerous of all animals, this generality holds true only in very rare instances. The shark-god is always powerful and respected, but generally he is regarded as a beneficent and protecting deity. It is only in the minds of modern, civilized man that he has become an abominable monster, inspiring disgust and unreasoning fear.

Each of these two attitudes seems equally unjustified. If they lead to self-destruction, both adoration and fear are disastrous emotions, and this is particularly true with regard to a formidable animal. I cannot help but think of the wisdom of those peoples of Polynesia who teach their children neither blind worship nor irrational fear, but a complete understanding of the menace, so that they may avoid it and, if necessary, conquer it.

TWELVE:
The Study of Sharks
A school for sharks.
Open sea.

Philippe Cousteau's narrative continues

An experiment was conducted by Doctor Eugenie Clark at the marine laboratory of Cape Haze, in Florida, to determine to what extent sharks could be conditioned to respond to complex stimuli. Years later, aboard the *Calypso,* Doctor Clark carried out another phase of the experiment.

The animals used in the earlier experiment were of two different species. There were two lemon sharks *(Negaprion brevirostris),* one male and one female, three feet in length; and three nurse sharks of the same size, all three of these male. The two lemon sharks had been captured in May 1958, five months before the experiment, and were perfectly adapted to their captivity, in good health and normally active. The others, although naturally slower, were in similar condition. The theater for the experiment was an enclosure, in fairly shallow water, of vertically planted squared-off shafts of wood, spaced about six inches apart. The enclosure measured forty feet by seventy feet and, aside from the sharks, contained only a few large sea turtles.

Throughout the experiment, the sharks were fed five times a week, from Monday through Friday, and always at three-fifteen in the afternoon. Earlier experiments with all types of animals had shown the importance of regularity in feeding times. Therefore, for six weeks — the entire period of the experiment — a target made of a fifteen-inch square of laminated plywood was lowered into the tank at precisely the specified time. This target was lifted out again following each feeding period, and was never left in the water at other times. It was secured at one end of a wooden bar in such a fashion that it could be placed in exactly the desired position, just below the surface of the water, regardless of the height of the tide. To complete the arrangement for the experiment, an underwater bell was placed two inches behind the target square. Whenever the target was pushed back to this extent, the bell would ring, and continue to ring so long as the target was held back. As soon as the pressure against the white square ceased, elastic bands returned it to its original position.

In the first two days of the experiment — September 22 and 23, 1958 — portions of food were dropped into the water at points closer and closer to the target. As of the third day, the food was attached to the center of the target by a short, fragile line. In order to secure it, the sharks were thereby forced to press their snouts against the white square. During the first week, the sound of the bell was very feeble, but in the second week it became loud and clear, audible even on the surface. Each time the apparatus was lowered into the tank, a portion of fish was already in place, and as soon as it was taken it was replaced with another. This was done by sliding the food down a length of wire running from the surface to the center of the white square.

The duration of each feeding period was reduced from forty minutes to twenty during the second week, and continued at this length of time for the remainder of the six weeks of training — or, rather, of conditioning.

In order to judge the effectiveness of the system and test the results, the target was lowered without food at the beginning of the seventh week, and whenever one of the sharks pressed on it hard enough to ring the bell a portion of fish was dropped to a spot next to the white square. A period of ten seconds was then allowed the shark to take his reward. If he did not succeed in snatching it from the line within this lapse of time, it was withdrawn from the water. This was done in order to associate the memory of the sound of the bell with the presence of food. Each week following this, the food was dropped a little farther away from the target.

The results were as follows: although, at the beginning of the conditioning period, the sharks had shown fear when the target was lowered into the water, they rapidly became accustomed to it. In this six-weeks period, the lemon sharks took the food and rang the bell five hundred and twenty-two times, and rang the bell but missed the food one hundred and sixteen times. Thus, the lemon sharks rang the bell a total of six hundred and thirty-eight times. The nurse sharks obtained the food and rang the bell seventy-nine times, and missed the food ten times. As a result of their greater ability to swim in place, they were able to feed seventy-five times without pushing the target far enough back to cause the bell to ring.

At the end of the conditioning period, on November 3, 1958, the target was lowered into the water without food. Within less than thirty seconds, the male lemon shark swam toward the target with his mouth already open. When he approached the empty target, he slowed down, closed his jaws and brushed the target with his snout, but not sufficiently hard to ring the bell. After ten similar attempts, he finally pressed the plywood square with enough force to set off the bell, and a portion of fish was immediately dropped. At the end of the first week, the male and female lemon sharks were perfectly conditioned to ring the bell by pressing on the empty target, and then to return for their reward. The nurse sharks approached the white square very rapidly, after the food had been dropped, and after the second time they stole the male lemon shark's reward. During the first experimental period of forty minutes, the nurse sharks obtained three portions of fish in this manner, and even blows on the head from above did not disturb them.

Throughout the month of November and the first two weeks of December, the two lemon sharks came and pressed on the target every time it was lowered. Then the temperature of the water dropped below twenty degrees Centigrade and they ceased taking the food. This state of affairs continued for ten weeks.

In conclusion, it can be said that these observations had shown no disposition on the part of the nurse sharks to associate the target with the presence of food. The male lemon shark had shown a strong tendency to approach the target first; often, the female, although swimming in the immediate vicinity of the white square, would not attempt to touch it until the male had taken three or four pieces of fish. More than 90 per cent of the time, the sharks would turn away in a clockwise direction after striking the target. Since the food was lowered to the left of the target, the most rapid means of attaining it would have been to turn to the left, in a counterclockwise movement. The additional time required for a detour to the right often made it possible for the other sharks to steal the food. The male seemed to have a greater facility for effecting this unaccustomed turn.

On February 9, 1959, the temperature of the water rose to twenty-two degrees Centigrade, and on the eighteenth of February, the sharks once again began accepting food. The experiments were begun again on the nineteenth and twentieth, and the sharks immediately resumed their earlier habits. In two days, the male pressed the white square twelve times, and the female pressed it four. Then, after a short cold period during which they again stopped eating, the experiment was continued until the middle of summer. When Doctor Clark decided to disconnect the bell from the target, the sharks, after a short period of hesitation, continued pressing on the white square and received their usual reward. This could mean that the absence of the sound stimulus made no difference in their reactions, and it could have been useless.

The experiment did demonstrate that, under the conditions described above, animals of the lemon shark species can be conditioned to associate the pressure on a target with the obtaining of food. In a few rare instances, the first sound of the bell would immediately attract a lemon shark who was swimming at the other end of the tank. At other times, the male lemon shark, after having pressed on the target with insufficient force to ring the bell, would turn completely around and swim back straight toward it. This time, of course, he succeeded in ringing the bell, and would swim promptly to the spot where the food was being lowered.

The fact that the female waited until the male had eaten several times before advancing on the target herself suggests that there may be some means of communication between them which is still unknown to us.

The habit of certain sharks of brushing their heads against inanimate floating objects — and even animate ones, like people — when they are hunting for food, can perhaps be explained by a peculiar ability of the shark, as I have mentioned earlier, to taste objects simply through contact with them. This characteristic may be responsible for the relative ease with which the subjects came to associate the target with food during the weeks of conditioning.

One final remark seems hardly compatible with the legends surrounding these monsters of the sea. It seems that, at certain moments, they are quite playful among themselves. Once their appetite was satiated, they sometimes swam back and forth, pressing on the target but making no effort to obtain the food which was then dropped to them. On several occasions, the male pressed the target and then left the food to the female. To me, this was certainly the most *surprising* discovery of this whole experiment, and confers on the killer some slight aura of gentlemanly delicacy.

The following stage of Doctor Clark's experiments was to determine the shark's capacity to make visual discriminations between different targets. It was this experiment that we planned to conduct on board the *Calypso,* using sharks at liberty in the sea as our subjects.

Eugenie Clark was aboard the *Calypso* at Djibouti on Saturday, September 23, 1967, when we left port, heading north for the islands of the Suakin group off the coast of Sudan, where the sharks were already familiar to us.

The *Calypso* was anchored just in the middle of the canal between Dahl Ghab Reef and a small uncharted reef which we christened Calypso Reef. The discovery of this reef was entirely due to chance and might have been disastrous, since we almost went aground on it, but it turned out, in fact, to have been providential. It formed a natural barrier against the strong ground swell from the southeast, and created a zone of near-perfect calm in which we could drop anchor and utilize all forms of our small boats and the most delicate equipment. The experiment we were about to attempt was to be the last and certainly the most significant of the expedition. The circumstances for it were almost ideal. For the past several days, the atmospheric conditions had been

During a long dive in any water, even the warmest, loss of body heat is extreme. The sun is most welcome.

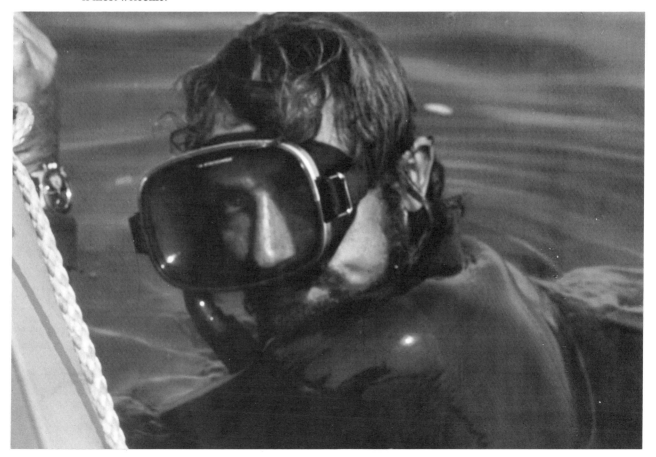

The red patches that you see in this bunch of squid are red tentacles. The tentacles turn red when the squid is in the process of mating.

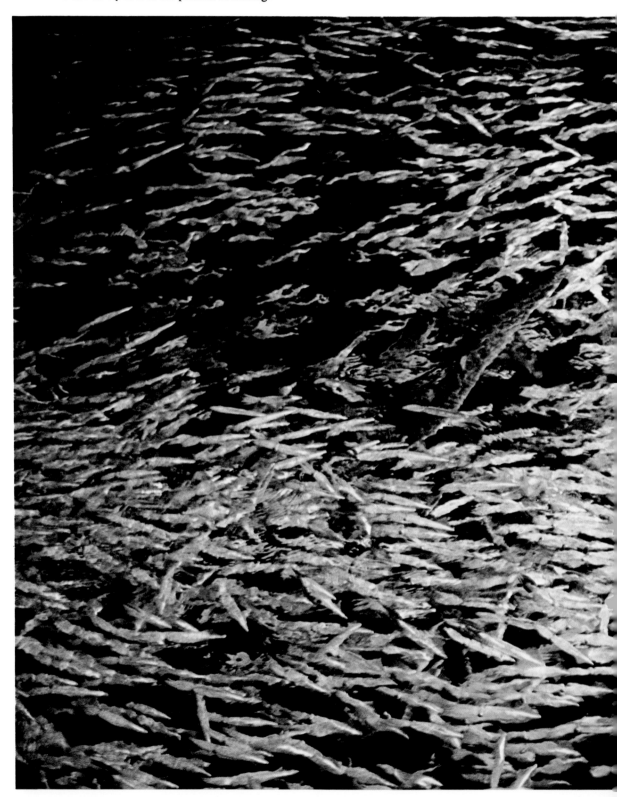

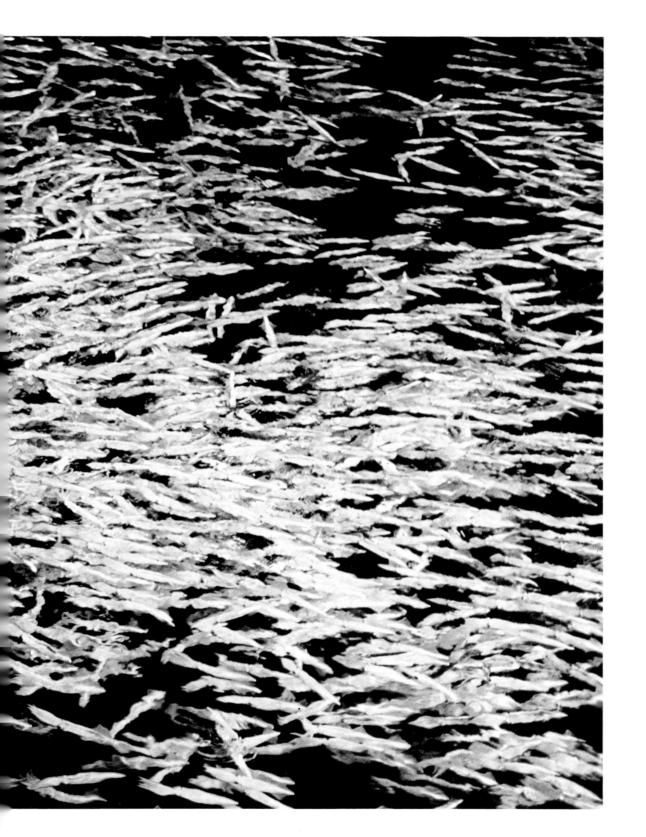

extremely favorable, and the absence of wind, the almost total calm, had allowed the water to clear to the extent that it was now of a crystalline transparency.

I have often noticed that the more clear the water is and the longer a period of calm goes on, the more active and glittering the life of the reef becomes. It is as if the movement of waves tended to carry the countless legions of timid little fish away from their sheltering clumps of coral. In order to survive, almost all the animal life of a reef has need of a hole, a crevice, a winding cleft, some branch or another in this immobile forest. Each of the little creatures, less swift and less well armed than any larger predator, depends for his very survival on the relative distance between the mouth of his pursuer and the entrance to his shelter of stone or coral. If the intruder moves toward him, the little fish draws closer to his hole, striving always to be certain of being able to reach it before the hunter can intercept him. If the sea is agitated, each wave creates a new and irregular current which obliges these little animals to remain constantly in the immediate proximity of their lairs, and the reef seems less populated, less brilliant, and less gay than it does in a period of calm. The fish, obviously, are perfectly conditioned to this state of affairs, and they know the near-futility of their efforts in bad weather, with the result that the constant hunt in which they must engage is really active along the slopes of the reefs only in times of flat calm. Since the action of the waves affects, to any major degree, only the first thirty or so feet below the surface, these observations are valid only for that region.

The experiment we were now set to attempt was scheduled to take place within that thirty-foot space, and, thanks to the persistent fair weather of the past days, the animal life here was proceeding at its normal rhythm. The predators had climbed from the intermediary depths, and were pursuing their constant search for food. Sharks, of course, were cruising among them, always ready to pounce on any wounded animal or to profit from any mistake in judgment on the part of a potential victim.

Doctor Clark had prepared the equipment to carry out here the experiment which had succeeded so well with captive sharks. This time, however, the sharks were free, perfectly at home in their element, and the behavior had not been affected either by capture, by unaccustomed imprisonment, or by an artificial period of fasting. We were all eager to go ahead, and the preparations had been painstaking in every detail.

Two square targets had been cut from panels of plastic, and painted with yellow and black stripes one inch in width. One of these targets was to be placed so that the stripes would be horizontal, while the other, although of the same pattern, would have vertical stripes. The two squares of rigid plastic were fixed in place at either end of a six-foot wooden bar. A small pulley was then placed at the center of the target with horizontal stripes and linked to a buoy on the surface with a pulley line of transparent nylon. This line, which was invisible in water, was for the purpose of bringing down bait in the form of pieces of fresh fish attached to a ring of galvanized wire. In this manner, we could send the portions of fish from the surface directly to the center of the target. The wooden bar to which the targets were fastened would be solidly attached to a fissure in the vertical wall of coral which formed the undersea façade of the reef. This façade, which is termed the "stay" of the reef, is a wall that begins at the edge of the coral reef and plunges straight down to a depth which often exceeds nine hundred feet. The waters surrounding it are the domain of the carnivorous animals of the deep, who feed on the leftovers from the sea-level plateau.

The sharks cruising in the immediate vicinity of the reef seemed to be sedentary, a fact that greatly increased our chances of success in the experiment. Working with the same subjects day after day should make it possible to condition them and to verify Doctor Clark's theory. A large steel shackle bolt and a short iron bar would furnish the sound source necessary for conditioning. Each time a shark seized the bait at the center of the horizontally striped target, a diver would strike the shackle with the iron bar, and the sound thus produced would be associated in the shark's mind with the idea of food.

This time, however, the experiment would be different from that carried out by Doctor Clark in Florida in that there were two targets, and we wanted to determine the shark's ability to differentiate between them. In the earlier experiment, the shark had only to learn to press on the target in order to obtain food, and the results had shown that some species succeeded in this without difficulty. Now, it would be necessary for the sharks to learn not only to press on the horizontally striped target to obtain food, but to select between the two targets, since, if they pressed the square with the vertical stripes, they received no reward.

In the first stage of the experiment, the horizontal square would carry portions of fresh fish at its center and the diver would ring his improvised bell. It was our hope that the shark would associate the design of the target and the sound of the bell with the idea of food. In the second stage, the hori-

The density of these animals is incredible. All those black dots seen grouped in two's are pairs of eyes. The bodies are almost transparent. They have no bones except what is called a feather, a transparent, flexible piece of hard matter serving as backbone.

zontal target carried no fish; the shark was to have learned to press on it, in order to have the diver ring the bell and then to be rewarded with a portion of fish. If he pressed on the wrong target (the one with vertical stripes), nothing happened. It was, therefore, a fairly complex experiment in two forms of conditioning that we were attempting.

Two days after our arrival on the reef, everything was in readiness and Canoë and I loaded the equipment into one of our small boats and set out to find a spot where the experiment might best be carried out. The requirements for this were fairly rigid: it must be an area in which we could not only attach the targets solidly to the cliff, but also find a shelter in a fissure in the immediate vicinity. We went into the water and began our explorations with a free dive, accompanied on the surface by the *Zodiac,* piloted by José Ruiz.

The spectacle we beheld was of a beauty as delicate as it was formidable. I swam along the edge of the plateau level, which seemed to mark the frontier between two worlds. To my left, there was a mysterious, disturbing void, which seemed to exhaust every nuance of color between blue and black. I could pick out vague forms, swift or lazy, lightly outlined in silver. They were tuna, powerful, enormous, and alone, ridged with scars of earlier battles. They were curious about us, and emerged from the infinite depths, approaching us, hesitating, and then swimming away. I do not know why, but even today this combination of power and silence impresses me. I am struck with a familiar and somewhat childlike idea: each of these magnificent fish has, through force of nature, lived for many years and engaged in incredible battles, swimming unceasingly through this world which permits me no more than awkward and too brief incursions. I was abruptly overcome by a whiff of jealousy — perhaps of love — and I turned away, suddenly conscious of being no more than an ungainly frog.

To my right, everything was reversed. The universe here was gay, vibrant with color and life. The sound of countless millions of tiny animals brought a constant echoing sound through the water, just as the strident sounds of insects carry through an Amazon jungle. It was a world of light and of serene mysteries, and yet, the combats which take place up here are no less bitter, no less pitiless than those that take place in the depths. In front of me, the edge of the plateau crowned the dizzying slope of a fringe of coral masses, extending out above the void like enormous petrified flowers. The swarm of timid little fish hovering around every jutting edge of stone shimmered before my eyes like a heat cloud on a summer day.

Canoë signaled to me, and I rejoined him immediately. He was swimming slowly around a kind of vertical fault which cut into the uniform surface of the cliff. On either side of the notch, which measured no more than six to nine feet in depth and six feet in width, the wall formed two advanced areas of stone, bordering the crevice as if they were two thick lips. The interior of the fault was riddled with twisting pathways and rich in hiding places, easily sufficient for a man. With a fluid, twisting movement of his body, Canoë dropped beneath the surface and swam straight down along the ledge, until he came to a little jutting branch of coral. There, he signaled to me that this spot would be perfect and returned lazily to the surface.

The region did seem made for our purposes and we set to work immediately. We fastened the targets solidly to the coral at a depth of about twenty-five feet. Just above and to the right of the targets, we prepared a hiding place for Canoë, who would be conducting the experiment. Since I was going to film the operation, there was no question of a fixed refuge for me; I would have to make do with improvised shelters anywhere in the area.

When everything was ready, Canoë speared a too-curious caranx and the sharks appeared at once. They had seemed to arrive from nowhere, and, as always, there was something of the miraculous about it. Suddenly, at a point very close to us, the water materialized into one and then two moving rocket forms, swift and disturbing. Their blue-gray color mingled so perfectly with the colors in the depths below that it provided at least some explanation for this apparent prodigy of nature. They had probably been there for a long time, watching our activity but outside our field of vision, and had not approached until they were alerted by the convulsive movement of the dying caranx. They were two sharks with white-tipped fins, *Albimarginatus,* audacious and fast. The larger of the two must have been almost ten feet in length, while the other was much smaller, no more than four feet long and considerably more nervous in his reactions. They seemed to have located the fish — which we had now planted at the center of the target — with no difficulty, but it was three hours later before they bit into it. Their age-old instinct constrained them to prudence. Our unexpected presence did not reassure them at all, and the way in which the food was presented to them was not the best proof of our good manners. The setting was unusual, and they disliked the colors. Through all this long period of waiting, neither Canoë nor I moved from our stations. The sharks would swim off into the distance and be lost to our sight, sometimes for quite a long time, but they came back and resumed their patrol in front of the target. Suddenly, a third shark, scarcely larger than the smaller of the first two, appeared on the scene, and that seemed to decide things for the largest. He made an abrupt full turn and swam directly toward the target. I started my camera, but it was a wasted effort. At about three feet from the target, he turned away again, seemed to hesitate for a moment, and then resumed his lazy swimming, back and forth, just in front of us. I think now that the scent of the other pieces of fish, which we had neglected to enclose in a waterproof sack, contributed to the sharks' confusion, and caused them to mistake the exact location of the bait we had set for them. However, I did not have to wait much longer. The largest shark, which, in addition to his size, was easily recognizable by a fin that had been cut almost in two in some long-past fight, turned back again, and this time he bit into the bait after only a fleeting hesitation. The sound of the improvised bell, which Canoë struck constantly while the shark was seizing and swallowing his prey, seemed to have no influence, either on him or on the others, who had closed in on the target as soon as he had seized the bait.

In the two hours that followed, the same shark took four portions of fish and missed his target four other times, while the smallest took only a single portion and the third shark none at all. We left the water after six hours of watchful waiting, exhausted but satisfied. The experiment was well under way.

The next morning, the same operation was begun again, but this time with less success. This session began, however, with a violent scene. When Canoë killed the fish we planned to use as bait, the big shark with the damaged fin surged from the depths like a torpedo, swimming straight toward Canoë, who retreated immediately to his prearranged shelter. Then, with a vicious contortion of his entire body, the enormous animal turned and swept toward me, his gaping jaws already opened. He was on a level with my head, and I could neither draw back any distance nor move to the right or the left. I tried to make myself as small as possible, and lashed out at him with the camera. I felt a shock and a sudden turbulence in the water that snatched the mask from my face, and then the camera was no longer in my hands. Flattened against the wall of coral, deprived of the mask that provided me with sight, I tried to make out the powerful form I knew to be somewhere just in front of me. I felt certain that he would return to the attack. It was only when the vague mass swimming in my direction was almost upon me that I recognized Canoë. He had picked up the camera, and it was he who

The vision of a large school of squid next to the ship at night is one of the more beautiful sights we encountered. Divers are swimming through them, and in the foreground is Delcoutère. Bernard Chauvellin is holding the lights next to Philippe Cousteau, who is at his left with the camera.

A quick surfacing to give instructions to Delcoutère and Chauvellin.

received the second attack. He managed, somehow, to evade it, and then found my face mask and held it out to me. I put it on and emptied it of water in a matter of seconds. The scene before me was clear now. The shark had gone back to his pose of nonchalant surveillance, just a few feet away. Canoë returned to his post behind the targets, and I checked my camera. Only the sun screen seemed to have been damaged, so we continued with the experiment.

This animal's attitude was strange, very unlike that of others of his kind. Never before had I seen a shark immediately attack, a second time, a prey he had missed completely on his first attempt. Moreover, in the course of the first attack, he had received a blow with the camera that was by no means negligible. Once again I thought of the phrase my father wrote in his book *The Silent World:* ". . . the closer we come to sharks, the less we know of them. No one can ever predict what a shark is going to do."

The experiment was continued for several days, and although its first results were extremely promising, we were forced to interrupt it. A cable from Paris announced the imminent arrival of a new doctor and two new members of the crew, and so we were forced to put back to sea, heading for the coast of Eritrea and the port of Massawa.

By the time we left, the sharks were coming regularly to the target with the horizontal stripes, in search of their meals. Throughout the entire experiment, I had never seen a shark brush against the vertical target. In comparing these results with those of Doctor Clark's earlier experiments, it would seem that sharks at liberty — the *Albimarginatus,* as least — learn more rapidly than their captive relatives.

THIRTEEN:
Conclusions
on Shark Behavior
Sharks among squid.
Understanding sharks.
Opinions for pessimists
and optimists.

Philippe Cousteau's narrative continues

We have surveyed the oceans but only to ridic-
ulously slight depths, and all the inroads man has made have done little more
than cross the magical frontier. Prisoners of air as we are, our ball and chain
floats at the surface, allowing us only short, ephemeral escapes. Marseilles,
Messina, Port Saïd, Massawa, the Maldives, Diego-Suarez, Dar-es-Salaam,
Djibouti, the Cape of Good Hope, Guadelupe, Nassau, Panama, Callao,
Cedros . . . So many angles to the path of our wanderings. Like ogres whose
appetites are too vast, we have scarcely tasted of our discoveries. Too many
visions have dazzled our eyes and flooded our hearts. There remains only a
memory, trembling and deformed as a mirage, neutral as sleep. The irony of
knowledge lies in its immateriality. Tomorrow I shall use everything I have
learned, just as I do every day, instinctively, without being aware of it. But
what have I learned of the shark?

The beauty of a supple line, the thought of possible menace, the exaltation of a combat in which I know nothing of the rules . . . but what more
than that? I have learned nothing of myself: fear has no gauge, and action
is but a need.

Yet, more than a year after my last meeting with a shark, a new adventure happened that showed me again the importance and the enduring effect
of experience. At the end of March 1969, the *Calypso* was anchored off
the west coast of Baja California in one hundred and fifty feet of calm and

Bernard Chauvellin is illuminating a shark right in front of him as seen through the surface.

The cameraman, Philippe Cousteau, swimming alongside the ship with masses of squid, which are illuminated by the lights held by Bernard Chauvellin.

limpid water. It was night, after a day that had been rich in action and movement; we had been filming sequences of gray whales, and sometimes we had leaped from our fast-moving boats onto their backs which were bleached by the spray. I was asleep now, deep in motionless sleep.

At about eleven o'clock, Bernard Chauvellin, our second lieutenant, who was on duty on the bridge, came to wake me. It seemed that millions of squid were surrounding the ship, forming an area around us that was white as snow. In the glare of lights from the ship, the whole surface of the water was a carpet of these animals, and their apparently disordered movements created a vast network of tiny waves, whispering through the air like the murmurings of leaves in the wind. Clinging to one another, multiplied to a number beyond reckoning by the reflections of their wake in the water, this multitude flowed back and forth like some gigantic hydra, flashing every color of the rainbow. The *Calypso* appeared to be surrounded by a living ice floe — but through the midst of it, swift-moving forms traced furrows as dark and irregular as the crevices of a mountain.

A dozen or more blue sharks of all sizes were striking lines of death through the living halo of the ship. Jaws wide open, the sharks swam slowly through the sea of squid, cramming their mouths full, then halted just long enough to swallow the gelatinous morsels in one great, convulsive movement of their bodies. Then they moved off again, still greedy, profiting from this incredible manna.

In its beauty, its darkness, and its vital cruelty, the scene had the aspect of a forbidden spectacle. We were intruders, allowed by some error to share a secret too mighty for us to comprehend. As we stood on the bridge of the *Calypso,* no one spoke. We could only watch this magnificent vision, in silence.

Sooner or later, however, we had to react. Within a few minutes, the cameras were ready and the underwater lights connected. The most experienced divers on board at the time were disabled with persistent colds, so it was decided that I would take with me Bernard Chauvellin and Jacques Delcoutère, who would carry floodlights to illuminate the scene I hoped to film. Bernard had been with us throughout the shark expedition, but he was not an experienced diver, and Jacques had joined us only recently. This was, in fact, his first mission. Bernard had taken part in several dives among the sharks of the Red Sea, but never at night, and although Jacques had been my friend for fifteen years, he had only just completed his period of training as a diver. In this living sea and this icy water, there is a great deal about sharks that would make an impression on divers far more experienced than my two comrades. But they put on their gear in silence, displaying no emotion. Then, as it always did, the dive began with the ungainly procession of the divers across the deck. We were, for the moment, awkward, waddling ducks, to whom the water would give some semblance of grace.

The shiver of water that closed in on me extended to the very tips of my limbs; the cold ran down between my rubber skin and my human skin, cutting off my breath for a moment. I was aware of the presence of Bernard, and then of Jacques, just behind me. Had I been right in allowing them to come with me to this meeting? For several seconds, as I watched the sharks swimming back and forth through the cloudy mass of squid, I was filled with apprehension. Then, quite suddenly, memory and instinct returned, and with them came certainty. The sharks would not attack — at least, they would not attack immediately. Just as it had been in our dives in the Red Sea a year before, I sensed, rather than understood, the ambiance of the water. The sharks surrounding us now were hunting and feeding on squid. They were concentrating all their faculties on a single situation. Only the taste, the form, the touch of a squid would bring them to bite. This was no longer a pack of wolves in search of prey. They had found their victims; it was an easy and abundant hunt, and they would not search for anything else.

We swam slowly into the zone of lights from the ship, and the reason for this enormous assemblage of squid became rapidly apparent. It was the mating season. The couples were swimming slowly together, one facing the other, their translucid bodies streaked with changing phosphorescence, their tentacles grasping each other in a multiple embrace. Sometimes, two or three other squid would attach themselves to one or another of the partners, like shipwrecked men clinging to a raft. A few solitary, more rapid individuals swam through the groups thus formed, sweeping brusquely from one corner to another, wrapping their arms around our face masks and our hands, around the camera and the lights.

The squid were gathered in such compact groups that it was almost impossible to see more than two feet ahead, and nose-to-nose encounters with a shark were frequent occurrences. At first, however, as I had thought, the sharks paid no attention to us. If, by accident, one of them bumped into one of us, he turned away immediately and started off in another direction, still devouring and swallowing the little creatures with which the sea was filled. We went down to a depth of about fifty feet, where the water became clear and dark again. Above us, the white mass of squid looked like a fleecy cloud. Bernard's floodlights attracted a few of the squid to us — either blinded or simply curious. Seen from below, the bellies of the blue sharks were astonishingly white, and their skin seemed very tender and fragile.

I had finished my reel of film, and decided to go back to the ship. But, during our ascent to the surface, I was abruptly conscious of a change in the ambiance around us. After more than an hour, the sharks seemed to have recognized our presence, and they were now reacting. The exploratory blows of their snouts were more violent, they were circling around us and coming back more often to brush against our diving suits, as if they thought they might perceive the true taste of our flesh through our covering of rubber. We were close to the surface now, and I could see Bernard Delemotte's face, as he leaned out of the boat, watching and waiting. A shark stormed brutally through a cloud of squid and smashed his head against the camera. He turned back, then apparently decided to attack again, changed his mind and disap-

The incredible number of these squid resembles a stream of white gelatinous matter going by the ship. They are usually very fast, but at this time of year they are very sluggish and consequently make for easy prey. This sight is fascinating as seen against the light on board the *Calypso*.

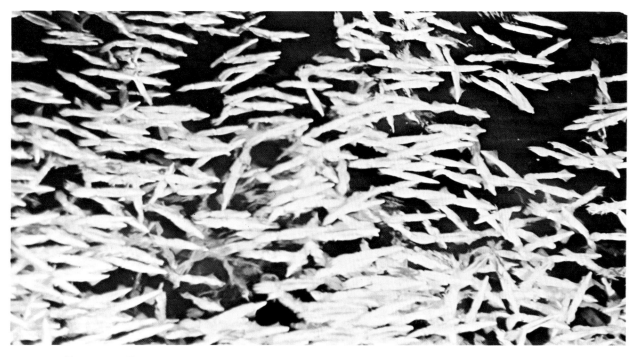

Even more discernible here than in the previous picture are the red tentacles of the squid.

peared. It was high time to leave the water. While Chauvellin and Delcoutère were ridding themselves of their equipment, Delemotte soberly told me that we had come out at exactly the moment when things were getting dangerous.

After all the months of forgetfulness, there still remained with us something of our adventures in the Red Sea: experience. For a few moments, I had the vague feeling of having acquired knowledge, and then the feeling disappeared. Many divers or swimmers, and many other people who simply want to learn, have asked us questions about sharks. Are they really dangerous? What species are the most dangerous? What can a man do against this animal? What are the best means of protection? And so on . . . For my part, I know that we have been protected in our encounters with sharks primarily by extreme prudence and great respect for the animal and his weapons of attack. Later, too, came experience and a more instinctive evaluation of danger whenever we made a dive.

Obviously, this kind of knowledge of the animal cannot be transmitted and is purely personal. A few simple bits of information may, however, help or at least prepare the diver for a confrontation with sharks, if it should prove inevitable.

Jacques-Yves Cousteau's comments

Until today, the majority of scientific experiments conducted with sharks have been carried out with animals in captivity. They are, therefore, interesting as indications of shark behavior, but they shed little light on the behavior of sharks at liberty.

Statistics concerning accidents due to sharks are still very poorly conceived. They center primarily on swimmers, and are almost always based on the highly disputable testimony of fishermen or on that of secondhand witnesses.

The observations of divers are more interesting, but they are infrequent and often contradictory. Moreover, the authors of these stories are quite often afflicted with a hero complex.

Experiments, statistics, and observations are all, therefore, subject to caution, and it is my considered opinion that it would be extremely premature to draw any conclusions about the dangers present in an encounter with sharks while diving.

But, if it is impossible to give this book very many *conclusions,* it is possible to express some *personal opinions.*

FOR PESSIMISTS

Every species of shark, even the most inoffensive, is anatomically a formidable source of potential danger. On paper, the most to be feared are the great white sharks *(Carcharodon carcharias),* with their enormous jaws and great, triangular teeth. But, in reality, this species is extremely rare. By far the most disturbing are the *Carcharhinus longimanus,* whose great rounded fins bear a large white circle at their extremities. These "lords of the long hands" are encountered only in the open sea, but everywhere in warm waters. They are the only species of shark that is never frightened by the approach of a diver, and they are the most dangerous of all sharks.

The youngest sharks — and therefore the smallest — are the most brazen. Even a very small shark, two feet in length, can inflict dangerous wounds.

Sharks race in from great distances to devour any fish in trouble. They can perceive the fish's convulsive movements by the rhythm of the pressure waves carried to them through the water. At a short distance, sharks are also extremely sensitive to odors, and particularly to the odor of blood. For both these reasons, underwater fisherman should not attach their catch to their belts.

Sharks are accustomed to attacking, without fear, anything that floats. They may, therefore, hurl themselves at the propellers of an outboard motor. This attitude makes them dangerous to swimmers, especially if the swimmer splashes about a great deal and makes considerable noise. For divers, the moments of entering and leaving the water are particularly dangerous.

The smallest bite of a shark is very serious, and may perhaps be fatal, since it always involves a considerable portion of flesh. In addition to this, the effect of shock is proportional to the quantity of damaged flesh. A victim of shark attack may die as a result of shock, even if the part of the body damaged by the animal's teeth is not vital.

There still exists no effective means of keeping sharks away from the area in which you are diving — either by chemical products, by sound waves, or by fields of electricity.

It is dangerous to dive at night or in troubled waters, and especially if there should be sharks in view, without using some strong protective device. such as a solid antishark cage.

It is dangerous to show fear of a shark; he knows this by instinct, and can profit from it.

It is dangerous to unleash the defensive reactions of a shark by attacking him (with a spear, a rifle, an explosive, or an electric shock) or even by frightening him (by pursuing him into a place from which there is no escape, for example).

When sharks are gathered together in a group, their behavior is unpredictable. A "frenzy" may suddenly take place, for reasons of which we still know nothing.

FOR OPTIMISTS

The real "man-eaters" are always "somewhere else." In Europe, the waters of Senegal, West Africa, are thought to be dangerous. But, in Dakar, you will be told to avoid the Red Sea and Djibouti. Djibouti prides itself on never having had a single accident, but people there will tell you that Mada-

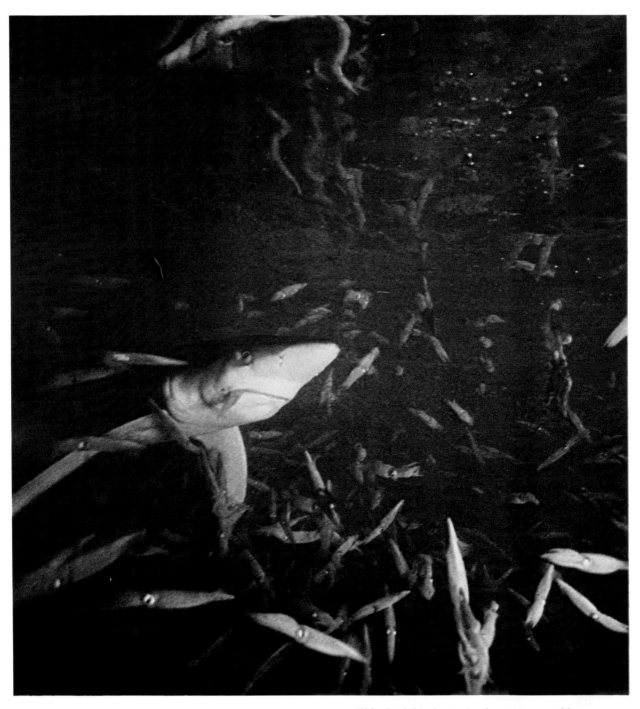

This shark has just gulped too many squid. One still hangs from his mouth, about to be very neatly cut in two. The reflection of the shark on the surface is a beautiful, changing shape gliding through the reflection of all the squid. At right, two pairs of squid show different colors. They can change colors very quickly. The eyes of these animals sometimes glow as brightly as stars in a dark sky.

gascar is infested with sharks, thirsting for blood. And, on the island of Madagascar, if you are on the west coast, the sharks are dangerous on the east coast, and vice versa.

The species considered most dangerous are also, as if by chance, the most rare. But this isn't very logical. If the white shark were really so terrible, it is probable that he would be more widespread, and we would have encountered him more often. Those we have encountered (rarely) have fled from us, seemingly terrified at our approach.

Sharks never "attack" a diver below the surface immediately. For a time that may be more or less long, but is generally considerable, they will circle around you, go away, and then cautiously return. You will have time enough in which to decide, calmly, whether to remain or to return to the surface.

In clear water, and in daylight, a diver is in no immediate danger if he encounters a shark. A team of two divers can easily survey two sharks. But,

Sharks are tearing through this mass of food, eating as much as they can of the unexpected meal. The two sharks in the lower-left-hand corner are about to collide, unable to see each other through the mass of squid. They are too busy eating to notice the divers. They often bumped into us unknowingly.

no matter how large the number of divers, it is always prudent to organize some form of shelter if there are three or more sharks surrounding you.

A solid object, two to three feet long, such as a film camera or, better still, a shark billy, constitutes effective protection against one or two sharks. The extremity of the shark billy should be provided with short points or nails, so that it will not slip off the animal's skin. It will serve the purpose of repelling the shark, and at the same time of increasing the distance between the diver and the shark. But, in order to avoid any defensive reaction, the shark billy should never be used to strike or wound your antagonist.

It is indisputable that many swimmers and many shipwrecked people have been bitten or killed. But to my knowledge there has been no documentation proving that deep divers have been wounded by unprovoked attacks — the divers themselves may have been guilty of what might be termed a lack of proper behavior.

The best protection lies in ease of movement in diving, swimming slowly and softly, and avoiding any abrupt change of position. Turn around often, to look back at your legs, which are normally out of your field of vision. If a shark should swim toward you, do not try to run away. Face him calmly, with your shark billy extended toward him. He will turn and circle before coming back to you.

If you have been cleaning or skinning fish, wash your hands and body before entering the water.

Today, even shipwrecked people can find a form of security in shark-infested waters, because of shark screens such as those we tested in the Red Sea.

All things considered, diving in tropical waters is actually much less dangerous than riding a motorcycle.

Now that I have summarized the lessons we have learned during twenty years of extensive diving among sharks in most parts of the world, it may be time to express my personal feelings. Sharks belong to the undersea environment. They rank among the most perfect, the most beautiful creatures ever developed in nature. We expect to meet them around coral reefs or in the open ocean, even if it is with a twist of fear. Their absence means disappointment for the divers, while their appearance is disquieting. When their formidable silhouette glides along the populated coral cliffs, fish do not panic; they quietly clear the lord's path, and keep an eye on him. So do we.

Appendix A

A NOTE ON PHOTOGRAPHY
AND
PHOTOGRAPHIC EQUIPMENT

All our underwater photographic equipment was built by CEMA (Centre D'Etudes Marines Avancées) in Marseilles. The cameras were designed by Armand Davso (from concepts by Jacques-Yves Cousteau), who used components of various existing types and make of equipment. They are not really dry cameras in watertight casings. The watertight casing is actually the outside of the camera. The inside contains the mechanism only — the spools for the film, the gate and the sprocket movement, and the shutter movement.

These cameras were designed five years ago and are frequently updated and perfected. We now have 16-mm. cameras with lenses ranging from the superwide angles to 25-mm. to 35-mm. focal length. In 35 mm. we also have the superwide angle and wide angle; 9 mm. and 18 mm. are commonly used, and we also have a 35 mm. for extreme close-ups.

For the stills we have built a watertight case for the Nikon camera, using it mostly with the 21-mm. lens. Of course, all the correction ports are ground by one of our specialists to the specification of each lens.

The film used is mostly in 16-mm Ektachrome 7255. We sometimes use the faster stock of 7242 or 7241, although they are much more difficult to employ because of their low tolerance for backlighting and wide differences in the amount of light. They are, in general, too contrasting. In 35 mm., of course, we use mostly the Eastman Color 5254 and 5251. For the stills we use Ektachrome X or Ektachrome High Speed in 125 ASA. We also use — but very seldom — Kodachrome 2 stock.

For our underwater lighting we use 1000-watt quartz lamps, with a color balance for 3200 K Degrees Kelvin. We also use the same type of quartz for lighting for still photography when we can, and when we cannot we use flash guns with Sylvania bulbs.

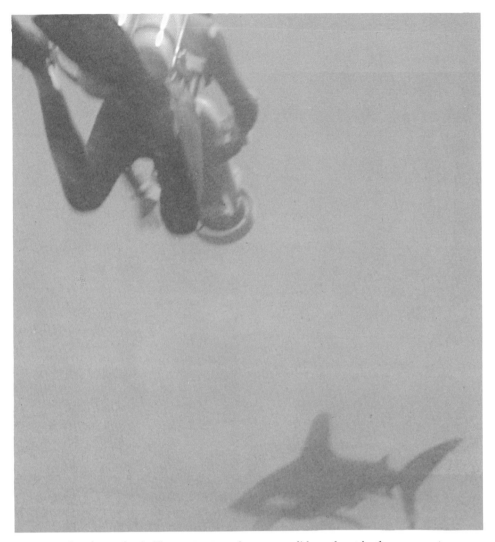

A cameraman shooting a shark. He must get as close as possible and out in the open water to do that, although he is protected by another diver immediately behind him (not seen here). This shot was taken on a day when the shark was not too aggressive.

The topside equipment is composed of several Arriflex 16, Arriflex 35, and Eclair cameras. Some are hand-held, very tiny Bell & Howell cameras, used in 35 mm. as well as 16 mm., for dangerous shots which might endanger the camera, as in the case of dropping into the water. In the event of accident it is not very important if the camera is damaged, so long as the cameraman is safe.

Sound recording is made with Perfectone equipment and very directional microphones. The sync is a quartz sync system that allows the camera and the recorder to be separated, and not attached by a cord. The use of wireless microphones also facilitates the use of this equipment; because then there is no cord from the subject to the camera or to the tape recorder, or from the tape recorder to the camera. They are three independent units.

Appendix B

DRAWINGS OF SHIPS, SHARKS, AND SEA-GOING EQUIPMENT

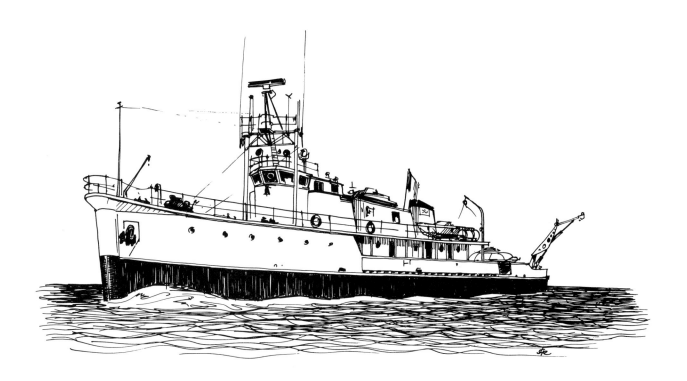

Figure 1. *Calypso.*

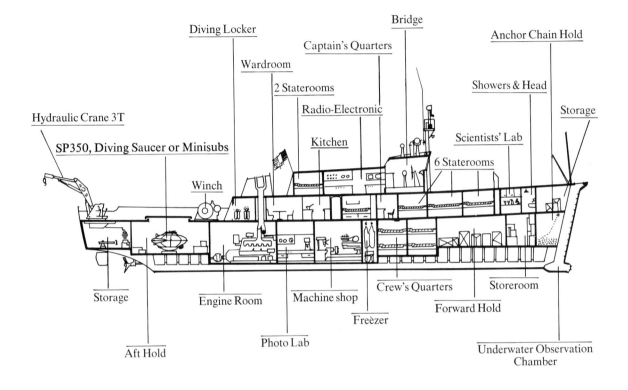

Diving Locker

Bridge

Anchor Chain Hold

Wardroom

Captain's Quarters

Showers & Head

2 Staterooms

Radio-Electronic

Storage

Hydraulic Crane 3T

Scientists' Lab

SP350, Diving Saucer or Minisubs

Kitchen

6 Staterooms

Winch

Storage

Engine Room

Machine shop

Crew's Quarters

Storeroom

Aft Hold

Photo Lab

Freèzer

Forward Hold

Underwater Observation
Chamber

Figure 2. How the *Calypso* is organized from within. Illustrated are all the modifications made before her departure on this shark expedition. The roof and control room were entirely changed; bunks were added in the main deck, forward portion, and accommodations were made to give more space to moviemaking—to the cameramen and their equipment. In the aft hold, the diving saucer rests on a stand. Every instrument in this hold is devoted to maintenance of the saucer or the two one-man submarines, the Minisubs.

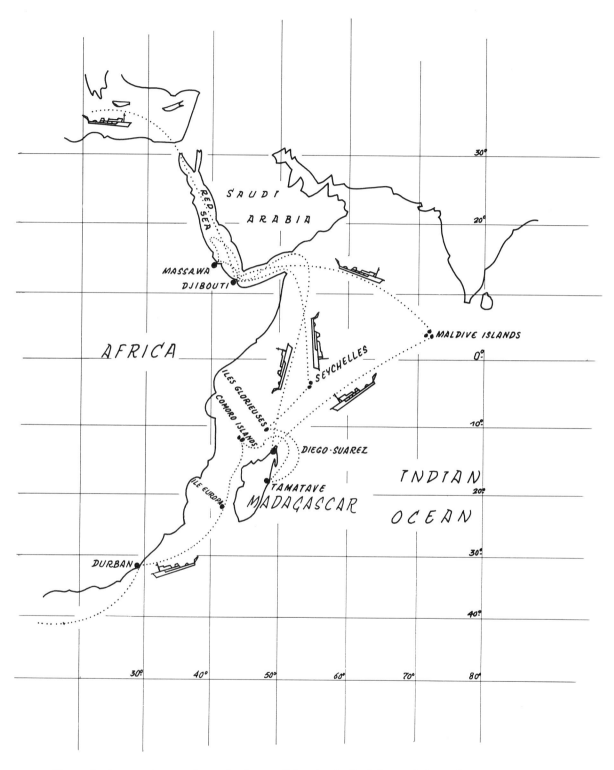

Figure 3. A general map of our shark expedition in the Red Sea and the Indian Ocean, indicating the areas most used by us. The *Calypso* left Marseilles in the Mediterranean in February 1967, went through the Red Sea and the Indian Ocean, and left Durban in the summer of 1968. The trip covered more than a year.

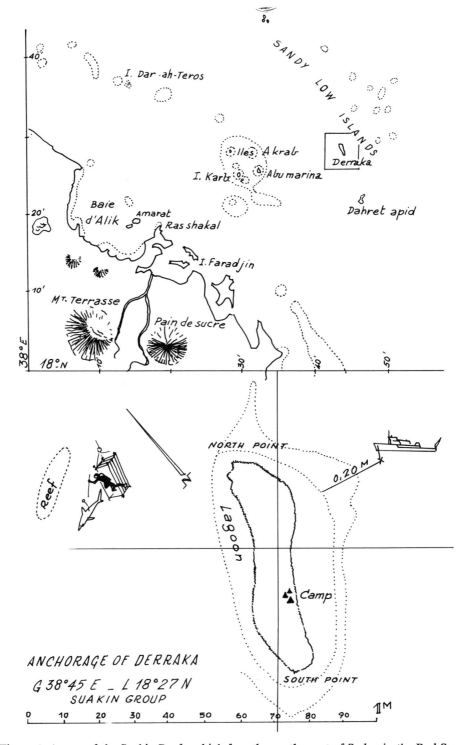

Figure 4. A map of the Suakin Reefs, which face the south coast of Sudan in the Red Sea. The lower drawing shows Derraka Island, where most of our experiments were carried out. The campsite is illustrated, in addition to the *Calypso's* favorite rough-weather anchorage. On the other side stands a small reef, which we dubbed "Calypso Reef" (it is uncharted) and the location where we did most of our tagging around Derraka. North Point was the most active area around the island, where we encountered the largest sharks and the greatest number of fish.

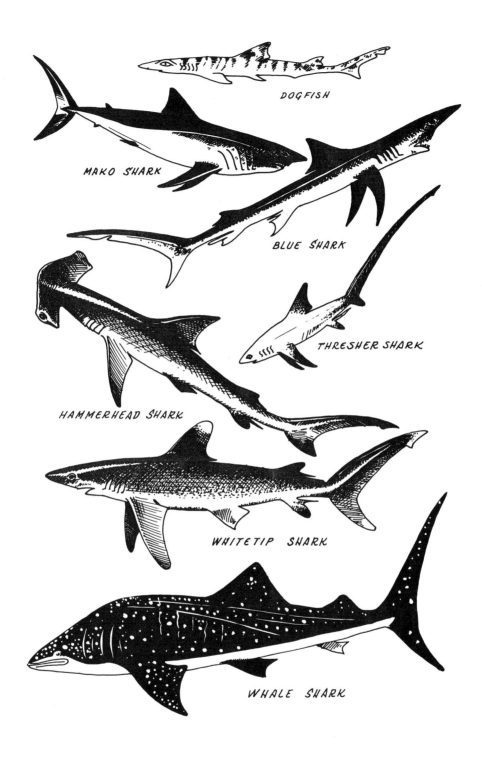

Figure 5. These are some of the most common species of shark. For comparative sizes see Figure 11. The dogfish is not considered dangerous, although it can tear some skin from a hand or foot. The mako shark is certainly one of the dangerous species, as well as the blue shark, the hammerhead, and the white-tip. Neither the thresher nor the whale shark is considered dangerous, although the thresher has a mouth that can inflict severe wounds.

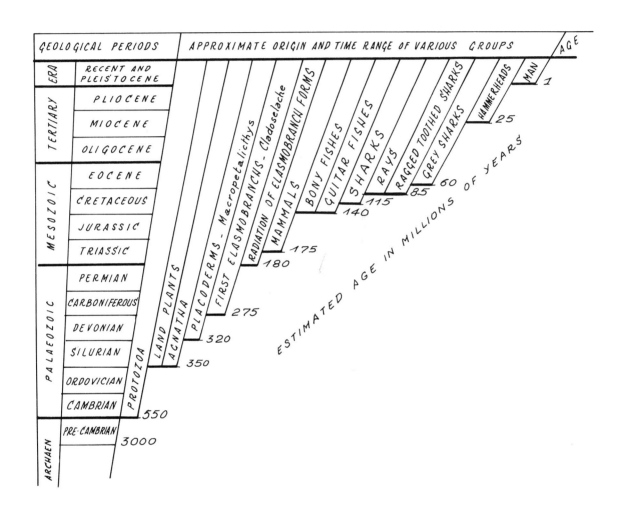

Figure 6. A self-explanatory comparison of the estimated age, in millions of years, of some marine species.

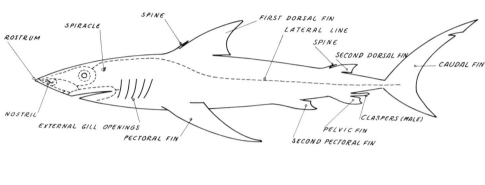

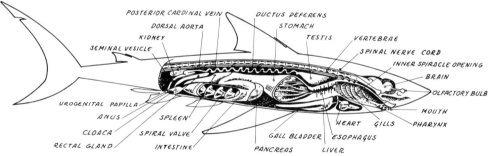

Figure 7. Both illustrations show the internal organization of the shark. Above, the location of the lateral line and most of the sensing devices grouped around the shark's head are delineated. Below are shown the shortness of the intestines, as well as the large stomach and extra-large liver. Inside the abdominal cavity the organs are not suspended by ligaments, and this is one of the shark's weakest spots.

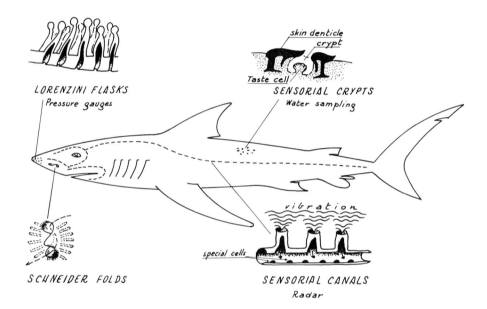

LORENZINI FLASKS
Pressure gauges

skin denticle
crypt
Taste cell
SENSORIAL CRYPTS
Water sampling

vibration
special cells
SENSORIAL CANALS
Radar

SCHNEIDER FOLDS

Figure 8. Drawing of the sensing devices of the shark. The sensorial canals moving along the lateral line are sensitive to vibrations and pressure waves. The Lorenzini flasks make it possible for the shark to sense differences in pressure. The Schneiderian folds cover the nostril of the shark, creating a canal through which the water flows. The shark's skin has sensorial crypts for water sampling and tasting of floating matter or possible prey. Most of these sensorial crypts are around the head. This combination of sensing devices is the key to the shark's perfect adaptation to his environment.

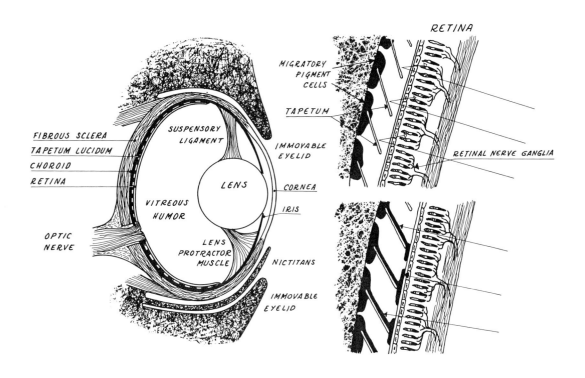

Figure 9. The interesting features of the shark's eye. On the left is illustrated the round lens of the eye. The shark's eye accommodates for distance; it does not focus by changing the shape of its lens, but by moving the lens in and out. In the upper-right-hand picture is shown how the tapetum, or silvery plates, reflect the light back through the retina, allowing the retina to be sensitized twice by the same ray of light. The migratory pigment cells at the base of these plates can be extended to cover the plates in bright light, as shown in the lower-right-hand picture, thus neutralizing the effect of the silvery plates. This whole system gives the shark's eye an extremely wide range of accommodation in both bright and very dim light.

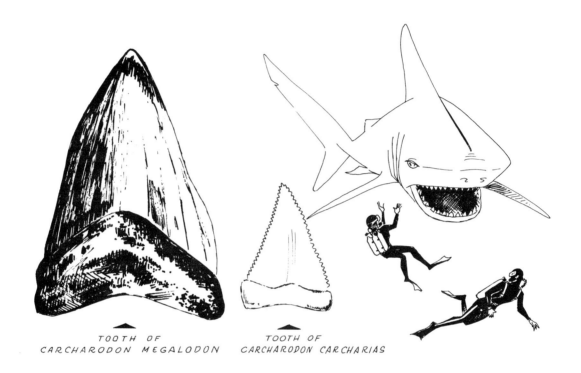

TOOTH OF
CARCHARODON MEGALODON

TOOTH OF
CARCHARODON CARCHARIAS

Figure 10. The fossil tooth of *Carcharodon megalodon*. This tooth is now in the Ocean-ographic Museum in Monaco. It was found in fossil layers. The shark to which this tooth belonged must have been of tremendous size, as noted in the drawing, which illustrates the scale of the shark as compared to man. The tooth next to it comes from a white shark *(Carcharodon carcharias)*. The white shark is considered one of the most dangerous species and largest predators. The difference in scale shows what a monster the *megalodon* must have been. The wildest nightmare conceivable to a diver would be to encounter such a beast.

WHALE SHARK _ 65 feet _

BASKING SHARK
45 feet

GREAT WHITE SHARK
36 feet

BLUE WHALER
20 feet

BIG-EYED THRESHER SHARK
18 feet

HAMMERHEAD SHARK
14 feet

WHITETIP REEF SHARK
9 feet

DOGFISH   3 feet.

WHITETIP OCEANIC SHARK.
12 feet

Figure 11. A self-explanatory chart depicting maximum sizes of the various shark species, as compared to man.

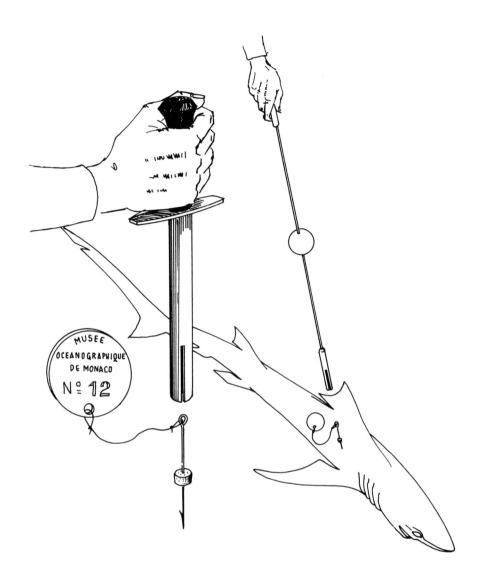

Figure 12. Our tagging apparatus. The short dagger was the one we used during the shark frenzies, because the longer one was not so practical. The long dagger was used out in the open sea, when there was only a maximum of one shark—perhaps two—not easily approachable. The tag illustrated is a sampling of what was marked on each of them. This is not a long-lasting tagging device, because the *banderillas* were made of steel, which would be rejected by the shark's skin after a period of four or five months.

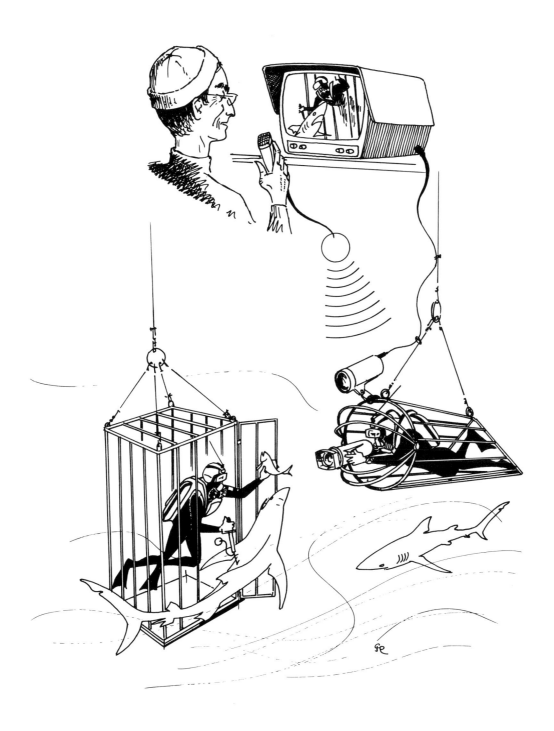

Figure 13. A shark cage used for the diver experimenting with sharks, and the cage used by the cameraman. This complete system is linked to the surface by television, where Jacques-Yves Cousteau, other members of the crew, and a scientist can monitor the action and communicate their ideas or directions to the cameraman, as well as to the diver in his cage. The system insures the accumulation of all data for the scientist on board—most of that time Doctor Eugenie Clark—and also makes for excellent safety insurance, since the viewer is able to detect danger and the cages can be pulled up immediately.

Figure 14. Depicted here is the equipment we used for filming the sharks feeding from the fish bait we'd caught, trolling in the Red Sea. Underneath the launch, *Calypso III,* are two movie cameras and one television camera. The cameraman aboard the launch sees what's happening on the TV screen and determines when to start the cameras rolling.

Figure 15. This is the setup devised by Doctor Eugenie Clark during her shark-behavior experiment in Florida. It is illustrated by a target with an electric bell, which rings in the water when the shark pushes the target. Immediately following, a reward of fresh fish is lowered to the shark.

Figure 16. This is the target experiment Doctor Eugenie Clark set up for us in the Red Sea, to help in our study of shark behavior. The diver just above the target is holding an iron shackle; he hits it to produce a noise, which contributes to the conditioning of the animals. The diver below him is holding a camera to record the experiment. The man at the surface drops pieces of fish, or whole small fish, on the vertical target, when cued by the diver.

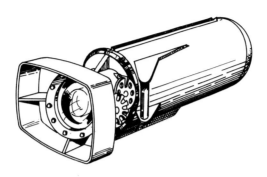

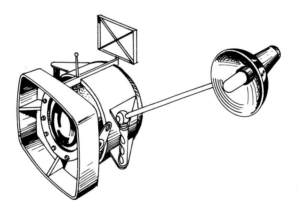

Figure 17. Shown at top, a typical camera used during our expedition. The controls are on the left near the handle, so they can be worked during shooting. On the other side is another handle, with a trigger to start the camera. All these cameras are made in our shop from Bell & Howell parts, and parts of other makes, and we use correction ports, ground to specifications, for each of our lenses. The drawing below illustrates a still-camera casing for a Nikon with 21-mm. lens and a correction port; also, of course, a flash gun.

Figure 18. A shark being attacked by porpoises. They hit the shark at top speed in the lower portion of the abdomen, the tender area of the shark, ripping apart the shark's delicate insides. They also destroy the gills by bumping them at top speed, thus destroying the shark's breathing apparatus.

Figure 19. Enemies of the shark.

The most dangerous enemy of the shark is man. Many hunt the shark not for self-defense against the killer, but merely for pleasure and excitement. Man seeks the shark to destroy him.

Boat propellers also tend to destroy sharks in the tropical seas. We have often observed the shark being mauled by the propeller of one of our launches or outboard motorboats.

The porcupine fish, which starts out as the shark's prey, becomes his killer when, as the shark begins to devour it, the porcupine fish inflates itself in the shark's mouth and asphyxiates him by preventing the water from flowing through his gills.

The great squid, too, is a killer of sharks in areas like the Humboldt Current. So are the alligators found at the entrance of Africa's rivers, for example, and the salt-water crocodiles, which massacre the sharks. The killer whale can devour a large shark at sea—an incident once witnessed by Professor Ted Walker near San Diego. Of course, as we have already mentioned, the dolphin is an eligible addition to the category of shark killer.

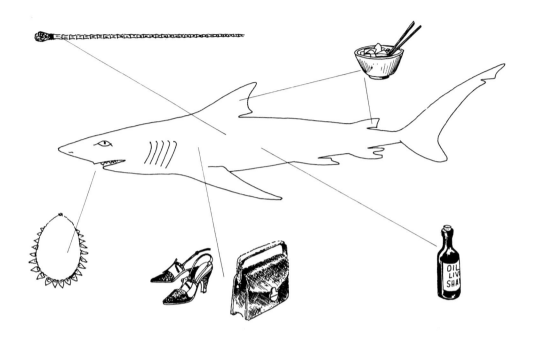

Figure 20. In many parts of the world, attempts have been made to exploit the shark for manufacturing by-products. Fisheries were once established—in South Africa and Florida, primarily. The principal product extracted from the shark was the oil in its liver. As shown in Figure 7, the shark's liver is extremely large and provides a great quantity of oil when treated. The oil, rich in vitamins, often was sold as cod-liver oil.

The shark's very tough and resistant skin has caused it to be used in the manufacturing of shoes, handbags, and other leather products.

The teeth provide assorted jewelry and ornaments, such as necklaces, bracelets, knife handles, sword handles.

The backbone is often used as a cane, supported by a piece of wrought iron which is run through the center of the vertebrae; the bone is filed and shaped. The handle of the cane is usually made of black coral, commonly found in the Red Sea.

The problem with the shark's skin is the treatment, which is a difficult, delicate process. The skin has a tendency to harden, unlike leather, which tends to be flexible. But this can prove advantageous, since the shoes, purses, and other items made of sharkskin are sufficiently resistant to last a long time. The skin has also been used in South Africa as sandpaper.

The fins are used by Orientals for food. In Lake Nicaragua, Central America, a fishery for fresh-water shark was officially established years ago. The fresh-water shark is a product of centuries of adaptation to these waters. It is related to the mako shark. The most important product of this fishery was oriental food for the Chinese colonies, made from shark fins. Today, most shark fisheries have disappeared. Cod-liver oil is usually synthetically manufactured, and shark leather has not proved commercially successful.

The shark is now fished mostly for its souvenir value in tourist industries of countries whose waters are abundant in sharks.

Figure 21. The squaloscope. Used for studying the shark in a confined area, the squalo-scope was designed in plastic and aluminum by Jean-Michel Cousteau. The structure proved efficient only for short-time study of the shark, because it was too small and the shark could not swim easily enough within the apparatus to ventilate its gills. After a while the shark would die as a result of lack of oxygen. The squaloscope was used pri-marily at Shab Arab Reef. It was not an easy structure to place in the water (being rather fragile), but it served an excellent purpose in allowing us to inject chemicals into the sharks to study their reactions. Most of these studies were made to determine the effect of tranquilizers.

Above the squaloscope, a one-man cage is being propelled, with the diver sticking his legs out at the rear end of the cage and paddling through the water. This mode of travel is absolutely safe, even in the worst shark frenzy.

Both cages were built in the south of France in our engineering plant, CEMA *(Centre d'Etudes Marines Avancées),* headed by Captain Brenot.

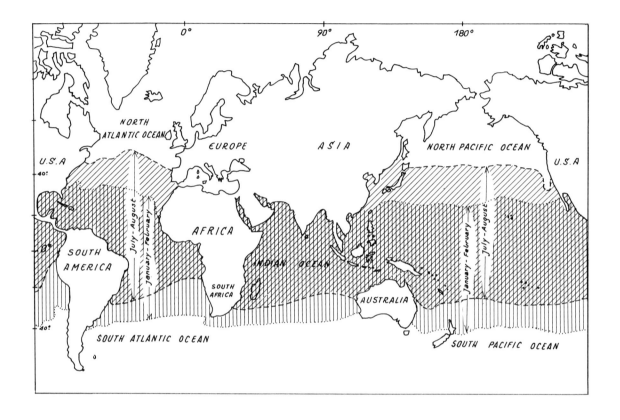

Figure 22. Illustrated in this map-temperature chart is the displacement, southward and then northward, of the warm-water belt around the world during winter and summer. This warm-water belt is certainly the area where most accidents occur. Most sharks are warm-water animals, except for the few species residing in the colder waters of the north. The warm-water belt is the area most often utilized by swimmers and divers, thus increasing the opportunity for accidental encounters. The chart was drawn from statistics accumulated by the Smithsonian Institution and other research organizations.

Index

CREDITS

Photographers whose pictures appear in this book

Philippe Cousteau
Michel Deloire
Raymond Deloire
André Laban
Yves Omer
Ludwig Sillner

Some of the topside photographs were selected from the personal collections of crew members.

Drawings in Appendix B by Jean-Charles Roux

Drawings in Chapter 11 by Juliana Sloane

Researcher: Miriam Perry

Photographic Assistant: Joan Lavine

The Undersea Discoveries
of Jacques-Yves Cousteau

DOLPHINS

The Undersea Discoveries
of Jacques-Yves Cousteau

Dolphins

Jacques-Yves Cousteau
and Philippe Diolé

Translated from the French by J. F. Bernard

Copyright © 1974, 1975 by Jacques-Yves Cousteau
Translated from the French by J. F. Bernard

All rights reserved. No part of this work may be
reproduced or transmitted in any form or by any
means, electronic or mechanical, including photocopying,
recording, or any information storage and retrieval
system, without permission in writing from the
publisher.

Published in 1987 by

Arrowood Press
166 Fifth Avenue
New York, NY 10010

This edition published by arrangement with The Cousteau
Group, Inc., 38 Eleven O'Clock Road, Weston, CT 06883.

Library of Congress Catalog Card Number: 87-71043
ISBN: 0-88486-015-9

Printed in Spain

CONTENTS

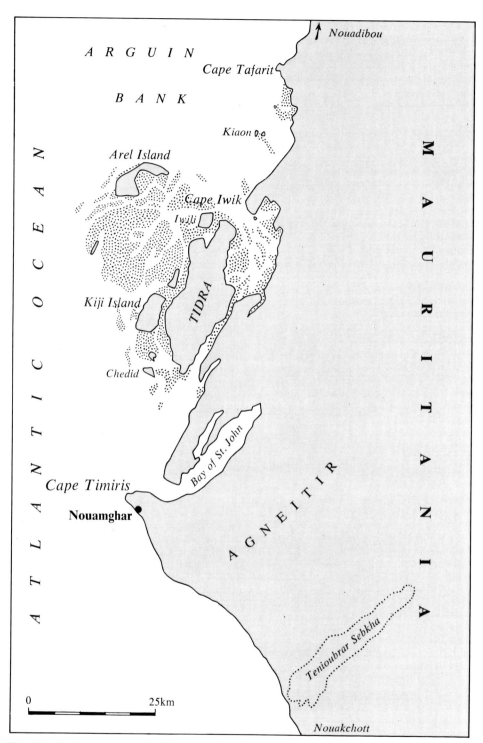

The Mauritanian coast, south of the Arguin Bank. This is the traditional fishing site of the Imragen

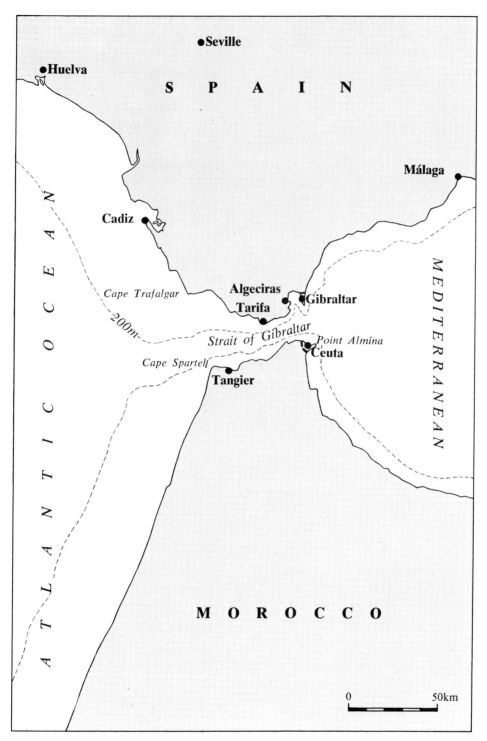

The Gibraltar Strait, where one can almost always spot cetaceans in abundance

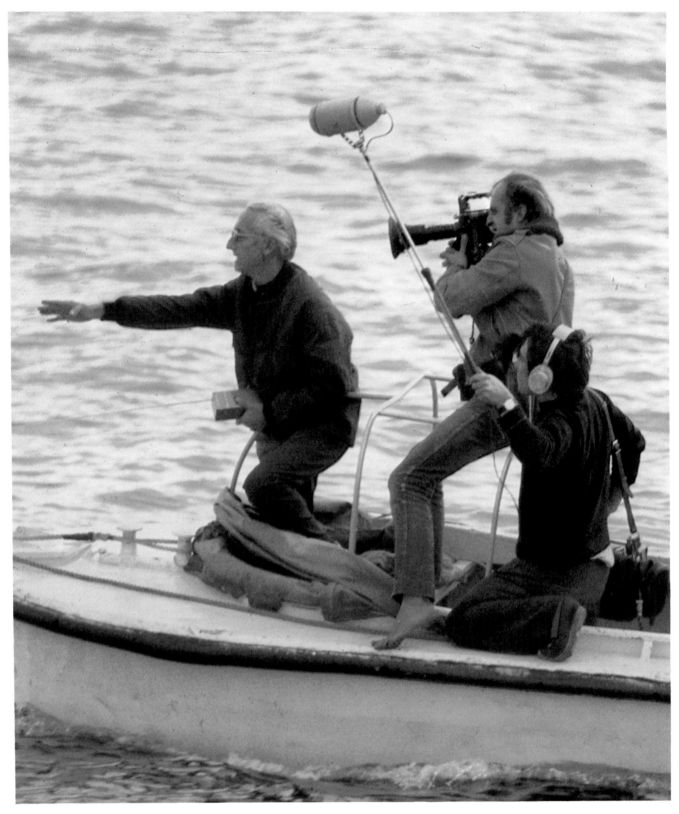

Captain Cousteau and Jacques Renoir, our cameraman and sound engineer, approach a school of dolphins.

Chapter One

FIRST ENCOUNTERS

The cruiser *Primauguet* cut through the water at full speed, its prow rising and falling among the waves and raising a great wave of its own as it pushed irresistibly through the liquid wall of the sea. It was an impressive sight. The cruiser, a ship of the French Navy, had just been released from dry dock and we were testing her in the waters of the Far East. At that moment, the *Primauguet*'s engines were wide open, and we were moving at a speed of 33.5 knots.

I was standing on the bridge, enthralled by the performance of the mighty cruiser as it cut through the sea with incredible violence. Then, I glanced to starboard. A school of dolphins was alongside, their fins regularly appearing then disappearing beneath the surface, their dark backs moving with graceful power through the rough water. I watched. And suddenly I realized that the dolphins were moving faster than the *Primauguet*. Swimming some thirty or forty feet away from the cruiser and parallel to her, they were passing her! I could hardly believe my eyes.

Then, suddenly, the lead dolphin altered his course and cut toward our prow. When he reached the crest of the wave raised by the thrust of the *Primauguet*'s engines, he hovered there until he was displaced by another dolphin, and then another. The dolphins had devised a game which they played in the midst of the waves: one by one, in turn, they rode the crest of the cruiser's wave, directly before our prow, for two or three minutes, then let themselves be carried to starboard or port so that the next dolphin could have his turn. It was an astonishing spectacle, but its importance to me at that time was practical rather than aesthetic. I realized that the school of dolphins, in catching up to and then passing the *Primauguet* as it moved at full power, must have been swimming at a speed of no less than fifty miles per hour!

That was forty years ago. Since then, I have had many encounters with dolphins, but I have never forgotten my first impression of those great mammals as they materialized in front of the *Primauguet*'s stem — faster, and infinitely more maneuverable, than the best machines that human ingenuity had yet been able to devise.

There is no seaman worthy of the name, regardless of his nationality, who is not familiar with dolphins. For centuries, mariners and dolphins have been friends. Sailors have watched these mammals following in the wake of their ships, as though they were fascinated by the vessels — or perhaps by the men on them. And for centuries sailors have been puzzled by the preferred position of a dolphin with respect to a ship: just forward of the stem. There has been much speculation over the dolphin's reasons for this preference. Some have concluded that the dolphin's purpose is utilitarian, in that the motion of the vessel through the water provides a free ride and allows the dolphin to conserve its strength so that, with a minimum of effort, it is carried at a considerable speed but over rather short distances. Yet, the fact remains, as I found out aboard the *Primauguet*, that the dolphin does not need a ship to attain great speed. Moreover, dolphins never stay very long forward of a ship's stem. So, it seems reasonable to surmise that the dolphin's purpose in choosing that position has little or nothing to do with location. By the same token, the speed of a ship does not seem to be an important factor. There is documentary evidence that dolphins maneuvered forward of ancient sailing ships as readily as they do before the stems of our mightiest warships today, and as readily as they still do with small sailing vessels, inasmuch as their speed is at least three knots.

We could say that, in such instances, the dolphins are "playing." But how can we possibly know what a dolphin considers to be a "game"?

It is possible that contact with the rush of water raised by a prow is pleasant to dolphins. It stimulates them, caresses them, "pets" them. The skin of the dolphin is quite sensitive, and the motion of the water may give them a pleasure almost sensual in nature. Or it may be that that same motion serves simply to cleanse their skins. But it would seem that the dolphin could be caressed or cleaned just as effectively aft of a ship, in its wake, as forward of its stem. Yet, dolphins never swim in a wake. . . .

It should be obvious by now that we understand very little about this behavior of dolphins. We know that these mammals like to come into contact with objects they find floating on the surface of the water. Occasionally, they actually swim with their bodies touching the hull of a ship. And sometimes two dolphins will place themselves on each side of the hull in this position, as though they are trying to support the ship and keep it afloat. Not all species of dolphin venture near boats and ships — only those who are most "gregarious."

A Sense of Direction

I have often had occasion to realize just how mysterious the life of the dolphin is and how little we understand it. In 1948, for example, I was aboard the *Elie Monnier*, a ship of the French Navy, when we set sail from Toulon for the islands off Cape Verde. Our mission was to launch the *FNRS II* — the bathyscaphe designed by Professor Piccard. En route, near Gibraltar, we took the opportunity to conduct an interesting experiment.

Marine mammals are particularly abundant in the waters around Gibraltar, and one sees large numbers of cetaceans: sperm whales, whales, and pilot whales. On this occasion, the weather was beautiful, the sea calm, and the dolphins particularly numerous. We set a westward course, to a point in the Atlantic where we wanted to take soundings at the mouth of the straits. By the time we had finished the job, we were about fifty miles from shore and we sighted a large school of dolphins obviously heading for Gibraltar. We made a half turn and joined them. Almost immediately, the dolphins took up a position directly in front of our prow and began leaping out of the water, playing, and always remaining ahead of our ship.

To all appearances, they were as certain of the course back to Gibraltar as we were, with all of our navigational equipment. I wondered if it was a coincidence. Then I decided to try an experiment. I ordered the *Elie Monnier*'s course changed ever so gradually and slightly. For a short time, the dolphins remained with the ship, then, suddenly, they left us and resumed the true course toward Gibraltar.

Several times we tried to lead them astray in this way, and each time the dolphins left us to stay on course. I could only conclude that here, some fifty miles from land, the dolphins knew the precise azimuth of Gibraltar and were on a direct course toward their destination. I was left wondering how

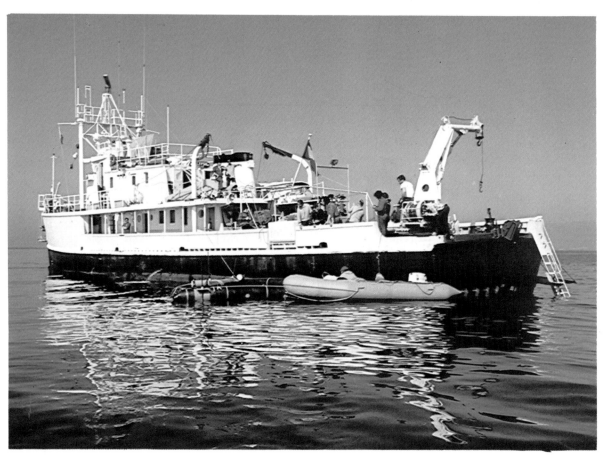

Calypso at anchor.

they could possibly navigate with such precision. Were they guided by the currents? By the topography of the bottom? By the composition of the water where the Mediterranean mixes with the Atlantic? I still do not know the answer to that question.

A Sense of Caution

During the same cruise, off the coast of Morocco, we cut our engines near a school of dolphins. The dolphins were following a southward course, playing as they swam.

The sea was calm that day, and, for the first time, we decided to join the dolphins in the water. We hoped that our diving gear would enable us to get close enough to film the mammals and, perhaps, even to touch them. Remember, this was in 1948, and it was a marvelous and exciting experience for us. Unfortunately, we were able to get only a few brief shots of the animals as

(Right) Dolphins in the open sea.

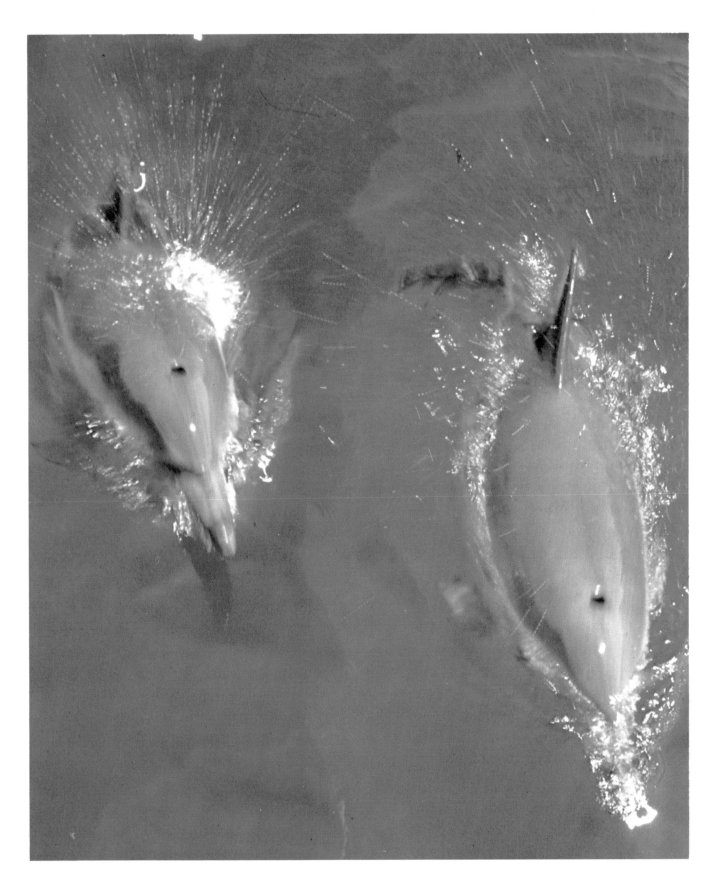

they dived toward the bottom or swam frantically away from us.

We learned that day that, in the water, dolphins are extremely wary of divers. And that conclusion has been confirmed many times since then. Dolphins in their natural environment never approach a man beneath the surface, regardless of whether the man is moving or remaining absolutely motionless. They seem less frightened of a man who remains on the surface, but, even then, as soon as the man dives, the dolphins flee. It may be that the human form represents a threat to them. A diver beneath the surface may appear to be a marine animal similar to a shark — the natural enemy of dolphins.

It sometimes happens that a dolphin will overcome its timidity sufficiently to swim a bit closer for a better look, but, almost immediately, he swims away again. We have never seen a dolphin in the sea remain among divers for any length of time. Even in areas not usually frequented by man, where the dolphins have no reason to fear man, they seem to regard a diver as a dangerous creature who must be avoided.

During *Calypso*'s oceanographic expeditions in 1951 and 1952, we often sighted schools of dolphins in the Red Sea and in the Indian Ocean. Sometimes these schools comprised several hundred individuals. We learned to recognize them at considerable distances by the great splashes the dolphins make by leaping out of the water.

As soon as we spotted a series of such splashes, we dived into the water. But, no matter how quick we were, we never succeeded in really getting close to the animals, let alone in swimming with them or joining in their games as we had hoped.

We used to daydream about these marvelous mammals, imagining that, somehow, we could work out a common life with them in the sea. We exercised great care in approaching them, doing everything possible to avoid frightening them. We did all that we could to present ourselves as friends. But how does one go about conveying an attitude of friendship to dolphins? We tried everything we could think of to reassure them and convince them of our good intentions, but they refused to take the bait. They did not even seem to notice the fishes that we offered them — which would have been snatched up immediately by a grouper or a shark.

At that time, we knew even less than we know now about dolphins and

(Right) A large school of dolphins traveling in the open water.

(Following page) Three dolphins swimming near *Calypso*.

about life in the sea. For us, dolphins were legendary animals, for we had read all the surviving literature of the ancients about them. That is not to say that we believed all that we read, but, even so, dolphins seemed to us to be the most attractive and intriguing form of marine life. And so, we were determined to make friends with them. But, every time we dived and tried to get close to them, they scattered in every direction, majestic even in their flight.

It often happened that, during our expeditions, we saw schools of dolphins swimming on a course parallel to *Calypso*'s. On such occasions, just as it had occurred some fifteen years earlier when I was aboard the *Primauguet*, the largest and strongest of the dolphins would take up a position directly forward of the stem. He seemed to take great pleasure in being pushed along by the water. Around this dolphin, the other dolphins gamboled, diving under the hull and making sounds as though they were demanding the best place and the game that was most fun.*

Sometimes a school of dolphins would continue these antics for fifteen or twenty minutes. At other times, the animals spent only a few seconds at it.

We were particularly taken by the grace and suppleness of the dolphins in the sea. As divers, we are hopelessly outclassed by them, and we can only envy an ability which we can never hope to match.

I have mentioned the "games" of the dolphins. If they do indeed play, their games are not haphazard or disorganized. They are community games which all participants begin at the same instant, as though by magic — or as though at a given signal. We have seen immense schools of dolphins suddenly begin leaping out of the water, turning, and raising great splashes of water as they fell back on their sides or on their backs.

In the water, one can see their white undersides quite clearly. Sometimes the animals stroke each other with their fins or rub the entire lengths of their bodies against one another.

The Silent World

In 1954, after having worked in the Red Sea, we headed toward the Persian Gulf on a petroleum-exploration assignment. As we were leaving Aden, we sighted a school of dolphins unlike any that we had ever seen and unlike any that we would ever see again.

These were the dolphins who were seen in *The Silent World*. Even that film does not convey an exact idea of that incredible gathering as we saw it.

---

*Dr. Kenneth Norris has seen dolphins "surfing" ahead of a large whale, just as they do with ships.

When we sighted the school from afar, the water was churning as though it were boiling. Our captain, François Saout, was on the bridge at the time. He sent for me immediately and reported: "I don't understand this at all. There's a reef dead ahead which doesn't appear on our charts."

It was not until we were closer that we realized that the "reef" was an incredible assembly of dolphins — no fewer than 10,000 of them, and perhaps as many as 20,000 — leaping playfully into the air. These leaps were so fantastic that we have never again seen anything like them in all our years of observing dolphins in the sea. We remained there for several hours, watching. Then night fell, and we lost sight of them. We have since tried to locate similar concentrations of dolphins, but we have seen nothing to compare with what we saw that day.

A friend of ours, Professor René-G. Busnel,† on a number of occasions has seen dolphins assembled in schools that stretched to a length of thirty-five or forty miles. In the Mediterranean, he has witnessed schools streaking past his ship — schools which extended for miles in both directions — with the dolphins swimming swiftly in single file, without even ruffling the surface. Once, en route to Dakar, his ship was completely surrounded by dolphins, with the animals spaced out so that there was only one dolphin to every twenty square yards of surface. He estimates that some of these schools comprised several million dolphins.

An Underwater Congress

In 1955, when we were filming *The Silent World*, we left the Seychelles and headed toward Amirante Island in the Indian Ocean. *Calypso* dropped anchor on the leeward side of a reef and remained there for two days while we dived. We noticed that, every morning at about ten o'clock, a school of dolphins passed near *Calypso*, apparently on a swimming tour of the reef. I wanted to follow them, and, since it seemed unnecessary to use *Calypso* for this, Frédéric Dumas and I set out in one of our launches. To this day, I have not forgiven myself for not taking a camera.

On the other side of the reef, we saw a dolphin rise to the surface to breathe and then let himself sink down into the water again, without swimming. We inched forward in the launch until we were as close as we dared go, then we dived. On this occasion, the dolphins did not flee as soon as we got

†Professor Busnel has either initiated, or participated in, several of *Calypso*'s cruises. He is currently Director of the Laboratory of Acoustical Physiology of the INRA.

Our Zodiac managed to maintain a position very close to a group of playful dolphins.

into the water. From the surface — we did not have our Aqua-Lungs® with us — we looked down and saw them turn their heads and stare at us. The sight that greeted us was one that we have never seen again. There were about fifteen dolphins — probably the school that we had seen going past *Calypso* every morning — in the crystal-clear water, on the side of the reef. They were *sitting* on the bottom, in a group, as though they were holding a conference. I say "sitting"; I mean that they were literally poised on their tails.

They remained where they were, stirring a bit and looking at one another. Then they continued with their meeting. But when we tried to move in closer to them, they swam away immediately. It was a unique and extraordinarily impressive sight.

The truth is that I still have no idea what they were doing. For the most part, the life of a dolphin — that is, of a dolphin living at liberty in the sea — is an enigma wrapped in a mystery. We understand a bit more — but not much

A dolphin can leap about ten feet above the surface.

more — about that part of the dolphin's life which takes place on the surface, when the animals are en route between two points and when we see them swimming and playing before *Calypso*'s prow. What they do with the rest of their lives, we have no idea. I cannot even offer a plausible explanation for the "congress" Dumas and I witnessed except to say that it did not appear to have anything to do with mating. I have described it only because I think Dumas and I are the only humans ever to have witnessed behavior of this sort among dolphins.

Ostracism?

We had an encounter of a different kind in the Mediterranean, in 1953. Again, the weather was magnificent and the sea was like a mirror. We were sailing around Corsica, and had entered the Tyrrhenian Sea, between Corsica and the Italian mainland. I was in the observation chamber, and from that vantage point I saw, for the first time in my life, a finback whale swimming on its back. The whale was in my field of vision for fifteen or twenty seconds. At first I thought it was a white whale. But then, when the animal righted itself, I saw that it was black, like other finbacks. It occurs to me that almost all mariners' accounts of white whales are based upon sightings of whales amusing themselves by swimming stomach-up slightly beneath the surface of the water. Albino whales are a great rarity, and I suspect that when navigators and whalers reported a "white whale," they were referring to an ordinary whale swimming in this position. In some cases, it may have been a case of confusion with the Beluga (*Delphinus leucas*), which is a Delphinidae of very large size.

The same day, we reached the vicinity of the Lipari Islands. However, we could not distinguish the coasts of the islands because, following a period of calm weather, weak currents, and a recent volcanic eruption, the water was covered with pumice stone. It was as though *Calypso* were moving through a sea of liquid rock, and the pumice made a constant crunching sound as it grated against our hull. A continuous noise rose from the water all around us, and it took an hour for *Calypso* to pick her way through that field of volcanic debris.

As the pumice stone began to thin, we sighted a black dot in the distance: a dolphin, floating vertically, with his snout protruding above the surface. From time to time, he moved his tail to maintain his position, that is, to keep his snout above the surface so as to breathe. But he was not swimming.

Calypso drew nearer, and still the dolphin did not move. It occurred to us that the animal might be sick, or even dead. When we were five or six yards from the dolphin, I ordered *Calypso*'s engines cut, and we dived into the water. It was obvious then that the dolphin was alive; he was watching us. We swam closer, and the animal's head disappeared beneath the surface, only to reappear a few moments later. There was no attempt at flight. He continued to return to the surface regularly for air.

We watched the dolphin for perhaps three quarters of an hour, until our ship's doctor, Dr. Nivelot, came to a conclusion. "The only thing I can imagine," Nivelot said, "is that he's sick. I'll have to see if I can do anything for him."

Canoë Kientzy brought a net from *Calypso* and gently wrapped it around the ailing dolphin. The animal did not attempt to resist, or to flee. Then we hoisted him aboard and placed him in a small boat filled with water. He floated in the water and appeared not unduly frightened. His breathing

Falco was able to lay hold of a dolphin in the water and to swim with the animal.

seemed normal, and there was no sign of any kind of wound or cut on his body.

After examining the dolphin, Dr. Nivelot concluded that a stimulant of some kind might be helpful, and he gave his patient an injection of camphorated oil. There seemed to be no immediate effect.

An hour later, the dolphin was dead.

We were all very upset, and Dr. Nivelot undertook an autopsy. He found nothing — no organic disorder, no sign of congestion. Nothing. We had taken the dolphin's temperature while the animal was still alive and found it to be normal (38°C).

The death of the dolphin was the occasion for much reflection on my part. Finally, I reached a conclusion which is perhaps somewhat daring. Nonetheless, it is a conclusion based upon long observation and experience since that unfortunate incident in the Tyrrhenian Sea. It is my opinion that the dolphin may have been ostracized by the other dolphins. Dolphins are gregarious beings who do not take well to solitude. When they are excluded from the company of other dolphins, they are in desperate straits indeed. Then, they try to attach themselves to anything or anyone. In our laboratory experiments at Monaco, we have seen dolphins who *allow* themselves to die. Dolphins are emotional, sensitive, vulnerable creatures — probably more so than we are.

It seems likely that schools of dolphins observe a form of discipline that we do not understand. There are probably rules which none of the school is allowed to transgress.

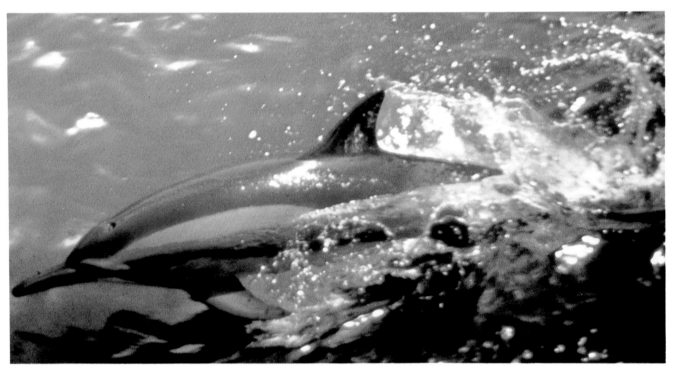

(Above) Dolphins in the open sea can swim at speeds in excess of 40 miles per hour.

(Right) From *Calypso*'s stem, part of our team watches a dolphin maneuver in the water.

The animal that we had taken aboard *Calypso* was quite young, so it is certain that she (it was a female, as we discovered) had not been turned out of the school because of old age. It may be that she had broken a rule of some kind. In any case, the pitiful death of that dolphin, so many years ago, made a deep impression on me.

Another aspect of the mysterious conduct of dolphins lies in their attachment to beings of other species. I am perfectly well aware that I am leaving myself open to criticism by attributing anything like emotions to dolphins. I should therefore begin by stating that there are certain documented facts which cannot be explained except by admitting that dolphins have certain emotional or affective drives. When marine mammals try to keep a drowning swimmer afloat, it may be because they have a tendency to push against, or to keep on the surface, any floating object. But what are we to think of the dolphin who, when his companion in captivity died, stubbornly kept the corpse from sinking? And what are we to say about the dolphin who, for over a week, kept the corpse of a tiger shark at the surface and resisted any at-

tempt to remove the corpse? He abandoned his efforts only when the tiger shark had begun to decompose.

Certainly, we may speculate that the actions of those dolphins indicate an incomprehension in the face of death, a refusal to accept death. It may be that such actions prove nothing. But they do give us food for thought.

In our own minds, our encounters with dolphins take on many of the characteristics of encounters with human beings. Why? No doubt, it is because each dolphin appears to have its own distinctive personality.

In any event, it is obvious that dolphins are often motivated by curiosity, and especially by curiosity about man. One can literally see it in their eyes. This is a fact that can be doubted only by someone who has never really looked a dolphin in the eye. The brilliance of that organ, the spark that is so evident there, seems to come from another world. The look which the dolphin gives — a keen look, slightly melancholy and mischievous, but less insolent and cynical than that of monkeys — seems full of indulgence for the uncertainties of the human condition. Among primates, one sometimes detects what appears to be sadness at not being human. This sentiment is alien to the dolphin.

When I had *Calypso* converted from a mine sweeper into an oceanographic-research vessel, I had a "false nose" built under the stem. This is a metallic well, at the bottom of which is an observation chamber equipped with five portholes. The observation chamber is about eight feet beneath the surface, and from that vantage point we can observe the sea around us. We can not only watch the dolphins as they move in the water, but we can also look at them as they look at us. And we can do so only because the dolphins themselves are willing. They see us through the portholes, and they press their snouts against the glass to see us. The rictus that crosses their cheeks, from the eye to the snout, gives them the appearance of wearing an eternal smile. Their "look" — mischievous, curious, observant — is that of a mammal and does not have the icy fixity of the shark's stare.

On two or three occasions, we looked at each other, and their eyes sparkled with an unexpected gleam of connivance, as though the most intelligent of the dolphins was about to reveal, at last, the great secret which would permit man finally to cross over the chasm separating humanity from animality, finally to restore to life its primordial unity.

This book makes no pretense of solving these mysteries. All that we can do is recount what we have done and what we have seen. Perhaps it will be taken in good part if we mention that in the past twenty-five years, *Calypso*'s team has had more direct experience with dolphins than man has ever had before. We have observed dolphins living at liberty in the open sea. We have seen them in semicaptivity, eager for contact with humans, eager not only to be fed but also to be petted. We have taken dolphins from the sea and released them almost immediately, having detained them only a few moments for an experiment. And, unfortunately, we have also seen dolphins living in close captivity, sad dolphins the sight of which was sufficient to cure us forever of any urge to deprive these creatures of their liberty.

Now, at the beginning of this book, candor requires us to confess that neither our own experiences nor the research of the hundred-or-so scientists, who are at work trying to solve the mystery of the dolphin, are sufficient to enable us to answer with any certainty the many fascinating questions that have excited the interest of the public: the meaning of the sound signals emitted by dolphins, the hierarchical structure of the dolphin community, the degree of the dolphin's attachment to humans, and so forth. All we can do is resign ourselves, at least temporarily, to our ignorance and continue to observe and to experiment so that, someday, we may arrive at the truth.

We have been careful, throughout this work, to refrain from making affirmations for which there is insufficient evidence; and, even at the risk of disappointing the reader, we have tried to remain well within the realm of the non-miraculous.

It is a peculiarity of the dolphin that it is the animal which most excites popular admiration and interest and, at the same time, which most elicits caution among scientists. This paradoxical situation is explained by the fact that, so far as the public is concerned, dolphins are a relatively recent discovery. It was only some twenty or twenty-five years ago that the dolphin became a circus and television star. And, almost immediately, people began talking about the dolphin's "language," its "intelligence," its "feelings." These are terms the indiscriminate use of which is enough to make any scientist uneasy.

We do not mean to imply that the exceptional qualities popularly attributed to dolphins are all exaggerations and myths. On many points, we share the feelings of the public with respect to the dolphin. And our long experience with dolphins has only served to strengthen those feelings in us.

Therefore, it is certainly not the purpose of this book to "demythologize" the dolphin. At the same time, we must not ignore the opinions and criticisms of zoologists, neurophysiologists, and acoustical experts — all of whom are, and should be, skeptics by profession. These specialists require proof.

For all of that, we do not believe that the adventure of the dolphins will lose anything of its capacity to elicit interest and admiration. Let us remem-

Ivan Giacoletto, one of *Calypso*'s divers, photographed this group of dolphins in the water.

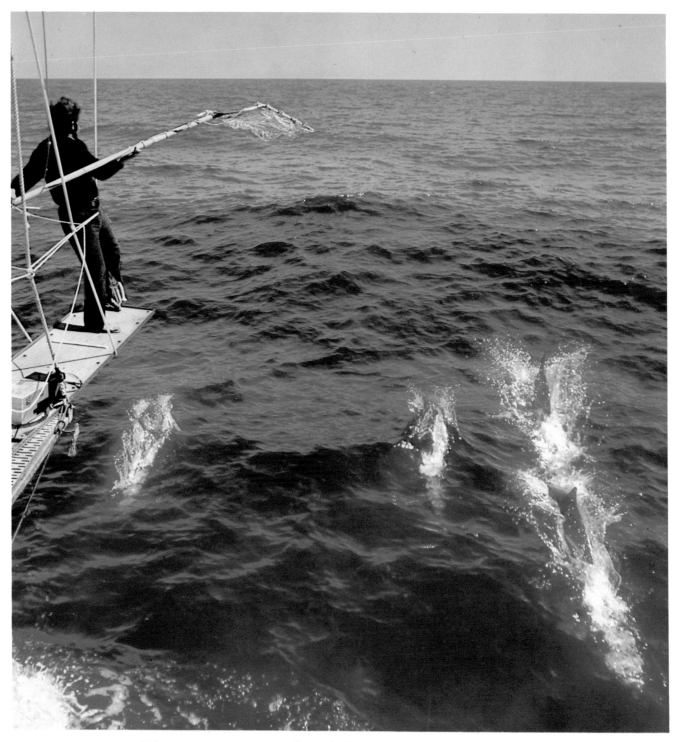

Falco attempts to capture one of the dolphins swimming before *Calypso*'s prow.

ber that this adventure is far from finished. It continues and grows from day to day. And let us remember too that life, in its exuberance, always succeeds in overflowing the narrow limits within which man thinks he can confine it.

Chapter Two

THE DOLPHINS OF MONACO

Our encounters with dolphins were, at first, more or less exceptional meetings in the course of our work, enjoyable distractions which occurred during *Calypso*'s expeditions. In our minds, we regarded the dolphin as a kind of friend in reserve, a rather mysterious and somewhat amusing friend to divers like ourselves engaged in the kind of work that we had undertaken.

It was our impression, at the time, that it required a certain amount of luck to sight a school of dolphins. We knew less about the sea then than we know now, and certainly much less about the kind of lives that animals lived in the sea. Even today, twenty years later, we do not know a great deal about the sea as a whole. The extent of the sea is so vast that even though a man may spend his whole life studying it, he can never know more than certain areas of the ocean.

One day in 1957, I decided that it was time to pay more attention to the dolphins we had seen in the Mediterranean. I had visited marinelands in the United States, and I had seen trained dolphins perform some extraordinary feats there. I had it in the back of my mind to obtain the same results for the Oceanographic Museum of Monaco.

I described my plan to Albert Falco, our chief diver. Albert, or Bébert, as we call him, is our most experienced diver, and he is also a man with a remarkable understanding of animals. I told Bébert that I wanted to try to capture some dolphins if it were possible to do so without harming them in any way.

"Capture dolphins?" Falco asked. "How on earth would we go about it?"

"Well, in America they lasso them."

"America is a cowboy country. They must have cowboy divers."

"Well," I said, "*Calypso* is going to be at Monaco for a week. We can devote that time exclusively to Operation Dolphin. At least it's worth a try."

Bébert shrugged.

As the first part of my plan, I had a platform installed on *Calypso*'s prow. The second part of the plan was to install Bébert on the platform, armed with a lasso which was attached to a pole.

Happily, the weather was perfect our first day out. Off Villefranche, we sighted a school of dolphins almost immediately. *Calypso* turned and began following a course parallel to theirs. As usual, the school quickly took up its position dead ahead of *Calypso*, and one of the dolphins placed himself so that he could ride along on the wave raised by our vessel.

The moment had come for Bébert to play cowboy.

Teetering on his platform, he swung the lasso and threw it. The rope struck the water, and the lead dolphin fled, closely followed by the rest of the school. In an instant, the sea was empty.

We then realized that if a lasso is thrown from a vessel moving at a speed of five or six knots, there is no chance that it will even penetrate the surface. Therefore, it is impossible to lasso a dolphin following that method. Nonetheless, Bébert was convinced that there must be some technique, some trick to it, that would make it possible to lasso a dolphin. For the next week, he tried one approach after another, but all in vain.

By then, it was time for *Calypso* to leave for an expedition in the Atlantic. When we reached Lisbon, however, Bébert left us to return to Monaco for the express purpose of pursuing his dolphin hunt. There was an old vessel there for him to use: the *Espadon*, a trawler which we would later convert into a ship for diving and oceanographic research.

Dolphins and Sharks

"At that time," Bébert says, "I knew practically nothing about dolphins. I had spent hours watching them playing around *Calypso*; and, for the past five or six years, we had been trying to dive with them in the water, but they

This is the *Espadon*, a converted trawler used by Falco in his first attempts to capture a dolphin.

would never let us join them. As soon as we got within ten or fifteen yards of them, they swam away.

"There was only one exception. During our expeditions in the Indian Ocean, whenever we passed near an island, we always went out in a launch or a Zodiac to inspect the bottom and the reefs, to see what kind of animals lived there. On this particular occasion in 1954, we were lying off the Farquhar Islands, to the northeast of Madagascar. And, following our usual practice, we went out in a launch.

"There were several dolphins in the water that took an immediate interest in the launch. As soon as we saw them, we cut our speed to a minimum and moved forward as slowly as possible so as not to frighten them. To our surprise, the dolphins did not run away, but remained at a distance of five or six yards from us. They were in relatively shallow water, and most of them kept their heads down. We could see their light-colored and somewhat plump bellies. For at least ten minutes, they remained motionless, watching us, with a mischievous expression on their faces.

(Following page) This photograph was taken at the precise moment that a dolphin, after having leaped through the air, struck the surface of the water again.

"I remember that, deeper in the water, directly below the dolphins, there were a number of sharks. We expected something to happen, thinking that perhaps the sharks would attack the dolphins. We had often heard, however, that dolphins were not afraid of sharks, that they were much more clever than sharks.

"In any case, the sharks and the dolphins left each other alone on this occasion. What struck me, though, was that this was the first time, in years of trying, that I had been able to get so close to a school of dolphins."

By the time he returned to Monaco, Bébert was convinced that if he was going to capture a live dolphin without hurting it, as I had instructed him, then he would have to devise some kind of special lasso for the job. He reasoned that the best place to lay hold of a dolphin with a lasso was just forward of its tail. This was the part of the animal's body which remained exposed the longest when a dolphin was swimming ahead of a boat. The problem was how to get a lasso around that slender part of the tail which lies just forward of the powerful tail fins.

Bébert approached the French Bureau of Marine Research — our research facility at Marseilles — and the Bureau manufactured a dolphin catcher of sorts for him. It was a kind of giant pincer, with two pawls designed to open on contact and then immediately close again.

Bébert did not give up his idea of a lasso. He designed a rigid hoop which was intended to hold the lasso open when he threw it. Then the device was modified so that it could be thrown by means of a hand harpoon or else shot by a harpoon gun. The idea was to slip the lasso around the dolphin's snout — a plan for which extraordinary speed would be required.

Designing an instrument capable of seizing — and holding — a dolphin is not as simple as it may sound. Bébert was dealing with animals weighing between 150 and 175 pounds and capable of leaping out of the water at a speed of thirty or forty miles per hour. His job was made more difficult by the fact that the dolphin's skin is extremely sensitive, and I had insisted that, above all, the specimen captured was not to be hurt in any way. Moreover, as we knew very well by that time, dolphins are very wary of man, and we had no idea of how a dolphin would react once it had been captured. We had often had occasion to note that the dolphin's snout is equipped with a large number of teeth.

The *Espadon* made its first attempt to capture a dolphin off the coast of Corsica. We had occasionally encountered schools of the mammals in these waters; and we did not know at that time that there were at least as many dolphins offshore from the Museum in Monaco, between Monaco and Nice, as there were around Corsica.

All in all, the mission of the *Espadon* in Corsican waters was a disappointment. By then, winter had set in and there were not many dolphins to be seen. There was a sufficient number, however, for Bébert to be able to try his new pincer device, and, as it turned out, the pincer was not nearly large enough. It was no larger, in fact, than the tail of a medium-sized dolphin. Moreover, the dolphin — a very sensitive and intuitive animal — seemed to be aware of what was afoot and always managed to avoid the pincer.

Bébert's attempts with his lasso were no more successful than the pincer had been, although the hoop he had designed, and the fact that the lasso could be launched by means of a harpoon gun, made it a more promising weapon. Unfortunately, the platform attached to the *Espadon*'s prow did not extend far enough over the water for Bébert to be able to position himself directly over the dolphin. He was therefore obliged to throw the lasso obliquely, which meant that when the rope struck the water it floated there, and the dolphin simply swam under it.

Here are a few extracts from Bébert's log during that expedition:

"At dawn today, we sighted three schools of dolphins. They all disappeared as soon as they saw us.

"I have the feeling that they see me standing on the platform and they know that something is up, so they are even more cautious than usual.

"I've tried the pincer, but it doesn't work. It's too narrow, and the dolphin always gets away.

"October 15 and 16. Bad weather. Very few dolphins. Those we do see don't even come near our prow. The *Espadon* is pitching wildly.

"October 17. My birthday. For a present, I'd like to catch a dolphin. The weather is right for it: clear, and a dead calm. Exceptionally good visibility. We are on a southward course, about ten miles offshore.

"We saw a sperm whale on the horizon, but no dolphins.

"We are putting in to Ajaccio for the night. I'm afraid we have become the laughingstock of the local fishermen.

"October 18. We have left Corsica and are returning to the mainland. During the crossing, I will work on a design for a new pincer."

The *Espadon*'s return to Monaco, therefore, was not exactly joyous. But the expedition had not been a total failure, for Falco had learned a great deal from the experience. He used the knowledge he had gained first of all to have the *Espadon*'s forward platform extended. Then it was suggested that he test a new means of capturing a dolphin, by using an arrow tipped with curare. By computing the amount of curare with great exactitude, he was told, it should be possible to immobilize an animal without causing it the slightest harm and, while it was unconscious, to hoist it aboard.

Bébert was skeptical about this device, but the "experts" who suggested it were so affirmative that he decided it would be unwise to ignore their advice. He felt that he should at least test their method.

At the same time, he decided that it would be useless to go all the way back to Corsica in search of dolphins. Instead, the *Espadon* would try to capture a specimen off Monaco, where Bébert had seen schools in coastal waters.

The test was run, with catastrophic results. The dolphin subjected to the curare was in no way immobilized. On the contrary, he embarked on a series of prodigious leaps out of the water and then fled at top speed. It was obvious that the animal had not been paralyzed, even briefly, by the drug. The reason may have been that the harpoon used was quite small and light, and it detached itself from the dolphin's body almost instantly. Moreover, Bébert saw blood flowing from the wound made by the harpoon, and he concluded that the curare was eliminated from the dolphin's system immediately.

Here is an extract from Falco's log:

"At 1 P.M., we were about sixteen miles from the coast when we sighted several schools of dolphins. I shot my famous curare-tipped harpoon at one of the animals, with the result that he made one fantastic leap and then disappeared, taking my harpoon, and my hopes, with him. Almost simultaneously, every dolphin in the area took off in the direction of Corsica at fifty miles per hour. It was total panic.

"We are now preparing a new harpoon, with an improved piston.

"October 29. The dolphin made off with my new, improved harpoon."

After several more days of tests, with identical results, Falco, by now totally disgusted, abandoned the "ultimate weapon" of the experts.

Once more, however, he had learned from his experiences. The *Espadon*'s venture into the waters off the coast of Monaco confirmed that dolphins were much more numerous in that area than we had previously suspected. And it also revealed that dolphins were much more creatures of habit than we had thought. What this meant, in practical terms, was that Falco had discovered he did not have to depend upon luck to sight a school of dolphins.

There are very few people who have the "feel" of the sea to the extent that Bébert does. Once he had established that there were dolphins in abundance nearby — within two or three miles of the coast, offshore from Villefranche and from Nice and in the Bay of the Angels at Var — he very quickly

(Upper right) A group of dolphins swimming at full speed off the island of Corsica.

(Lower right) As the Zodiac draws near, a dolphin suddenly turns and dives.

familiarized himself with their routine and habits. Facts unsuspected by those who had never observed dolphins in the sea were now, for Bébert, truths based upon evidence: simple truths and useful truths.

Yet, it was six months before Bébert succeeded in capturing his first dolphin.

The species of dolphin that is usually seen giving performances in American marinelands is a species common in Florida's waters, the *Tursiops truncatus*, or Bottlenosed Dolphin. This species adapts fairly well to captivity and has a robust constitution. It is also found in the Mediterranean; but there, the most numerous species is the *Delphinus delphis*, or Common Dolphin, which is smaller and lighter than the Bottlenosed Dolphin. It is also considerably more delicate than the latter, as we were soon to discover.

The *Espadon*'s team, equipped with binoculars, quickly learned to spot schools of dolphins; and the ship's captain, Jean Toscano, developed the art of steering his vessel into a position parallel to the dolphins.

"We had to lure them toward the stem," Falco said. And whether they were "lured" or not depended on the time of day, the weather, and the condition of the sea.

Usually, the dolphin who takes up a position directly forward of a ship's prow keeps close watch on the ship. He is extremely cautious. At the slightest sign of activity aboard, he stops playing. Sometimes he leaves, taking the others of the school with him. Therefore, when Falco was on his platform above the spot where the dolphin was playing, it was necessary for him to assume the appearance of a part of the vessel. He had to remain absolutely motionless. When the dolphins came within range, he says, he pretended to himself that he was a figurehead on the prow and did not move a muscle. He had to choose the proper instant to strike — and then he had to move with the speed of lightning.

Meanwhile, at the Museum in Monaco, workmen were busy constructing a large pool to house the dolphin that Bébert hoped to capture.

By this time, Falco had returned to his idea of a pincer device for capturing dolphins, and he had succeeded in perfecting a pincer that he was sure would work. The device, once it had been manufactured by one of the Museum's mechanics, resembled a pair of giant scissors. Its U-shaped arms were covered with a layer of soft rubber so as not to bruise the sensitive skin of the dolphin. The two arms of the scissors were locked open by means of a plastic pin; then, on contact with the dolphin, the pin was released and the arms were snapped shut by a spring. The whole apparatus was mounted on a harpoon. Then, a yellow buoy was attached to the pincer by means of a line.

A dolphin was caught during the first tests with this device, but he suc-

Albert Falco, Canoë Kientzy and Armand Davso carefully lay a captured dolphin on a pair of air mattresses.

ceeded in freeing himself from the pincer. It was therefore necessary to double the size of one of the arms of the pincer.

The next time, the pincer held, but the dolphin began thrashing about in terror, tearing his skin on the apparatus. The *Delphinus delphis* was more high-strung than anyone had suspected. Falco therefore released the dolphin.

So far as methods were concerned, it was back to the drawing board. Finally, a rather complicated procedure was worked out among Bébert, Maurice Léandri, and Canoë Kientzy. Bébert would fire the pincer, and then Léandri would immediately throw the yellow buoy as far as possible from the ship. The instant that Maurice had thrown out the buoy, Canoë was supposed to dive into the water. And the captain, at the helm of the vessel, would give a

Dolphins leaping at the entrance to the Bay of Villefranche.

turn to the right before ordering the engine to be cut and the gears to be disengaged.

Canoë, meanwhile, was supposed to be over the side with the inflated rubber mattresses. (The purpose of the latter was to avoid bruising the dolphin's skin.) He was to wrap the mattresses around the dolphin, remove the pincer, and then take the dolphin alongside the *Espadon*, where there was an open hatch aft to port.

The first tests, carried out off Monaco, Villefranche, and Nice, had given Bébert the opportunity to discover what areas were most frequented by the dolphins and also to observe their habits. He noted that the animals followed a fairly regular schedule. In the area between Monaco and the mouth of the Var, for example, the dolphins seemed to swim in from a southeasterly direction, heading toward Nice and staying at a distance of about three miles from the shore. During the day, there were few dolphins to be seen, but they began

to arrive from the open sea late in the afternoon, about 4 or 5 P.M. They never ventured into the water flowing from the Var into the Mediterranean, but stayed on the fringes of that water so as to take advantage of the abundance of fishes to be found there. When darkness fell, the animals disappeared toward the southwest, swimming at top speed and leaping out of the water. It is likely that, during the night, they swam in a large semicircle in the open sea so that, the following afternoon, they would arrive once more from the southeast.

The First Capture

Here is the definitive passage from Falco's log:

"October 31, 1957. Everything appears to be ready. I think that the pincer is working perfectly, and everybody on the team knows exactly what he is supposed to do. The weather is good, and the *Espadon* is no longer pitching.

"Luck is with us. We spotted dolphins on the horizon — a very large school of two or three hundred specimens off the Monacan coast. We had hardly completed our turn to the rear of the school when three dolphins, trailing behind the main body of the school, caught up with us and took up their position forward of our prow. Fortunately, I was already on the platform, holding the loaded harpoon gun. I fired. It was a good shot, and the pincer closed around the tail of one of the dolphins. Immediately, Maurice threw the buoy into the water. Captain Toscano stopped the engines, and Canoë jumped into the water with his mattresses as Captain Alinat and I leaped into the Zodiac and sped out to the buoy. By then, the dolphin had been in the pincer for about three minutes, and was apparently exhausted by his struggle to free himself. He was floating on the surface, not moving.

"This was the moment that we had been anticipating for the past three months. I jumped into the water near the buoy and swam the few yards to the dolphin, pulling the buoy behind me. Finally, the animal was within reach. I grabbed his tail, and immediately he dived, giving me such a blow with his tail that I was lifted out of the water. I fell back and began swimming toward the spot where I had guessed that the animal would surface. We reached it almost simultaneously, and this time when I grabbed the tail I was able to keep my hold. The dolphin's breathing was short and shallow. Apparently, the effort of diving had drained what little strength remained in him. With the help of Canoë and his mattresses, and of Alinat in the Zodiac, I removed the pincer and slipped a lasso around the dolphin's tail. Then we hauled him back to the *Espadon*.

"As soon as he was aboard, we began sprinkling his skin with a gentle shower from a hose. This seemed to facilitate the dolphin's respiration which, until then, had seemed difficult. Meanwhile, the dolphin's dark eyes watched us closely, following the movements of the men around him.

"Meanwhile, the *Espadon* was racing back to Monaco. When we sailed past the Oceanographic Museum, we radioed a message. Then, as soon as we had docked, the dolphin was carried off on an inflated mattress and gently placed into a truck dispatched by the Museum."

By 2:15 P.M., the dolphin, which had been captured at 12:30 P.M., was swimming in its tank at the Museum.

It was immediately evident that a captive dolphin's reaction to humans is very different from his reaction to man in the sea. So long as the dolphin is in his natural environment, man is a source of terror. But, as soon as the animal is removed from its environment and is alone, the situation changes radically.

When the dolphin was first put into his tank at the Museum, immediately upon arrival from the *Espadon*, Bébert got into the water with him and held him at the surface so that he would not drown. The dolphin was trembling and suffered a series of convulsions. As he was growing visibly weaker, we tried holding a tank of oxygen next to his blowhole, and, with the first few breaths, the dolphin seemed to improve noticeably.

Thereupon, Bébert began walking the dolphin around the tank so that he might familiarize himself with his new home. We had learned that this was an extremely important part of the acclimatization process, for dolphins usually panic if they strike an obstacle while swimming. Since dolphins cannot swim backward, they apparently feel trapped if their snouts encounter a wall; then, they fall prey to an overriding sense of terror.

By the time Bébert climbed out of the tank, the dolphin seemed gradually to resign himself to his new situation. He was swimming unaided now, in a narrow circle, and his breathing was more or less normal. Nonetheless, Bébert and Canoë remained with him, watching him every moment from the side of the tank, throughout the afternoon and into the evening.

It was already dark when, after hours of careful observation, Bébert and Canoë decided that there was no reason for them to spend the night with the dolphin. All indications were that the animal was now reacting normally and that he would not require their attention during the night. They started to leave, and then, as an afterthought, decided to remain by the tank a few minutes more. At that moment, they saw the dolphin sink slowly to the bottom of the tank. He was obviously unconscious and in serious danger of drowning. Immediately, both men dived into the tank and brought the dolphin to the surface. Then they began walking him around the tank so as to help him breathe. Canoë and Bébert were later joined by Boissy, and the three men took turns in the tank throughout the night.

By late that night, the dolphin was able to swim unaided for a while. Then, suddenly he was helpless again and would have sunk to the bottom if the men had not been there to support him in the water. His eyes were almost completely closed, and his tail seemed to be paralyzed. Once more, the oxygen tank was held over the animal's blowhole.

It was not until ten o'clock the following morning that the dolphin's condition had improved sufficiently for him to be able to swim more or less normally and even to attempt a few dives (although the tank was too shallow for this kind of sport).

Falco had taken the dolphin's temperature twice. During the night, it was 38.6°C; in the morning, 38.2°C. Falco had also observed his breathing. During the night, the dolphin had breathed from two to four times a minute, but, in the morning, the rhythm had slowed.

When Dr. Beck arrived in the morning, in answer to Falco's call, he also inquired about the animal's pulse — a reading which Bébert had learned to take by jumping into the water, holding the dolphin in his arms, and placing his hand over the animal's heart.

"It was sixty during the night," Falco replied. "But for the past few hours, it's been only forty-eight."

"That's normal," Dr. Beck assured Bébert. "When he was first captured, the dolphin was excited. Traumatized, if you will. Since then, he has calmed down, and his pulse has slowed. Actually, he seems in fairly good condition — considering that he's obviously still in a state of shock. The capture itself was hard enough on him, but confinement in this tank must be very difficult for such a sensitive animal. I recommend a regime of vitamins and minerals."

So far as I was concerned, vitamins and minerals were all very well, but I suspected that something more was needed. That feeling was confirmed when Falco told me the following story:

"During the night we spent with the dolphin, Canoë and I left the animal alone for a few moments to see if we could find some coffee upstairs in the Museum. Suddenly, we heard a series of shrill sounds coming from the tank. They weren't loud, but they were piercing, like the cries of a child trying to call someone. We returned to the tank immediately and got into the water with the dolphin and began talking to him. The crying stopped at once. I feel certain that just our being there with him was enough to restore his calm."

"Bébert," I said, "I don't want the dolphin to be left by himself any more. We'll have to try to find a companion for him."

We discovered that the greatest danger in capturing a dolphin was not only from the wounds that the pincer device might inflict, but also from the psychological impact on the dolphin of the capture, that is, the shock to its nervous system. Bébert had noticed in capturing the dolphin, and also in his previous unsuccessful attempts, that the moment that the mammal was touched by anything — lasso, harpoon, or pincer — it seemed to go into a state of paralysis for a few seconds, apparently as the result of that contact. The result was the same, regardless of whether at that moment the dolphin was in the sea, or on an inflatable mattress, or in a tank. The animal simply became immobile, as though stupefied, and began to shake and tremble. It appeared that the dolphin could not accept the fact that he had been stopped, seized; that he had lost his freedom.

It was this shock that may have been the chief problem with our dolphin in the Oceanographic Museum. The animal — upon discovering that "he"

(Right) A dolphin spurns Falco's attempt to offer a friendly gift.

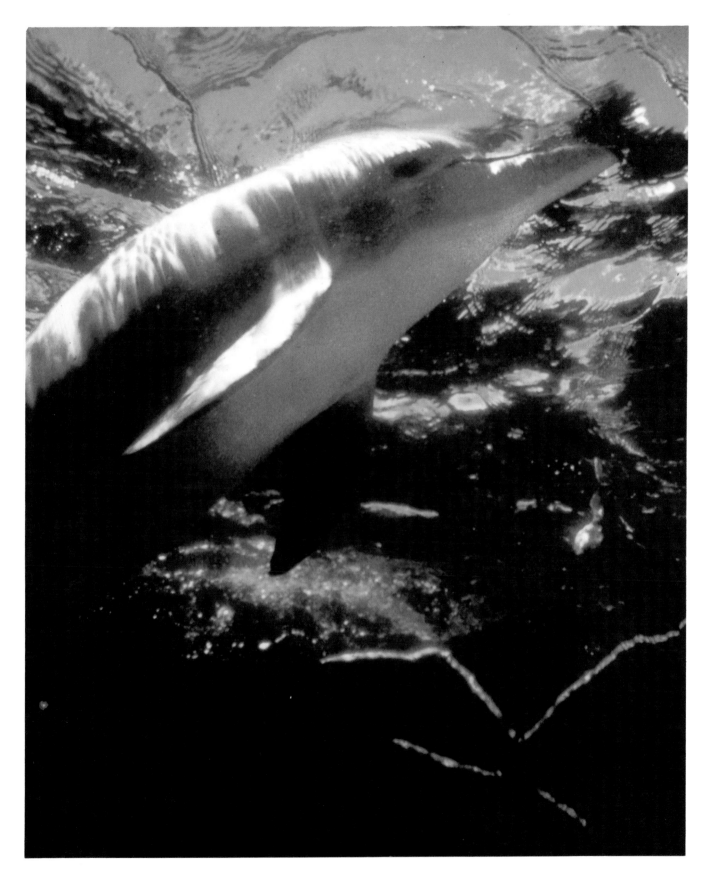

was, in fact, a female, we had christened her Kiki — of course was not exposed to public view. Nonetheless, a large number of people had access to the tank, people whom, for one reason or another, we could not exclude: journalists, radio and television commentators, and so forth.

The *Espadon*'s team was now living in a small room near Kiki's tank, and Falco was with the dolphin night and day, watching for any sign of irregularity or difficulty in her breathing. For days on end, he barely slept. As a safeguard against accidents, he installed an inflated plastic balloon under each of Kiki's flippers so that she might remain on the surface even if she lost consciousness. On one occasion, Kiki fainted. One of the balloons slipped, and the dolphin sank. Almost immediately, Bébert was in the water.

"Kiki had become very attached to me," Bébert said. "She used to look for me. Obviously, she knew that when I was with her I did what I could to help her, to give her as much relief as I could. Sometimes she tried to swim a bit, but if she ran into one of the walls of the tank, she immediately went into a panic. It happened occasionally that she inhaled water through her blowhole; and then she'd come to me so that I could hold her."

November 2, 1957. There has been no improvement in Kiki's condition, and upon Dr. Chalazonitis' recommendation, we gave her morphine by means of a suppository.

We are all aware that the dolphin is in pain. Sometimes she trembles and shivers uncontrollably. She does not seem to mind when we take her temperature, but remains motionless.

November 3. Everything was quiet last night. We took turns staying with Kiki throughout the night. The veterinarian was here this morning, and his prognosis is favorable. Kiki's temperature is now 37.4°C. Her respiration: four per minute.

Today we gave her the first penicillin injection.

Kiki has eaten nothing at all since her arrival at the Museum. We have tried force-feeding her, but she vomits anything that she swallows. In spite of all this, she has never once tried to bite any of us, although she has a set of very impressive teeth.

We gave her injections of theramycin at 3 P.M., 9 P.M., and 4 A.M.

The nights are most difficult for us because we must constantly be ready to dive into the tank to help the dolphin. During the night, we gave her two camphor suppositories.

November 6. The veterinarian visited Kiki today at 6:30 P.M. In the course of his examination, he discovered that her heartbeat had returned to normal. Her temperature: 36.3°C.

Falco threw three live mullets into the tank, making sure that they hit the surface with a splash. Kiki immediately gulped them down. Apparently, the fact that the mullets were alive and moving had much to do with her decision to eat them. This is a consideration that we will have to keep in mind for the future. We also fed her a dozen smaller fish, which she ate with good appetite. Obviously, this is not much food for a dolphin of Kiki's size, but it is a good beginning, and everyone is overjoyed at Kiki's progress.

Although Kiki now seems able to swim normally, we have continued to use the plastic balloons at night. The problem with these balloons is that they prevent the dolphin from submerging her head, with the result that the skin on her skull is dry and cracked. We have begun dampening her head with a cloth at regular intervals during the night.

Another sign of progress: Kiki's tail is no longer paralyzed.

November 7. We have finally found a tank of sufficient size to accommodate Kiki comfortably. I have obtained permission from the management of the Palm Beach Hotel to put Kiki in their swimming pool, which is about 150 feet long and 60 feet wide — a magnificent expanse of water.

Falco left aboard the *Espadon* in search of a companion for Kiki. Offshore near Nice, he succeeded in capturing a male specimen weighing 125 pounds, and the dolphin — we call him Dufduf — has now joined Kiki in her pool at the Palm Beach.

The first meeting between the two dolphins is something to remember. First, the male pushed his snout into Kiki's genital area, then he began swimming gracefully around her. The two elongated bodies, covered with gray, satinlike flesh, twisted, turned, crossed one another. Occasionally, they brushed against one another, then separated, and, a few moments later, touched again. They rubbed their bellies against one another for twenty minutes, then they began swimming side by side in perfect synchronization. But they did not mate.

Falco threw some sardines into the pool for Dufduf, and the newly arrived dolphin gobbled them down without hesitation. We all had the impression that Kiki had persuaded her new friend to eat.

Despite the fact that both animals are eating and exercising, they seem to be growing thinner. On their bodies, next to their flippers, there are hollows indicative of weight loss.

March 1, 1958. This morning, we found Dufduf at the bottom of the pool, dead. An autopsy was performed, and pieces of wood and cloth were found in his stomach. When a dolphin is fatally ill, he tends to swallow any-

(Following page) The dolphin's "smile" gives the animal a sympathetic look.

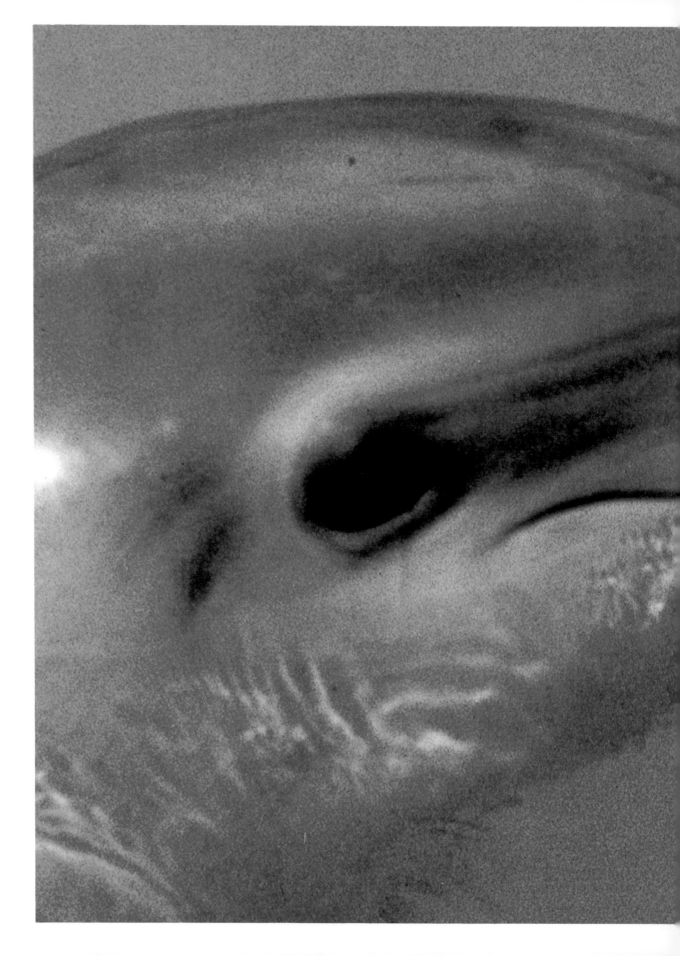

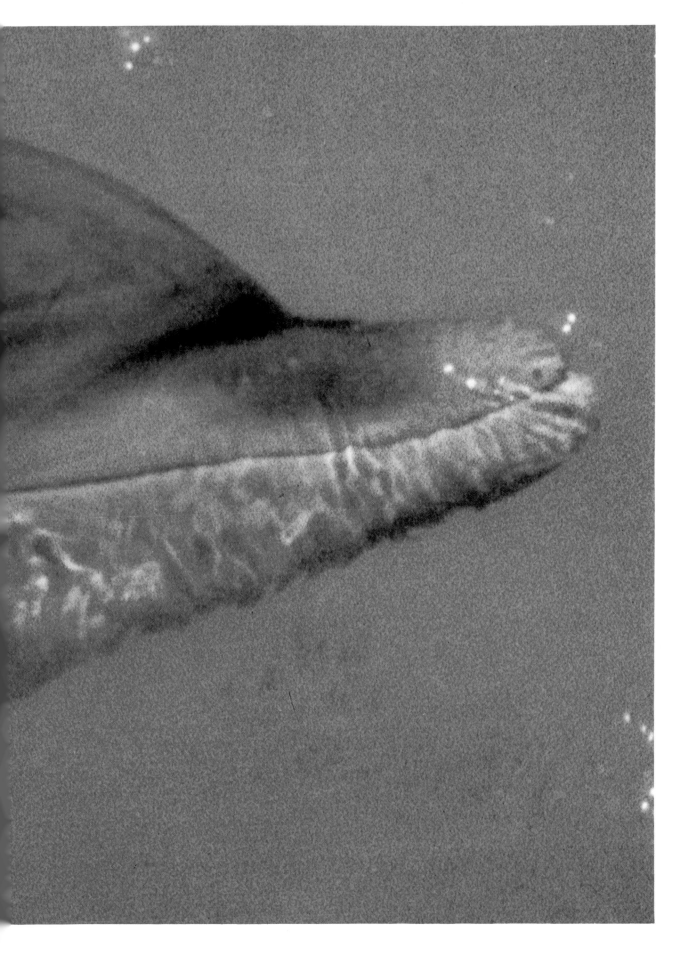

thing within reach. Falco has observed this phenomenon on several occasions. Thus far, no one has been able to devise a satisfactory explanation for this behavior.

Immediately we gave Kiki a massive dose of Vitascorbol and of cod-liver oil. She swam around the pool constantly, making her shrill, crying sounds. We all had the impression that she was searching for her lost friend. I think that we had better find her a new companion as soon as possible.

One of the most obvious conclusions we reached in the course of these first experiments was that dolphins are group animals. They are utterly incapable of living alone. If they have no companionship, they are extremely unhappy and do not adapt to captivity. Left alone, they sink into a torpor and remain inactive. But as soon as they are given a companion, they spring to life again.

Almost immediately after Dufduf's death, Falco left again on the *Espadon* to search for another dolphin. At first, he had no luck. There were many dolphins in the Bay of Angels, but they were all females with young; and as soon as the *Espadon* approached, they fled in every direction.

On March 16, we removed Kiki from the Palm Beach pool and returned her to the tank at the Oceanographic Museum. The hotel's clientele was beginning to arrive for the season, and few of the Palm Beach's customers would have enjoyed the company of a dolphin during their morning swim.

On the same day that Kiki returned to the Museum, Falco captured a dolphin — a female — which seemed unusually large and heavy. He brought her back to Monaco and we put her into the tank with Kiki. Almost immediately, the dolphin broke free of Falco's grip and crashed into the wall of the tank. Falco succeeded in grasping her in his arms. He raised her from the bottom, spoke to her, tried to calm her. But she wrenched herself free again and once more smashed her skull against the wall with a terrible noise.

At one-thirty in the afternoon, the dolphin was dead. She had killed herself by swimming at full speed from one side of the tank to the other and crashing into the walls. Her agony was horrifying. She lay on her side at the bottom of the tank, her body quivering. Then she began to stiffen, and her lungs filled with water and she was dead.

Falco was alone at the time, and it was not until the dolphin was dead that he could leave the tank to call Dr. Beck. The two men cut open the female and removed a perfectly formed baby dolphin, weighing three and a half pounds, from her womb. Unfortunately, the infant dolphin was already dead.

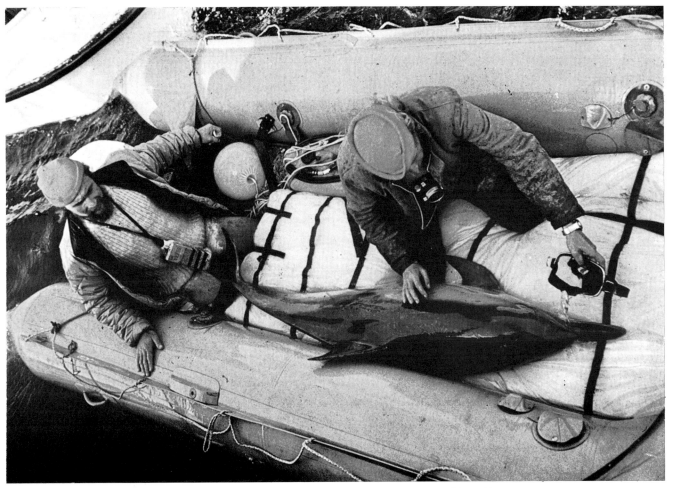

A captured dolphin is taken aboard a Zodiac by Bernard Delemotte and Jean-Pierre Genest.

Falco was deeply moved by this tragedy which bore such a marked similarity to suicide.

Shortly afterward, a male was captured. We called him Beps. He died as the pregnant female had died, by smashing his head as hard as he could against the walls of the tank. On the third attempt, he succeeded in killing himself.

Despite the horrible deaths of the companions we had tried to provide for her, Kiki seemed to thrive for a few months. Then she, too, died in her sixth month of captivity — perhaps out of loneliness. She had no companions of her own species, and Falco, whom she seemed to recognize and to regard with affection, was now far away from Monaco on an expedition. It is possible that she might have lived longer if she had not been deprived of the company of a human whose presence seemed to comfort her.

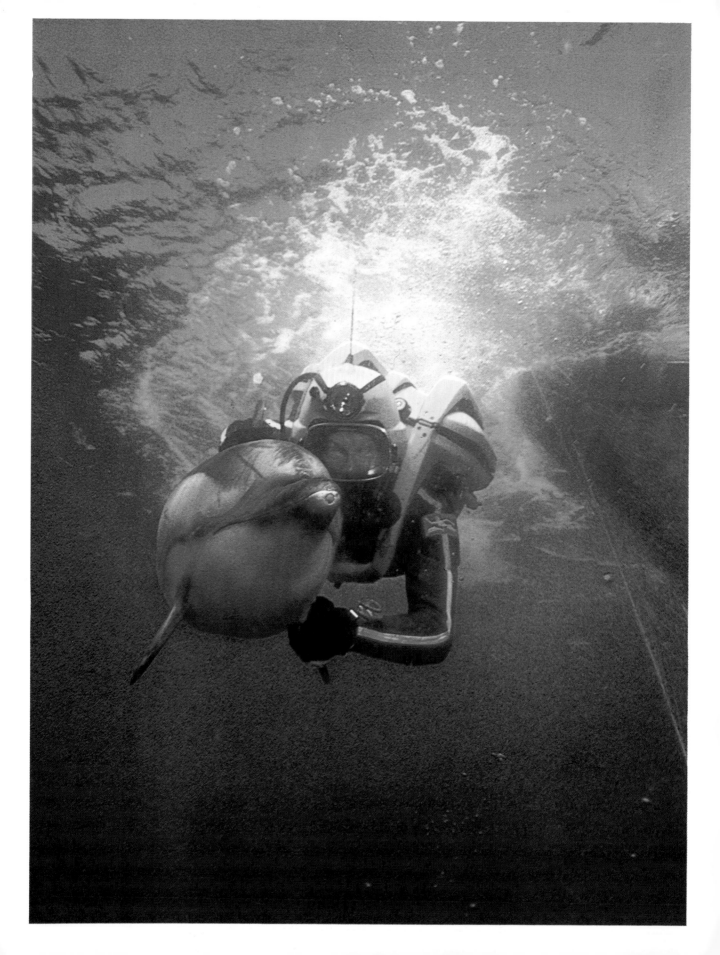

Chapter Three

THE LAWS OF THE CLAN

Our pursuit of dolphins during 1957 and 1958, as clumsy as it was, taught us many things. Our attempts to acclimatize dolphins to new surroundings ended, eight months later, in failure because at that time we knew so little about marine mammals — certainly far less than what we know now, sixteen years later. Sixteen years in the study of marine mammals is a long time, and yet, at the same time, it is so very little. . . .

The extended mission of Falco and his team in pursuit of dolphins provided us with much valuable information on the reactions of dolphins not only during and after capture but also, and paradoxically, on dolphins living at liberty in the sea. We learned, for instance, that the event of capture is an enormous shock to a dolphin, both physically and psychologically.

The pincer device developed by Bébert, while not perfect, was quite effective. Bébert had discovered that the device must be fired vertically and that the dolphin was immobilized for several seconds by the shock of impact.

(Left) A diver from *Calypso*, Jean-Pierre Genest, swims alongside a dolphin.

It is during these few seconds that the dolphin must be seized, so as to avoid any struggle and consequent injury to the animal.

We learned to care for and cure a dolphin's wounds. And, in so doing, we observed that dolphins never, in any circumstances, manifested the slightest hostility to man. Even when we held an animal in our arms, or applied pressure to a wound — which certainly must have caused considerable pain — there was no aggressive response. The dolphin consistently allowed us to do whatever we wished, without making the slightest attempt to defend itself. Even though it was sometimes necessary to force an animal's mouth open in order to feed it, never once was any of us bitten — a remarkable record, considering that a dolphin is a very highly strung and nervous animal.

One of the most pressing and immediate problems, in fact, was persuading a captive dolphin to eat. Falco eventually succeeded, thanks to his patience and ingenuity. Sometimes it was necessary for him to throw out a fish a hundred times before the dolphin would take it. And even then, the animal often refused to eat it. The noise of the fish striking the water might attract the dolphin, who would then approach the fish, nuzzle it, pick it up in his mouth, play with it, and then lose interest when the fish sank to the bottom. One can imagine, therefore, what a chore it is to get a dolphin to eat the ten or twenty pounds of fish a day that it needs. As we know, the easiest method consists in having an acclimatized dolphin in the same tank. The presence of this animal encourages a newly arrived dolphin to eat.

Sensitive Skin

The most serious problems we encountered with the Common Dolphin were caused by the extreme delicacy of its skin. The slightest bruise during capture, the least scratch, results in a wound which appears almost immediately. The *Espadon*'s team learned to judge the degree of seriousness of such a wound from its whitish color. The Common Dolphin, we concluded, required very clean water. The slightest impurity not only aggravated any wounds but also threatened the general health of the animal. In this respect, certainly the *Delphinus delphis* is much more vulnerable than the Bottlenosed Dolphin.

In the course of our experiments in Monaco, we observed that the behavior of our captive dolphins was determined largely by the extreme sensitivity of their skin. If an animal remained out of the water for several hours and was not kept damp, its skin dried, wrinkled, and looked as though it had been burned.

According to our observations, one of the chief concerns of marine mammals is to avoid contact with any solid object. When we were making our film on whales and were diving with humpback whales, these great mammals always were extemely careful to avoid touching us with their flippers.* At first, we thought, rather naïvely, that the whales were making an attempt to avoid hurting us, but now I believe that they were chiefly concerned with avoiding any shock to their skin.

The scientific research of the past twenty years has seemed to present the dolphin as an animal living in a world of sound, an animal whose acoustical talents are highly developed. This is true, of course. But this aspect of the dolphin's abilities has made us lose sight of the fact that a dolphin in a tank, despite his highly developed and fully functioning "sonar," lives in mortal dread of colliding with the walls of the tank. Life in a tank or pool entails a certain disorder in the sensory perception of the dolphin. And, from that, results a psychological disequilibrium, a distortion of behavior patterns, which, at least in the case of the Common Dolphin, causes the animal to weaken and to die.

It is true that the Bottlenosed Dolphin, which is sturdier than its Mediterranean cousin, adapts more easily to confinement; but, even then — as we shall see in the course of this book — the animal is profoundly modified by the fact of captivity.

It should be understood, of course, that one cannot make anything more than general statements in this respect. We must keep in mind, when comparing the *Delphinus* and the *Tursiops* (or other species), that specimens of the same species adapt to captivity with varying degrees of success. Some animals bear captivity better than others. Some adapt readily, while others never adapt.

Another phenomenon illustrated by our experiences at Monaco was the fact that the dolphin is an eminently social animal. He is a group animal, and he is not happy except in the company of one or more of his own kind. There was a striking difference between the behavior of a dolphin alone in a tank and that of a dolphin with a companion of the same species — regardless of the sex of either dolphin.

At the same time, it must be said that when a dolphin is ill or lonely, man seems to represent a possible companion on whom the dolphin may center its

*See *The Whale*, by Jacques-Yves Cousteau and Philippe Diolé, Doubleday & Co., New York, and Cassell, London, 1972.

(Following page) The waters of the Indian Ocean were like a lake when we encountered this school of dolphins.

attention. It appears reasonable to say that the food provided by man is not the principal cause of the dolphin's attachment to humans, for, in most instances, a captive dolphin initially refuses to eat. It seems that the presence of a human being, who caresses and cares for the dolphin, inspires trust in the animal. There is much evidence for this in Falco's log:

"The dolphin pressed herself against me so that I could hold her up to the surface. . . . As soon as she saw me get into the water, the dolphin swam to me and gently rubbed against me. When I approached the tank, the dolphin began emitting little cries which I'm inclined to interpret as sounds of joy."

I think that Falco's most valuable observations were those which he made at sea, while the *Espadon* was searching for dolphins off Monaco, in the Bay of Angels and at the mouth of the Var. While he was there in the month of February, he saw groups of fifty or sixty mother dolphins accompanied by their young. Sometimes, at night, Falco observed a few larger dolphins in the sea, not together but swimming 150 to 200 yards from each other. When the *Espadon* approached them, these dolphins leaped into the air. (A dolphin can leap as high as ten feet out of the water and for a distance of ten or twelve feet.) Then they watched the ship for a while before diving and remaining out of sight for a few minutes.

Not all of the dolphin's day was spent leaping and playing. There was a schedule of activities. For a part of the day, the dolphins remained beneath the surface, coming up only for air. Then, suddenly, one satin-gray body would leap into the air. As though on signal, it was followed by other bodies. This was the propitious moment for the *Espadon* to move alongside the school in order to attract some of the dolphins toward the prow. It was observed that females with young never played forward of the ship — with one exception. The exception, Falco reported, was a female who obviously was unable to resist the temptation offered by the prow. She cut in front of the *Espadon* and took up her position, while her offspring went off to join another female who had a calf of her own. The mother stayed before the prow for two or three minutes, then she gave up the game and returned to her baby.

There seemed to be a large number of young of all ages in the area. A baby dolphin at birth weighs only from four to six pounds. By the age of one year, they may weigh as much as seventy pounds. Usually, young dolphins do not play before a ship's stem. They are extremely timid. If a ship approaches them, they dive under the hull and remain at a depth of fifty to sixty feet. (When the water is clear, they can be seen from the surface.) Then, as soon as the ship has passed, they surface to port, to starboard, or aft.

On February 10, 1958, Bébert captured a female weighing 175 pounds.

The female had a calf; and the infant, without hesitating or trying to find its mother, went to another female of the same school. After a few seconds, the school, seeing that the captured female was unable to join them, swam away.

It sometimes happened that a young dolphin would take up a position forward of the prow. Almost immediately, however, its mother would arrive and push him away, forcing him to rejoin the school.

"From the platform," Falco says, "I once saw a young dolphin come directly under the platform. His mother was nowhere to be seen. Possibly she was hunting for food. In any case, the calf remained there, directly beneath my feet, for several minutes. The temptation was too strong for me. I took the pincer and fired, and the calf was caught. I could see the buoy behind him. I dived into the water right away so that I could remove the pincer. The skin of a young dolphin is even more delicate than that of a full-grown animal. I took the calf into my arms. He could not have weighed more than twenty-five or thirty pounds.

"As soon as I had a grip on the dolphin, I saw its mother streaking toward me. My first thought was that she was going to attack. Instead, she began swimming around us, making a series of little cries as she swam, sometimes brushing against me. She was a handsome specimen, probably weighing between two hundred and two hundred and fifty pounds. She was much larger than I and incomparably more agile in the water. I confess that I was more than a little frightened at first. Then I understood that the dolphin had no intention of attacking me. She was pleading, calling to her calf. She wanted her child back, but she also wanted to avoid harming me.

"I did not know what to do. I wanted to take the calf back to Monaco with me, for I felt that, at his age, it would not be terribly difficult to tame him. It was truly a dilemma. The mother, circling frantically around us, screaming, was more than I could take. I was very moved. I opened the pincer and freed the calf. He rushed toward his mother, and the pair dived immediately and were lost to sight."

Falco is so familiar with dolphins that he is able to locate a school of them by certain signs. For example, the presence of sea gulls circling overhead is often an indication that a school of dolphins is nearby, hunting for bluefishes, sardines, mackerels, and anchovies. The sea gulls remain in the area to eat what the dolphins leave.

"It is very difficult to see exactly how dolphins hunt," Bébert says, "since they move so quickly. I've noticed that they have difficulty seeing something that is directly in front of them. Regardless of what is generally believed about the bilateral vision of dolphins, I myself have seen them turning their heads from one side to the other. They probably do not do this in captivity,

but only in the excitement of the hunt. It may be that the purpose of this movement is to enable the dolphin to use its teeth on its prey rather than to see it. For dolphins rush into a school of fish and swallow anything they can, any way that they can. But, before a dolphin can swallow a fish, he must turn it in his mouth so that the fish goes down headfirst. Otherwise, the fish's fins and bones will cut the dolphin's throat as it goes down. It is likely that a dolphin loses some of his prey, when he tries to turn it in this way, and that the sea gulls seize the fish."

Dolphins have a larger number of teeth than any other mammal, marine or land: between 88 and 200 of them. These teeth, however, are all conical and all have the same function: to hold the dolphin's prey rather than to cut it or chew it. At the same time, the jaws of a dolphin living at liberty crush its prey into cylindrical form so that it will be able to cross the larynx and penetrate into the esophagus. In captivity, however, dolphins swallow fish whole. One can drop one fish after another down a captive dolphin's mouth without stopping — like dropping letters into a mailbox.

Dolphins eat at more or less the same time every day, and their meals last approximately one hour. When they have had enough, the dolphins assemble into a large group for a few moments, then break up into smaller groups before heading out to sea again. Their normal swimming speed is about ten knots.

The composition of these groups of dolphins seems to vary according to the season. In autumn and winter, the largest group comprises females and their calves. We know that the mothers help one another in watching over their offspring, just as they help one another in giving birth. This has been observed among dolphins in captivity, and it is a subject to which we will return later in this book.

For part of the year, the male dolphins live separately from the females, although they remain in the general vicinity of the main body of the school. The essential social unit of the school seems to comprise three or four adult dolphins. The females of this unit, under the authority and protection of the male, care for their young until the latter reach the age of six to nine months. The school is composed of a number of these fairly large family units. The school increases or decreases in size, according to circumstances, in order to

(Upper left) A gathering of dolphins at the mouth of the Var.

(Lower left) The *Espadon,* cruising off Agay, in search of dolphins.

In the Marineland of Florida, two dolphins display their expertise at catching fish. (Photo, courtesy of Marineland of Florida.)

form groups comprising from fifty to a hundred individuals.

Quite often, when a large group is being pursued, it will break into smaller groups of three or four dolphins. These smaller groups are probably family units.

It is not known whether male dolphins have "harems," like male sea lions and elephant seals.† We have been able to observe sea lions on land, and we know that one male will sometimes be lord and master of as many as eighty females. But dolphins, obviously, have never been observed on land. All that we know of their mating habits is what has been observed in aquariums, where their behavior may be different from what it is in the dolphin's natural environment. A dolphin in captivity does not appear to be attached exclusively to one particular female.

We know that dolphins sometimes divide themselves into groups according to sex, with the males in one group and the females in the other. But, in general, these are not mature dolphins.

†See *Diving Companions* by Jacques-Yves Cousteau and Philippe Diolé, Doubleday & Co., Inc., New York, and Cassell, London, 1974.

It is difficult to determine the precise age of these young animals. They are "adolescents," perhaps eighteen to twenty-four months old. They form extremely close-knit groups, and, at a given moment, the entire group leaves the adults and goes off together, striking out on their own. Perhaps these are less fond of playing and frolicking than the adults. They are very "serious." They know that they are still weak and vulnerable. Nonetheless, when they act together as a group, they are virtually invincible. They are capable of wild pranks.

Yet, these young dolphins are extremely wary of divers. It is impossible to get close to them. When they were younger, they played with their elders around ships; but, beginning at a certain age, they no longer care to take such risks. They remain together, in their group, and all their activities are group activities.

Later on, the males and females, when they are grown, are united into a single group.

The most exact observations on this subject have been made by Japanese scientists, who have captured entire schools of dolphins and are thus able to study the division of sexes according to age within a large group.

A dolphin allows himself to be petted by Falco.

Dominant Animals

We know that there exists a hierarchy among dolphins which is probably as well defined as that found among African elephants. However, it is not known precisely what the function of that hierarchy is, or what its criteria are. There is probably a leader dolphin, and probably there are dominant dolphins.‡

In this respect, we know more about the sperm whale, which is also a toothed whale, than we do about the dolphin. Some schools of sperm whales

---

‡It is possible that these ranks are temporary. Dr. Kenneth Norris is of the opinion that there is no permanent leader among free dolphins.

are led by old males, although usually old males do not live with a school. Other schools, however, have females as their leaders. We have no way of knowing what, precisely, qualifies a particular individual, male or female, as the leader of a school.

It appears that, in nature, it is the oldest males who mate with the females. This is true both of marine mammals and of land mammals who live in groups, such as lions.

In capturing marine mammals, we have observed that it is not the leader of a school who, in order to save a school, will destroy an obstacle or tear through a net. This function devolves upon a male of the second rank, as though the life of the leader were too precious to the future and fecundity of the group to be risked.

There are not only dominant individuals but also dominant species. We have observed that in large schools of cetaceans, species are mixed. We have seen pilot whales mingling with the Bottlenosed Dolphin, for instance; and during our expedition on the coasts of Mauritania, we saw a *Sousa teuszi* in the same school as two other species, of which one was probably the Bottlenosed Dolphin.

In captivity, according to Caldwell,* certain species seem to dominate others. But are these truly dominant species, or is the fact of their domination merely a function of the limited space available to captive animals?

It is much more difficult to observe marine animals who live in groups than to observe land animals. We know more or less how elephants and antelopes live. But, so far, it has been impossible to get an idea of the social structure of dolphins living in the open sea. We can only surmise that that structure exists, and we think that it must be well defined.

To the extent that it is possible to judge, it seems that the hierarchies which exist in our marinelands are even more stratified than in the sea. This phenomenon is observable in marinelands — such as those in St. Augustine, Miami, San Diego, and Los Angeles — where some of the tanks are large enough to accommodate twenty or twenty-five animals.

In these tanks, each animal occupies a special territory corresponding to his rank in the hierarchy. This situation also obtains in zoos, among land mammals occupying the same enclosure. In a tank, the most desirable place, and that occupied by the dominant animal, is in the center of the tank, or next to the opening through which fresh water is pumped into the tank. Each animal seems to have its own "miniterritory," which it defends with vigor.

*David K. Caldwell and Melba C. Caldwell, *World of the Bottle-Nosed Dolphin.* Philadelphia, 1972.

Observations made at the Marine Studios of Florida† indicate that, except while mating, the dominant adult male dolphin usually swam around his tank alone. Occasionally, he was accompanied, at least briefly, by a female or by a younger male. Although generally peaceful, it sometimes happened that the dominant male showed signs of aggressiveness — often without provocation. At times, however, the provocation was obvious: another animal took some of the male's food, or a younger male approached the female swimming with the dominant male. In such instances, the male bit his presumptuous rival, or struck him with his tail, or even pursued him. Usually, the younger male was scratched or cut and bruised. But when the offender was a female, or a very young or small animal, the leader did not harm it.

At the Marine Studios, the highest ranking dolphin, after the dominant male, was a female named Pudgy, who had already borne several calves. Pudgy by no means lived in the glorious isolation affected by the dominant male. On the contrary, she was a constant point of interest and activity in the tank. She was not afraid to take chances, and she made it a point to investigate any strange object that appeared in the tank. After a series of increasingly daring inspections of the object, she would inform the dominant male that there was no danger, and then he would venture forth.

If the intruder was an unknown diver, he was treated as though he were a dangerous object, even though his equipment was exactly the same as that of a diver known to the dolphins.

Pudgy was the only female whose company the dominant male would tolerate outside of the mating season.

Directly below the dominant male and Pudgy in the hierarchy, there were a certain number of animals, all of approximately the same rank: old females and other, younger females who were carrying their first calves.

A second group comprised three males, of which one was the "boss" of the other two. The third group included the younger animals, who had all been born in the same year and who were not yet weaned. All social activity in the tank centered around the first group, of which Pudgy was the animating spirit. There was another female who, although quite young, belonged to the circle of older females. She served as Pudgy's adjutant, and she supervised the calves in the tank.

This outline of social life in an aquarium tank is sufficient to indicate how complex must be the relations among dolphins living at liberty in the sea. It is also an indication of how little we know in this area. We only suspect the existence of a hierarchy, but we have good reasons to think that dolphins in the sea have "territories" — but territories which belong to the school as a

†See Margaret C. Tavolga, "Behavior of the Bottlenosed Dolphin," in *Whales, Dolphins and Porpoises*, University of California Press, 1966. K. Norris, Editor.

whole. In Hawaii, Kenneth S. Norris observed a school that remained for several weeks, and perhaps even several months, in the same place.

The Florida habitat of the Bottlenosed Dolphin is not very large — a stretch of rather shallow water about fifty to a hundred miles long. Many Bottlenosed Dolphins sojourn at the mouth of the Mississippi. An albino dolphin, who was quite easy to spot and who was finally captured, made it possible to gather some interesting data on the movements of the Bottlenosed Dolphin. There are cases of dolphins who have remained in the same area for as long as three years. It is quite possible that, especially in Florida, the movements of the dolphins are confined to a relatively small area, and that the dolphins cover the same stretch every day. Falco had remarked that, near Nice, the dolphins arrived from the southeast in the morning and departed in the evening toward the southwest. They were probably following the movement of the fishes who themselves follow the movement of the sun.

This is also what occurred during our research in the Gulf of Málaga. During the morning, we were rather certain of being able to find dolphins on the left side of the Gulf, and in the evening, on the right side.

It has been claimed that the *Tursiops* of Florida prefers shallow water to deep water. But we must remember that what is true in one part of the world may not be true in another. Professor Busnel, for example, has encountered the Bottlenosed Dolphin at depths of 10,000, 12,000, and 15,000 feet. According to Busnel, the Bottlenosed is not specially a shallow-water mammal. It is found in Florida's coastal waters because it follows the schools of fish — especially mullets — which come to feed there.

The Bottlenosed Dolphin as well as the Delphinus delphis is also found near the coast; but it is found, too, and more frequently, in water from 2,000 to 2,500 feet deep, at the edge of the continental shelf.

Various observers have indicated that dolphins move in aligned ranks, like an army on the march. In such cases, the animals all rise to the surface, at the same time, in order to breathe. Professor Busnel has seen schools of dolphins in this formation.‡ It may be that these groups are formed of animals of the same age and sex. It is also possible that that particular formation is employed only when the dolphins are moving over a considerable distance.

It will undoubtedly require much time for us to become acquainted with the social life of dolphins in the sea. Only detailed and repeated observation by divers will finally reveal what occurs in groups of marine mammals subject to the authority of one or several leaders.

‡David K. Caldwell has observed the same phenomenon.

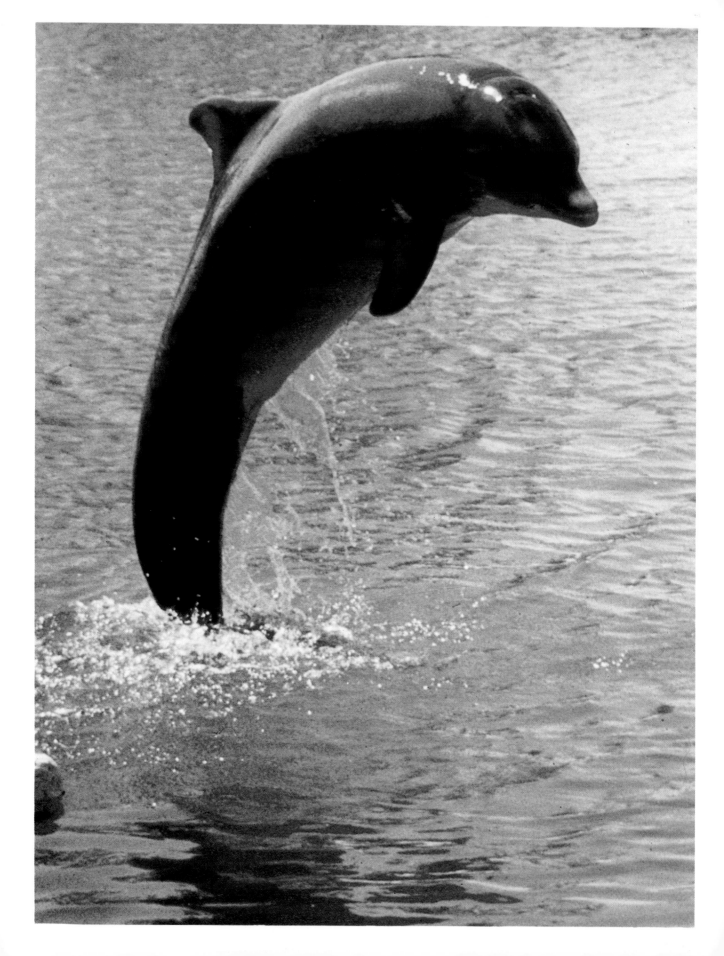

Chapter Four

THE STORY OF DOLLY

I think that the most interesting phase of our observation of dolphins was that which dealt with dolphins who had entered into relationships of various kinds with humans, but without giving up their liberty in so doing.

There are many instances of this phenomenon in the United States, Australia, New Zealand, and Great Britain.

The attraction of dolphins to human beings is attested to throughout human history. There are documents, for example, which cite numerous instances of this attraction in the period of Antiquity — instances which, for many years, were regarded as myths.

One of the most celebrated of these legends may be that of Arion, a Greek poet born on the island of Lesbos. Arion was saved by a dolphin after he had been thrown overboard by the crew of a ship on which he was traveling.

No less an authority than Plutarch has recorded the story of Korianos, a native of Asia Minor, who pleaded with a group of fishermen to spare the life of a dolphin caught in their nets. Shortly thereafter, Korianos himself was

(Left) Dolly playing near the Asburys' dock in Florida.

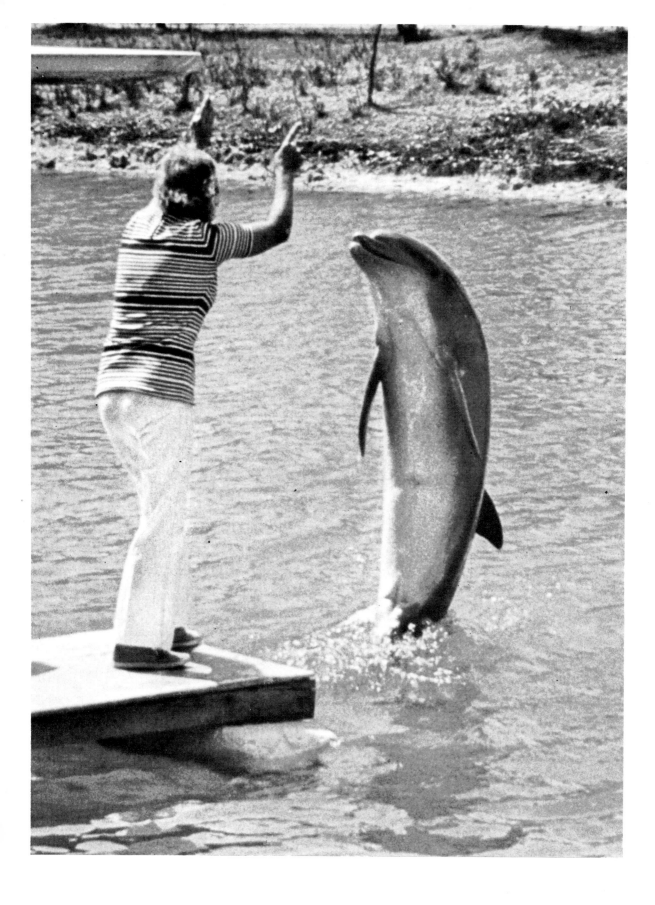

shipwrecked, and his life was saved, Plutarch assures us, by a dolphin.

Today, we know enough about dolphins to be able to see a core of truth in these anecdotes of Antiquity. We know that a certain number of dolphins, living at freedom in the sea, seek out the company of humans, become attached to them, and persist in returning to the places where they have encountered swimmers — and especially where they have encountered children. And we know that dolphins are fun-loving and dependable creatures who, upon occasion, act as lifesavers. There are numerous, well-documented cases which demonstrate that the ancients, in believing that dolphins were friendly and benevolent toward humans, were not quite so naïve as we "superior" men of the twentieth century might like to believe.

In the Keys

One of the most touching and best documented of such adventures is that which occurred to an American family in our own time. The Asbury family includes the father — who happens to be President Nixon's helicopter pilot — his wife, Jean, and their two daughters: Kelly, who is eight, and Tina, ten. There is also a dog named Puggy.

The Asburys live in Florida, on one of the numerous canals of the Keys. The house is several miles from the ocean, although it is accessible by means of the canals.

One morning in May, 1971, the Asbury family was startled to see a Bottlenosed Dolphin appear not far from the pontoon on their property. The dolphin reared his head above the surface, showing all his teeth in a "grin" and making characteristic crying sounds. The Asburys watched as the dolphin came closer. Then Jean Asbury ran back to the house and returned a few moments later with a fish, which the dolphin eagerly accepted. The dolphin ate what he was offered, while the two little girls watched in utter enchantment.

Only Puggy the dog seemed to disapprove.

From that moment, the Asbury family regarded the dolphin as one of them. They fed her regularly, named her Dolly, and made her the official family pet. Even Puggy eventually was won over.

Dolly, a handsome female, four or five years of age, weighing about 425 pounds and measuring seven feet in length, became the swimming companion of the Asbury children. Kelly and Tina held on to Dolly's dorsal fin and

(Left) When Jean Asbury calls, Dolly comes.

Jean Asbury offers Dolly a fish from her mouth.

the dolphin towed them through the water.

Dolly seemed truly to enjoy such activities, and it soon became evident that she had adopted the Asbury family as well as been adopted by them. She showed only perfunctory interest in the other humans living along the canal, and most of her time was spent at the Asbury dock.

The star in Dolly's firmament of humans was undoubtedly Jean Asbury, who fulfilled the role of "mother" to Dolly as well as to Kelly and Tina.

The affective relationship implicit in this situation is very difficult to interpret. We know that affection among humans is sensed by animals. Jean Asbury's maternal love, the affection she radiated, was certainly not lost on Dolly. Jean's gentleness, patience, and obvious interest no doubt influenced Dolly considerably. Thus, the relationship established between Jean and Dolly seems to have been essentially emotional and maternal. At the same time, we must take into account that it was Jean who fed Dolly, who usually played with her, and who taught Dolly the tricks that the dolphin had learned to perform. Mr. Asbury was often absent for several days at a time, and the two daughters were usually at school during the day.

Communication

Jean and Dolly often had lengthy "conversations." As Jean spoke softly, Dolly held her head out of the water and listened with an attitude expressive of eager attention and of intense desire to communicate.

Dolly was able to understand the sense of certain words — "yes" and "no" for example. She seemed to understand when Jean scolded her for being naughty or expressed pleasure over something that Dolly had done. She was able to distinguish certain objects and to carry them to Jean upon command. All of which seems wonderful indeed until we remember that many household pets, such as dogs, do these things.

The Asburys constructed a shelter for Dolly next to their pontoon, and the dolphin used this shelter when she wanted to rest. Using the shelter was one of her best tricks, for she had learned to open and close the door unaided.

She knew how to catch rings, to fetch a ball and put it into a basket, and to leap high out of the water upon command. One of Dolly's games was to tow a small plastic boat with Puggy, the dog, as her somewhat hesitant passenger.

One of the tricks Jean Asbury taught Dolly was to distinguish various coins. Jean would throw a handful of change into the water, and Dolly would collect and return to Jean only the dimes — a difficult task, considering the muddy bottom of the canal, the size of a dime and the relative size of Dolly's snout. Yet, Dolly never made a mistake and brought back the wrong coin, and she never failed to bring back every dime that Jean had thrown out. The dolphin's "sonar" obviously was powerful enough to penetrate the layer of mud on the bottom, into which the dimes sank.

Dolly did not spend every moment of her day with the Asburys. She was beginning to be known in the neighborhood, and sometimes she swam in some of the other canals. Occasionally, she visited other people, but she showed an unmistakable preference for the Asburys and their property. She knew the canals very well, and she never failed to return promptly to her "home" with the Asbury family.

A Draftee

The Asburys, by a series of inquiries, learned something of Dolly's background. It seems that the dolphin had belonged to the U. S. Navy and had been assigned to a dolphin-training base at Key West. The base was known officially as a "study center," since the Navy is reluctant to have it known that these animals are being trained for military service.

One of Dolly's former trainers told Jean that when the "study center" had been transferred from Florida to California, he had decided at the last minute not to have Dolly shipped to the new facility. Dolly, it seems, was regarded as undisciplined and undependable — in short, a bad recruit. When she was ordered to take an object to a particular location, she did so; but then she insisted on carrying the object back to the man who had given it to her originally. It was obvious that such behavior during military operations might present problems. She was therefore given an "undesirable discharge" and turned loose near the Florida coast. But she had become accustomed to humans and apparently was unwilling to give up their company. She therefore swam toward shore and entered the network of canals in the Keys, where she had been lucky enough to encounter the Asburys — a family which satisfied her need for contact with man.

Voluntary Prisoners

There is no doubt that a dolphin who lives among humans for any length of time undergoes a deep psychological modification. There are many examples of this in addition to Dolly. On several occasions, captive dolphins have regained their liberty, either accidentally or because they were intentionally released by their keepers, and yet continued to seek out human contacts.

Perhaps the most celebrated instance of such a dolphin is that of Tuffy, a male Bottlenosed Dolphin who was used as a bottom-to-surface messenger during an American underwater-survival project. Tuffy was confined in a floating pool off the California coast when a passing fisherman spotted him and opened the gate of the cage, setting Tuffy free. The dolphin was probably extremely puzzled. The opening of the gate had always been preceded or accompanied by a ceremony of sorts: whistles, the giving of orders, the assignment of a mission. But he was not so puzzled as to refuse to take advantage of the opportunity thus presented.

An immediate and extensive search, by sea and air, was launched for the missing Tuffy, who was, after all, extremely valuable and almost irreplaceable. The dolphin was found very quickly, and he returned, with undisguised pleasure, to his trainer.*

A similar case was reported at the Lerner Laboratory at Bimini, in the

---

*See David K. Caldwell and Melba C. Caldwell, *World of the Bottle-Nosed Dolphin.* Philadelphia, 1972.

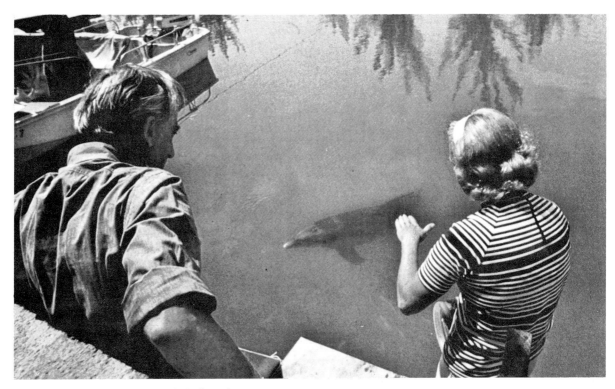
Captain Cousteau and Jean watch Dolly swim.

Bahamas. The gate of a dolphin's tank was accidentally left open, but, in this instance, the dolphin simply refused to leave. And at the Marineland of Florida, a dolphin was intentionally set free, just as Dolly had been. The dolphin remained in the vicinity of the Marineland for quite some time; finally, he must have concluded that there was no access possible from the sea back into the tanks, for he eventually went away. A few months later, a team from the Marineland captured a "wild" dolphin with suspicious ease. The dolphin, of course, was the animal who had been turned out of the Marineland's tanks and who had finally succeeded in getting himself captured once more.

At the St. Petersburg Beach Aquatarium, on Florida's Gulf coast, a dolphin who suffered from a physical deformity was released in the Gulf. This dolphin was recaptured — not once, but several times. He had discovered the secret of getting captured: whenever he saw a fisherman's net, he threw himself into it. Finally, the Aquatarium officials gave in, and the dolphin was admitted back into their tanks.

Saved, by Force

Calypso's diving team, headed by my son Philippe, went to Florida to make Dolly's acquaintance. They were warmly welcomed by the Asbury

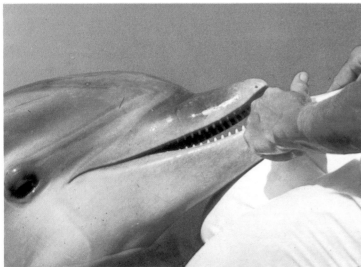

Dolly's various expressions during her life with the Asbury family; Dolly playing with a ball and a rubber ring; Dolly resting her head on Jean Asbury's lap.

family, and by Dolly herself. After two or three days, the dolphin had learned to recognize the divers, and she adopted them. She was so interested in them that there were times when she made a pest of herself. It was impossible to go into the water without being obliged to play with Dolly. The dolphin insisted that Philippe and his men dive with her, or that they allow themselves to be towed while holding her dorsal fin. Playing with Dolly became something of a chore.

Dolly was perfectly trustworthy, but, even so, one had to be careful when playing with her. She was very strong, and sometimes she did not know the precise rules of the game being played. The divers used their Aqua-Lungs® when they went down with her; and since Dolly had been taught to pick up objects on the bottom and carry them to the surface, she insisted on latching on to a diver by his belt and taking him back to the surface. There was no point in struggling, since it was impossible to break away from her. The unhappy diver simply had to resign himself to returning to the surface. Perhaps Dolly thought that the divers at the bottom were drowning, or it may be that it was no more than a new game for her.

On the surface, she adopted the opposite tactic. She forced her snout and head between the arm and the body of the divers and then dragged them to the bottom.

Dolly was so friendly that she eventually suffered for it. She lifted her head above the surface so frequently, in order to call the Asburys or to talk to them or to play or simply to see what they were doing, that she became sunburned, especially on the top of her head. It became necessary to apply sunburn lotion to relieve the pain.

Fear of the Ocean

We spent six weeks trying to find out exactly what the relationship was between Dolly and her adopted family. The most striking aspect of that relationship was that Dolly absolutely refused to return to freedom in the sea. We attempted a number of times to release her in the ocean, away from the Keys, but without success. Our purpose was to film Dolly in the open sea, since the water in the canals is often cloudy. We tried luring her out of the Keys by gifts of fish, a task in which the two Asbury children helped by talking to Dolly along the way. In this endeavor, we used a Zodiac around which Dolly was fond of playing. At first, we got no more than a mile or two from our point of departure before Dolly turned around and went back to the Asbury dock. It is unlikely that Dolly's decision to remain in the canals was based upon any inability to find her way into the open sea, for, I had already observed, dolphins seem to have an extraordinarily accurate sense of direction. As our efforts continued, we managed gradually to entice Dolly farther and farther away from the Asbury property, but it was never possible to get her to remain in the sea. We could not even persuade her to venture onto the level roof which borders the main reef — let alone get her away from the reef into deep water.

If Dolly was rejected by the U. S. Navy as being unfit for military service, it could not have been because she lacked anything as a swimmer. On the contrary, she was a rare spectacle of suppleness and grace in the water.

We have seen many "shows" at aquariums and marinelands, and we have filmed many spectacular "acts" outside of such places; yet, we had never before had the opportunity to live for several weeks with an animal like Dolly who, as time went on, became increasingly co-operative.

It is very rare — indeed, it may never have happened before — that humans are able to spend time in the water with a dolphin who is completely free to come and go as she wishes and to do precisely as she wishes. We felt that we had entered into a new stage of the relationship between man and animal, for most studies and observations of dolphins had, until then, been carried out in aquariums, with the dolphins held captive in tanks.

During our life in common with Dolly, we had only one inconvenience. The water in the canals, as I have mentioned, was very cloudy, and it was almost impossible to do any filming. If the water had been clear, we would have been able to get full-faced shots of Dolly swimming toward us — something that is virtually impossible in the sea. It is possible only with a tame dolphin. And it is rare one encounters an animal which is both tame and free.

Obviously, then, the sequences that we were able to film, for the most part, show Dolly performing the tricks that Jean Asbury had taught her — the same kind of performance that we could have filmed in an aquarium. Yet, the surroundings, the ambiance, were totally different. Dolly was not living in a tank. She was swimming freely in the Florida Keys. She could have run away if she had wanted to. But she did not. She always returned to the Asburys and to us. Every morning, she was there, waiting for us, asking for nothing more than to be allowed to swim with everyone else, or to be able to play and to invent new games — such as taking over the Zodiac, ramming it, and turning it over.

At first, we were afraid that Dolly might be struck by a passing boat, or might be injured by a propeller. But the canal on which the Asbury property is located leads nowhere. It is a dead end, and there is very little boat traffic. All the neighbors knew and loved Dolly. And Dolly herself had learned that certain boats were dangerous because of their speed, and she always avoided them.

It was impossible to discover whether Dolly caught fish for herself, or whether she lived exclusively on the food provided by the Asburys. It seems likely that her own hunting was very limited, for the canals do not abound in fish.

Every day, we tried to take Dolly for a promenade in the canals. We would call Dolly, take the Zodiac (which Dolly liked because of its round form and its feel), and start off at a very slow speed. It was a great pleasure to watch her swimming level with the Zodiac and then, with a mischievous look in her eye, suddenly shoot ahead of it.

Unfortunately, the Asbury house is quite distant from the sea. When we began to get rather far from the canal on which they lived, Dolly seemed to be seized with fear. She slowed down and eventually turned and swam back to her "home" without us.

The Oar

It seemed especially puzzling that Dolly was not tempted to leave the Keys and return to the sea in order to find a mate. For it was clear that she was not naturally inclined to celibacy. One day, an oar fell overboard, and Dolly immediately mounted the oar, tried to straddle it, and rubbed herself against it. Obviously, nothing came of all her activity. The oar was constantly slipping away from her and floating away. Then Dolly swam about nervously, making little cries.

This pitiful scene was repeated several times.

Dolly was obviously in the throes of sexual desire, and there was nothing she could do about it. Whenever she could, she brushed against the divers, pushed them with her nose, or attempted to lay her body against theirs. She seemed to relish contact with the divers' vinyl suits, which she no doubt found soft and pleasant. The shape of the divers, however, seemed to come as a surprise to her, and she often seemed puzzled.

Sexual desire was not the only reason that Dolly rubbed herself against

(Right) Jean and Dolly engage in an animated exchange as Philippe Cousteau looks on.

(Below) Dolly eating from Captain Cousteau's hand.

the divers' suits. She was actually obeying a law of her species and attempting to satisfy a deep need. For dolphins are intensely social animals, and their social activities are based upon physical contacts. Whether swimming at liberty in the sea or in marinelands and aquariums, dolphins brush and rub against each other. They touch each other with their snouts and flippers. All these gestures are undoubtedly of great importance as functions of the structure of the group and also of the place of each individual animal in the dolphin hierarchy.

Dolly, isolated from other dolphins as she was in the canals, was deprived of these social contacts. To some extent, she had adapted herself to human contacts, and she even sought them out. She loved to be petted by the Asburys and by our divers because she was unable to participate in the physical contact with other dolphins which plays such an important role in their social life.

Dolphins, unlike land mammals, have no sense of smell, and therefore they have no "scent." Instead of smelling, they touch, particularly around the genital area. This may be a means of recognizing one another and of publishing one's rank in the hierarchy. The slightest turbulence in the water makes it possible for a dolphin to sense the proximity of other dolphins or of a diver.

The skin of a dolphin is so soft and pleasant to touch that it is comparable to that of the most seductive woman. "But in the case of a dolphin," Michel Deloire pointed out, "one never knows what the reactions of a four-hundred-pound female will be at the moment of ecstacy."

It was obvious, on the other hand, that Dolly's attachment to Jean Asbury was free of sexual overtures. The dolphin was attracted by Jean's maternal warmth, and she responded to the woman as any child would have responded; while Jean, on her part, treated Dolly with boundless patience and affection — despite the fact that taking care of Dolly involved more work than if Jean had had another child on her hands. Her life necessarily had come more and more to center around Dolly's needs. The dolphin remained in the neighborhood constantly, and, when she was lonely, she called. Jean then had to drop whatever she was doing to go out to talk to Dolly. Her conversation consisted of words without any particular meaning or logic and were intended to calm and pacify the animal: "Good girl. Pretty girl . . ." The conversations ended with Dolly "kissing" Jean, that is, giving her a lick with her tongue which scratched Jean's cheek.

Like a spoiled child, Dolly insisted on constant attention. The situation reached such a point that Jean could no longer be away from the house. She could not go to a movie, or visit friends. And, obviously, a vacation was out of the question. The Asburys attempted to find someone who could keep Dolly company while they were away — a dolphin-sitter, as it were. But the experiment was a fiasco. Dolly had a tantrum and refused to eat.

A relationship like that between Dolly and the Asburys is a marvelous and exciting adventure, but it entails a responsibility to the animal which eventually monopolizes the lives of the humans involved.

We recently received a letter from Mrs. Asbury telling us that after the departure of *Calypso*'s team, "Dolly was heartbroken." Undoubtedly, she missed the "walks" with the divers in the Zodiac and the various games that she played with them. Dolly became so fond of the Zodiac, in fact, that once, when the Asburys had let an entire day go by without using it, Dolly tried to start it up herself.

Dolly had not yet found a mate, although she had had the opportunity to do so. In July 1972, during the Democratic National Convention, Dolly was taken to Miami to campaign for the protection of marine mammals. In her letter, Mrs. Asbury says: "When time came to go home, we couldn't catch her with a net, so we swam her sixty-five miles through rough and open water to Key Largo. Along the way we passed some wild dolphins. Dolly stopped to play for a while, but when time came to continue our journey she came along willingly. She did stop to play with some sea turtles, but she wanted to stay with the Zodiac because she knew we were going home. We stopped at the Anglers Club on Key Largo for the night. Dolly was tired from her long swim, so we were invited to stay for a week so she could rest. She was so weak her skin had turned white. On July 17 we decided to take Dolly home by truck. Finally, after many long hours, we caught her. She was very happy to be back home.

"Dolly loved to make nightly visits to the neighbors, but one afternoon she came home with a steel rod wrapped around her. The only thing we could figure was that she had brought it to show to me from one of the local construction sites. We untangled her and treated her cuts with gentian violet. I was heartbroken and didn't know what to do. Dolly would lie in my lap and all she would do was cry.

"With this happening, plus various other things, in March I decided to board Dolly over at the Sugar Loaf Lodge with another dolphin, Sugar. Dolly doesn't like it over there and she has lost a lot of weight from moping, but I feel it is the best thing for her. If things get better, I will bring her back home. I go over every day to feed her and Sugar, and Dolly is teaching Sugar some new tricks. Tina and Kelly go over to swim with them when they can. I still talk with Dolly at night. Our relationship is just as close as before, if not closer. Dolly is improving now. We took the Zodiac over to help her adjust.

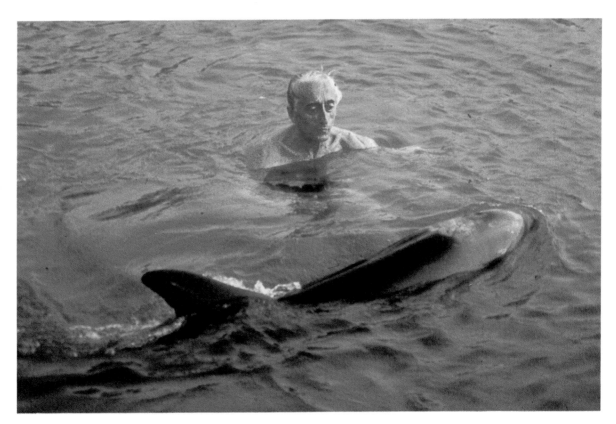

(Above) Captain Cousteau and Dolly take a swim together.

(Left) Jean Asbury's daughter, Kelly, and Dolly are great friends.

She is beginning to gain back some weight, but I know she hates captivity."

A Certain Smile

Such is the story of Dolly. We have been witnesses to it. We spent several weeks with the dolphin, and we have tried to judge her behavior as objectively as possible. What intrigued us initially, when we first heard about Dolly, was the question of whether it is possible for an emotional relationship to exist between man and marine mammals. In other words, can there be a real exchange of affection between them?

The experts are generally negative in this respect, including our friends Busnel and Albin Dziedzic,† who have both participated in expeditions aboard *Calypso*. In their opinion, only man is capable of feeling an emotional attachment. A dolphin is not attracted to any particular individual human but seeks out human contact with any available human being.

This is also the opinion of most American scientists, as well as of the

†Albin Dziedzic, like Professor Busnel, is attached to the Laboratory of Acoustical Physiology of INRA.

dolphin trainers at the various marinelands.

Is it true that the dolphin has no "heart"? That he is less affectionate, less loyal than, say, a dog?

"Yes," says Professor Busnel, who feels that we have been led astray by "a certain smile." The smile to which Busnel refers is that engaging rictus which is the permanent expression on the face of the Bottlenosed Dolphin — an expression which it is tempting to interpret as a smile or a laugh.

Other marine mammals, such as the killer whale and the pilot whale, and the fresh-water or river dolphin, do not awaken our sympathy to the same degree as the Bottlenosed Dolphin. And yet, they are at least as clever as the latter when we see them in our marinelands. Trainers say that these species learn even more quickly than the Bottlenosed Dolphin.

The Bottlenosed Dolphin, like most stars today, was launched by television. The "Flipper" series has popularized the photogenic smile of the dolphin; and, by now, there is no scientific argument which could possibly persuade the general public that Flipper's expression is not, in fact, a smile.

Konrad Lorenz has studied at length the animal signs and gestures which man tends to interpret as favorable or unfavorable and to which he attributes an unwarranted, or a totally false, meaning. The dolphin's "smile" may indeed be as misleading as many of the signs cited by Lorenz. But the total absence of aggressivity in the dolphin, the fact that the dolphin will not bite a human, even when the animal is subjected to the most horrifying tortures — such as having metal hooks driven into its skull with a hammer — these are documented facts which cannot be denied. In one experiment conducted in the United States, twenty-nine dolphins were killed, and not one of them ever attempted to bite, or harm in any way, the men who were tormenting them. It would be difficult to think of any animal, other than the dolphin, who exhibits such patience, forbearance and magnanimity toward human aggression. Even a faithful dog sometimes turns on his master; and there is no household pet, however thoroughly domesticated, that will not, when sufficiently provoked, bite or scratch. We sometimes speak of the animal kingdom as a world of "tooth and claw." And so it is, indeed, a kingdom where animals turn their natural weapons against one another and, if need be, against human beings. The dolphin, for a reason which we have yet to fathom, seems to be the exception — at least as far as his dealings with humans are concerned.

Unless one has actually seen it, it is difficult to imagine the trust shown by the dolphin who, of his own accord, places his head into the hands of the man who is going to put blinkers over the animal's eyes. And it is difficult to deny that dolphins show a special attachment to children — as we shall see in the course of this book — and sometimes to a particular child.

Dolly and her favorite oar.

We are perfectly willing to admit that affection cannot be sketched out by means of a diagram. It cannot be measured on a scale, or recorded on a tape. Dolly never said or wrote: "Dolly loves Jean." But Dolly, when she was suffering, did go to Jean, and to no one else, and lay her head on her adoptive mother's lap. Can this be conditioned behavior? Or a sentimental illusion? Scientists, in their quest for certitude and proof, tend to reject the marvelous, and, in so doing, they sometimes risk not seeing the forest for the trees.

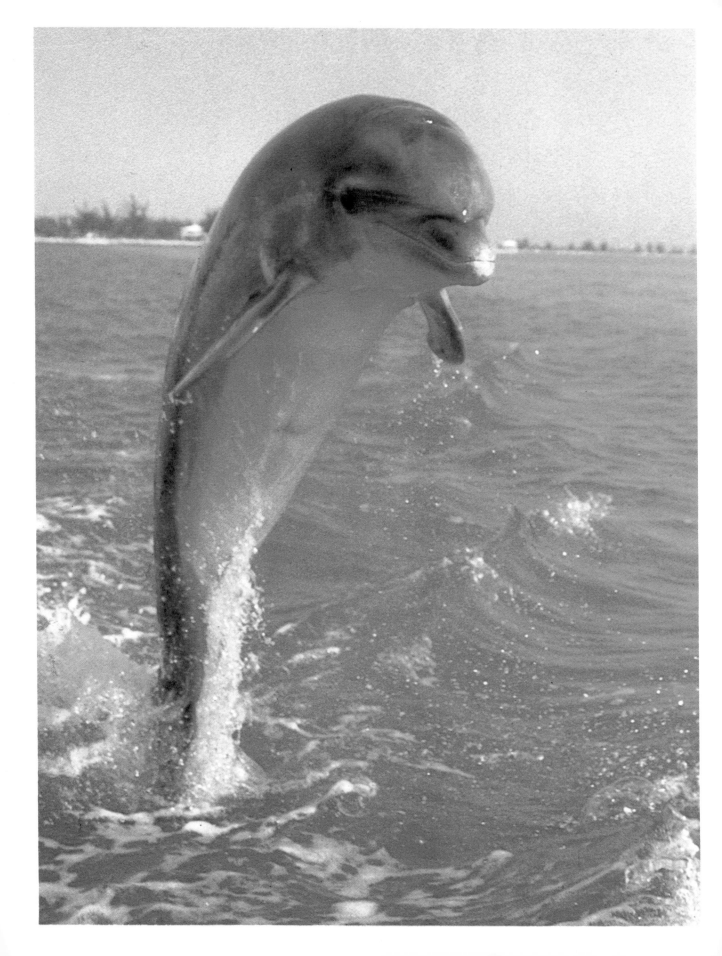

Chapter Five

LIFE WITH MAN

The case of Dolly, described in the preceding chapter, is hardly unique. There have been several dolphins who have acquired more or less permanent fame by associating with humans. One of the most celebrated of them was Pelorus Jack, who became known in 1888. Pelorus Jack lived in Cook Strait, which separates the two principal islands of New Zealand, between French Pass and Pelorus Sound. It is from the latter that the dolphin took his name.

Pelorus Jack was a *Grampus griseus* (Gray Grampus, or Risso's Dolphin). It was never discovered for certain whether Jack was, in fact, a male or female. But, for almost a quarter of a century, he (or she) was a world-wide celebrity. He was mentioned by many writers, including Kipling and Mark Twain. One of the most famous journalists of the time, Frank T. Bullen, made a special trip to New Zealand to write an article about Pelorus Jack.

Unlike Dolly and some other dolphins, Jack was never in direct contact with human beings. He was fascinated by ships, and there was hardly a vessel which entered Cook Strait that Jack did not accompany on part of its journey.

(Left) The tail fins of dolphins are very powerful. Dolphins can literally stand on their tails.

The Opononi dolphin of New Zealand allowed children to ride on his back. (Photo, courtesy of The Auckland *Star*.)

He rubbed against the ships' hulls, swam before their prows, and dived and leaped around them.

Jack's usual station was at the entrance to the Strait. He was there so often that many people journeyed to the Strait solely to see him. Sometimes two steamers arrived simultaneously, then, Jack would invariably choose to accompany the faster of the two. He tended to ignore mere yachts and other lesser craft.

The Opononi dolphin playing with bathers. (Photo, courtesy of The Auckland *Star*.)

The *Penguin*, a steamer which frequently passed through the Strait, on one occasion inadvertently rammed Pelorus Jack, and the dolphin was rather seriously injured. From then on, whenever the *Penguin* entered the Strait, Jack was careful to keep his distance from that particular vessel.

Pelorus Jack disappeared in 1912. Some have attributed his disappearance to death from old age, and this explanation is quite plausible. Others have claimed that he was killed by a Norwegian whaler at the entrance to Pelorus Sound.

Opo and the Children

It was also in New Zealand, in Hokianga Bay, in the North Auckland District, that another man-loving dolphin appeared in 1955. This dolphin first became conspicuous for its habit of following pleasure boats, and it was widely believed at first that the animal was, in fact, a shark. It was actually a female dolphin, quite young – probably an orphan whose mother had been killed by one of the Mighty White Hunters who seem to be always with us. In any case, the dolphin was not yet one year old. She loved to have her back scratched with an oar or a broom, but even then, she initially kept her distance from humans.

When summer came, the dolphin began to mingle with the bathers at Opononi beach. Which of the bathers first got up the courage to pet the dolphin? It is not known. It may well have been a child, for the dolphin, whom the bathers called Opo, showed a marked preference for young people.

Opo spent most of her time at Opononi beach, or, if she was not there, she quickly arrived at the first sound of a boat's engine. Soon, thousands of people were going to Opononi to see the dolphin and, if possible, to pet her. The fortune of the innkeepers and businessmen of the modest village was assured. Ice cream and beer were sold at an unprecedented rate. The grateful population formed a committee for the protection of dolphins and installed large signs at the entrance to the village: "Welcome to Opononi. But do not try to kill our happy dolphin."

It was Opo's delight to swim among groups of children. She seemed to invite petting, for she sought out those children who were affectionate and avoided those who played too roughly. Her favorite was an excellent swimmer, Jill Baker, a girl of thirteen. "Whenever Opo saw me go into the water," Jill said, "she left the other swimmers to come to me."

Opo often dived between Jill's legs, then picked her up and took her for a ride on her back. At first Opo had seemed to dislike being touched, or having her dorsal fin grasped by the children. But, as soon as she realized that the children had no intention of hurting her, she allowed them to do whatever they wished.

It is difficult to believe that Jill Baker merely imagined that Opo preferred her to the other children, or that the witnesses to Opo's preferences — tourists, journalists, and fishermen — were all victims of an illusion in believing that Jill was Opo's favorite. The only conclusion possible is that Opo recognized Jill and was able to distinguish her from the other bathers.

Some of the fishermen in the neighborhood sometimes offered Opo fish from their catch — mullets, especially — but she would never accept their offers. She preferred to catch fish on her own.

A Local Celebrity

One day, a swimmer gave Opo a multicolored beachball. The dolphin invented a game with it, which consisted in throwing the ball high into the air and then swimming out, as fast as she could, to catch the ball when it came down.

She also enjoyed searching for empty beer bottles on the bottom. She picked up the bottles in her mouth and then threw them as far as she could. When she had performed a particularly spectacular trick and there was applause and shouts of admiration from the beach, Opo would leap into the air in a sort of triumphal jump. It seems that she heard the people's shouts, understood their meaning, and was pleased. She became a star.

At times, there were so many visitors to Opononi beach that Opo was overwhelmed. Some tourists were so avid to touch the dolphin that they ran into the sea fully clothed. A few people handled Opo inconsiderately, pulling her tail roughly, or trying to turn her over on her back, or attempting to block her. She showed her displeasure at such treatment by swimming out of reach, though without undue haste. The only sign of irritation was the constant beating of her tail. Never did she give any stronger indication of resentment than that.

Opo was in her glory when the children of the Opononi school held their school picnic on the beach. The children were playing in the water when one of them suggested forming a circle and holding hands. Opo, as though she knew what was expected of her, came right into the center of the circle and performed her tricks with her beach ball, to the delight of her audience.

In March 1956, a law was passed forbidding anyone to capture, hunt, or otherwise molest dolphins in Hokianga Bay. A few days later, it was noticed that Opo was conspicuously absent from her favorite haunt off Opononi beach. Four boats were sent out to search for the dolphin, but they found no trace of her.

A clam digger found her, dead, her body squeezed between two rocks. It seems most unlikely that Opo would have deliberately swum into that position. The probable explanation is that the dolphin was the victim of an explosion and was thrown into the rocks, for, in that area, there are men who fish with explosives.

Opo's body was carried back to the beach and buried there. The people of the village covered her grave with flowers.

The Dolphin of La Corogna

It was our good fortune to take part in an adventure similar to that of Opo. We were in Paris, about a year and a half ago, when we received a letter from Spain reporting that there was a dolphin, near La Corogna, which was accompanying fishing boats and swimming among the bathers at the local beach. In other words, it was obviously a particularly sociable dolphin.

Jacques Renoir, who was shooting our film on dolphins, went to La Corogna, where he was warmly welcomed. He was immediately driven to Lorbe Cove, about twelve miles from the town, which seemed to be the spot most favored by Nino, as the dolphin had been named.

Renoir, wearing his diving suit, dived into the water. A few minutes later, he saw a handsome dolphin coming toward him in the water. He came near, turning, twisting, and brushing against him. Then, without the least sign of fear, Nino slowly rubbed the whole length of his body slowly against Renoir's. Jacques began stroking Nino gently, and suddenly the dolphin rolled over on his back, showing his light-colored underside — a position characteristic of females in heat. Renoir caressed the dolphin in a more precise way and extended his arm. Nino, of his own accord, began rubbing himself against the arm. Jacques's Spanish hosts, who were watching him from the surface, were obviously shocked but were too polite to say anything.

When Jacques returned to the surface to climb back into the boat, Nino tried to stop him. He no doubt wished to continue sampling the pleasures of which he had been deprived.

It remained for Jacques to explain to the Spaniards that their Nino was really Nina — an eight-foot female *Tursiops truncatus*, weighing about four hundred pounds. She was an adult specimen and was probably ten or twelve years old.

The next day, Jacques dived with a local diver who was employed as a dock builder. This diver knew Nina well because, whenever he was in the water, the dolphin came to circle around him.

Nina's Story

José Freire Vásquez, who knew the story of Nina from its very beginning, told me about his meeting with her:

"The first man to make the acquaintance of our dolphin was a diver named Luis Salleres, who worked in the Lorbe clam beds. Salleres was working in the beds one day when he looked up and, to his surprise, saw a dolphin nearby, watching him. The following day, the dolphin was there again, and this time the animal came closer. Salleres tried to pet her; and not only did the dolphin not flee, but she actually seemed to enjoy it.

"Salleres told some friends of his in La Corogna about the dolphin, but no one believed him. He came to see me because he knew I was interested in marine biology and in animal behavior. I must say that, at that time, I wasn't really convinced of what he told me. Nonetheless, the following day I went to Lorbe with Salleres, and we went out in a small boat. Salleres had his diving suit with him, and he got into the water. Very shortly, as I watched, I saw a dolphin approaching our boat and then diving toward the spot where Salleres had gone down. A few seconds later, Salleres and the dolphin both surfaced and began swimming around side by side.

"I was astonished. And I couldn't resist the temptation to join them in the water. The dolphin was perfectly willing to play with me, but it was obvious that she was more interested in her friend the diver.

"Then something notable happened. After playing with the dolphin for a while, Salleres returned to the boat to get his underwater camera. I was still in the water with the dolphin. The water was quite cold, and I'm not really a good swimmer. Suddenly, my legs felt as though they were paralyzed. I was terror stricken. I began waving my arm to attract Salleres' attention. At that instant, the dolphin, as though she understood what was happening, came very close to me and remained absolutely motionless in the water next to me, so that I was able to put my arms around her body. With the dolphin supporting my weight in the water, my fear vanished, and I simply waited for Salleres to return from the boat."

Nina and Jacques Renoir dived together for a week. Jacques's boat was anchored in about forty feet of water, and, using his Aqua-Lung®, he ordinarily dived down to the depth of the anchor. It usually took about five

Nina with the Spanish diver, Luis Salleres.

minutes for the dolphin to make her appearance. She approached on the surface of the water, and then, as she drew nearer the boat, she dived, spiraling down the anchor line until she reached Jacques. No doubt, the feel of the line against her body, as she descended, was an agreeable sensation.

When Jacques saw her, he held out his hand, and Nina immediately went to him and rubbed her genital area against his hand.

"We played together for thirty or forty-five minutes," Renoir recalls. "There always came a time when Nina began leaping into the air, then she would fall back and return to me, wildly eager for more fun and games. It was an extraordinary situation, as though the barrier between man and animal no longer existed. There was some sort of strange understanding between us. It

When other dolphins came to play in her bay, Nina ignored them.

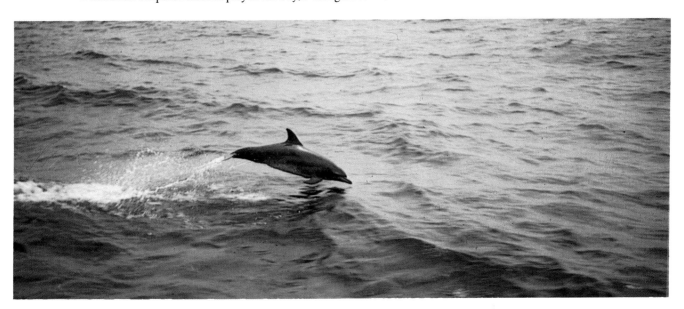

would be very difficult for me to say exactly what our feelings were for one another, but there was undoubtedly *something*. Luis Salleres, the Spanish diver, had the same sort of feeling for Nina. In fact, he told me that his wife was jealous of the dolphin and sometimes made scenes over her."

A team of divers from *Calypso*, including Bernard Delemotte and Yves Omer, went to La Corogna to take part in filming sequences for our dolphin film. "You'll see how beautiful Nina is in the water," Jacques Renoir told them when they arrived. "She's like some gorgeous woman. . . ."

"They laughed at me, of course," Jacques relates. "But the first time they dived and saw her, they told me: 'You were right. She *is* beautiful. We could never have imagined anything like her!'"

Nina had won them over.

A National Glory

La Corogna is a small town, and the adventure of Nina, added to the presence of our divers, created a sensation. All the chief men of the town were involved in the affair, and the newspapers in the area began devoting whole pages to Nina. The dolphin, who had started out as a local personality, quickly became a national heroine. The Spanish television network sent a team to Lorbe to make a film which showed Nina playing with a group of swimmers, among whom Franco's grandchildren figured prominently. Nina became the symbol of the link between the Spanish people and the sea. Tourists flocked to the area, and the town's only bistro was jammed to the rafters. The price of land began to rise, and speculators made a great deal of money.

The local fishermen, who had always been poor, suddenly prospered as tourist guides. Now, they earned in a day what it had previously taken them a month to earn. And every weekend there were monstrous traffic jams which were the despair of the local police.

Nina, like any star, gave of herself for her public. She allowed herself to be petted. She mixed with the bathers. She played near any boat that put out into the water.

The tourists loved her. When she swam on one side of a sightseeing boat, everyone rushed over to that side; and when she crossed over to swim on the other side, everyone rushed back to the other side so that the boats were often in danger of capsizing. Some people fell into the water. There were shouts and screams and a constant coming and going of craft of all sizes.

Nina's patience seemed inexhaustible. Sometimes, on Sundays espe-

Even when Salleres put his arms around her, Nina did not seem to mind. (Photo, Jose Freire Vasquez.)

cially, there were as many as two thousand people in the water, all determined to touch Nina. Some of the tourists climbed onto her back. The children tugged at her tail. But she never showed a moment's irritation or impatience.

When she had had enough, she simply disappeared for a half hour or so, then returned, apparently ready for another appearance before her fans. Like any performer, she could not do without her audience. Her stage was always the same, an area some nine hundred feet from the beach. She never dived so deep as to lose her audience.

It is interesting to note that Nina showed a marked preference for swimmers wearing diving suits.

She played constantly throughout the day except for a period of approximately one hour, around noon, when she disappeared, perhaps to eat. In any event, she never accepted food from any of her admirers.

Except for the fact that Nina was a dolphin and that she liked humans, there is very little similarity between her case and that of Dolly. Dolly was a dolphin who had been captured, trained, and then released. She sought out the company of human beings because she was accustomed to them, had

Shooting a sequence.

lived with them, and been fed by them. She behaved like a trained animal who, when released, refused to go "wild" again. She was conditioned by her education, and she asked for nothing more than to be allowed to perform her tricks. What was extraordinary about Nina, on the other hand, was that, so far as it was possible to discover, she had never been trained. There is no aquarium or marineland in the vicinity of La Corogna. And it is most unlikely that, alone, she had crossed the Atlantic to Spain from the United States.

Moreover, her behavior gave no reason to believe that she had undergone any special training, or that she had been previously conditioned in any respect whatsoever. She performed no tricks. She was not eager to play, or to leap out of the water. All she wanted was to be with humans and to be petted by them. Her attitude was as spontaneous as that of Opo. Except that Nina had no favorites among her admirers. She liked everyone, and, for that reason, she was particularly vulnerable.

A Monument to Nina

The civil authorities of La Corogna and the Spanish Navy, accepting responsibility for Nina's welfare, passed certain measures designed to protect the dolphin who had brought prosperity to La Corogna. It was forbidden to use outboard motors around Nina, lest the dolphin be injured by the propellers. No net could be lowered into the waters of the cove, lest Nina become entangled in it and perhaps drown. And no one was allowed to tug at Nina's tail, which was judged to be fragile.

One evening, there was a banquet attended by the mayor, the commandant of the naval district, and the district prefect. Jacques Renoir was invited to speak at the banquet. In halting Spanish, he said:

"We all know how much Nina has done for this area. She has attracted crowds of tourists. She has caused the value of property to double. And she has brought a great deal of business to the town. Nina has done all these things for La Corogna. But what is La Corogna doing for Nina?"

"We love her," someone answered.

"That is not enough," Jacques responded. "There should be a monument to Nina — on the La Corogna jetty, for example."

The next morning, the newspapers launched a fund-raising campaign for Nina's monument. It was proposed that a statue be commissioned, representing a diver with his arms around a dolphin. There was an enthusiastic public response.

The Final Enigma

"At the end of November," relates José Freire Vásquez, "a group of fishermen reported that they had seen Nina near one of the clam beds and that she seemed very ill. Luis Salleres and I went to Lorbe immediately. We searched the bay thoroughly in a boat, without seeing any sign of her. If she had been there, Nina would certainly have come to us, as she always did.

"Five weeks later, at the neighboring beach of San Pedro, the decomposed body of a dolphin washed up onto the sand. Luis and I inspected the corpse and immediately recognized it as the remains of poor Nina.

"It is difficult to say what caused her death. It may have been an accident. Certain individuals in this area use grenades to fish, and Nina may have been the victim of an explosion. Or she may have become entangled in a fisherman's net and drowned. It was winter, and the fishermen, who worked as tourist guides during the summer, had returned to fishing when tourists became scare. They had to earn their living, and they wanted to use their nets again, although it was forbidden by law to do so, precisely because of the danger the nets presented for Nina."

Nina had spent five months in the area of La Corogna, seeking human companionship. She seemed to have given up living among her own kind. Once, a school of Bottlenosed Dolphins was sighted outside the cove. Two of the school entered the cove and spent about a quarter of an hour with Nina. Then they returned alone to the school, and Nina remained in her cove.

Why would a dolphin voluntarily give up living among her own kind for the sake of contact with human beings? There is no way for anyone to answer that question at the present time. It may be that she had been banished from her school for some reason or other, that she was condemned to exile, and that she sought relief from her loneliness among humans.

In Captivity

The love life of dolphins has rarely been observed in the sea, but it has been studied in aquariums. In that environment, the sexual act is preceded by an extended period of love play. The male nips at the female and caresses her. The female flees and generally plays the coquette. Both dolphins swim around at full speed, splashing water in their tank. It is very likely that there is more sexual activity in captivity than in the natural environment of dolphins. This is usually the case among animals confined in zoos.

One pair of dolphins, observed in captivity, behaved as follows: The

(Above and right) Jacques Renoir and Nina

male dolphin, beginning in the spring, showed an extraordinary interest in one of the females, whereas, during the preceding year, he had played indiscriminately with all the other members of the group in the tank. He undertook a real courtship of his inamorata, giving her little pats with his flippers, nipping her on the snout, pushing her with his nose, uttering little cries, and clicking his jaws. This characteristic procedure, which was observed on different occasions, continued for several days. Then the female began to respond in her own way. Her response climaxed in a brief mating. Immediately, the male lost interest in this particular female and began courting another one.

The act of copulation itself is of very brief duration. Dolphins, like all cetaceans, have fibroelastic penises similar to those of Artiodactyls, which differ from the vascular penis of carnivores and primates. Coitus is therefore extremely rapid, lasting from one to thirty seconds, for erection, rather than being caused by an influx of blood into the penis, results from muscular action. Yet, coitus can be repeated (especially among Common Dolphins) several times, at intervals of fifteen minutes.

Mating usually takes place at the surface of the water and is easy to observe in aquariums. That of the Bottlenosed Dolphin has often been described in various publications.

It frequently happens that the female will take the initiative and position herself in such a way that the dorsal fin of the male penetrates her sexual

(Following page) Two dolphins photographed in the open sea.

orifice. Among some species (Pilot Whales, Bottlenosed Dolphins, and Pacific White-sided Dolphins), the female indicates that she is in heat by taking the initiative in amorous games. For dolphins, lacking a sense of smell, cannot catch the characteristic scent of a female in heat as land mammals do.

Female dolphins have a clitoris located at the vaginal orifice, which is about two inches in depth. The male organ is flat and triangular and ordinarily remains within a sheath in the dolphin's body. It emerges like a knife from a scabbard. The dolphin has conscious control over the muscular action which results in erection, and he is therefore able to attain erection very quickly.

The prenuptial games of dolphins sometimes represent scenes of great beauty.* The animals intertwine their flippers, twist and turn, lay their heads on the neck of their partners, and swim gracefully side by side. They dance a veritable ballet of love. Sometimes the male seizes the female around the middle of her body with his flippers. They nip at one another, and their whistles and cries can be heard above the surface of the water.

These amorous preliminaries may last as long as thirty minutes to an hour. The sequence is somewhat less tender. The male rushes at the female as though he intends to ram her head on. At the last second of his charge, he turns, and the partners' bodies rub against each other vigorously. It is during this rubbing that the male's penis makes contact with the female's ventral area. At the moment of climax, the male slides under the female and almost perpendicular to her, with the hind part of his body and his tail folded over her.

This position is reminiscent of the right-angular position taken by sharks. But there are variations. At the Florida Marine Studios, mating takes place during the night or very early in the morning. The male approaches the female from the rear, slightly to the side, either perpendicularly or at a lesser angle. Erection follows immediately.

Among Bottlenosed Dolphins, coitus occurs in either of two ways. The penis enters the female for only half its length, and coupling lasts only ten seconds; or else it penetrates for its full length, and then the act continues for thirty seconds. Coitus is often accompanied by rhythmic movements of the pelvis.

Another mating technique has been observed among Killer Whales, Stenella plagiodon, and Steno which copulate belly to belly on the surface of the water, but in a horizontal position.

During pregnancy, the female Bottlenosed Dolphin stays somewhat apart from the rest of the group but remains in the company of the other

*Some of these have been described by Antony Alpers in his book, *Dolphins, the Myth and the Mammal*, Boston, 1961.

female who will assist her during labor. The expectant mother diligently performs what can only be described as prenatal exercises: she bends her head and tail toward the bottom of the tank, then raises them toward the surface. Some pregnant females continue these exercises for sixty minutes at a time.

Usually, a dolphin gives birth to only one calf at a time. Gestation lasts for one year among Bottlenosed Dolphins and eleven months among Common Dolphins. Lactation continues for sixteen months after birth.

The first birth of a cetacean in captivity occurred at the Brighton Aquarium, in England, in 1914. But the calf was stillborn.

In February 1947, a Bottlenosed Dolphin named Mona, who had been captured pregnant, gave birth in the Florida Marine Studios. Her offspring, a female, was alive and healthy and was christened Spray.

The birth of Spray made it possible to collect some important data. The calf is born not headfirst, but tailfirst. The umbilical cord breaks spontaneously. Since the newborn calf's lungs contain no air, it will drown unless the mother takes it to the surface at once for its first swallow of air. In this endeavor, the mother is usually aided by another female dolphin, known as the

Nina diving. This photograph was taken only a few days before Nina died. (Photo, Jose Freire Vásquez.)

"aunt" or the "midwife." The two females push the calf toward the surface with their snouts. Perhaps this necessary raising of their young to the surface is at the origin of the dolphins' ability to use their snouts to throw balls or rings, and even to save drowning humans.

Some specialists maintain that the mother does not push her calf to the surface. According to this opinion, the calf rises of its own accord, accompanied by the mother.

A newborn dolphin is already rather large and heavy at birth, and it already possesses all the organs of an adult. This no doubt is the reason why the period of gestation is of such long duration. An infant dolphin's body weighs approximately 10 to 15 per cent of its mother's weight and measures a third of the length of the latter's body. For a newborn dolphin must be strong enough to maintain its body temperature and to react against the cold.

Female dolphins, like all female cetaceans, are devoted mothers. They keep constant watch over their offspring, who swim against the mother's body, and defend them courageously against such enemies as sharks. The mother's milk is unusually rich. The mother's breasts are located in pairs, next to her genital organs. A mammary muscle makes it possible for the dolphin, like the whale, to turn slightly on her side and send a jet of milk into the waiting mouth of her offspring.

The milk of cetaceans is composed of 35 to 40 per cent fatty materials, which makes it possible for a young dolphin to grow very rapidly. But a calf is unable to feed itself until it grows teeth — usually at the age of five to seven months. It sometimes happens that the calf continues breast-feeding long after its teeth have grown in, until the age of two years.

A newly born male dolphin is able to have an erection only a few hours after birth. These erections are stimulated by contact with the mother. The first attempts at copulation take place during the first few weeks following birth and have the mother as the sexual object.

The proximity of the mother's breasts and genital orifice is no doubt a factor in this sexual precocity. The calf, in nursing, stimulates the sexual instinct of the mother, and it is not rare that the mother herself causes the calf's erection. She then turns on her side and encourages copulation. This is the young dolphin's first lesson in sexuality.

A male dolphin is unable to impregnate a female until he reaches the age of seven years — the same age at which the female attains sexual maturity.

Sexually, dolphins are extremely active animals. Jacques Renoir is by no means the only witness to this phenomenon. Remington Kellogg, a renowned expert on cetaceans, was passionately loved by a male dolphin in a marineland — so much so that the animal tried every means possible to make Kellogg fall into his tank. On two occasions, the dolphin succeeded; and on both occasions he manifested his affection in an unmistakable manner

Some dolphins are homosexual. It has happened that two males attacked a female who was put into their tank. The female had to be removed in great haste, for the males would obviously have killed her.

In the course of a series of experiments at the St. Thomas Laboratory, in the Virgin Islands, John C. Lilly requested that one of his assistants, Margaret Howe, live with a dolphin for two limited periods. The first period lasted seven days; the second, two and a half months.

During this time, Miss Howe was to remain with the dolphin, named Peter, day and night. The purpose of the experiment was to give the dolphin a "cram course" in language.

In the center of Peter's tank, a platform was constructed. And, on this platform, Margaret Howe installed her bed. At night, Peter rested in the water alongside the bed. During the fourth week of the experiment, Peter began to show unmistakable signs of having something more than a student-teacher relationship in mind. By the end of the month, Miss Howe was writing: "I find that his desires are hindering our relationship. When Peter was upstairs in the Fiberglas tank, he would occasionally become aroused, and I found that by taking his penis in my hand and letting him jam himself against me he would reach some sort of orgasm, mouth open, eyes closed, body shaking, then his penis would relax and withdraw. Now, however, I am completely in the water with him and because so much of my body is exposed . . . I am completely vulnerable to him. . . ."

The remedy devised was to place Peter in a tank with two female dolphins. The following morning, his ardor had noticeably abated.

During the next two weeks, under the pretext of playing ball, Peter succeeded in calming Miss Howe's fears. At the same time, he devised a form of love play which consisted of nipping at Margaret's legs, or holding them gently in his mouth without biting. Peter had become very gentle in his sexual approaches, and he no longer tried to push against Miss Howe, or to knock her over.

At the end of two months, Peter had demonstrated beyond doubt that he would not bite Miss Howe's arms or legs and that he could be trusted. At the same time, he had demonstrated his trust in his mentor by allowing her to handle his sexual organ.† This is the closest contact known between a dolphin and a woman.

---

†John Cunningham Lilly. *The Mind of the Dolphin*, New York, 1967.

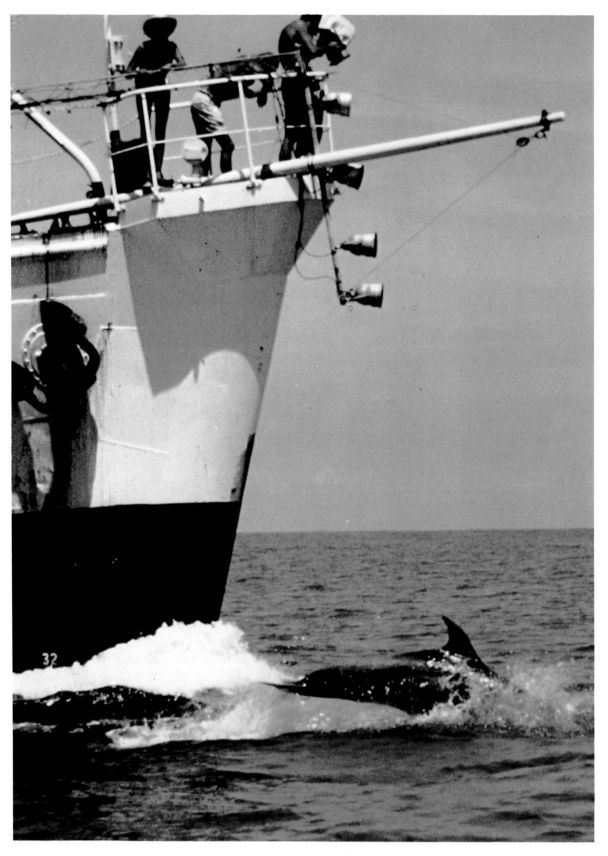

Michel Deloire, our cameraman, getting footage of dolphins surfing in *Calypso*'s wake.

Chapter Six

THE ROAD TO FREEDOM

For a very long time, it had been my intention to devote an entire film to dolphins. Yet, I could never bring myself to use dolphins from aquariums and marinelands as subjects in the film, for these dolphins seemed to me to be deformed and perverted by their captivity and their contact with man. I felt that trained animals — performing animals — could not give us a true representation of the way that marine mammals lived in freedom in the seas. Moreover, the behavior of dolphins in captivity had often been described and filmed.

Therefore, if I wanted a film on dolphins, my subjects would have to be free dolphins. I felt that with our team of divers, and with all of *Calypso*'s resources, we might be able to contribute something to man's understanding of dolphins. We are among the few divers who have had numerous opportunities to observe dolphins in the sea — often at close quarters — either when they came to swim around *Calypso* or when we followed them in our Zodiacs.

The experience we had acquired with dolphins, and especially Falco's observations on the *Delphinus delphis*, seemed to indicate that we might make the film I had in mind. And so, in 1970, I entrusted the project to Jacques Renoir.

During our earlier expeditions, we had seen large numbers of dolphins in the vicinity of Gibraltar and offshore at Málaga. For that reason, I decided to begin our filming in that part of the Mediterranean.

We were aware from the very beginning that it was not easy to film dolphins in the sea. There was no way for our divers and photographers to come near them in the water, and, from *Calypso*, we could never get a frontal view of them. The dolphins swam before our prow, and we could get shots only of their tails, whereas what we really wanted was shots of their heads, their "smiles," their expressions.

With this purpose in mind, I had an arm constructed which extended over *Calypso*'s stem. A camera was attached to this arm, with the lens aimed at the prow. It seemed reasonable to expect that, with this device, we might be able to film what had always eluded us before: a frontal view of dolphins swimming in the open sea.

Yves Omer, our underwater cameraman, supervised the installation of this new piece of equipment. A supporting arm was attached to the stem and then heavily braced to prevent vibration as much as possible. A marine camera and a television camera were coupled in a mobile compartment the position of which could be changed to allow for shots from different angles. Both cameras were remotely controlled.

Calypso's underwater observation chamber made it possible for us to observe dolphins approaching and also to check the action of the cameras.

A Mistake in Yellow

January 17, 1971. We are lying off Málaga and, as we expected, there are many dolphins in this area. We are ready to begin filming, but, to our great disappointment, the dolphins seem reluctant to take up their usual position forward of our prow. It is possible that our new camera arm, extending in the water from the stem, frightens them. It has been the same all along the coast of Spain and around Gibraltar. No school of dolphins that we have encountered will even come near *Calypso*'s prow. And yet, our captain, Philippe Sirot, employs the greatest skill in maneuvering so as to attract them. *Calypso* catches up to the schools slowly and moves parallel to them as gently as possible. But it does no good. I am sure it must be the camera arm. Dolphins have never been afraid of *Calypso* before. . . .

I have now discovered what the trouble was. I went forward and leaned over the side to look at the arm. The braces attached to *Calypso*'s hull, and the compartment housing the cameras, have been painted a bright yellow, a color

Professor Busnel and Captain Cousteau study the movements of dolphins on closed-circuit television from *Calypso*'s bridge.

that can easily be seen in the water. The only thing to do is to take down the whole installation and paint it over, in the same color as our hull: dark red.

We returned to Málaga and the repainting was undertaken immediately. Then we set out to sea again. The first school of dolphins we sighted surrounded *Calypso* without hesitation. Yves Omer and I went to the bridge to watch the television screen. And, for the first time, we saw a frontal view of dolphins swimming in the sea.

"It Works!"

Yves and I were enthusiastic. "It works!" we both shouted.

There were a number of dolphins visible through the portholes of the observation chamber, each one, in turn, taking his place in the wave raised by *Calypso*'s prow. They seemed to swim effortlessly, their tails moving at regularly spaced intervals. Long ago, aboard the *Elie Monnier*, I calculated that in order for a dolphin to attain a speed of ten knots, its tail must beat 120 times per minute, or two strokes per second. But now, the dolphins were moving their tails at a much slower rate. My guess was an average of a stroke and a quarter, or a stroke and a half every second.

The dolphins do not place themselves directly before the prow. Their bodies are at an angle to it, sometimes slightly to one side or slightly to the other. This is very likely intended to enable them to keep an eye toward the surface. "They really are cautious," Yves says. "They obviously want to swim

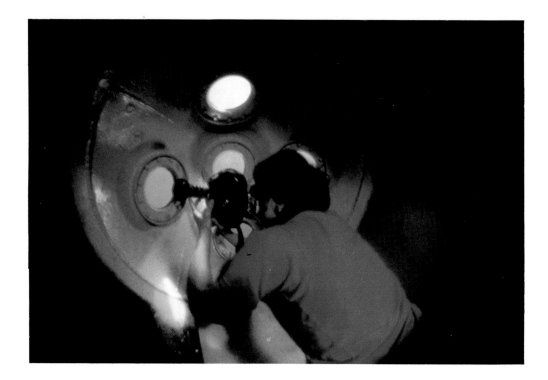

at the prow, but, at the same time, they are uneasy about it."

Despite this cautious approach, some of the dolphins are sufficiently courageous to pass between the prow and the camera. They move from one side to the other, obviously ready to dive at the slightest sign of danger. Sometimes they lie on their sides and we can see their light bellies. We are struck by their suppleness in the water — and by their speed, for it is apparent that they can outdistance us whenever they wish.

"Imagine," I told Yves, "we have 1200 horsepower in our engines. And these animals can swim circles around us!"

Indeed, the dolphin has more power, in proportion to the weight of its muscles, than any other animal.

Yves and I estimate that there are probably a thousand dolphins around *Calypso*'s prow, and we are fascinated by the way they move. The dolphin does not use its lateral flippers to swim, and its dorsal fin probably serves only as a stabilizer. It is able to move so rapidly because of its marvelously hydrodynamic shape and because of its powerful tail. The tail moves up and down horizontally, rather than vertically as in the case of fish. It can also move at an angle on both sides even when the animal is swimming at a rapid pace.

In aquariums, the Bottlenosed Dolphin can be seen swimming back and forth at the surface of its tank, at high speeds, with its tail much lower than its head. All these movements are possible because of the heavy musculature of the caudal peduncle, which is located both above and below the vertebral column. And yet, the tail of the dolphin is essentially the same as that of land mammals. The only difference is that it has adapted perfectly to life in the sea.

(Left) From his vantage point in our observation chamber, Gerard Petiot films dolphins in the sea.

(Right) Dolphins viewed through a porthole of the observation chamber.

(Below) A dolphin swims past the observation chamber and the automatic camera located at *Calypso*'s fore.

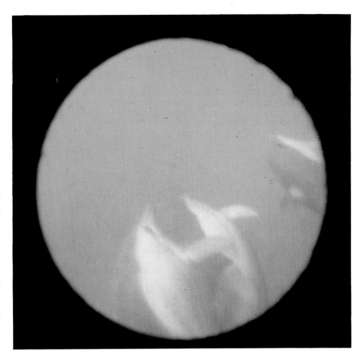

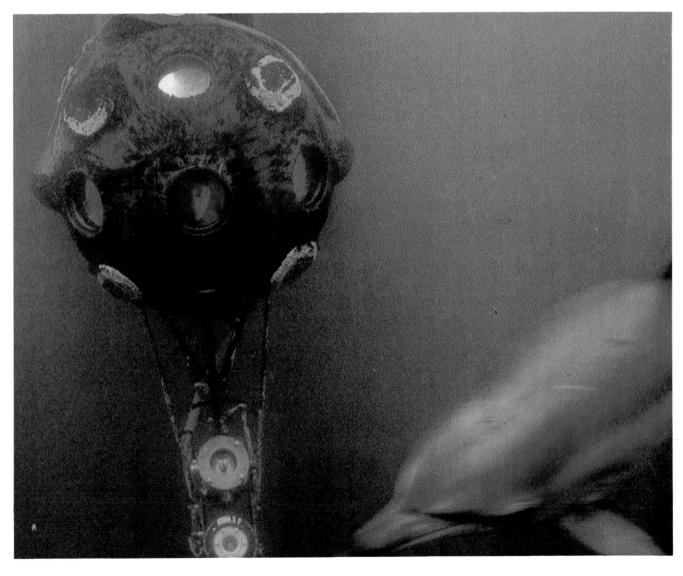

The body of the dolphin still contains traces of the animal's land origins, especially in the bones situated near the anal region which were once a pelvis and two limbs. Similarly, the dolphin's flippers contain all the bones of the hand, the wrist, and the arm.

A New Tank

I invited several researchers to participate in our dolphin expedition. Among those aboard *Calypso* are Albin Dziedzic, research engineer at the Laboratory of Acoustical Physiology; Alain Hellion, researcher at the Institute of Physics and Chemistry at Lyons; and Bernard Gautheron, a technician at the Phonetics Institute. Professor René Busnel joined us later.

We have a floating tank designed by Albin Dziedzic and built by the Laboratory of Acoustical Physiology. The tank is a triangular pool twenty feet in length. It is surrounded by air bags, which give it buoyancy. A net, which goes down to a depth of fifteen or twenty feet, is attached by these floaters. The shape of the net is maintained by rigid inserts located at the bottom of the net. We intend to place animals in this pool, for very brief periods, in order to study them. They are then to be released immediately.

We have already tested our new tank in the sea, off Málaga. All went as planned.

January 19.

We are leaving Málaga, despite heavy weather from the southwest. We are going to try to catch a dolphin.

A platform has been installed on *Calypso*'s stem, and Bébert Falco is going to try to capture a dolphin, using the same method employed thirteen years ago.

Now, however, we have the benefit of a new pincer, designed by R.-G. Busnel. This pincer is U-shaped, like the one Falco used earlier, but it has a long wooden handle at its extremity. A net bag is attached to the pincer by means of some rather fragile string. It is no longer necessary to use a harpoon gun to launch the pincer. It is simply held before the dolphin's snout. When the dolphin pushes against the device with its snout, the strings break and the net falls. The metal pincer itself never touches the dolphin's body, since it never leaves Falco's hand. A nylon line runs to the Zodiac which follows the dolphin.

The first tests of the new pincer have been unsuccessful. The weather was rough, *Calypso* was rolling, and it was impossible to take proper aim at the dolphin. The platform on *Calypso*'s prow makes it difficult to hold the pincer at an absolute vertical. We have, therefore, replaced it with a beam, which once was used to lower a sounding device into the water. This beam goes to within ten feet of the surface and makes it possible for the pincer device to be positioned directly over a dolphin swimming forward of our stem.

I should note here that not all species of dolphins like to swim in the wave of a prow. The Common Dolphin, the White-sided Dolphin, and often the Bottlenosed Dolphin are those who favor this kind of game. So does the Steno. (Professor Busnel captured a specimen of the latter, which was the first one to be taken alive.*) Pilot whales occasionally swim before a prow, but Harbor Porpoises never do.

We have also had to modify our pincer somewhat. The knots in the netting were too large and bruised the animal, and the fastenings were too weak and too stiff. I think that we now have an apparatus that will do the job for us.

First Capture

January 24. Falco, perched on the beam of *Calypso*'s prow, was unable to aim properly at a dolphin swimming directly under him. So, he chose another target: a dolphin swimming slightly to the side. However, he held the pincer in a vertical position.

The net has a great advantage in that the animal was so surprised that it very quickly came to a halt. Simultaneously, *Calypso* did likewise, and the Zodiac raced out, leaping from the crest of one wave to the next. But the sea was so rough that it was difficult for the little craft to maintain its speed. Nonetheless, Delemotte and Giacoletto, who were in the Zodiac, acquitted themselves with their usual competence and caught up to the dolphin. They then loaded him onto the Zodiac and brought him aboard. The animal was trembling.

The whole procedure lasted no more than sixty seconds. Speed is of the essence, since, if the dolphin goes into shock, there is a danger that it may suffocate. Not once did we ever have any problem of this kind during the first phase of our operating procedure. The co-ordination between Bébert and the men in the Zodiac was absolutely flawless.

*The Steno Dolphin was first described, and its existence known, in 1880, when a dead specimen was found.

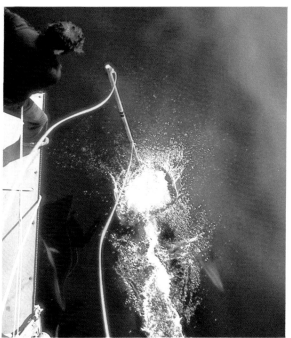

The various phases in the capture of a dolphin by Falco. The net must cover the dolphin's head. Then the animal is picked up by the Zodiac.

As soon as the dolphin was aboard, Busnel gave him a cortisone injection and a tonicardiac.

The weather is so bad that no experiments are possible, and we are en route back to Málaga. Meanwhile, the dolphin is dehydrating, and we are giving him continuous doses of glucose.

The vat in which we have placed the dolphin, on *Calypso*'s rear deck, is quite small, and the sea is so rough that the animal was thrown up against the side. We have covered the bottom and sides of the vat with foam rubber so as to form a protective cushion around the dolphin and to keep him from being thrown against the sides.

Upon docking at Málaga, we lowered the floating tank into the water and put the dolphin into it. We've attached orange ribbons of nylon to the net, because we're afraid that the animal will not see the knots and will bruise himself against them.

As soon as the dolphin was in the tank, Falco went down also and spent a quarter of an hour with him. The animal seemed dazed and was not moving very much. By the time that Bébert came back aboard, however, the dolphin was swimming normally. Nonetheless, we want to make certain that his blowhole is above the surface at all times; so, we have placed small bolsters under his snout.

During the night, the storm reached its peak, and even within the port the waves were so high that *Calypso* broke two of her hawsers. At the height of the storm, the floating tank became unbalanced and twisted. By the time that one of our divers managed to work his way into the tank, the dolphin had become entangled in the netting and had drowned. We are all very sad.

January 25. The weather is better this morning, and we are setting out to find another dolphin. . . .

There was no problem in capturing the first dolphin we encountered — a specimen weighing over two hundred pounds. Falco has lost none of his skill. He captured the animal on the first try. The sea was calm and still, and Bébert was able to lower the pincer almost to the surface. Then, as soon as the dolphin came up to breathe, Bébert quickly put the pincer around him and the dolphin was caught in the net without injuring himself.

The dolphin is neither a Bottlenosed nor a Common Dolphin, but a *Stenella styx*, which is grayer than the Common Dolphin.

The tank was immediately lowered into the water. It is light but handles rather clumsily. We keep it on the aft deck, with its air bags always inflated. We have got the knack of getting it into the water, but getting it back aboard is something else again. The whole team has to work at it, and we must be extraordinarily careful to keep the net from snagging. Naturally, it tends to hook onto anything within reach. With all its problems, however, it is still an ingenious device.

As soon as we had the tank in the sea, the dolphin was placed into it. The animal positioned himself vertically in the center of the tank and then refused to move. Occasionally, he sank deeper and then rose to the surface again, but he would not swim around in the tank. Our dolphin was so obviously unhappy that I decided to free him. He was no sooner out of the tank than he shot out of sight as though he had been fired from a cannon, proving that he could, after all, swim like any other dolphin.

January 26. Today, Falco captured another dolphin. We put the animal into the tank, and very soon it was swimming round in a circle.

We've decided to install hydrophones in the tank so that we can record the dolphin's whistles and cries.

Just our luck. We've captured a taciturn dolphin. Thus far, he's made three sounds. One when he was captured and two during the night. Thereafter, he has absolutely refused to speak.

January 27. We've spent the day waiting for our dolphin to "talk." We are beginning to feel slightly ridiculous. . . .

At 6 P.M., a squall from the east caught up with us. It is too dangerous to the dolphin to keep him in the tank in this weather, so I have ordered him set free. I think that Falco will be glad to see him go.

We are hauling in the tank as fast as we can. . . .

The weather is too bad for us to be able to work effectively. Moreover, *Calypso* has other assignments waiting for her. We will have to interrupt Operation Dolphin for a while.

A Merry-Go-Round

On April 5, *Calypso* returned to Málaga, and we were ready to begin the next phase of our dolphin project. This time, we were going to work in the vicinity of Gibraltar. The television and movie cameras were in place, aimed at our prow, and we set out with high hopes.

We were not disappointed. Very shortly, both screens were filled with the fantastic spectacle of a crowd of dolphins swimming in circles, pushing and brushing against one another. It was an incredible, animated merry-go-round. Occasionally, we caught a frontal view of a dolphin with its broad smile, then, everyone on the bridge laughed.

We were able clearly to distinguish the stream of air bubbles rising from their heads as they were whistling.

(Above) The dolphin has now been taken aboard the Zodiac.

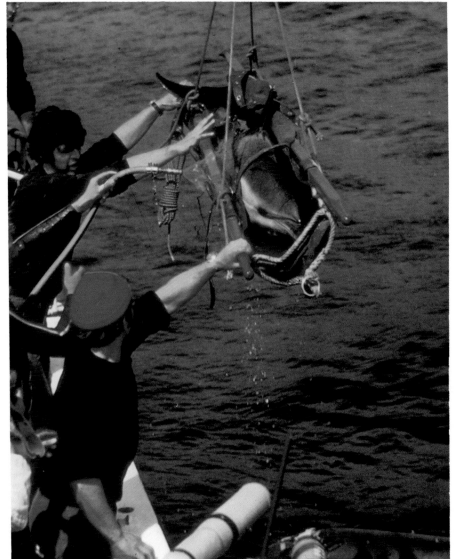

(Left) The captured dolphin is hoisted aboard *Calypso*.

(Right) Yves Omer gives first aid to the dolphin, which is now in a tank on *Calypso*'s aft deck.

Falco, meanwhile, had taken his position on the beam at our prow, and, on the first try, he was able to capture a female dolphin. She was immediately placed into the floating tank. It took only a short while for her to become accustomed to the tank, and she swam around without fear of ramming into the sides. Occasionally, however, she pushed her head against the air bags, obviously searching for a way out of the tank.

Professor Busnel advised us that a dolphin weighing 150 pounds required at least eighteen or twenty pounds of fish per day.

The sea had become so rough that it was necessary to remove the dolphin from her tank and place her into one of the two large vats that we kept on *Calypso*'s aft deck.

The ceremony of getting a dolphin into the vat always followed the same

pattern. Falco would take the animal in his arms and pass her gently to Bernard Delemotte. Delemotte would hand her to Yves Omer, who was standing next to the vat. Everyone had to be extremely gentle, for dolphins, out of the water, are unable to support their own weight. When they are moved, they must be supported at all times, for their vertebrae are very fragile.

Falco was not the only one concerned about the health of whatever dolphins we had aboard *Calypso*. Bernard Delemotte kept constant watch over them, and he summoned our ship's doctor at the slightest pretext.

"I can't tell you how often Delemotte has awakened me in the middle of the night," Dr. Joseph François says. "It's always the same. He wants me to examine one of the dolphins who, he says, 'looks funny.' And he insists that I do it immediately. He reminds me of one of those nervous mothers who call the doctor whenever their child sneezes. They are always sure that something is wrong."

Fortunately, most of Bernard's alarms were false. Nonetheless, we felt obliged to keep very close watch indeed over our dolphins. We knew that *Calypso*'s rolling and pitching would throw the animals against the walls of the vats, or even empty the vats and leave the dolphins without water. Even though we lined the vats with foam rubber to protect the dolphins, we did not lower our vigilance.

The bruises which appeared on the dolphins' bodies were a source of constant worry to us. Their skin is so tender that moving them from the tank to the vats, or from the vats to the tank, no matter how gentle we tried to be, caused lesions which quickly became infected.

Falco regarded it as a challenge to feed our female dolphin. He slid sardines into her mouth at every opportunity — fresh sardines, caught that very morning by means of a *lamparo*. The dolphin's eyes shone, but she refused to swallow the fish. Finally, by means of gentle insistence, Falco was successful. The dolphin began eating.

April 15. There are many dolphins here around Gibraltar, and Falco has captured a male weighing two hundred pounds. The sea is quite calm today, and we were able to lower the floating tank and to put the dolphin into it without delay. Dziedzic and Gautheron used their hydrophones to record the dolphin's whistles when it was captured, that is, as soon as the animal realized that it was a prisoner. These sounds continued for fifteen or twenty minutes. Then, when the animal began to swim around in the tank, he fell silent. When there are other dolphins in the area, they respond to these whistles, but, as soon as they see that there is nothing they can do for their friend, and that he is silent, they leave.

Our second dolphin was christened Fox Trot.

Aboard *Calypso*, the two dolphins were tossed about in their vats by the ship's rolling. We noticed that they seemed unwell, and we knew what was wrong! They were seasick. We had noted before that marine mammals are no more immune to this affliction than man.†

Later, more bad weather obliged us to put our second dolphin into the other vat on *Calypso*'s aft deck. The two vats were twelve feet apart, and we had the impression that there was constant communication between the dolphins. The female turned her head and whistled. The male immediately raised his head and whistled back. This exchange continued for over two hours, without pause.

"I suppose," Falco said, "that the female told the male that we were going to give him something to eat, and that it would be all right for him to accept it."

Falco was obviously right, for the male dolphin ate four sardines without hesitation. (We were fortunate enough to have made the acquaintance of a fisherman from Málaga who was very interested in our work and who provided us regularly with fresh fish.)

We put the two dolphins together into the floating tank, and they seemed overjoyed. Both animals performed acrobatics to express their pleasure. The female, who was familiar with the tank, served as guide to her companion to keep him from becoming entangled in the net. She kept her body pressed against him as they swam together.

At night, we were afraid that the animals might be caught in the netting, and we brought them back aboard *Calypso* and put them in their vats. However, we used a stretcher that Dr. François had among his supplies, and this device, in combination with our crane, worked perfectly in hoisting the animals aboard. Of course, we were careful to be as gentle as possible, but I was saddened by the sight of the dolphins being tossed about in their tanks. Captivity, no matter how well intentioned, is no life for a dolphin.

When both animals were together in the tank, everything seemed to go smoothly. They did not make a sound. But as soon as the animals were separated, the female began to utter cries. She seemed to panic and dived toward the bottom, with her mouth open. On several occasions, she became entangled in the net, and Yves Omer was obliged to go down and release her.

The male dolphin occasionally performed an interesting maneuver. He placed himself in a vertical position, then bent down upon himself. It would have been an amusing trick for a marineland audience. However, we had no

---

†Commandant Alinat has invented a non-rolling aquarium, which we use aboard *Calypso* to house rare coral fishes destined for the Oceanographic Museum of Monaco.

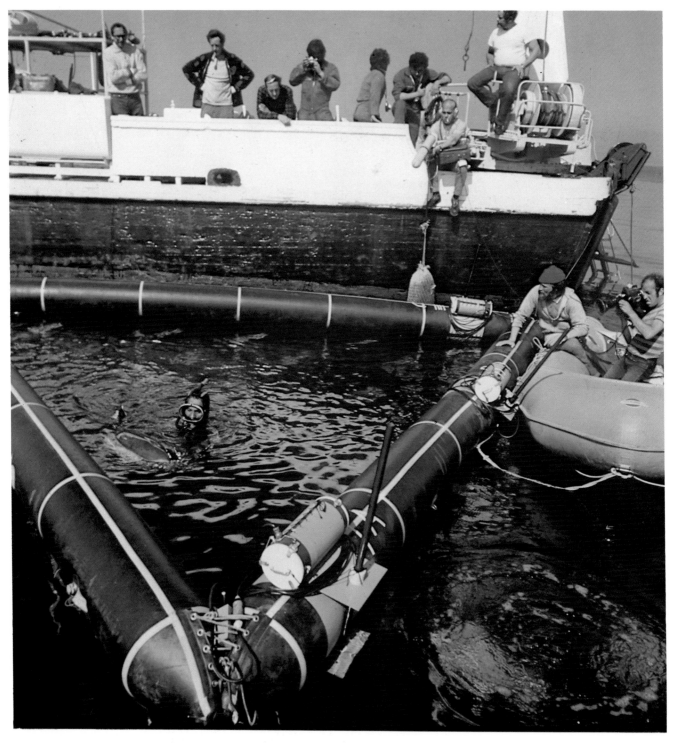

(Above) Falco joins the dolphin in our triangular floating pool.

(Right) Once in the floating pool, the captured dolphin begins to make sounds. Notice the **bubbles** rising from the animal's blowhole.

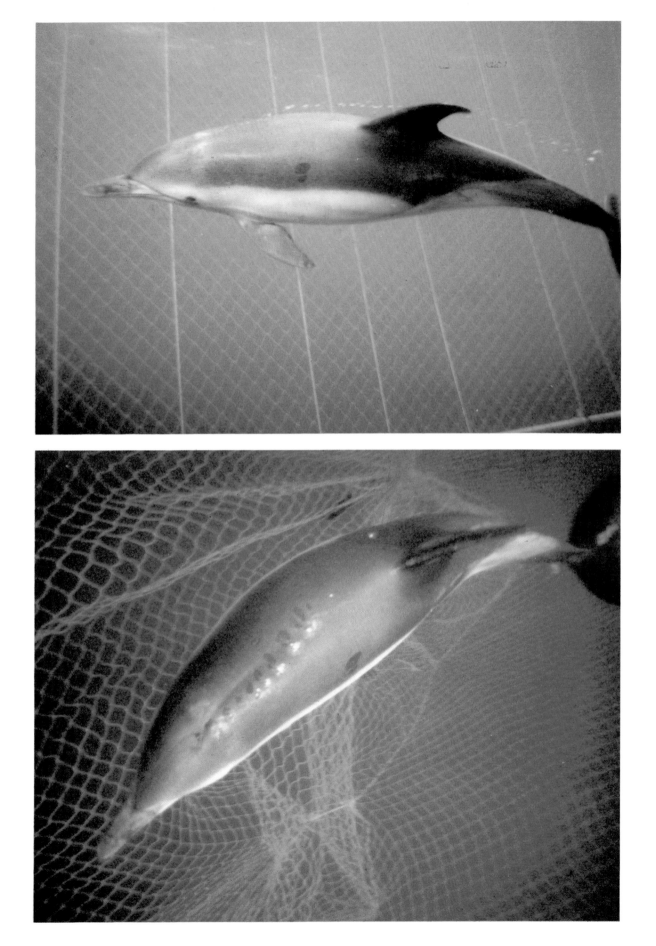

intention of turning these dolphins into performing animals. At the time, all we were interested in was using the tank's acoustical equipment to maximum advantage in order to record the sounds of dolphins living in circumstances which approximated freedom.

On one occasion, we left the female (who, by then, was quite tame) alone in the tank. *Calypso* then moved a fair distance away, for the sounds of our engines and of the propellers turning interfered with underwater sound recordings.

We hoped that the dolphin, left to herself in a tank in the sea, would call to other dolphins, and that a school would be attracted by her cries. And that is exactly what happened. As the dolphins approached, our sound engineer recorded their calls. The animals came to a halt some thirty feet from the tank — undoubtedly listening to what the female was telling them. But what was she saying? "Help me"? Or "Swim away, these creatures are dangerous"? We do not know. In any event, after a short time, the school of dolphins swam away and the female, perhaps disappointed, fell silent.

We were surprised that the female dolphin never attempted to leap over the side of the floating tank. Certainly, she would have been able to do it easily enough. In aquariums, dolphins sometimes move from one compartment in a tank to another simply by jumping over nets in one leap. But these are obviously dolphins who are accustomed to captivity. It seemed likely that our dolphin had no idea that a barrier might be passable. She was accustomed to the vastness of the sea. Anything that loomed before her, therefore, was something strange and unfamiliar. Never, during our observation of dolphins on this expedition, did a single dolphin attempt to jump out of the tank — despite the fact that an adult dolphin is capable of leaping to a height of ten feet. Sometimes, our dolphins inspected the net closely, but they always ended by swimming away from it. They seemed afraid that, if they pushed against it, they would become entangled.

Animals not yet deformed by captivity were necessary for the kind of experiments that we had in mind. We intended to place blinkers over the female dolphin's eyes so that we might observe how she would guide herself when she was sightless.

The dolphin allowed us to put the blinkers on her, but the kind of blinkers that we were using obviously were uncomfortable for her. She rubbed herself and thrashed about and was evidently unhappy. We therefore removed the blinkers.

Albin Dziedzic had another pair of blinkers, which attached by means of suction. We tried them on the dolphin, but these seemed as uncomfortable as the others. Everyone therefore set to work to make a blindfold of foam rub-

Before beginning our experiments in echolocation, the dolphin is blindfolded.

ber that would not hurt the animal. When it was finished, it was held over the dolphin's eyes by the strap from a diver's mask, which was passed under her neck. The animal showed no signs of discomfort.

Although deprived of her sight, the dolphin swam around the tank without the slightest hesitation and without touching the net. Falco was in the water with her, and he reported that there was no discernible sound as she swam. It was obvious that the sound waves, used by dolphins as "sonar," are emitted at a frequency which makes them inaudible to humans. Falco, however, felt that the dolphin's success may have been due to her knowledge of the location of the net and of the air bags.

To test Falco's theory, we installed iron bars around the tank at intervals of about two feet, then we dropped the net. The dolphin, wearing her blindfold, swam among the bars without touching them. With the net gone, there was no longer any barrier between her and freedom. Yet, she did not dare swim away. The fact that she could not see had most likely made her even more cautious than usual. Falco then led her back to the center of the tank.

The experiment was repeated several times as Jacques Renoir filmed it.

The following day, we put the same blindfold on the male dolphin and then turned him loose in the tank with the unblindfolded female. They swam side by side and were never apart for an instant, with the male swimming against the female and imitating every movement she made.

We then removed the female from the tank and returned her to her vat. The blindfolded male at first had no trouble swimming alone, but then, he grew tired. A current began to move through the tank, and it was enough to

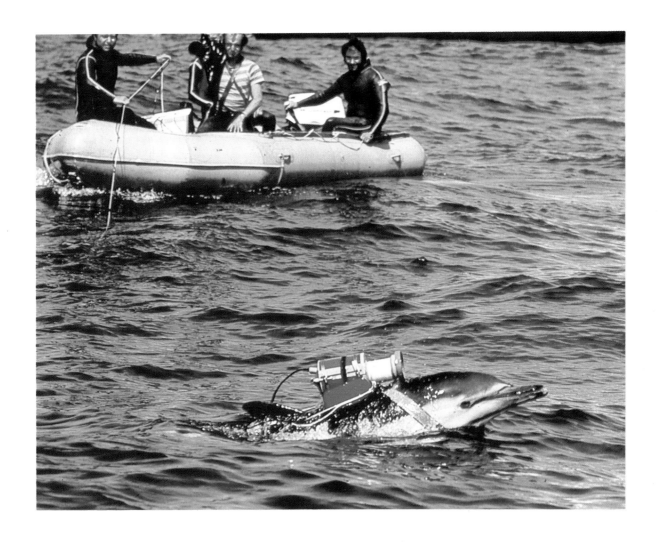

(Left) The blindfolded dolphin is about to find his way around the pool by means of sound.

(Above and below) A dolphin equipped with an underwater camera is freed in the hope that he will rejoin his school and film their movements for us.

send the dolphin against the net and to entangle him in it. The first time this happened, the animal tried desperately to free himself, but thereafter he knew that a diver would come to free him immediately, and he simply waited, motionless, for help to arrive.

Our friend Dziedzic was delighted by the results obtained by means of the floating tank and the system of hydrophones and other recording equipment with which it was equipped.

"I was able to get some absolutely incredible recordings," he reported later, "which it took me almost a year to analyze. I was able to follow the movements of a dolphin within the tank solely on the basis of his echolocation signals and by using the hydrophones to triangulate."

Some dolphins were better subjects than others and lent themselves very well to experiments as well as to filming. Nonetheless, we never kept any dolphin, even the best subjects, for more than two days. As soon as an animal showed the least indication of fatigue or weakness, we released him immediately. Falco was responsible for deciding at what point a dolphin was ready to return to freedom in the sea.

"Falco's diagnostic ability is really astonishing," Dr. François says. "He knows dolphins so well that he was able to know intuitively when they were not well. He simply looked at them. I think that he could tell somehow from the way an animal moved, just as some specialists are able to tell if a dog is sick by the way it walks or moves its spine."

It had occurred to me, on more than one occasion, that it would be worthwhile to attach a camera to a dolphin's back. I felt certain that one or more dolphin cameramen would be able to film some extraordinary scenes of the group life of dolphins. My plan was to have the dolphins return to their school, and then we would recapture them later and remove the cameras from their backs.

For our first venture, we chose a particularly large, strong animal. The capture had been difficult precisely because he was so strong. Then we put a harness on him and attached a camera to it. This procedure required a considerable amount of time, and when we had finished our work, the school was already one or two miles away. As soon as we released the animal, he headed directly toward his friends; but he did not catch up to them, either because he was exhausted by the ordeal of his capture or because the camera slowed his speed.

Several dolphins from the school swam toward him, but they remained a safe distance away from him and ended by returning to the school alone. When one animal sees something abnormal in the appearance or behavior of another animal, there is a tendency to avoid the latter.

On April 18, we captured a 275-pound male and, following the same procedure, we attached a camera to his back. The dolphin was able to swim, but his speed was hindered by the camera. His companions in the school swam past him, without waiting for him. Soon, our dolphin cameraman was alone in the sea. We recaptured him, removed the camera and harness, and then released him.

For each of these attempts, we used a different, fresh dolphin. But at no time did any of these animals succeed in swimming at his normal speed while carrying the camera. The harness and the socle impeded him, and the camera was obviously cumbersome. None of them managed to catch up to his school or to remain with his companions. And the film that was taken by our dolphin cameramen was totally without interest.

Our experiences with the camera-carrying dolphins lead me to believe that the Americans, who were trying to train dolphins to carry explosives, may have been disappointed in the results they obtained. It should be remembered, however, that they were working with Bottlenosed Dolphins, which, at a length of eight feet and a weight of over four hundred pounds, are more powerful than the Common Dolphin of the Mediterranean.

Still, we did not give up our attempts to find out how dolphins behave among themselves when they are alone in the sea. We simply turned to other methods. One of these was to equip a dolphin with a radio transmitter, following the example of William Evans of the Naval Undersea Research Center.‡ Once again, however, we found that the harness used to attach the transmitter to the dolphin's back hindered the animal's movements and reduced his speed. Even worse, the flexible antenna of the transmitter actually acted as a brake. Obviously, we had no trouble in finding our radio dolphin after the experiment, since he never succeeded in getting very far away from us in the first place, or in catching up to his school.

We made use of a completely different approach by having a diver attach a bag of fluorescein to a dolphin. (Even a small amount of this substance will leave a long, green trail in the water.) We thought that we would thus be enabled to see where he went and what he would do.

Our divers stood by, ready to relieve one another in following the dolphin's trail, and we were just congratulating ourselves upon our ingenuity when the dolphin suddenly dived and disappeared. Of course, it was impossible for the divers to see where the dolphin had gone — because of all the fluorescein in the water.

To this day, the secrets of the free dolphins are safe.

‡See Chapter Eight.

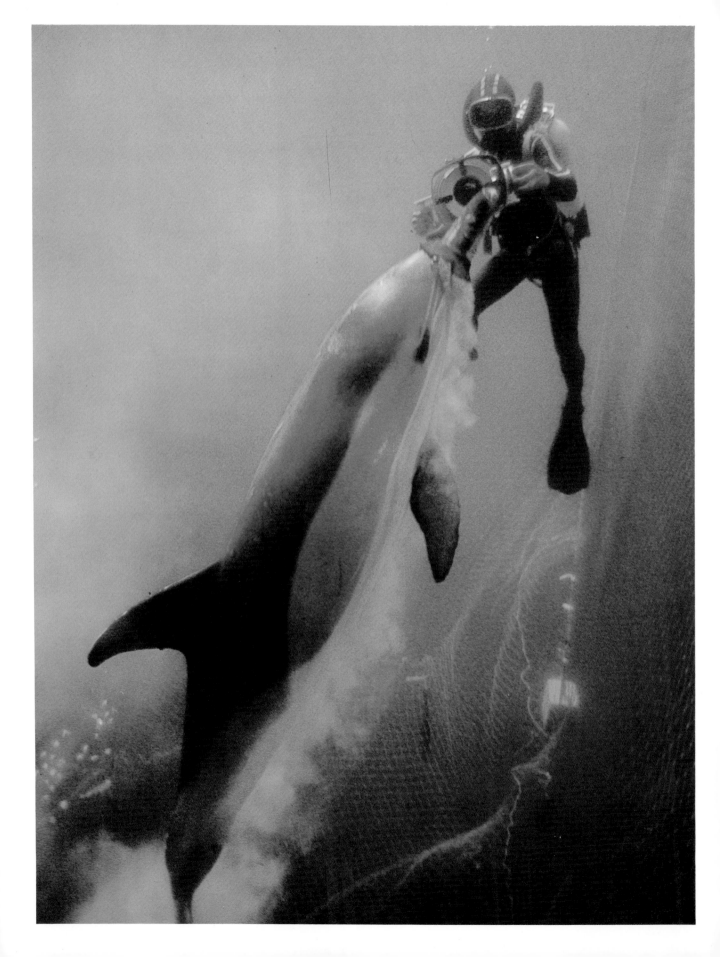

Chapter Seven

A WORLD OF SOUND

We were in the Mediterranean, off the coast of Spain, near Almeria. The weather was splendid, and we were able to lower the floating tank and record the sounds of the dolphins at our leisure. As in our previous recording sessions, we were using three antennaed hydrophones which had been arranged at three different angles in the tank. Two underwater television cameras had also been positioned in the floating enclosure, so that we could relate the animals' sonic signals to their movements.

On this occasion, there were three dolphins in the tank, all of them captured the previous day. They were perfectly calm and seemed already to have adapted to their tank. Their movements were normal, as was their respiration. Every twenty seconds or so, they rose to the surface to breathe.

The sea was absolutely flat, and *Calypso*'s equipment was able to pick up every sound from the tank without interference. By analyzing these sounds by means of our oscilloscope, and by synchronizing them with the images being received on our television cameras, we were able to put together an audio-

(Left) A diver marks a dolphin with a fluorescent chemical so that we can follow his trail in the water.

visual record which constituted a glimpse into the sonic world of the dolphins.

It is a world very different from our own. The first reason, obviously, is that it is a world of water, and also that dolphins are capable of emitting and perceiving sound at frequencies higher than those at which humans are able to hear. Moreover, the human ear is not equipped to hear in the water.

The noises which we picked up were weak and occurred at intervals. These sounds were the well–known "clicks," as they are called; and even "attention clicks," that is, infrequent, but regular clicks which indicate that the dolphin is attentive to its environment. It is that clicking sound which, when accelerated, repeated, and intensified, makes it possible for the dolphin to perform a sonic exploration of the world around him. He perceives the echo of the sounds he makes and, from them, is able to deduce the existence and the shape of the obstacles in the area. This is the "echolocation" system of the dolphins.

Contrary to what is commonly believed, the dolphin does not make continuous use of this system. When an animal is in a tank or pool, where the water is clear and where he is familiar with the location of the walls, he does not need it, or use it. The dolphin's sense of sight is acute, and a few clicks are sufficient to give him an adequate idea of the size of his tank. If, on the other hand, a dolphin is placed at night into a tank with which he is unfamiliar, a steady series of echolocation clicks will be forthcoming.

As soon as our three dolphins came near the nets which circumscribed the floating tank, the rhythm of sonic emissions accelerated noticeably. The larger openings in the nets, which were harder to locate, seemed particularly to disconcert them, and the clicks increased. These might be called "warning clicks." Then, as soon as we threw a fish into the tank, the clicks became much louder to enable the dolphins to locate their prey.

Obviously, the dolphin's echolocation system is not nearly so simple as the above description might lead one to believe. For one thing, the so-called "clicks" of the dolphin are not constant with respect either to quality or to loudness. Sometimes the signals are amplified and transformed into sounds so unexpected as to startle observers: grindings, clapping noises, squeaks, and so forth. And sometimes these same clicks are inaudible to us because they are emitted at too high a frequency.

It is noteworthy that in none of these variations does the dolphin make bubbles in the water.

A blinkered or blindfolded dolphin's sonar system is so acute that it enables him, at a distance of fifteen or eighteen feet, to distinguish between two fishes. This has been verified by experiment, and it shows that the dolphin's echolocation system is extremely sensitive. The ability to identify and classify an object, demonstrated by this experiment, obviously presupposes the existence of mental processes which go beyond simply locating a fish. A systematic choice between two objects presumes the ability to retain and to make use of stored data. In other words, it presupposes the existence of memory and of the ability to recognize forms by means of sonic silhouettes. We are far from being able to analyze and judge these abilities in the dolphin. But, for the moment, it may be said that "what is clearly evident, and what is most remarkable, is the dolphin's ability to adapt his sonar to the most varied situations."*

The Mysterious Organ

It is not known which of the dolphin's organs is used to emit the clicking sounds. One of the subsidiary mysteries is this: How can the dolphin make sounds without having vocal chords? There has been much discussion of this and other questions, but no positive answers have yet been produced.

For the past twenty-five years, thirty or so laboratories in various parts of the world have been engaged in breeding dolphins for study by perhaps a hundred specialists. Thus far, the only certitude we have is negative. We know that the dolphin's sonar signals do not come from its blowhole, and they are not accompanied by air bubbles — unlike the communications signals which we will discuss later.

It seems generally accepted that all of the precise data that a dolphin gathers when he is near his prey, or in the vicinity of an obstacle, can be obtained by a signal which passes through his snout.

Directional sensitivity plays a most important role in the echolocation process. In commercially produced radar and sonar systems, manufactured for the purpose of locating objects of various kinds, the finest possible sonic "brush" must be used. In the dolphin, the rostrum, or beak, assumes the function of the sonic brush when the animal is near its prey.

For long-distance acoustical perception, it is likely that the dolphin makes use of an organ common to other toothed whales: a hollow, located in the forward part of its head, which contains a fatty matter not unlike wax. Within this mass is a network of tissues which may act as an amplifier which serves to magnify sound at a higher rate than the surrounding tissue. The role of this "amplifier" (a role which is possible but over which there are disputes) would be to focus, by successive reflections, the sonic waves which occur with

---

*"Les systèmes sonars animaux," in *Congrès de Frascati*, Vol. I, p. 444. R.-G. Busnel, editor

(Above) The pool, with its electronic equipment, is left to float alone in the sea with its captured dolphin.

(Left) The pieces of iron in our floating pool are used in our echolocation experiments.

a certain incidence. (There are commercially produced directional antennae based on this principle.)

The clicks made by a dolphin for purposes of echolocation are of uncertain origin. Some say that the sound is produced by muscular action, just as the human larynx can be used to produce a clicking sound.

It is known that the dolphin's tongue plays no part in these sounds.† It should be noted, however, that the sounds are sometimes produced at the rate of 800, 1,000, or 1,200 clicks per second — faster than can be produced by any muscle, or any vibrating membrane, known in nature.

It is obvious that the dolphin's clicks, as important as they are in the animal's life, remain a mystery so far as man is concerned.

Ulysses

The range of the dolphin's clicks extends from audible low frequency to the ultrasonic range, the latter being at frequencies ten times higher than

†The bat, an aerial mammal, uses its tongue to modulate the sounds. Some bats produce the echolocation "clicks" with their tongue.

those audible to the human ear. There have been times, aboard *Calypso*, when the sounds made by the dolphins were audible only to Ulysses, our dog. If Ulysses understood what the dolphins said, he did not tell us.

The dolphin, thanks to its sonar ability, is able to find its way and to pursue its prey even in the cloudiest water. He is able to perceive sounds of 150,000 hertz. The question, however, is how, and by means of what organs, he exercises this extraordinary ability. His ears — which probably were once those of a land mammal, covered with fur — have been reduced to openings no larger than pinpoints. These open at the level of the dolphin's skin, just behind the eyes, and at the base of a small groove. The disappearance of the pavilion of the ear may be due to hydrodynamic exigencies, or it may be a consequence of diving and water pressure. At this point, we have no way of knowing the reason.

Researchers have the experimental proof that the dolphin perceives echoes and his own sonic emissions through the intermediary of his lower jaw. That jaw contains major nerve terminals connected to tissues which, in turn, are connected to the animal's complex and highly developed internal ear.

The theory of the lower jaw has been corroborated by means of an experiment. A dolphin, who was trained to find a sonic source in his tank, when blinkered, put his lower jaw against that source. To achieve this he had to lie on his side or on his back. This indicates that the lower jaw of the dolphin is highly sensitive to sound. The jaw contains a fatty, almost liquid tissue which transmits the sound to the internal ear. (The cochlea of the dolphin is about the same size as that of humans, but his acoustical nerve is much larger and contains thick contact fibers.) The dolphin is therefore especially well equipped so far as hearing is concerned, and it is not surprising that sensory life is controlled largely through its sonar. The dolphin is primarily an audial creature, while man is primarily a visual creature.

The dolphin, of course, is not the only animal who uses echolocation. Bats make use of the same system, and their sonar abilities have been studied at length.‡ Busnel and Dziedzic have demonstrated that a blindfolded Harbor Porpoise can detect and avoid metal wires measuring .2 mm. in diameter. For a blindfolded bat (*Myotis lucifugen*), the diameter of the wire detected is from .07 mm. to .12 mm.*

---

‡The ability of the bat to guide itself by echolocation was first observed 160 years ago by Lazzaro Spallanzani, an Italian scientist; but Spallanzani's discovery was forgotten for many years. See *Les systemes sonars animaux*, R.-G. Busnel, ed.

*The reason for the differences in performance by porpoises and bats very likely has to do with the different densities of their respective milieux.

At Narragansett Laboratory, Marie Poland Fish has recorded the underwater sounds of four hundred species of fish, twenty-five species of cetacean, and ten species of seals. Echolocation, therefore, is hardly a rarity among living beings. And the more zoology widens its field of endeavor, the longer grows the list of the animals who make use of it. There are birds and one fish as well as large mammals who live in water such as the hippopotamus. According to Dr. W. M. Longhurst, the hippopotamus can detect obstacles and prey by making use of sonar, without being obliged to emerge from the water when the visibility is less than twelve inches.

Even among humans, there are blind people who have learned to guide themselves by the echo of clicks made by their tongues or their canes — clicks which bear a strong resemblance to the clicking sounds made by the toothed whales.†

Professor Leslie Kay, of the University of Canterbury in New Zealand, basing himself on the ultrasonic guidance systems of dolphins and bats, has designed a sonar system for the blind: eyeglasses which emit ultrasonic waves, the echoes of which are perceived by the blind person. The latter is thus able to detect an object eighteen to twenty feet in front of him. The principle of this device is a "sonic image," transmitted by the eyeglasses, of the person's surroundings, which enables one to distinguish the nature of obstacles — a wall, a passerby, a street lamp, etc.

Communications Signals

As intriguing as the dolphin's echolocation system may be, we were even more interested in studying the sounds by which dolphins communicate with one another. For we know that dolphins "speak" to one another and that they send out calls and warning signals.

On *Calypso*'s television screens, we were able to observe the air bubbles which rise from the dolphin's blowhole when it sends out signals of this kind. Some of the photographs, reproduced in this book, show these bubbles trailing like strings of crystal beads behind the animals. Sometimes, a single large bubble rises above a dolphin's head. It is claimed that, when observed in

†See "Les systemes sonars animaux," in *Congres de Frascati*.

(Following page) A school of dolphins in the open water off Málaga.

aquariums, this release of one large bubble corresponds to a threat, a gesture of dissuasion, or a warning.

Dolphins sometimes also exchange whistling sounds. These sounds are communications signals quite distinct from the sonar whistles in series by means of which a dolphin locates an object or an obstacle. It is beyond doubt that dolphins communicate as do many other species (birds, insects, and fish, for example). Bees, as Von Fritsch has demonstrated, have a language which is danced rather than articulated. A bee who has discovered a particularly rich source of pollen is able to explain to other bees how far away the source is, in which direction, and how plentiful it is.

Voices in the Sea

Long ago, we learned to listen to the voices speaking in the silence of the seas. In the Far North, we have heard the extraordinary sounds of the Weddell seals, which are perhaps the noisiest of the marine mammals. Their cries reverberate under the arctic ice with a strangely pathetic, almost painful note.

In the waters off Bermuda, my son Philippe and our sound engineer, Eugène Lagorio, have spent entire nights taping the extravagant concerts of the humpback whales — the singing whales, as we call them. Sometimes, there were a hundred whales exchanging roars, bellows, and mews — words that I use reluctantly to describe the sounds of the humpback whales, for those sounds, in fact, resemble those of no other animal. They are sounds which resemble trills, and the clanking of chains, and the squeaking of doors. In my mind's eye, I can see Eugène sitting in his Zodiac, the glittering sky above him and the dark, eternal sea stretching endlessly around him . . . listening to those alien voices from the sea, voices which might have come from another universe and another time.

The fact that dolphins speak is not a recent discovery. Aristotle knew it twenty-three centuries ago. Since his time, however, the land-bound civilization of the West forgot that there were indeed voices in the sea — countless voices and sounds which, to us, are still incomprehensible.

For it is not only the dolphins who speak. All marine mammals do so, and the phenomenon is only rendered more striking by its universality.

An Unknown Source

How can the dolphin produce sounds, since it has no vocal chords? It is likely that, among most species, sounds are produced only in the water. A dolphin must be in a marineland or a laboratory, and he must have the benefit of a trainer, before he can learn (quite easily) to "speak" or "sing" in the open air.

With respect to the means of producing these whistles and squeakings, it must be admitted that we know next to nothing. The sound may originate at two or even three levels, in the laryngeal passage and in the nasal passages. The formation of sounds may be attributed especially to the epiglottis comprised of two tonguelike strips surrounded by a powerful sphincter. At the upper level, in the nasal passages, there are "nasal valves" also controlled by a large muscle. These valves are able to close off the nasal passage, and they may be responsible for originating sound by partially closing the passage, or by some controlled modification of it, so that a stream of air passes through and begins to vibrate.

The secret of this phenomenon lies between the laryngeal cavity and the blowhole. What is known for certain is that the dolphin has two separate means of making sound, for he can produce, simultaneously, clicks and sounds through his blowhole.

What is the meaning of these sounds, which we call communications signals or relational signals? Do dolphins really "speak" to one another? Do they have a language? These, obviously, are the questions that everyone is asking. And the answers given to them are far from positive.

Vocabulary

Before we can determine whether or not the dolphin's sounds mean anything, it would be helpful to distinguish them and enumerate them. Obviously, it has not been possible, up to the present, to do so with "wild" dolphins. In our aquariums and marinelands, however, where one can record and study such sounds over a period of years, it is believed that a wide range of sonic signals has been detected. Researchers have tried to analyze and assort these sounds, and they distinguish some two thousand different whistles. On that basis, one might conclude that the language of the dolphins is composed of two thousand sounds — or we might say two thousand "words." It is said that Racine wrote his tragedies with a smaller vocabulary than that. In any event, the active vocabulary of the dolphin would be somewhat greater than that of many humans.

Unfortunately for our understanding of dolphins, these signals are not always the same, even among individuals of the same species. Indeed, some

(Right) With the greatest of care, we attached a radio transmitter to the dolphin's dorsal fin.

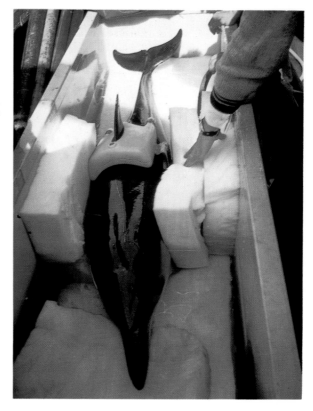

(Facing page) Then, the dolphin was turned loose in the sea.

of them seem to mean nothing at all, and those which have a precise meaning are quite few. It seems that certain series recur insistently, but we are unable to affirm that identical signals correspond to identical situations. Animals living in captivity in aquarium tanks have a much smaller vocabulary than was originally believed. And, so far as the "cries and grindings" that dolphins have been taught to make in the air, it is likely that they have no meaning at all for the dolphins.

David and Melba Caldwell have asserted that each individual dolphin has its own signal, a personal sound, which may be perceptible and even intelligible, but which is nonetheless untranslatable and untransmittable.

So far as the dolphin's famous "distress signal" is concerned, it is difficult to identify it with certainty, since it is not always the same in every case. John C. Lilly has recorded and transcribed this signal in the form of an inverted "V"; and Professor Busnel and Dziedzic have done the same in the form of an upright "V."

Of course, it may be that, if the distress signal differs from case to case, it is because it does not always have the same meaning. A harpooned dolphin, for example, may want to communicate any number of things: "Help!" or "Escape!" or "I am in pain" or "Wait for me" — at least, if we are willing to admit that these translations from man's language may correspond to the reality of an animal's behavior.

It is possible that dolphins living in their natural environment may be capable of expressing many things which elude us. As Professor Busnel has

pointed out, "Given our present knowledge of dolphins, we must admit that we know nothing of the semantics of the sounds made by dolphins."

Even so, it seems impossible to deny that dolphins make use of communications signals. They appear to be capable even of describing complex situations, of recounting what they have seen, to other dolphins. Reliable witnesses report cases in which individual dolphins are sent ahead by a school to reconnoiter a passage or to scout for danger. It would therefore seem that there must be communication of some sort — communication which, like communication among bees, implies an elaborate range of expression.

An Unsuccessful Experiment

Professor J. Bastian, of the Scripps Institution, designed an experiment intended to demonstrate that dolphins are able to exchange information — even complex information — among themselves. He placed two dolphins in a tank: a male and a female who had known one another over a long period of time. The tank was then divided into two parts by means of a net. A light signal was installed on each side of the tank. When the signal was given, each dolphin was supposed to press on a right pedal or a left pedal according to whether the light blinked or shone continuously. When a point was reached at which the dolphins' response was 97 per cent satisfactory, the light signal on the male dolphin's side of the tank was disconnected. Yet, the male continued to respond satisfactorily by means of information provided by the female.

The two animals seemed to exchange numerous acoustical signals while in the tank, and these signals were picked up by the experimenters by means of hydrophones and then recorded on tape.

In order to ascertain whether the information passed from the female to the male was indeed communicated through these signals, Professor Bastian separated the dolphins by soundproof neoprene panels. The male's responses were then satisfactory only in 54 per cent of the cases. But as soon as an opening was made in the panels, the male's performance leaped to 86 per cent satisfactory.

Thus, it was demonstrated that dolphins are able to communicate, and that one animal can explain to the other what must be done in a particular instance.

So far so good. Yet, we must remember that, when dealing with dolphins, very little, if anything, is what it appears to be. Professor Bastian's experiment was repeated — and failed. Bastian himself no longer believes in the validity of the experiment. He now believes that some unintentional exterior signal indicated to the dolphin what he was supposed to do. And that stimulus, of course, has negated all the data of the experiment.

It is true, nonetheless, that a captive dolphin communicates to a newly arrived dolphin everything that the latter must know to live in the tank, and everything that he must expect or tolerate from his human captors. Aboard *Calypso*, we have had ample opportunity to observe this phenomenon in our floating tank.

This does not necessarily presuppose an "exchange of thoughts" between two animals. The behavior of a new dolphin in an unfamiliar situation may be explained by imitation — a process readily observed, in a highly developed form, among chimpanzees. In this instance, one dolphin would swim slowly around her tank, showing its boundaries to another dolphin who had just been placed into the tank. The latter would follow the first dolphin closely. Rather than an exchange of thoughts, therefore, there would be an exercise in social help.

Dialogue

Killer whales have an acoustical system at least as well developed as that of dolphins. T. C. Poulter, an eminent specialist, has provided us with an account of conversation between a captured specimen and a group of killer whales which remained at liberty.

In 1966, Edward I. Griffin, Director of the Seattle Aquarium, purchased a twenty-three-foot killer whale, weighing four tons, from two Canadian fishermen for the sum of $8,000.‡

The animal was located at the mouth of the Bella Coola River, near the village of Namu. In order to get him to Seattle, it was necessary to manufacture a gigantic net supported by forty-one empty oil barrels. The whale, enclosed in the net, was then towed from the mouth of the Bella Coola to Seattle. Throughout its two-week journey southward in the Pacific, this bizarre convoy was escorted by a school of killer whales. A male and two females — perhaps the family unit of the captured specimen — exchanged whistles and cries with the captive in what can only be described as a dialogue. But what kind of dialogue? We have no way of knowing. What did they say? Were the sounds calls, or complaints, or expressions of emotion? Were they sounds of encouragement and advice? In any event, the captive killer whale, though responsive and obviously sensitive to these whistles, never once attempted to escape from the net. The only indication of his nervous state consisted in movements of his dorsal fin.

Calls in the Night

During our expedition in the Mediterranean, we attempted to learn at least whether a captive animal could carry on a conversation with the school to which he belonged. We therefore captured a female dolphin and placed her in the floating tank. *Calypso* then moved away, leaving the dolphin alone in the tank. We remained at a distance of six and a half kilometers (about four miles) from the dolphin, but we were in constant contact with the tank by radar and radio.

In the middle of the night, the isolated dolphin began to make sounds. These were not ultrasonic noises. They were perfectly audible to us; and Albin Dziedzic and other experts in animal acoustics described their reception as perfect.

We were surprised by the persistence of the sounds made by our captive dolphin. And we thought that we sensed in her "voice" a certain note of emotion, of pathetic appeal. Her cries intensified and resembled those of a wounded animal. Was it a distress signal?

‡See *The Whale: Mighty Monarch of the Sea*, by Jacques-Yves Cousteau and Philippe Diolé. Doubleday & Co., Inc., New York, and Cassell, London, 1972.

Two captured dolphins swim side by side in the floating pool.

(Right) Experiments in the pool are filmed by *Calypso*'s cameramen.

The female's cries were of such a wide range that our tapes of them represent truly an embarrassment of riches. Every indication is that the dolphin was calling in the night to the school from which she had been separated. If so, her efforts were not in vain. The school came, and other cries resounded in the dark water. But, as we have often observed on such occasions, as soon as the school understood that there was nothing it could do for its captured member, it fell silent and swam away.

A Non-Language

It should be kept in mind that the school of dolphins, even though it did nothing, nonetheless came to see what had happened. Therefore, there must have been a moment during which information was exchanged between the dolphin in her tank and the dolphins in the open water. But does this exchange imply the existence of a language, in the sense in which linguists accept that term?

"No," says Professor Busnel. The dolphin's sounds were merely relational acoustical signals. They were indeed signals, but not language. They were composed of elements which cannot be broken down; and those elements cannot be assembled according to the rules proper to language, that is, into combinations forming words and phrases. For language does not consist essentially in signals, however numerous, but in the ability to put these sym-

bols together according to a system which engenders a more or less unlimited number of combinations. This is what is known as "syntax." But when two dolphins communicate, they make use of a single signal, or of successive unrelated signals. This is what specialists call a "pseudolanguage," or a "protolanguage," or a "zero-syntax language."

It is not impossible that, someday, dolphins may arrive at a true language. For the present, however, we have no proof either that dolphins speak, or that they are capable of speaking.

Moreover, language is expressive of abstract notions: the past, the present, and the future. This is what characterizes human language and also what makes it possible to extend the human vocabulary to the infinite. We have no experimental proof, at the present time, that free dolphins are capable of devising a vocabulary, or that they are able to increase their capacity for expression.

Finally, language depends in large measure upon culture, life styles, and environment. It is possible that dolphins, living at close quarters with humans, may come to acquire some sort of language. Language can be learned over a long period of time. A human infant normally does not begin to speak before the age of two or two and a half years. What is required is an intimate common life with the mother and the affectionate monologue concomitant with that life. (This, in effect, was what occurred with Jean Asbury and Dolly.) We know, for example, that children left to themselves — "wolf children," as they are called — do not speak and cannot learn to speak once they pass a certain age.

The American researcher J. C. Lilly claimed to have taught English to dolphins — a claim which was strongly contested and criticized in scientific circles, notably by a Soviet scientist, L. G. Voronine. Lilly asserted that the Bottlenosed Dolphin was capable of imitating the human voice and of learning words which designated objects. Since that time, many experiments in American laboratories have shown that dolphins are capable — as Lilly claimed — of producing aerial sounds which some authorities have assimilated to imitations of the human voice in a different acoustical register. And Dr. Lilly was probably quite right in thinking that he heard, on a tape, the sound of a dolphin imitating the laugh of Lilly's secretary. However, no one has observed a similar phenomenon since that time.

Because dolphins have no vocal chords, however, the sounds that they make resemble whistles more than words, and one must have much patience to be able to recognize a word like "ball" or "hat" in the sound emanating from the blowhole of a dolphin.

There is nothing particularly astonishing in the fact that a trained dolphin is able to "fetch" a hat, a ball, or a ring floating in its tank when the name of the object is spoken. This may merely be the result of training, of voice obedience — as it is in trained dogs. The animal would learn the sonic signals which are first of all the symbols of objects and then the symbols of actions. It has been experimentally demonstrated that, in practice, the dolphin relies more upon the trainer's gestures than upon his words.

This limited success does not necessarily imply that there is a possibility of a "dialogue" between man and animal. The actual communications among dolphins, or between men and dolphins, are programmed and limited, whereas language in its proper sense is a non-determined operation — that is, an open operation in the course of which the speaker is free to combine, in an unpredictable order, the signals at his disposal.

The crux of the problem is to determine whether or not dolphins will be able to "combine" in this way one day. We know that a chimpanzee has only recently succeeded in doing so. The young animal, raised by a human family, is able to express abstractions: the past and the short-term future. He invents gestural signs.* He is able to associate sounds in a logical manner in order to communicate a simple, but new, idea. He combines signals so as to arrive at an expression more complex than the one that he has been taught. He *creates*. This particular chimpanzee, therefore, has a language. It is, of course, an individual language and one which is operative only between the chimpanzee and the human who created the language.

Primates apparently have outdistanced dolphins on the road leading to human mental activity. There is no reason to believe that the dolphin may not catch up to the chimpanzee. Experiments with primates have been going on for much longer, and are much more advanced, than those with marine mammals. We are in an era of new knowledge with respect to the brains of primates.

Dr. Dreher, in California, has taken a different tack from that adopted by Dr. Lilly. Instead of trying to teach dolphins to speak English, he has tried to learn "dolphinese." He isolated several whistle signals, which he then reproduced in an aquarium. These signals seem to have a definite meaning. However, it has not been possible to draw any positive conclusions from this experiment.

The whistles made by dolphins are modulations in frequency. There are

---

*At the University of Oklahoma, Professor Allen Gardner and his wife have taught the deaf-mute sign language to three monkeys. The animals are able to put together simple sentences by combining nouns and verbs. Professor Rumbaugh has taught a monkey to operate a computer keyboard, and the monkey is able to put together sentences in Yerkish — a language of geometric designs. In a similar experiment, Professor Premack and his wife, using colored blocks, have succeeded to teaching a monkey an optic language.

whistled languages among human beings which make use of the same kind of modulations. Professor Busnel has made a study of whistled languages still in use in various parts of the world: at Kuskoy, in Turkey; in France's Ossau valley, at Aas; and above all on La Gomera,† one of the Canary Islands; and in Mexico. Whistled languages are used in areas where the human voice is lost in the wind, or where it does not carry because of topological barriers. At La Gomera, for example, the cliffs are so steep that the natives invented a whistled language as a means of communicating so as to avoid having to climb up and down the cliffs or walk around them. Whistlers on Gomera "speak" at distances of up to six miles. The record, it seems, is eight miles.

There is a remarkable analogy between the "sonagrams"‡ of the whistled languages and those of the underwater whistles of dolphins. The dolphins' sounds represent the same kinds of modulation, though their modalities are much more limited and are produced at a much higher frequency.

An analogy between physical structures therefore allows one to hypothesize that the whistling sounds produced by dolphins could, in theory, be used as the phonetic elements of a true language.

To the extent that the dolphin's sound-modulations are variable (modulations which, unfortunately, have not yet all been recorded), one is justified in thinking that they constitute a system of acoustical communication analogous to that found among many other animal species. Nonetheless, even if we concede the existence of a certain vocabulary — the extent of which is unknown — we still lack a vital element in deciphering that vocabulary. As Professor Busnel says, "We have no Rosetta Stone to give us the key to the dolphin's whistles." That is, even if we assume that each whistle has a particular meaning, we have no way, at present, of knowing what that meaning is.

It is known that whistled human communication may be, and is in fact, a prop for language. On La Gomera, a whistler — a *silbador* — can express formulas like the following: "Don't forget to buy a loaf of bread on your way home tonight," or, "Take the sheep to the meadow up there." Such a language, obviously, functions as well as one which makes use of words.

The point, as made by Busnel in Washington, is that if we are going to teach a language to a captive dolphin, it would be better to use a whistled language than a vocalized, articulated language. A whistled language is one

---

†Many other whistled languages are used around the world: in Oubangui and in the Island of Fernando Poo, in the Gulf of Guinea, where the "Bubis" use a very elaborate language by blowing in whistles.

‡The graphic transcription of frequency, time and intensity, by means of special devices, of sounds produced.

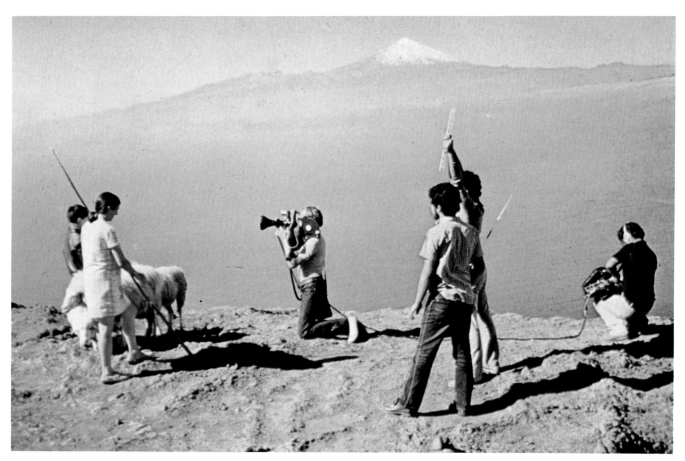

On the island of La Gomera, Jacques Renoir films the natives who make use of a whistled language.

which a dolphin would find it easier to perceive, analyze, and repeat.

It may seem an idle dream to think of communication between dolphins and human whistlers; but it may also be the beginning of a communication between the two species. For whistled languages represent a "language skeleton" which is adequate to express what one wishes to say. This mode of expression may be the vehicle of human communication with dolphins — so long as dolphins have something to say. And that is the real problem.

It is necessary, nonetheless, to translate our vocalized language into a whistled laboratory language as a means of starting the linguistic apprenticeship of dolphins. In this way, we would be able to teach them signals which would not necessitate the use of organs (vocal chords) which dolphins do not possess, and which would be contained within the dolphin's own acoustical register.

W. Batteau, an American acoustician, became interested in this idea and, with Professor Busnel's approval, built an electronic device capable of converting the sound of the human voice into a whistled voice. This machine was used in an experiment with two dolphins in Hawaii. After several months of work, it was shown conclusively that the dolphins were capable of assimilating this whistled language. It was demonstrated that they were able to learn, to memorize, and to repeat twenty-six different messages. However, the dolphins had not reached the point where they were able to associate the sonic signal with the object which it signified. At that point there was a tragedy. Dr. Batteau was drowned off Hawaii, and the experiment was abandoned.

After having placed much hope in the possibility of a dialogue with dolphins, we must recognize today that our projected dialogue was perhaps a dialogue of the deaf, or at least an illusion. At the moment, research has paused so that we may take stock of where we are. It has occurred to us that, before being able to "talk" to dolphins, it might be better to get to know dolphins better and, above all, more objectively. This, no doubt, will be the work of several years.

It is our own firm opinion that present studies of the intelligence and the sounds of dolphins are violated by the conditions in which they are carried out. Captivity represents a dramatic handicap. The shock experienced by these sensitive animals, at the trauma of capture, disturbs them profoundly. In captivity, they are given shots of antibiotics, stuffed with vitamins, and fed protein compounds. These dolphins — who are usually adults — are wholly without preparation for this kind of treatment.

Moreover, the species most often used for study is the *Tursiops truncatus*, or Bottlenosed Dolphin, because the Bottlenosed is more robust and more docile in captivity. But he is not necessarily the most intelligent of the dolphins. The ability to learn, to imitate, and to obey, which the Bottlenosed possesses in a marked degree, is surely not a definitive indication of intelligence. Indeed, this ability may complicate research rather than facilitate it.

The fundamental problem of captivity is one of space and freedom. One can only imagine the suffering of an animal enclosed, even for a short time, in a container where there is barely space for its body. It is true that captured dolphins are placed into larger tanks as soon as they arrive at the aquarium or marineland to which they are destined. But it is equally true that, in these tanks, the slightest sound the dolphin makes is echoed from the tank's walls. The animal therefore moves in water filled with incomprehensible echoes. Yet, we know that sound plays a primordial role in the life of a dolphin. We can only conclude that a dolphin in such an environment must exist in a state of total disorientation.

In our marinelands, dolphins find companions in captivity. They do tricks. They participate in shows. They have fans. But the behavior patterns which they develop in these conditions have very little to do with those which obtain when a dolphin lives at liberty in the sea.

We have succeeded in creating a personality common to captive dolphins. And it is that personality that is being studied, without taking into sufficient account that we are dealing with animals that have been spoiled and perverted by man.

It may be said that we have studied dolphins in captivity only because there was no way for us to study them in the sea. Yet, it has always been our intention, aboard *Calypso*, to do precisely that: to study marine life in its natural environment. We learned, at the very beginning of our efforts, that it was extemely difficult, but not impossible. We have succeeded on two separate occasions. Given the time and the means, this approach should at least be tried. It would certainly provide us with some unexpected information on the social life and behavior of dolphins.

The method we used during our expedition in the Mediterranean represents a compromise. It certainly is by no means an ideal solution, but it may offer the advantage of a rather good opportunity for observation.

Dolphins captured very quickly and painlessly were not made to undergo the ordeal of imprisonment in a concrete tank. Our floating tank probably reduced to a minimum the stress which is so harmful to dolphins. Our three inflated air bags supported a net which was almost forty feet deep. This space was sufficiently large for a dolphin to feel practically free. They were in their proper *milieu*, that is, in the sea. The net, with its widely spaced knots, allowed them to see the water around them, to see other dolphins, and to hear them. They were not isolated, as they would have been in an unfamiliar environment.

It is true that the dolphins were obviously somewhat alarmed at their capture. But they did not have the opportunity to adapt to captivity, or to be deformed by it, for we never kept a dolphin in the tank for more than two or three days. Often, they were detained for much shorter periods than that. Some of them were set free on the same day they were captured, or during the night, after one experiment.

We always hoped that the group remained in the area, for we had an idea of how desperate the "prisoner" could feel if its calls were not heard. We already knew that dolphins were social beings. They are extremely attached to one another. But we had particularly striking proof of the attachment, in the vicinity of Málaga and Gibraltar, during our Mediterranean expedition. It is difficult to imagine the degree of comfort that one dolphin is able to give another in captivity. As soon as two dolphins were alone in their tank, their behavior underwent a transformation. They swam side by side. They rubbed against one another. And none of these manifestations seemed to have sexual characteristics. One might say that dolphins have an intense need for affec-

Dolphins have no sense of smell and no "scent." In order to recognize one another, they must touch — as this male and this female are doing.

tion. Their emotional lives are highly developed.

Perhaps the best procedure would be to capture two dolphins simultaneously, both from the same school, so that the bond of affection between them would already have been formed in the sea rather than in a tank. The two dolphins would not necessarily have to be a couple. The emotional bond between individuals of the same sex seems stonger and more durable than that between male and female. We have observed that males in the sea do not swim with the females. The two sexes associate only during the mating season. Then, as soon as mating has taken place, they lose interest in one another. It is possible that we will find dolphins are more amenable to friendship than to love. . . .

Chapter Eight

THOUGHT IN THE SEA

It was morning. Aboard *Calypso*, everyone was absorbed in his work. The mechanics were disassembling an outboard motor under their green canvas shelter on the aft deck. The cameramen were working on their underwater camera. On the bridge, Jean-Paul Bassaget and Chauvin were bent over their charts, and, behind them, the radioman was performing the mysterious rites of his office. A typical workday.

The sea was like a pond under a sky ablaze with sunlight.

Then there was a shout: "The dolphins!"

It came from Francois Dorado, who was repairing the Zodiac on the aft deck. The fact that he shouted "The dolphins!" rather than a simple "Dolphins!" is significant. To us, these mammals are indeed *the* dolphins, and an encounter with them is a happy event, an event which involves its own rites and requires an immediate series of interventions on our part.

Instantly, everyone aboard *Calypso* swung into action. Prezelin, Bonnici, and Delemotte rushed to the prow, from which vantage point they could observe the dolphins more closely. Delcoutere raised the hatch leading to the observation chamber and disappeared down the stairwell so that he could watch the dolphins beneath the surface. On the bridge, Bassaget and Chau-

vin were watching them through binoculars. It was a large school — large enough, certainly, to make it worth our while to investigate. Bassaget ordered the engines cut, and *Calypso* now moved noiselessly through the water on her own momentum.

All around us there were dolphins, their dorsal fins plainly visible above the silken surface of the sea. One of them leaped from the water, and, for a moment, the graceful arch of its light gray body flashed in the sunlight. In the blue immensity of sea and sky, the point at which *Calypso* had come to a halt seemed a privileged space, a tiny enclave reserved for the meeting of dolphins and men.

I have often wondered why these encounters with dolphins have always taken on a festive appearance among us; why everyone aboard *Calypso* is suddenly so joyful and enthusiastic. It is certainly not because we are unaccustomed to contact with marine animals. We have dived with them for the past quarter century. We have played with groupers in the Red Sea, with octopuses at Seattle, with humpback whales at Bermuda. . .

The divers would say: "It's not the same thing at all. Groupers are ugly, and octopuses are alien. Whales are too big. But dolphins are beautiful, and they're just the right size — hardly bigger than humans, and much more agile."

All that is true. But I know that there is more to it than that. When we meet dolphins, it is like meeting friends, or relatives. We feel that they are beings with whom we share the secrets of the sea. *Calypso*'s divers are proud of their intimacy with the sea, and dolphins are living symbols of the unusual life that they lead. No, they are more than symbols: they are witnesses.

A Long Experience

Perhaps it will not be taken amiss if we say, in all modesty, that we know more about the behavior of free dolphins than anyone else. Other observers have confined their observations to dolphins in marinelands, aquariums, and laboratories. But, for the past twenty-five years, *Calypso's* team has encountered, followed, and observed dolphins in the sea — something that has been possible to no other team. Our advantage has been, obviously, that we have observed dolphins in their natural environment. That is, in the open sea. No aquarium, no tank in a marineland, however spacious it may be, can begin to

(Left) Even though we never keep dolphins for more than a short while in our floating pool, they quickly become accustomed to the presence of our divers.

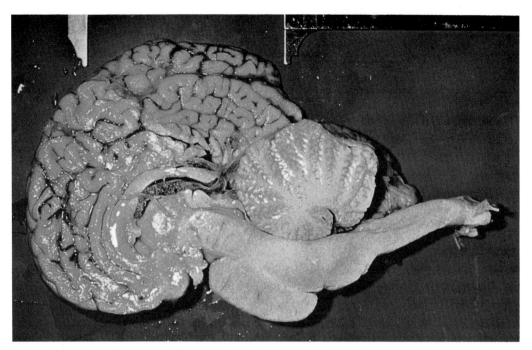

The brain of a dolphin. (Photo, Naval Undersea Center.)

duplicate the conditions of the sea. And no dolphin who inhabits one of those aquariums or one of those marinelands can be described as a "normal" dolphin. Therefore, the conclusions drawn by observing the behavior of such dolphins are often misleading when applied to dolphins as a whole.

Having said that, let us add immediately that twenty-five years of observing dolphins has not begun to reveal the secrets of these marine mammals. It is hardly likely that even another quarter century would suffice. Yet, we have learned enough to know for certain that the direct observation of animals living at liberty in the sea has a much greater value than the experiments and research undertaken with captive animals as subjects.

If there is one conclusion we can draw from our twenty-five years of experience, it is this: So far as the dolphin is concerned, the essential questions asked have been asked in the wrong terms. The result has been mass confusion, with the scientists on one side, demanding proof, and an enthusiastic public on the other side, weaving fables and anthropomorphism into a saga of science fiction.

It is our opinion, in fact, that all the efforts made to judge the behavior of the dolphin, and to measure his "intelligence" or to understand it, are exercises in futility.

In order to speak of intelligence, one must know what intelligence is. Intelligence depends upon the physiological and sensory equipment of a given species. If we base ourselves purely upon anatomy in this respect, we can say that the dolphin comes right after man on the scale of evolution. Indeed, the brain of the dolphin weighs more than that of a human — 1,700 grams for the dolphin, and about 1,450 grams for man. Only one human brain is known which weighed more than that of the average dolphin: that of Georges Cuvier, the French zoologist and palaeontologist, which weighed 1,800 grams. The size of the dolphin's body relative to that of its brain is only very slightly more than that of man.

The size of the Bottlenosed Dolphin's brain at birth is comparable to that of a human infant at birth. But the rate of growth of the dolphin's brain is considerably faster than that of the human brain.

What is most striking is the extraordinary exterior resemblance of the dolphin's brain to our own. There is a major development of the cerebellum and of the cerebral surface, a considerable size of the cerebral hemispheres, and a high cellular density. It is an extremely structured brain; and it is likely that, in comparison to other species of animal, the dolphin has at least the mental capacity of the chimpanzee — if not more.

With respect to the brain and the cerebellum — that is, the co-ordination of movements and the nerve center of the intellect — the relationship between the two is slightly better in the dolphin than in man. There are certain anatomical differences in the cortical structures of dolphins and man. For instance, the thickness of the cortex is not the same, the cortex of the dolphin being thinner than in the analogous areas of other large brains. Human intelligence depends primarily upon the cortex. The area of the cortex which has to do with sound is much larger among dolphins than among humans, while that having to do with sight is smaller. The olfactory lobe of the dolphin is atrophied.

But, as we shall see, though the dolphin may be lacking in certain sensory areas, his existing sensory equipment is capable of supplying abundant and precise information — information sometimes superior to that at man's disposal — which is necessary to life in the sea.

The physiological equipment of living beings does not absolutely or automatically imply a certain level of "intelligence." There is no direct correlation between the size and the structures of the brain.

Intelligence, in the sense that that term is generally accepted, is partly the product of a social and cultural environment. It is not merely a composite of our physiological possibilities. The intellectual potential of our brain can be activated only by a certain number of factors — the accumulation of knowledge by the communication of information, by means of one's life style, and so forth. Otherwise, it remains untapped.

The Four Conditions

Therefore, when we try to measure the "intelligence" of a monkey, or a

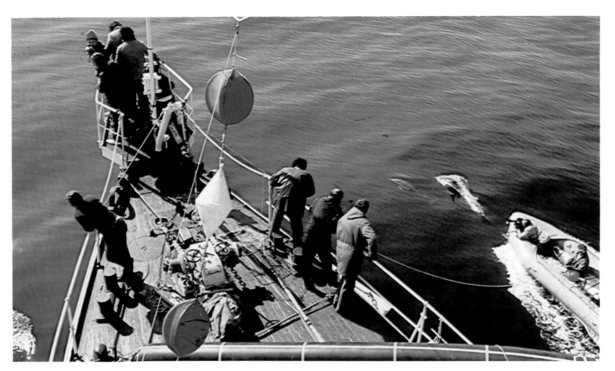

Jacques Renoir, in the Zodiac, films dolphins swimming around *Calypso*'s stem.

dog, or a dolphin, by basing our determinations on the weight of the animal's brain or on its neurological equipment, we are creating a problem which does not exist in reality. It may, in certain cases, be permissible to compare animals among themselves; but animals cannot be compared to man or measured by his standards. For man is the only being who preserves the four prerequisites necessary for the elaboration of a civilized society: the brain, the hand, language, and longevity.

Dolphins fulfill three of these conditions. Their brain is almost the equal of our own. And even though they may not have a language in the strictest sense of that term (although that remains to be proved), they are undoubtedly able to communicate among themselves. They live a sufficient number of years — at least twenty or thirty years, or as long as prehistoric man — to be able to acquire experience and knowledge. What they are lacking is the hand, which is the essential tool of civilization.

There are also other factors which come into play.

The offspring of humans are born helpless. They must be watched over and cared for over a period of years. That period is used by adults to educate the child and to initiate him into human language. Human children develop mentally over a span of years, and this development presupposes both the constant attention of the parents and an environment where virtually everyone speaks the same language, uses the same objects, and resolves most of the same problems by acquired formulas.

Infant dolphins, on the other hand, are already complete when they are born. Education can add little to what they are. Physiologically speaking,

A dolphin allows himself to be carried along by the wave from *Calypso*'s prow.

they are finished beings at birth.

Finally, dolphins do not live in the same element as man. Water is their home, and they cannot leave it without dying. This imposes a heavy burden on them, for it is water which turned the hand of their ancestor into a flipper.

The dolphin's struggle for survival in the sea has not had the same formative effect on him as man's struggle on land. "Cetaceans," says Alpers, "have lived in the sea, cut off from all contact with other mammals (except for man and sea lions) for sixty million years or more. During all that time, unlike monkeys, dogs, cats, elephants, and horses, they have not been compelled to share their environment with other intelligent or semi-intelligent animals. Their only companions, and their prey, have been fishes, who are their inferiors. We do not know what degree of intelligence they possessed when they first went into the water, or if that intelligence has increased or changed since the time when they changed their environment."

It is intriguing to speculate whether the potential which the dolphin possessed in one environment — on land — might not have been stunted in another environment. Is it possible that a mammal who was "off to a good start" on land has been spoiled by an easy, non-competitive life in the sea?

Sensory Equipment

The senses of the dolphin have developed unequally, and this is the reason why their relational lives are so different from our own. In certain respects, they are better endowed than we; and in others, they are inferior. Unlike ourselves, for example, and unlike most mammals, toothed whales are probably completely devoid of a sense of smell — a sense which plays such an important part in the lives of fishes.

So far as sight is concerned, dolpnins are superior to man and to fishes but approximately equal to other mammals. The fields of vision of the two eyes overlap considerably in a forward and downward direction, which makes possible the dolphin's stereoscopic vision. The eyes are extremely mobile and can turn upward, forward, downward, and even backward, along the dolphin's side. Even more remarkable, the dolphin's vision is as good in the open air as it is in the water. Trained dolphins can leap fifteen or eighteen feet into the air and seize a fish held in the mouth of their trainer. This trick presumes that the dolphin can go from subaquatic vision to aerial vision with exceptional rapidity and assurance. In fact, a captive dolphin's tricks in and out of the water, with balls and rings and fish, attest to his great visual acuity. Pilot whales and killer whales are capable of the same sort of performance and have the same exceptional vision. Man, on the other hand, is not well equipped to see in the water.

There are, however, blind dolphins: dolphins who live in fresh water, or in estuaries in India and in South America where the water is very cloudy, and whose eyes have atrophied. These dolphins depend on their echolocation system in order to locate and seize their prey.

The dolphin's acoustical equipment, as we have mentioned, is especially well developed. The dolphin's life is based upon constant acoustical exploration. He listens and watches constantly in the sea. Obviously, therefore, sight and hearing are the two senses which are most important to him. The auditory nerve (the eighth cranial nerve) is highly developed and is the largest of the cranial nerves. In the cortex, the auditory center is exceptionally large. And the dolphin's ear is modified for use in the water.

The sensory cells, which allow the dolphin to perceive the highest frequency sounds, are of large size, and each one has its own nerve fiber. (In man, several cells are in connection with one fiber.) The same nerves are equally developed in other animals, such as mice and bats, who depend largely on hearing.

According to Dr. Winthrop Kellogg, formerly Professor of Experimental Psychology at the University of Florida, the acoustical system of the dolphin "has undergone a remarkable adaptation in the course of geological time, and this marvelously sensitive organ is specially equipped to perceive vibrations in the water."

Experiments have shown that dolphins hear frequencies of 150 kilohertz, i.e., 150,000 vibrations per second. The limit of human hearing is 14 to 16 kilohertz, which corresponds to the sound of a strident whistle. The limit of monkeys is 33 kilohertz; that of cats, 50 kilohertz; and that of mice, 80 kilohertz. Only bats, at frequencies of 175 kilohertz, have keener hearing than dolphins.

Hearing undoubtedly plays a more important part than sight in the search for food, in the finding of directions, in the perception of depth, and in communication among dolphins. A blindfolded dolphin is able to skirt around a line stretched ten or twelve feet above the surface, simply by relying on his echolocation system.

The dolphin's sense of taste, which has been little studied, has not atrophied like his sense of smell. At the base of his tongue, the dolphin has numerous papillae containing taste buds similar to those found in man and in herbivorous animals. It is not known precisely what role taste plays in the sensory life of dolphins, but it is possible that the gustatory terminals which cover a part of their palate and tongue enable them to follow their schools and to detect the presence of certain fishes. As Bébert Falco has observed in our floating tank, dolphins open their mouths frequently. It may be for the purpose of obtaining certain information through their sense of taste.

A Marvelous Skin

No one who has ever touched the skin of a dolphin is likely to forget the silken, elastic, soft feel of it. The fact that the dolphin's skin is sensitive and delicate has a great influence on the animal's behavior, both because the dolphin is very cautious of any action that may damage its skin, and because, once a dolphin trusts a human, he enjoys being petted. All dolphin trainers and keepers are aware that the contact of the human hand, once a dolphin has come to permit such contact, is a decisive factor in training an animal.

In mating, or merely in their social lives, dolphins rub against one another, caress one another with their flippers, or even rub themselves against a brush in the tank or against the shell of a tortoise.

The dolphin's skin undoubtedly has much to do with the animal's "stunts" in the water, since it allows him to attain greater speed. The body is

(Following page) Although the dolphin was swimming at full speed, our Zodiac managed not to lose sight of him.

absolutely smooth. The ears are no more than minuscule holes. There is no scrotum. The dolphin's hydrodynamic lines, in other words, are perfect. Even at high speeds, their movement through the water causes little turbulence which would act as a brake. In the United States and in the U.S.S.R., studies have been undertaken to determine why the dolphin is able to move through the water with a minimum of resistance.

The skin's tegument and its fatty layer surely have something to do with this ability. Even more important are the longitudinal folds which are formed on the surface of the skin, while the dolphin is swimming. These folds help increase speed by eliminating turbulence. "These marvelous swimming machines," Professor Budker has remarked, "move as though by magic and are capable of producing ten times more power per pound of muscle than any other mammal." Indeed, experimentation with a Bottlenosed Dolphin has revealed that the power developed by a swimming dolphin was only about two horsepower. As early as 1936, Sir James Gray, of Cambridge University, pointed out the great disproportion between the power developed by the dolphin and the speed which was attained. Since then, this phenomenon has been known as "Gray's Paradox." Sir James observed that "the form given by Nature to the dolphin is more effective than that of any submarine or torpedo conceived by man."

Researchers have generally assumed that the secret of the dolphin's speed in the water has something to do with the animal's shape. In 1955, Max O. Kramer, a German engineer who was a refugee in the United States, asserted that it lay instead in a peculiarity of the dolphin's skin. He noted that the animal's exterior tegument, far from being impervious to the water, was permeable and that under it was a harder layer of interior fat about 1.5 mm. in thickness. This fatty layer covered a multitude of small vertical grooves filled with a spongelike substance which is absorbent in water and which can squeeze out four fifths of the water it absorbs. Kramer theorized that this "second skin," which is sensitive to pressure, was able constantly to absorb the oscillations which appear on the surface when a wave, or turbulence of any kind, is caused by water resistance.

Respiration

The respiratory rhythm of dolphins, and other toothed whales, varies according to the conditions in which the animals find themselves at any given time. It should be noted, however, that observations on this subject were made almost exclusively in laboratories.

When the dolphin is not disturbed, and is swimming in a normal manner near the surface, he breathes once or twice per minute. But when he is disturbed, excited, or frightened, the rhythm increases considerably and reaches a rate of five or six times per minute.

Before a deep dive, which may last seven minutes and probably longer, the dolphin hyperventilates his lungs by a series of deep, rapid breaths. This procedure increases the oxygen content of the lungs and facilitates the elimination of carbon dioxide.

Unlike man, a dolphin empties and then refills his lungs almost totally with each breath, even when swimming normally.

The depth to which dolphins can dive varies greatly according to species and even according to individuals who may be more or less trained. The Bottlenosed Dolphin normally swims at a depth of between 100 and 150 feet; but the celebrated Tuffy, who participated in Project Sealab, was accustomed to diving to a depth of 1,000 feet. And there is some evidence that dolphins descend to depths of perhaps 2,000 feet.

The tractability of dolphins has made it possible to use them in experiments which may contribute to an increased knowledge of the physiology of diving. One dolphin was trained to exhale the residual air in its lungs after his deep dives, while he was still under water. The air was exhaled into a funnel connected to a tank. It was therefore possible to study and analyze the composition of this air, which had been modified by deep diving.

To Sleep — Perchance to Dream

A dolphin cannot sleep for more than five or six minutes at a stretch without the threat of drowning. It appears that the animal, in its state of half-sleep, sinks slowly downward in the water, and then rises again without ever really losing consciousness. His breathing, unlike our own, is not automatic and unconscious. But, since dolphins are not subject to the effects of weight, it is likely that they need less sleep than humans do.

A sick or injured dolphin, if he is greatly weakened or loses consciousness, sinks and drowns. In such circumstances, dolphins help each other. An incapacitated dolphin is sometimes supported at the surface for hours, or even days, by one or two other dolphins.

When a school of dolphins begins to doze, it is quite likely that one or two individuals remain awake to act as guards. This is also the case among certain groups of land mammals.

I have witnessed the awakening of a school of sleeping dolphins off the coast of Africa. The school was spread over a fairly wide area, with the indi-

A Zodiac and one of our other small craft approach a school of dolphins.

vidual animals a good distance from each other. When *Calypso* drew near, one dolphin roused all the others by crying. The entire school was suddenly awake in the sea around us, and the water churned with their movements.

Mutual Assistance

The social sense of dolphins and their often remarkable behavior have sometimes given the impression that they help one another, and even that this mutual assistance is one of the laws of the school.

We have often witnessed scenes which attest to the social solidarity of which marine mammals are capable. Aboard *Calypso*, in the open sea, we have noticed that when a dolphin was injured, two or three other dolphins of the school approached to help him and support him. Meanwhile, the entire group came to a halt a short distance away, as though waiting to see what

Two free dolphins photographed while diving.

would happen. If, at the end of a certain time, the "relatives" or "friends" were not successful in getting the injured dolphin to rejoin the school, the school simply continued on its way. Those who had gone back to assist the unfortunate animal were obliged to swim after the school, for a dolphin cannot survive alone in the sea, away from others of his own kind.

If mutual assistance is a law among dolphins, it must be recognized that it is not an absolute law and that there are exceptions.

Here are two distinct instances, the first of the law and the second of the exception:

In 1962, during one of *Calypso*'s expeditions, with Busnel and Dziedzic, we tried to capture some pilot whales — animals particularly cautious and difficult to approach in the water. We were following them in the sea, trying to get near enough to use a light harpoon. Finally, we succeeded in placing the harpoon in one of the whales, but the Zodiac, in its haste to reach the animal, became entangled in the harpoon's line and was unable to move. The pilot whale then began to cry as loudly as he could. Almost immediately, two other whales arrived and positioned themselves one on each side of the wounded whale. They moved their bodies against his and, thus supported, the whale was able to free himself to swim away.

In 1965, Albin Dziedzic also tried, with a vessel of his own, to capture a pilot whale. He encountered a large school of them near Alicante and managed to harpoon a young male in the midst of the school. The whale dived immediately, but the harpoon line held firmly and the animal was unable to escape. He therefore began to cry very loudly. Although he was literally surrounded by innumerable pilot whales, not one of the other members of the school came to his aid. After a few minutes, several of the school dived, then returned to the surface, and the entire school swam away, leaving their wounded companion alone.

It should be obvious how dangerous it is to generalize about the behavior of toothed whales, and how that behavior can differ from instance to instance. It may be that the social hierarchy plays a role indicating the conduct of the group so that assistance is given to a leader, or to a female in danger, but not to immature young whales. This is obviously a hypothesis, since we are just beginning to learn about the social structures of pilot whales and about the impact of such structures on the lives of individuals in the school. We know only that such structures exist and that they are very likely of great importance.

Games

There is one activity of dolphins which, while not confined to them, never ceases to astonish us. I am referring to their games and to their love of play. Many other species of animal love to play — cats are a notable example — but dolphins, by the powers of observation they display and by the ingenuity they show, lead us to attribute to them a behavior not unlike our own. Perhaps it is because they show signs of a sense of humor while playing.

In the Florida Marineland, for example, a dolphin amused himself by making a surprise attack on some pelicans and pulling out their tail feathers, but without harming or biting the birds. And a female dolphin chose a sea tortoise as her toy, pushing it with her snout around the tank.

All trained dolphins seem to take pleasure in performing their stunts, but they also love to play among themselves. They sometimes spend hours throwing a fish, or a piece of cloth, or a ring.

One dolphin discovered that if he placed a feather near the water-outlet valve of his tank, the feather moved rapidly away, then stopped. He therefore repeatedly placed the feather in the proper place to watch it move away. Another dolphin saw what the first dolphin was doing and immediately took up the game.

We know that such behavior is not inspired by the boredom of captivity, and that it does not result from training, for dolphins also play when they are at liberty in the sea. They push any floating object before them — a piece of wood, or, like Opo, an empty bottle.

Dolphins also love to surf, and they allow themselves to be carried on the crests of waves, just as human surfers do. (In Florida, on at least one occasion, dolphins actually joined human surfers.) And, like humans, they wait for a particularly big wave.

This spontaneous behavior, which resembles playfulness and presupposes the existence of a well-developed spirit of invention, is sometimes considered as evidence of a highly evolved form of intelligence. And here, of course, we are once more face to face with a problem of our own creation.

Outside the Animal Kingdom

Much that has been written and said about dolphins tends to set them apart from other animals, to locate them somewhere outside the animal kingdom. The public looks on them as less than human, but as nonetheless in the process of becoming our equals.

Such an attitude has serious consequences with respect to our treatment of dolphins. In view of the intelligence of dolphins, we would have particular obligations to them. Beings so close to man would merit special consideration, particularly in the form of that respect due to brothers who are not our inferiors. To the physiological and psychological problems presented by dolphins, therefore, would be added a new problem, one of the moral order.

We should point out, first of all, that the reasoning in the above paragraph is specious. We have obligations not only to dolphins, but to all animals, and to all men. Man today is ready to believe in and to respect a moral animal, whether it is a horse, a dog, a cat, or a dolphin.

Physiologists, acousticians, biologists, and experts on cetacean life — all except Dr. Lilly — are of the opinion that dolphins are not essentially different from other mammals; that there is no natural difference between a dolphin and, say, a monkey or a dog.

This is an opinion which many people will find unsympathetic. We are inclined to attribute a kind of superiority to an animal whose brain weighs more than the human brain. At the same time, the social mores of the dolphins, comparable to those of man and of monkeys, seem to indicate the existence of a bond between us and them. It also inspires us with an affection and a curiosity which we do not feel for other animals. Indeed, it must be admitted that the relationship between man and dolphins is, above all, an emotional one.

The Affective Aspect

If our scientists can be blamed for any fault, it is that in their concern with objectivity, they have failed to give adequate consideration to those things which cannot be measured and analyzed. I mean, to the affection and devotion which dolphins seem to offer to man.*

The answer to that statement has been made already, and it will no doubt be repeated. "This aspect of sentimentality," say Professor Busnel and Albin Dziedzic, "was created by man out of his romantic illusions. Dolphins feel no more affection or emotion with respect to man than a dog does. Probably even less."

It would be possible to retort, or course, that the dog has been man's friend and companion for the past 60,000 or 100,000 years. The dog was created and formed by man. It is a product of human civilization. Whereas the dolphin, marooned in his aquatic world, isolated from us, was unable to experience a common life with man until very recently.†

It is only today, by reason of man's new curiosity about life in the sea, that we have taken an interest in the dolphin and have noticed that the dolphin has probably been interested in us for a long time. He mingles with swimmers, he rides children on his back, and he saves drowning humans.

Ten or twelve thousand years ago, dogs circled around neolithic campfires, seeking the company of man, warning him of the presence of wild animals, and trying to help him in the hunt. Today, the dolphin protects swim-

---

*Some of these emotional states are able to be measured. For species of so-called laboratory animals, there are tests which yield quantitative values. So far as the dolphins are concerned, however, since the number of subjects available for experiments is so limited, such problems have hardly begun to be studied.

†The exception may have occurred in the course of the Minoan civilization (2500 – 1300 B.C.), as we shall see in a subsequent chapter.

Two dolphins swimming side by side.

mers against sharks and helps fishermen find a catch of mullet. Who can tell what the dolphins will be to us in eight or ten thousand years? Will our remote descendants look back in wonder at the twentieth century, when dolphins were regarded as "mysterious" animals with strange ways and an even stranger "language"? Will our great-grandchildren perhaps wonder how we ever managed to survive in the sea without the aid of the dolphin?

Captain Cousteau and Professor Busnel in conference before *Calypso*'s closed-circuit television screen.

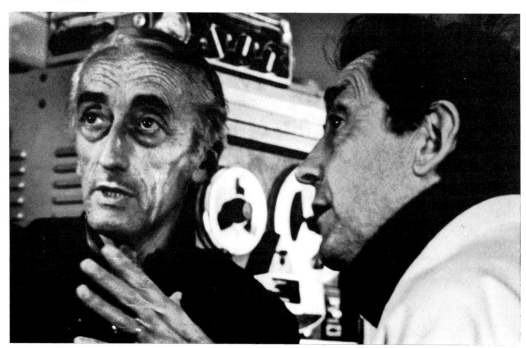

Chapter Nine

THE EDUCATION OF DOLPHINS

The docile nature of dolphins, and the fact that they have never bitten any-one, inclines many people to regard them as part of the human adventure and to make domestic animals of them. Thus, one or more species of cetaceans would become the marine equivalent of the horse or dog on land. For *Tursiops* is not the only marine mammal to have been revealed as a potential auxiliary of man. The pilot whale, as well as the killer whale, has also given evidence of qualities equal, if not superior, to those of *Tursiops.*

For over twenty years, toothed whales have been subjected to experimentation in numerous laboratories and in the thirty or so marine circuses. The first free dolphins to accomplish missions in the sea, assigned to them by man, were released in 1964.

It is clear that this vast effort has not yet allowed us to learn which of these animals is more suitable for collaboration with humans, any more than it has enabled us to reach a consensus on exactly what to expect of the marine mammals.

At the present time, the Bottlenosed Dolphin is highly favored for exhibition in the marinelands and aquariums of the United States. They are captured off the Florida coast and near the mouth of the Mississippi. The

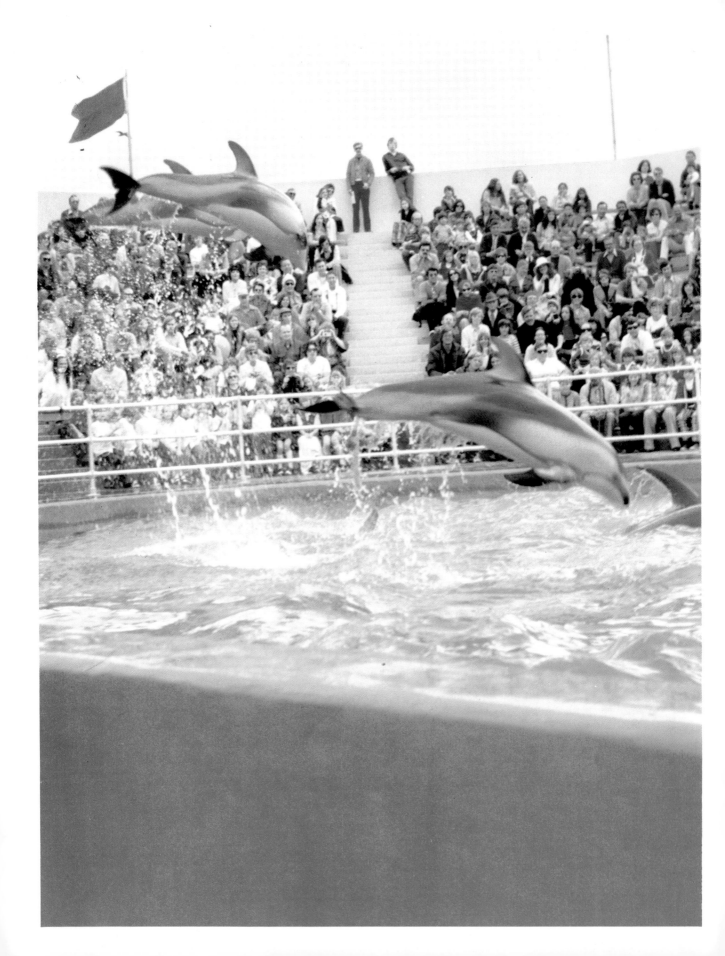

preference for the Bottlenosed is based upon the ease with which they may be trained. However, other species, such as the Spotted Dolphin (*Stenella*), make equally good students. Since 1970, a number of American establishements, particularly on the West Coast, have killer whales living in capitivity, and these mammals have given evidence of exceptional qualities. Caldwell cites the case of a "false killer whale" who, having seen a performance by dolphins, performed the same tricks as the latter without benefit of having been taught them.

The fact is that it is still too early to be able to know which of the marine mammals is most suitable for collaboration with man. They have simply not been tested sufficiently as yet. We should remember that it required ten thousand years or so for the animal breeders of the prehistoric and historic periods to create the domestic animals we have today. These helpmates are the end product of a very long process of selective breeding and crossbreeding. We have not yet even begun this process with marine animals. It is a task which presupposes a knowledge of all the available forms of toothed whales, whereas, in the Delphinidae family alone, we are aware of the existence of some forty-eight species. And there are approximately ninety species of "small cetaceans," including Delphinidae.

The Capture

A number of Americans have learned to specialize in the capture of dolphins in the sea and even in training these animals before selling them to aquariums and marinelands. One of the best known of these entrepreneurs was the late A. V. Santini. Santini pursued a dolphin in a speedboat, threw a net over it, then dived into the water to complete the capture by hand. It is said that Santini was able to calm and immobilize a dolphin simply by placing his hands on him. It is worth noting, in this respect, that some marine mammals cease struggling as soon as they sense that there is no hope of escape.

One trainer at Key Largo, Florida, sold fifty dolphins in an eight-month period. The price of a trained dolphin depends on the kind of performance he is capable of giving, but even an untrained dolphin in 1970 was priced at $400.

It often happens in dolphin hunts that animals are injured. Moreover, no

(Left) The dolphin show at the Palos Verdes Marineland.

more than one or two of every five captured are actually kept. Those one or
two are the dolphins who will consent to eat, or those who are young enough
to be amenable to training. The others are turned loose in the sea in more or
less good condition.

It is impossible to determine beforehand whether or not a particular
dolphin will be able to adapt to captivity. Professor Busnel reports that, in his
laboratory in Denmark, dolphins captured in the Baltic were literally eating
out of his hand ten minutes after they were taken, while there were others
who would accept no food at all.

The capture of dolphins for commercial purposes is now forbidden in the
United States, and the law prohibiting such capture is enforced with great
vigor. In France also, a decree was issued in November, 1970, at the request
of professors Busnel and Budker, which reads: "Considering the contribution
of Delphinidae to the ecological equilibrium of the seas and their value in the
area of technical and scientific research, it is forbidden to destroy, pursue, or
capture, by any means whatever, even without the intention of killing such
animals, all marine mammals of the Delphinidae family [dolphins and por-
poises]. These restrictions do not apply to operations undertaken solely for
purposes of scientific research."

Captivity

The behavior of dolphins in captivity varies from one individual to
another, as we have already mentioned, and cannot be foreseen. Such behavior probably depends on factors of which we are not yet aware. When a
dolphin is being captured, it is impossible to know whether he is a young male
who is dominant or dominated. We cannot determine his social status, or
even his age. This is the basis of the varying behavioral patterns which seem
so incomprehensible to us. The same holds true of primates, some of whom
adapt to captivity while others never resign themselves to it.

Falco's experiences, in trying to feed dolphins at the beginning of their
captivity, are common in all American aquariums. A keeper at the Florida
Marineland, exasperated at his inability to feed a newly arrived dolphin, began to bombard the unhappy animal with fish and even to strike him with
them. The dolphin opened its mouth and, inadvertently, swallowed one of
the fish. Whereupon he began eating the others voluntarily.

There are now several foods commercially available for marine animals,
just as there are for cats and dogs. These have a protein-compound base.
Captive dolphins eventually lose the habit of eating live fish. Caldwell gives

an account of a dolphin who was fed a live mullet. When the dolphin felt the fish squirm in his mouth, he was so overcome with terror that he dropped the fish and fled to the far end of the tank. The dolphin refused to eat for the next twenty-four hours. The Harbor Porpoises raised by Professor Busnel and his team were so accustomed to being fed by hand that they simply ignored the live fishes in their tank.

Animals like these, who wait for man to provide food for them and who give up hunting, are not very far from domestication.

Generally, the process of adapting to captivity takes place rapidly, within one or two weeks. It is unusual for a dolphin to try to escape, and he ordinarily becomes sufficiently accustomed to the presence of man that, at the end of several days, he will allow himself to be petted. Indeed, a captive dolphin often appears to seek out such contact.

Affection

It is extremely difficult to determine the exact nature of the bond between the animal and his trainer. Does a dolphin become attached to his master? Indeed, does a dolphin have a "master," in the sense that a dog has one?

All trainers maintain that they know their dolphins and that their dolphins know them. We do not really know whether training would be possible, at least from the standpoint of the trainer, unless there were an affective link between man and animal. Teachers all have their favorite pupils. Trainers likewise learn to know the most intelligent animal, the one who learns fastest and who occasionally shows signs of surprising intuition and imagination.

According to Professor Busnel, the affection of a dolphin for his trainer exists only in the imagination of the trainer. It is an illusion and a myth. Busnel has run a series of experiments demonstrating that a trained dolphin will obey his trainer even if the latter is dressed as a woman. He will also obey a woman — and he will even obey a piece of wood so long as the dolphin perceives the signal to which he has been conditioned. A Beluga whale, taught to kiss its trainer, kissed him even when the man was wearing a gas mask. The conclusion drawn by Professor Busnel is that there is not a great deal of difference between the animal's behavior toward his trainer or toward another person who takes the place of the trainer.

The same phenomenon may be observed among other species. Some animal trainers teach tricks to lions and then pass the animals on to a "lion tamer" — any lion tamer — who is able to make the lion repeat the tricks

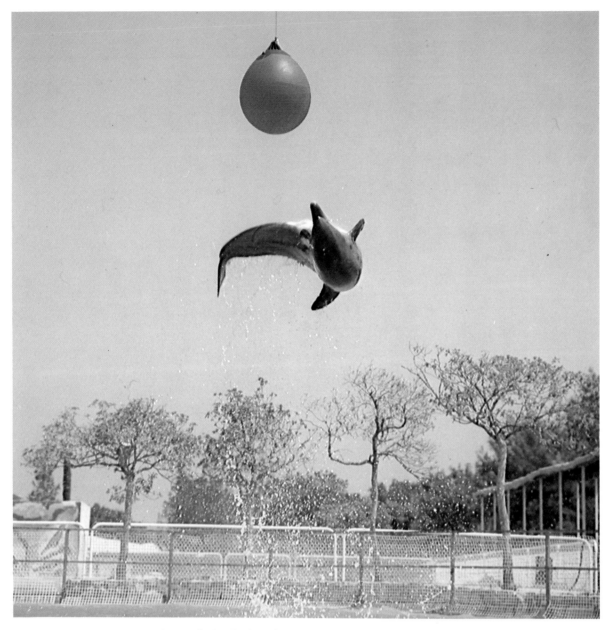

At the Marineland of Antibes, the dolphins make prodigious leaps. (Photo, Jose Dupont, Marineland d'Antibes.)

before an audience. This does not mean that the lion has no affection or aversion for the trainer or for the tamer. It means simply that a lion, upon receiving a signal to which he has been accustomed, will perform the trick corresponding to that signal.

I am not altogether certain that Professor Busnel's experiments demonstrate that dolphins are incapable of recognizing their keeper, or that they do not feel a particular affection for him. Indeed, Caldwell points out that some dolphins work better with their first trainer than with any successors; and

One of the dolphins at Antibes is able to catch a child's ball. (Photo, Jose Dupont, Marineland d'Antibes.)

some will not work at all for anyone but the first trainer. This seems to indicate that dolphins do recognize the trainer, and even that they appreciate him.

Certainly, scientists are quite right in arguing for objectivity in dealing with dolphins. But, even if we refuse to admit that the dolphin is "an animal endowed with reason," we must recognize that the dolphin is not trained as other animals are, and that he succeeds better than others in performing difficult stunts.

It is useless to attempt to constrain a dolphin, and if we strike him or punish him, we run the risk of never being able to train him at all. On the other hand, the dolphin does willingly what we ask him to do. He does so simply for the pleasure of playing, or "to please us." It is not necessary even to reward a dolphin every time he obeys. However, it does happen occasionally that a dolphin will be distracted, or will refuse to perform as requested. In such cases, the dolphin may be ill, or afraid.

Every marineland has a champion dolphin capable of giving an exceptional performance. Some of these animals execute a triple somersault. One dolphin, named Pedro, who weighs eight hundred pounds, high jumps over a bar twenty feet above the water. Others specialize in playing with balls. There is a team of two Bottlenosed Dolphins who perform a series of simultaneous leaps. Their movements are perfectly synchronized and indicate a total mastery of their bodies both in the air and in the water, as well as the perfect coordination of born acrobats.

The most extraordinary trick, perhaps, is that of the dolphin who, upon his trainer's command, will climb out of the water and lie on the edge of his tank. This act is absolutely contrary to the dolphin's nature and can be explained only by the animal's desire to please his trainer.

Happiness and Unhappiness

There is a vexing question which is often asked: Are the captive animals that one sees performing in aquariums really unhappy?

There is no certain answer to that question. Surely, dolphins performing tricks in an aquarium are better situated than the animals condemned to inactivity in a zoo. We might even say that the presence of the public, the applause, the atmosphere of admiration — all these things are agreeable to dolphins. A few minutes before show time in the Miami Seaquarium, the dolphins can be seen swimming nervously at the bottom of their tank, like jittery actors before stepping onto the stage.

It sometimes happens that dolphins will go through their whole repertoire of tricks for their own amusement and without having been ordered to do so.

We should not be misled by such signs of spontaneity. Captivity is always a terrible ordeal for an animal. Yet, there is one argument to which we cannot close our minds: the dolphins, pilot whales, and killer whales used in marine zoos and in training centers never try to escape. (The same holds true for most land animals that have adapted to captivity.) There is a common anecdote told to illustrate this phenomenon — a story which, in my opinion, is more touching than it is convincing. It seems that while A. V. Santini was supervisor of the Porpoise School of Florida, the "school" and everything in it was demolished by Hurricane Betty. Tanks, boats, and nets were all washed out to sea, along with Mr. Santini's twelve captive dolphins. All twelve of the dolphins returned to the school. Some came the day after the storm; some, a week later; and others, a month later. The returnees watched the workers rebuilding the school and splashed and sprinkled them as though they were eager for the work to be completed on the new tanks so that they could return to their homes.

Deformation

The public often imagines that because dolphins in captivity seem so friendly, they are easy to study and make perfect subjects for experiments in behavior.

It is true that dolphins have been used in experiments of all kinds. It is also true that, living together in their tanks, in contact with the public, dolphins form habits and invent or imitate certain forms of conduct so as to please their trainer. Thus, new "cultures" are being formed; cultures which are more or less capable of being passed on; cultures which are peculiar to each marineland and which conform to its characteristics, its program, and its life style. In this respect, a group of captive dolphins is comparable to a human group.

Experiments performed in marine zoos may be interesting and instructive so long as we do not forget that the subjects used in these experiments have been conditioned and deformed, and that they bear little resemblance to dolphins living in freedom in the seas. It is especially important to bear this in mind when dealing with the psychological aspects of beings as complex as marine mammals. It is certain that the study of human psychology, if it were undertaken exclusively in prisons, would also lead to misinterpretations and absurd generalizations.

The dolphins that one sees in aquariums today are often representatives of the third generation of dolphins in captivity. These grandchildren of free dolphins have never seen the sea. And, among the surviving grandparents, it is understandable that the memory of liberty has faded somewhat. Some of these older dolphins have been in prison for fifteen years. It is hard to believe that, in that period, their behavior has not been modified drastically.

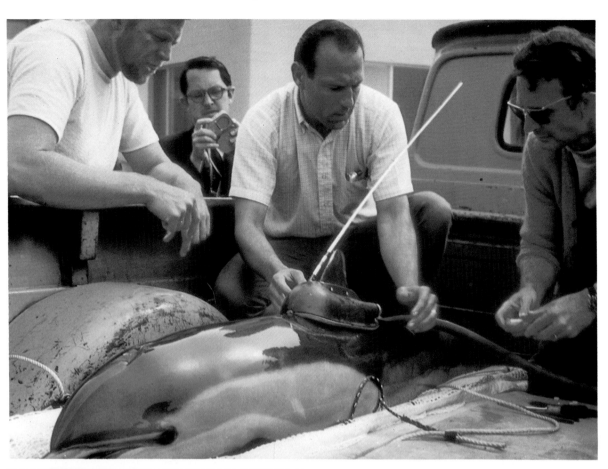

(Above) At the Marineland of Florida, a dolphin was photographed while giving birth. Notice that the baby dolphin emerges tailfirst. (Photo, Marineland of Florida.)

(Upper left) William E. Evans' team, at the Naval Undersea Center at San Diego, attaches a transmitter to a dolphin's dorsal fin. (Photo, Naval Undersea Center.)

(Lower left) A submerged dolphin equipped with a radio transmitter. (Photo, Naval Undersea Center.)

Regarding the life span of the dolphin, we have some fairly accurate data. The age of a dolphin can be determined by an examination of his teeth; and, on that basis, it appears that a dolphin lives for twenty to twenty-five years, and perhaps longer. (The pilot whale lives for twenty-six years — but senility sets in at the age of eighteen.)

It happens frequently that dolphins become ill. They seem especially prey to human disease caught from visitors. They are subject to epidemics of influenza and to hepatitis. When a dolphin is ill, he no longer eats or plays. Then, his temperature is taken, he is given injections, and sometimes he is even X-rayed.

Since breathing is a conscious function among dolphins, the use of anaesthesia has always proved fatal to them. Now, however, progress has been made in this area, and it has become possible to undertake surgical procedures.

Naval Training

The U. S. Navy has undertaken to train dolphins and other marine mammals, such as killer whales and sea lions. The dolphins used in these experiments were trained for use in studying the physiology of diving, as messengers and carriers of tools and as scouts assigned to detect and recover submerged objects. Caldwell affirms, however, that these dolphins were not used to carry explosives, or to attach explosives to the hulls of ships, as is generally believed.

The two main training centers for dolphins are the Naval Undersea Research and Development Center, at San Diego, and the Oceanographic Institute of Hawaii, at Honolulu. At the Mote Marine Laboratory, in Sarasota, Florida, Dr. Perry Gilbert is studying methods of training dolphins to combat sharks.

Training begins in a tank which can be opened to communicate with various enclosures. The dolphin is first taught to press a button which rings a bell, then to go down a passage after having received a signal. Next, he learns to carry a ball or ring to a swimmer or diver. All these things are designed to persuade the dolphin of the necessity of learning. Or, as the trainers say, the dolphin must be taught to learn.

Once a dolphin has been taught to learn, he is transferred outdoors to a complex of floating enclosures. It appears that this transfer necessitates a new education, for the transferred dolphin seems to have forgotten, at least for the first few days, everything he had learned up to that point.

In this new training area, the dolphin is taught to return to its trainer on command, since this is indispensable if a dolphin is to be regarded as dependable. This training is not very difficult. The greatest obstacle is to teach a dolphin to overcome its fear of swimming from one enclosure to another and, strangely enough, of swimming down the passage which leads into the open sea. Dolphins seem to feel not the slightest urge to escape. Sometimes they return to their tanks from the sea even before they are called.

The specific signals or commands for the numerous exercises must be as different as possible, so as to avoid confusing the animal. And each signal must correspond to a well-defined activity.

Next, the dolphin is trained to work with a boat. At first, the boat remains motionless on the water. Then it moves, and gradually it increases its speed. The dolphin becomes accustomed to leaping above the surface and to diving deeper and deeper. This phase of the dolphin's training occupies at least two weeks and takes place in the bay next to the Hawaii Research Center. Finally, the training area moves into the ocean and remains there for several weeks, some two hundred yards offshore.

Impressionable Recruits

Obviously, it is not nearly so easy to train a dolphin as might appear from the above paragraphs. The training process depends upon many factors,

The mother dolphin turns on her side to facilitate nursing. The mother's breasts are situated on either side of her genital orifice. (Photo, Marineland of Florida.)

Dolphins like to tease the sea turtles with which they share their tank (Photo, courtesy of **Marineland of Florida.**)

not the least of which is the character and the physical and psychological state of each animal. One finds the same types among marine mammals as among army recruits. Some are goldbricks, some are lazy, some are stubborn, and some — perhaps the minority — are "good soldiers."

One major factor in training dolphins is the impressionable nature of these animals. They are easily frightened and confused. A new situation, or an unfamiliar object, is sufficient to disturb their behavior patterns. Training must therefore progress by stages. Change should be as slight as possible so as to allow the dolphins to pass from one stage to another almost without being aware of it.

Despite all the precautions that one may choose to take, success is never certain in training dolphins. No matter how conscientious and experienced the trainers are, even dolphins who have completed their training are known to stage incidents. They may refuse to work, for example, or even to enter their enclosures. At that point, a new course of training must begin. It may also happen that dolphins training in the open sea are distracted by the fish swimming around them. That is natural and understandable, but it nonetheless upsets the training schedule.

Even in such cases, escapes are very rare. At **Point** Mugu, the first such training center established by the American Navy,* over a period of five years, which included 1,600 work sessions with dolphins and 600 sessions with sea lions, the center lost only one dolphin and one sea lion permanently. The other animals who escaped all allowed themselves to be recaptured or returned to the center on their own, sometimes after having been away for two weeks.†

The primary purpose of all these centers is to train dolphins who will eventually be turned loose in the sea to accomplish certain assignments. At the San Diego Center, there are several dolphins, as well as a killer whale and several sea lions, who live in the ocean near the center and respond to the calls of their keepers.

To achieve this result, it is necessary to be as familar as possible with the life style of marine animals living at liberty in the sea, regardless of the good will and the learning ability of the animals involved. Persuasion and affection are of much more importance than constraint. Training, in this instance, does not follow the usual pattern of alternating rewards and punishments. A dolphin usually obeys willingly and does whatever he is told to do, out of curiosity or out of playfulness. But any attempt to use force, or any kind of rough treatment, reduces the animal to helplessness or makes him ill.

A Dolphin Researcher

Dr. W. E. Evans, a biologist at the Naval Undersea Research Center, has specialized in the study of dolphins at liberty. In the pursuit of his specialty, Dr. Evans makes use of a catamaran designed as an observation craft by the center. Between the two hulls of the catamaran, there is a plastic underwater observation chamber from which two observers, with cameras, may follow the movements of the dolphins and sharks which, in the autumn, are especially numerous off the California coast. This device makes it possible to

---

*The Point Mugu center was closed in 1970 and its functions divided between the facilities at San Diego and in Hawaii.

†This information was provided through the courtesy of Mr. Blair Irvine, of the Naval Undersea Research and Development Center.

record the cries of dolphins in their natural environment and to gather data on the social conduct of dolphins in the sea, on their sexuality, on the compositions of schools of dolphins, and on the hierarchy which prevails in those schools.

Dr. Evans also makes use of other means of investigation. He was the first one to use a dolphin as a research agent among his own kind. But, instead of strapping a camera to the animal's back, as we did, he has attached a radio transmitter to a dolphin's dorsal fin. This transmitter sends out various data on the duration and depth of a dive, on the route followed, on "territory," on the relationship between the depth of a dive and the depth at which plankton are located, etc. The transmitter begins to operate as soon as the animal returns to the surface to breathe.

When using the transmitter, Dr. Evans avoids interference from boat engines and propellers by making use of a sailboat, the *Saluda*. Philippe Cousteau and Jacques Renoir were Dr. Evans' guests aboard the *Saluda* for a week while he conducted his experiments. It was proved once more that it was possible to attach recording devices to marine mammals and perhaps even to train them to play a part in gathering data on the life of dolphins in their natural environment. But it was also demonstrated that a dolphin carrying a radio transmitter is slowed in his movements — just as our camera-bearing dolphin was in the Mediterranean. Or even more so, since Evans' transmitter contained an antenna which seemed especially to hinder the dolphin's movements. Nonetheless, Dr. Evans was able to follow the movements of a dolphin for seventy-two hours, and it was possible for him to establish that the transmitter-bearing dolphin, despite the fact that his form had been modified, was accepted by his school.

By using a goniometer, Dr. Evans was able to locate the dolphin with the transmitter whenever it surfaced to breathe. But, hampered as the dolphin was by the radio, he tired rather quickly. The clamps by means of which the transmitter is attached to the dorsal fin loosens when the magnesium solder which holds them in place begins to dissolve in the water. It would seem that it would perhaps be better to study the possibility of using miniaturized devices.‡

‡We once attached an underwater camera to a gray whale named Gigi, and she seemed not at all inconvenienced by the camera's presence. However, the relation between the strength of the whale and the weight of the camera was quite different from that of Dr. Evans' dolphin and radio transmitter.

(Right) One of the Marineland's dolphins has dragged his ball down to the bottom of the tank. (Photo, Marineland of Florida.)

From his underwater observation sphere, Bill Evans observes the behavior of sharks and dolphins. (Photo, Naval Undersea Center.)

The information sought by Dr. Evans had to do with swimming speed of free dolphins and the number of times and the depths to which they dived. A special device was supposed to provide such data.

A dolphin swimming toward a distant destination moves at a speed of eight or nine knots. During this moderate effort, he dives but not very deeply, and he normally remains without breathing for five-minute periods. There are instances of dolphins remaining in a dive for fifteen minutes. It is known that they dive to a depth of three hundred feet and that they may attain a depth of one thousand feet. From our minisub, we have never seen dolphins at great depths.

Tuffy: Liaison Agent

Tuffy, a male Bottlenosed Dolphin weighing three hundred pounds and measuring over six feet in length, was trained at the U. S. Naval Center at

An assembly of sharks around Bill Evans' sphere. (Photo, Naval Undersea Center.)

Point Mugu, California. Subsequently, he was used by the Navy in two experiments in undersea living: Sealab II and Sealab III.

Tuffy's assignment was to act as liaison agent between the undersea houses and the surface. He carried messages back and forth, and, occasionally, tools. Dolphins have an enormous advantage over divers in this kind of work. Since they are not subject to decompression accidents, it is not necessary for them to observe the various stages of ascent. Tuffy would dive to a depth of more than three hundred feet, and then, upon command, he would shoot to the surface like an arrow.

Tuffy had another very important assignment, which was to guide lost divers back to the undersea house. Since the men occupying the house had nitrogen in large quantities in their blood, when they became lost on the bottom it was essential that they find their way back to the house without delay. They could not rise to the surface without making long stops for decompression, or without being placed in a decompression chamber. Therefore, each diver had been supplied with an electric bell for use in summoning Tuffy. The bell was audible to Tuffy at a distance of 1,500 feet. As soon as he heard it, he seized the end of a nylon line, which was wound on a spool and attached to the entrance to Sealab, and carried it to the diver.

Experiments conducted at Point Mugu have shown that dolphins are able to tow three times their own weight. A four-hundred-pound dolphin has no difficulty at all in towing a half-ton load.

One of the greatest problems in training a dolphin for a particular task is to find out at what point the conditioning to which the animal has been subjected makes it possible to rely on him. When can a dolphin be "turned loose"? What will he retain of his training when he is once more alone with the instinctive impulses which have guided his species for millions of years? One is certain of success only when a liberated animal returns to his home port after having accomplished his mission.

Training of this kind is unprecedented. Therefore, those who undertake it are obliged to rely upon their intuition and to improvise training methods.

It is a well-established fact that dolphins spontaneously come to the aid of man in the sea. We have already mentioned several anecdotes, some of them going as far back as the time of Pliny the Elder, which attest to this behavior.

During World War II, a dolphin pushed a raft, containing six American airmen shot down by the Japanese, to a small island.* The U. S. Air Force, perhaps encouraged by this example, has studied the possibility of supplying its pilots with a small transmitter which would reproduce the distress signal of dolphins. The purpose of this transmitter would be to summon dolphins to the rescue of airmen adrift in the sea. The problem, as we have already pointed out, is that the dolphin's distress signals vary greatly. And we have described the controversial nature of the problem of the dolphin's sonic signals.

One area in which the dolphin's reputation is well deserved is that of fighting sharks. Dolphins do battle with sharks and usually emerge victorious from such encounters. Their superiority lies in the fact that they attack as a group and are able to devise tactics, whereas the shark fights alone. Moreover, dolphins are able to charge an enemy with incredible force and ram into its most sensitive region (the ventral area) with their tough snouts. A stroke to

*Airmen Against the Sea, by George Llano.

(Right) A pilot whale, or blackfish, performs with the dolphins at the Marineland of Palos Verdes.

the shark's liver — which is the dolphin's customary tactic — is usually enough to put the shark out of commission. (The abdominal cavity of dolphins is very large, and their highly developed livers make them invulnerable to such attacks themselves.) It does not appear that, in these battles, the dolphin makes use of his teeth to bite his enemies.

Dolphins do not attack sharks on sight. In captivity, the two animals sometimes live peaceably together — as sharks and dolphins do in the Miami Seaquarium. Sometimes the shark will take the initiative and attack a young or ill dolphin. Then, the entire group of dolphins will unite to attack the predator. It is certain that there is no love lost between dolphins and sharks.

The hostility of dolphins toward sharks has been useful in training dolphins to protect swimmers against attack by sharks. In South Africa, Professor Taylor has taught two dolphins, Dimple and Haig, to chase away sharks from swimmers' beaches.

In Sarasota, Florida, Dr. Perry Gilbert is making a systematic study of the reciprocal behavior of dolphins and sharks. He places specimens of both species into a single tank and observes their reactions according to each species and according to the respective size of the animals. The encounter is filmed, and the sounds of the animals are recorded on tape. The experimenters are particularly interested in discovering whether the dolphin's acoustical signals have the effect of terrorizing the shark or keeping it at a distance.

The progressive training method consists first in placing the dolphin into a tank with a motionless, dead shark. Later, the dead shark is pulled through the tank on a line. And, finally, the dolphin is confronted by live sharks of different sizes.

Of the four dolphins subjected to this course of training, only one was recognized as a champion shark fighter, and he was released to stand guard before a Florida beach.

It has not yet been determined precisely what kind of assistance we can expect from dolphins in the sea; but it seems that, with a minimum of training, they are capable of assuming the role of protectors and guards.

The training program undertaken by S. Fitzgerald is not designed to teach dolphins to attack sharks on sight, but to train them for a more complex function: patrolling and giving the alarm when sharks are sighted. In so doing, dolphins would truly become man's helpers in the sea.

Chapter Ten

THE FISHERMAN'S FRIEND

Oppian, a Greek poet of the second century and the author of poems on fishing, states that dolphins were in the habit of pushing fishes into the nets of fishermen. But Pliny the Elder was even more explicit than Oppian. This Roman writer lived in Gaul, and around 70 A.D., he was procurator of the Province of Narbonne. He was a man of insatiable curiosity, and he was constantly assembling material for his *Natural History*, a massive work in thirty-seven books. There is a passage in Book IX which seems based on Pliny's own observations:

"There is, in the Province of Narbonne, in the territory of Nimes, a pond named Latera, where dolphins fish with humans. On a certain day, a boundless school of mullets leave the pond and head for the open sea through a narrow channel which connects the two bodies of water. This channel is too narrow to allow the use of nets; and no net would be strong enough to support the weight of such a mass of fish. These mullets know the time of the flood tide, and then they make straight for deep water, hastening through the only place where it would be possible to block their passage. As soon as the fishermen become aware of this movement, a great crowd of people assemble at that spot, eager to see whatever may be seen. Everyone calls out in a loud

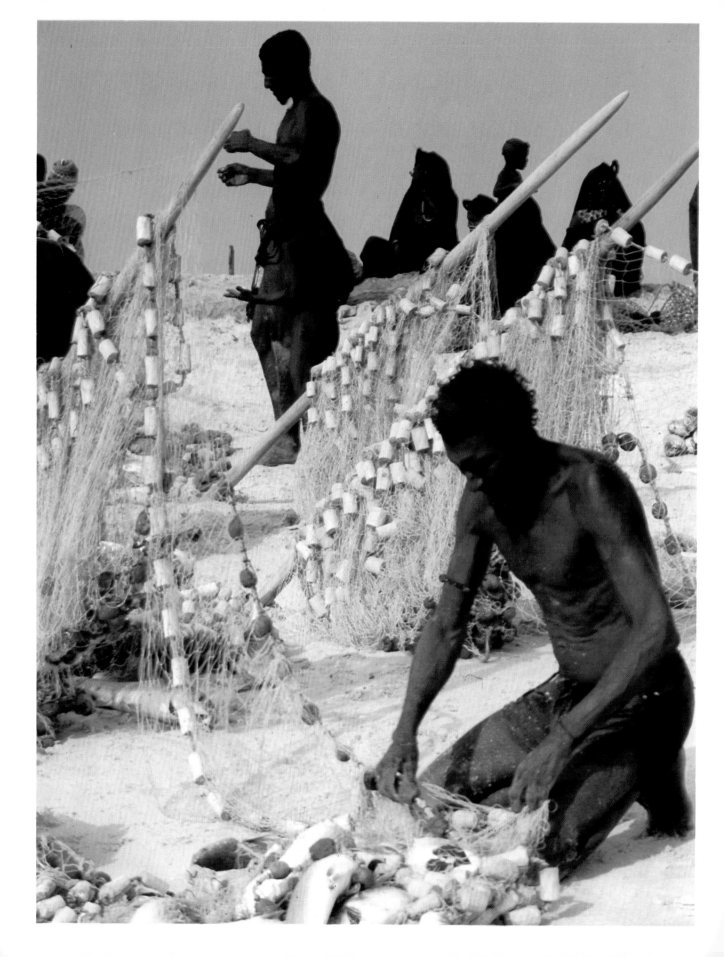

voice: 'Simon!' [Apparently the popular name for dolphins at that time.] Then the dolphins come, arranged in ranks as for battle. They block·the way into deep water and push the frantic mullets back toward the shallows where the fishermen encircle the fishes with their nets, which they hold by means of forked sticks. Nonetheless, the mullets try to jump over the nets, but they are caught by the dolphins who, for the moment, are content to kill them and to defer their meal until the victory has been won. When the battle is at its height, the dolphins take pleasure in allowing themselves to be encircled by the nets so as to press agains the mullets; and, so that this pursuit does not cause their enemies to flee, they slip softly among the boats and the nets and the swimmers so that there is no opening left for escape. And, although they leap in the water, none of the dolphins tries to escape from within the nets, except when the nets are lowered before them. When the fishing is over, the dolphins divide the mullets they have killed; but, as though conscious of having deserved more than the recompense for a single day, they wait until the following day, and they eat not only the fish, but also bread dipped in wine.

"That which Mucian relates concerning the same method of fishing in the Gulf of Iasos differs from the present instance in that here the dolphins come without being called to receive their share from the hands of the fishermen. Each boat takes one of the dolphins as a partner, even though this all takes place at night, by torchlight."

Since the period of Antiquity, Pliny's story has been regarded as a popular fable, and it has often been cited as an indication of the author's credulity. No doubt, Pliny was credulous to a point, but in the present instance, at least, he seems not to have been victimized by the imagination of the Gauls of the South. The name of the pond, Latera, is preserved in that of the village of Lattès, in the South of France; and the channel "too narrow to allow the use of nets" still exists at Palavas-les-flots, where the waters of the ponds of Méjean, Le Grec, and Pérols empty into the sea. There is no doubt, therefore, that Pliny was scrupulously accurate, at least so far as the setting of his story was concerned.

And how about the dolphins today? Fishermen in the area still cast their nets for mullets, but the dolphins no longer come to their assistance. Somewhere between the time of Pliny and our own, contact seems to have been lost with the friends of the fishermen.

Still, Pliny's story is not as improbable as it may sound. In Mauritania, a long distance from the South of France, and at a spot along the Atlantic,

(Left) Imragen fishermen on the beach at Nouamghar, in Mauritania.

fishermen still count on the help of dolphins, as they have for thousands of years, to catch mullets weighing from seven to nine pounds. Members of the Imragen tribe claim to have recourse to the help of the dolphins to push mullets into their nets as the mullets pass along the coast during their migrations.

Archaeological discoveries lead us to believe that, during the neolithic age, and perhaps even before, fishing was practiced along this stretch of the African coast. It is probable, in any case, that men have fished there uninterruptedly, in the same spot, since prehistoric times. The Imragen are a very ancient tribe who are neither Arabs nor Berbers. They have always been tributaries of more warlike peoples and of the Marabouts who were their oppressors.* They turned toward the sea for their food, while the Moors remained attached to their deserts and occupied themselves with pillaging, slave trading, and camel racing.

Even today, on this coast of arid dunes, where the desert touches the Atlantic, there is a human island, a tiny group of people who, having turned their back to the Sahara, place all their hopes in the sea. These people are divided among four or five miserable clusters of huts. But they are not a sedentary people. They roam the desolate coast of Mauritania, where only a few shrubs grow and where salty ponds and mudholes alternate with dunes and banks of bare, hard sand.

This is the domain of the marine birds: the pelicans, cormorants, pink flamingoes, and white spoonbills. It is also the home of clouds of buzzing flies.

It was here, in 1816, that a sailing ship ran aground — a ship the wreckage of which is famous: the *Medusa.*

It is one of the most desolate, sinister, and sun-baked areas on the face of the earth.

The Imragen, who number no more than three hundred today, move along the coast to follow the movement of the fish. Whenever they halt, they erect their *tikitt* — miserable shacks of straw — or their tattered tents.

The Water and the Fish

Some of the Imragen fish almost the whole year, while others fish for only two or six months. In the spring, they gather around the rare water holes, where a brackish, muddy liquid oozes through holes in the sand. For the main preoccupation in this arid country is to locate water. For food, the people have only fish. And during the summer, when there is no more fish, they join

*Raphaelle Anthonioz, "Les Imragen, pecheurs nomades de Mauritanie," in *Bulletin de l'IFAN*, t.XXX.

the Moors in the desert and drink camel's milk.

The abundance of fish along this coast is incredible. The stretch of water between Cape Blanc and Cape Timiris — a distance of about eighty miles — is reputed to be one of the richest in the world in marine life. From September to the end of February, vast schools of mullets follow each other in their migration southward. These schools cover areas hundreds of yards long, from twenty or thirty yards wide, and one to two feet in depth.

The mullets are so abundant that the Imragen, it is said, sometimes make a catch, according to their traditional methods, of six to eight thousand pounds. They then place the fish in the sun to dry.

It is not known precisely who the Imragen are. The word *Imragen* is of Berber origin and appeared in comparatively recent times. It means "those who hunt" or "those who cultivate the land." We know only that the Imragen are not of Moorish stock — though some of them may well be of mixed Moorish and black antecedents. In any event, they were an enslaved and captive people who paid tribute to the more powerful Moorish chieftains until they were liberated by the French colonial administration. Even under the French, however, the Imragen continued to pay tribute, in kind, to their Moorish overlords.

The Imragen have no ethnic cohesion, in the sense that they are united neither by blood nor by religious belief. Their only bond is their common and exclusive activity: fishing. In pursuit of that activity, they have remained on the shore of the Atlantic since time immemorial, while, inland, their oppressors and captors changed with the ebb and flow of historic tides: Sanhadja Berbers, Hassanic Arabs, Moors.

It is not beyond belief that the Imragen were fishing from these same beaches in neolithic times. At Ganeb el Hafeira, in the southwestern Sahara, small balls, marked with a groove, have been found in a prehistoric site. It is interesting to note that the present-day Imragen weight their nets with terra-cotta balls almost identical in shape to those found at Ganeb el Hafeira. (The Imragen call them *idan*.) Moreover, numerous prehistoric fishing implements have been found along the coast frequented by the Imragen.

According to a tradition, the origins of which are lost in the mists of antiquity, the Imragen, from the earliest times, were aided by dolphins in their mullet fishing. They still consider the dolphin as a benevolent and prestigious animal, and it is forbidden to kill any dolphin. In exchange, it is expected that the dolphins, like those mentioned by Pliny, will push mullets into the nets of the Imragen.

We were greatly intrigued by this "legend" of the Imragen, and we resolved to see what was true and what was false in it. We therefore sent a team

(Above) The Imragen, sitting beside their nets, watch the first dolphins arrive.

(Right) The first mullets are taken in the nets of the Imragen fishermen.

to Mauritania, under the supervision of Jacques Renoir. This team was assured of the co-operation of Professor Busnel and of the support of General du Bouchet.

We had chosen the period at which fishing was best, that is, the period from December to February. Our team of divers and cameramen departed in December, from Nouakchott, to journey to the land of the Imragen tribe at one of their preferred fishing spots — Nouamghar, three miles from Cape Timiris, on the Bay of El Merdja.

Our men found not a village but a grouping of several families surrounded by screaming children and swarming flies. There were fewer than ten *tikitt*; windowless, and even smaller and more ill-smelling than one would think possible.

There were a few odoriferous fish drying in the sun, and the nets had already been cast. But we had chosen badly. Fishing was not at all good, and the mullets were late in arriving that year. Thus far, no one had spotted a single dolphin, even though watches had been posted at the summit of the

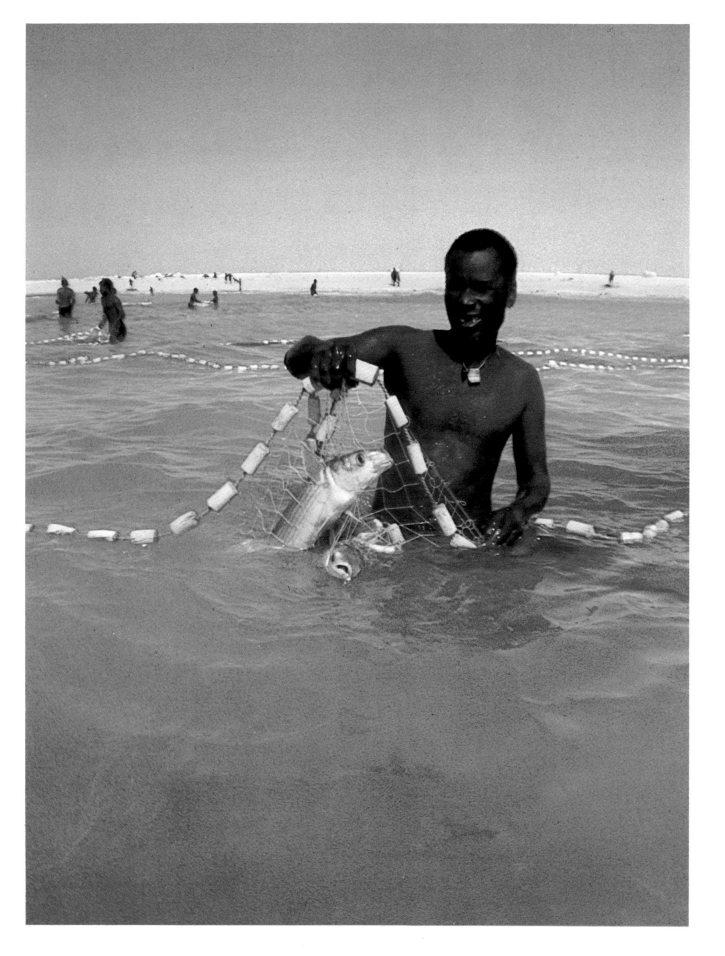

dunes to scan the surface of the sea.

Our expedition had required a considerable amount of equipment. From jeeps and station wagons we unloaded an air compressor to fill our air tanks, tanks of compressed air, cameras, diving gear, floodlights, jerrycans of fuel, and a Zodiac with two motors. All this was piled on the beach and on the dunes, where it had been unloaded, while our men busied themselves with raising their tent.

The Imragen women had hidden themselves in their huts, while the menfolk sat on the sand and watched the new arrivals without a flicker of sympathy. The fishermen, as we learned later, were upset by the absence of the dolphins. The mullets are their only source of food, and without dolphins, they could not catch the fish. This was good reason indeed to worry. For selling salted fish provided them with the small amounts of money the Imragen needed to buy the other necessities of life: sugar, salt, and tea.

When darkness fell, campfires began to appear among the huts, and the divers approached warily, offering cigarettes and attempting to engage the Imragen in conversation. The women — the older women first — began to appear in the doorways of the *tikitt*. These women, it was learned, were most hostile to the divers. They were afraid that the presence of our team would prevent the dolphins from approaching the beach to help the fishermen. Apparently, they had understood that our friends intended to swim in the sea and to go near the dolphins. For centuries, the Imragen had regarded the dolphins as their special friends, and as the friends of no one else. No doubt, they felt that the dolphins would not like these Frenchmen who breathed in the water. We meant absolutely no harm, of course; and if we believed for a moment that our presence would have deprived these poverty-ridden people of the help of the dolphins, we would have decamped immediately. By then, however, we had had sufficient experience with dolphins to know that these mammals do not restrict their benevolence to any particular segment of mankind.

It was not easy to persuade these women of the truth. They shook their black-veiled heads obstinately. What was diving to them? Or cameras and film? They were concerned about their familes and their children. If the Imragen have not experienced famine for centuries, it is because of the mullets and the dolphins, who come from the sea. Therefore, anything that comes from the interior could only be hostile. For that was where the warlike Moors came from. . . .

Fishing plays such an important role in the activities of the Imragen that it is at the very center of their mental lives. It is surrounded by superstitions and religious observances. Our divers were not unsympathetic to the anxiety of these poverty-stricken tribesmen. Eventually, the conversation grew more candid, and the chief of the fishermen asked Renoir and Falco not to go into the water and risk preventing the arrival of the dolphins.

The divers did not know quite what to do. Their equipment was piled on the beach. Was it to go unused? Would their work and hopes all be in vain because of the superstitions of these poor people who alternately pleaded and threatened in their frantic attempts to dissuade them from diving? Finally, a compromise was reached. Falco and Renoir agreed not to go into the water so long as the dolphins had not yet made their appearance.

The following morning, a long period of waiting began. Imragen and the divers sat next to each other on the beach, their elbows on their knees, looking at the sea as it sparkled in the sun. Occasionally, one of the watchmen on a dune shouted: a school of mullets was approaching. Immediately, a fisherman began striking the surface of the water with pieces of wood. This was the signal intended to attract the dolphins. But no dolphins appeared. The school of mullets passed along the beach, but not even the smallest dolphin intervened to push the fish toward the beach where everyone and everything was ready. The fishermen were sitting two by two, each holding the extremity of a net which ended in a stick. Yves Omer and Bébert Falco were in the diving suits, the camera on the sand next to them, trying to be as inconspicuous as possible. They were faithful to their agreement. They would go into the water only if and when the dolphins made their appearance.

A Marabout, kneeling in the sand and surrounded by moaning women, muttered incantations.

The Killer Whales

Suddenly, far out in the water, a fin appeared, followed by others. They were not the fins of dolphins, but of killer whales. The presence of the school was probably what kept the dolphins at a distance. Dolphins are frightened of killer whales, and they flee at the first sight of the latter's huge triangular dorsal fins or at the first sound of their shrill whistles. The divers understood at once why the dolphins had not appeared on schedule; and they knew that they would not come so long as the whales were in the area. Obviously, something would have to be done. Otherwise, the Imragen would be convinced that we water-breathing Frenchmen had deliberately deprived them

After the dolphins have herded the mullets toward shore, the fishermen use sticks to push the mullets into their nets.

of their catch and, therefore, of their livelihood. Even worse, these poor fishermen along with their wives and children, would face a year of virtual starvation.

Falco and Omer jumped into the Zodiac and sped out toward the killer whales. In the small craft, they charged each of the mammals in turn, forcing them out to sea. The *corrida* lasted for more than an hour. Finally, the killer whales, deafened by the din of the outboard motors, and confused by the maneuvers of the Zodiac, decided to withdraw.

Falco and Omer had barely returned to the beach when the sea began to churn and boil. The dolphins had finally come, and they were pushing the

mullets before them.

Immediately, Jacques Renoir and Michel Deloire grabbed their camera equipment and ran into the water.

Fishing

The mullets, rolling one on top of the other, were already nearing the beach. They churned frantically in the water as the dolphins encircled them, forcing them into a compact mass and then throwing them into the air in a brilliant explosion of shining scales. The dolphins themselves seemed to be in the grip of a frenzy. They seized fishes in their mouths, turning them to swallow them headfirst, and then threw themselves back into the middle of the school.

Meanwhile, the Imragen, who had removed all of their clothing except a leather loincloth, were raising the nets by placing the pieces of wood at the ends of the nets on their shoulders. Then they ran toward the water and, swimming vigorously, spread the nets and, with a wide, turning motion, herded the mullets toward the beach. A second net was thrown farther out, and then another still farther.

Dolphins and men mingled in the water. The mammals swam among the fishermen, their mouths gaping open as mullets leaped around them.

A dog moved along the beach, half running and half swimming, in pursuit of mullets. The dog belonged to a blind man who was in the water with his net. There were so many mullets that even he caught his share, and he gathered them with an eagerness that was touching to witness.

On the beach, the women were shrieking with joy, while their naked children jumped and shouted.

The first enthusiasm had created much disorder in the water, but in order to take advantage of the wealth which was literally pushed up to the feet of the Imragen by the dolphins, a bit of discipline was necessary.

The fishing of the tribe is regulated by very strict customs. The fishermen, divided into teams of two men each, do not all go into the water at once. The elders of the village decide, by drawing lots, who will be the first to fish. Then they send out the other teams, one after the other. There are mullets enough for everyone.

Despite their poverty and their privations, the Imragen revealed themselves to be real athletes. Under their bronzed skin, strong, well-defined muscles were clearly visible. Their way of fishing must keep them in shape.

With a net measuring sixty to ninety feet in length, each team caught from 250 to 300 pounds of fish at once and returned to the beach carrying a wriggling, struggling, shining yellowish mass of mullets whose scales glittered in the sun with the fire of diamonds. As each team returned, they were met by women who loaded the fishes into other nets which they placed upon their heads. They then set off at a slow trot, bent under the weight of their loads, their bare feet sinking into the sand. Occasionally, our men saw a mullet work free of the net and fall to the sand, where it twisted and turned under the blazing sun.

Visibility Zero

Jacques Renoir and Michel Deloire, in the midst of fishermen, mullets, and dolphins, rolled in the water. The other divers joined them. Occasionally, one of them succeeded in touching a passing dolphin. Sometimes, everything disappeared into a mass of foam.

The cameras were aimed, but it was necessary to record the movements of the dolphins and the details of their intervention. The cameramen therefore left the center of the struggle and moved away. But they could no longer see anything. The water was cloudy. It is truly clear and calm only when the wind is from the east or northwest — which should be the prevailing wind at that time of year.

It is certain that, without the dolphins, the fishing would not have been nearly so good. They are excellent fish beaters. A dolphin does not need clear water to seize, with astonishing precision, a jumping mullet. His echolocation system enables him to locate his prey and seize it in one effective gesture.

Yves Omer, despite the lack of visibility, filmed the scene as best he could. He could hear distinctly the clicking of the dolphins' sonar as they pursued the mullets at full speed.

Finally, the number of mullets lessened. The dolphins went back to the open sea. And the fishermen returned to the beach to estimate the results of their first fishing of the season. They were smiling broadly. They knew that our team, by chasing away the killer whales, had enabled the dolphins to return. The atmosphere was noticeably warm and friendly.

The Man-Dolphin

Our cameramen and divers returned to the beach wondering whether they had gotten any usable footage in the cloudy water. They stood on the sand, discussing the film as they removed their diving gear. Jean-Clair Riant pulled off his hood, and his mass of blond hair tumbled around his ears.

No Imragen had ever seen a blond before. And Riant, to confuse matters, also had a blond beard. The women of the tribe swarmed around Jean-Clair, asking one another if this was not a man-dolphin. The men remarked that our vinyl diving suits indeed resembled the soft, supple skin of the dolphins.

On the Mauritanian coast, everyone knows that the dolphin's reproduc-

The mullets are initially piled up on the beach. Later, they are taken to drying huts.

The mullets leap from the water in an attempt to escape the dolphins.

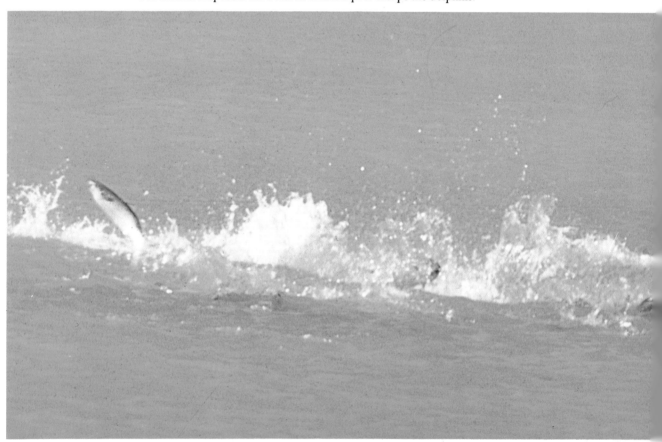

tive organs are located within his abdominal cavity. This arrangement accounts for the animal's perfect hydrodynamism. Was it the same for Jean-Clair Riant? Jean-Clair was obliged to remove his diving suit to show that he was a man like other men. It was a moment of universal hilarity.

An hour later, there was an alert. The watchers signaled the arrival of another school of mullets. The children began beating the water with their sticks, and the dolphins obediently appeared, their dorsal fins erect, their backs humped, pushing mullets before them to the beach.

For the Imragen, fishing is a matter of life and death. For the dolphins, it seems to provide the opportunity for an orgy. But so far as the mullet itself is concerned, does the combination of man and dolphin pose a threat to its survival as a species? The general opinion of experts is that it does not. The fishing of the Imragen, as spectacular as it may be, is actually less murderous than it appears. It has been calculated that 90 per cent of the mullets herded by the dolphins and the Imragen manage to escape.

A Difficult Chore

After the fishing is over, there are still difficult chores to accomplish. The fish must be prepared and dried. This is the work of the women and children,

but, if the fish have been plentiful, the men also help in this task. First, the head of the fish must be cut off. Then the fish is split in two and its bones and entrails are removed, along with its eggs. It is then washed in the sea.

Some fish are simply set out to dry, while others are salted. The eggs of the fish are placed between two planks to be flattened, then they are salted and dried for seven days. Poutargue, a dish made from these eggs and from the salted fish, has a ready market along the Mediterranean coast.

On this occasion, fishing had been exceptionally good. The Imragen were no longer hostile toward us, and they no longer felt that our presence was unlucky. After all, we had driven away the killer whales, the enemies of the dolphins. Women, children, and fishermen, everyone sang our praises. We were invited to participate in the celebration that would be held that night to honor the return of the dolphins and the abundance of fish.

In the dim light of carbide lamps and of campfires fueled by the bones of the mullets, we watched the Imragen express their joy in singing and dancing to the sound of drums. These songs and dances distinguish the Imragen from the Arabs and the Berbers; for dancing is held in contempt by the Moors, while it is widely practiced among the Imragen, who dance to express their joy in happy circumstances. Until late that night, we listened to the sounds of that modest celebration in honor of the dolphins and of the sea which, since prehistoric times, has fed the men of the desert around the edge of this bay. For the Imragen may be miserable indeed. They may have no trees or lands or flocks, but at least they have never gone hungry — thanks to the dolphins.

A Problem In Identification

Professor Busnel was astonished to see the dolphins hunting mullets so near the shore, sometimes in very shallow water only a few yards from the beach. The dolphins were from seven to ten feet in length, and they were difficult to identify. We were certain that they were not always the same dolphins, for there were differences in length. Moreover, judging from the shape of the dorsal fin, they seemed to belong to two different species. They were black, or very dark maroon. We found a skull on the beach and sent it to the British Museum for identification. It is now "the largest specimen that we have in all the collections of the British Museum," wrote F. C. Fraser, the celebrated cetologist.

We wondered whether the dolphin in question was the *Tursiops* — perhaps a species other than *truncatus*. The *Tursiops*, or Bottlenosed, is vaguely defined. The Mediterranean *Tursiops* does not resemble that of Japan or of Florida; and the *Tursiops* of Mauritania may be different from the others, at least in size. We still do not know the answer to those questions.

Professor Busnel identified one dolphin which is considered to be rare. In the course of two fishing sessions, in a group of from ten to fifteen large dolphins, Busnel noticed a specimen with the humped dorsal fin characteristic of the *Sousa teuszi*, which was identified in 1892 when one of the species washed ashore near Duala. Professor Busnel is the first specialist to see a live specimen.

It is possible that the gratitude of the Imragen toward the dolphin is not entirely justified. It seems unlikely that the dolphins intentionally "collaborate" with man by helping him to fish. They push the mullet school toward the beach so that they themselves can capture them more readily. Yet, it would be very difficult to convince the Imragen that the dolphins, as sacred animals, do not show a special benevolence in driving the fish into their nets.

One may suppose that the fishing, which has been practiced for millennia in this favorable spot, exercises some attraction for the dolphins, just as it does for the humans who live in the midst of the hostile desert. One dare not say that man and dolphin eventually became accustomed to one another's presence here. In any event, it appears that there is greater attachment on man's part to the dolphin than on that of the dolphin to man.

There are other instances of similar collaboration in other parts of the world. In Florida, many local fishermen are convinced that dolphins maneuver in such a way as to drive the fish into their nets.

Less unlikely are examples of association between men and dolphins in fresh water. In Burma, for instance, each village has its dolphin (*Orcella fluminalis*), which answers to its name and participates in the village's fishing. In 1954, F. B. Lamb* witnessed the activity of another fresh-water dolphin (*Inia geoffrensis*) in South America on the Tepegos River. A fisherman began by tapping his boat with his oar. Then he whistled in a particular manner. The dolphin appeared. As the boat advanced, frightening the fishes and sending them toward the bottom, the dolphin pursued them and forced them to rise within the reach of the fisherman.

It may be that, one day, the dolphin will truly become man's helper in the sea; that he will consciously and ingeniously send schools of fishes into our nets. But we have not yet reached that stage.

*Professor R.-G. Busnel, *Symbiotic relationship between man and dolphins*, Proceedings of the New York Academy of Sciences, 1973.

Imragen fishermen always work in pairs, and these two-man teams enter the water one after the other.

Nets are laid out all along the beach at Nouamghar. To the left, one can see dolphins herding mullets toward the nets.

Chapter Eleven

THE RIGHT TO RESPECT

For a long period of time, at least during the whole of Antiquity, man honored and respected dolphins. There was a true alliance between dolphins on the one hand, and fishermen and seamen on the other. Poets hymned the virtues of dolphins; and it was forbidden to kill these animals both because they rendered such estimable service to mankind and because of the superstitious fears that a dolphin's death awakened in man.

Much later, during the modern era, when sensitivities had been blunted, respect for marine mammals gave way to organized massacre, carried out with murderous weapons. European fishermen began using larger and larger boats, and, in the the course of the twentieth century, they observed that their catch had diminished alarmingly. The fault, they complained, was that of the dolphins, Beluga whales, and seals, and they succeeded in persuading their governments of this libel. The results were predictable. In France, for example, the Naval Registry required that fishing boats carry a firearm aboard, and there was a bounty paid for every dolphin's tail that a fisherman brought back with him.

The regulations, and the bounty, no longer exist. But the belief somehow lingers that dolphins are the enemies of fishermen.

Once, such beliefs may not have seemed important. There were many dolphins in the sea, and it was difficult to believe that they might one day be in danger of extinction. But today, when dolphins are being hunted and killed by the hundreds of thousands for commercial purposes, the danger has become very real. Whales, finally, are protected by law. But dolphins are not. Everywhere in the world, they are being slaughtered to provide canned food for dogs and cats, since the price of meat has made it expensive to use beef or pork for such purposes.

Tuna Fishing

An even more imminent danger to dolphins is represented by modern tuna-fishing methods, as they have been practiced commercially for the past twenty years, especially in the Pacific.

Fishermen are aware that schools of dolphins and schools of tuna move together in the sea. The dolphins swim at the surface, and the tuna swim beneath the dolphins, at the same speed. The dolphins are therefore visible from the surface, and the fisherman who spots a school of dolphins knows that there may be a school of tuna underneath.

For many years, a hook and line, with live bait, was used in catching tuna. In the 1940s, however, fishermen began using a net of cotton fibers, a material which tears easily. Sharks attacked the nets, and this, combined with the cotton fiber's tendency to rip, resulted in the escape of great numbers of tuna. Nonetheless, the use of these nets quickly became common.

Between 1956 and 1961, the American tuna fleet was completely modernized. Now, nylon nets were being used, along with new fishing techniques, and the catch of tuna increased considerably. By 1966, 62 per cent of the tuna caught with nets in the American tropics of the Pacific were found under schools of dolphins. One can imagine what the consequences were to the dolphins.

In the course of our encounters with dolphins, and while we were diving with them, we frequently observed that they were accompanied by schools of tuna.

Little is known about the reasons for this association between species. At first, it was believed that dolphins and tunas were in search of the same food, but recent observations have failed to confirm that hypothesis.

Another explanation was offered: the tunas sought out the company of dolphins in order to protect themselves against attack by sharks. If so, the security thus obtained is precarious indeed, for sharks have often been seen swimming through schools of dolphins without being attacked or even hindered.

A third hypothesis is that tunas tend to group near objects floating in the sea.

The California Fisheries Bureau, after numerous experimental studies, arrived at the conclusion that tunas seek out the company of dolphins in order to take advantage of the latter's directional ability. For dolphins, as we have mentioned, have a perfect directional sense and are able to orient themselves even on the surface.

In the Trap

In the midst of the confusion concerning the reasons for the association of dolphins and tunas, one fact remains: tunas seem to follow dolphins very closely. The present technique of tuna fishing is based upon the supposition that this is so, at least as tuna fishing is practiced off the California coast and also, to a lesser extent, in the waters of Brazil, Peru, and Canada, by boats of 1,000 to 1,500 tons, equipped with refrigerated compartments.

When a school of dolphins is sighted, the ship comes to a stop and small boats are lowered. The latter engage in a "round-up" of the dolphins, herding them together while a powerful speedboat deploys a heavy net in an attempt to encircle the dolphins.

The purpose of this maneuver is to confine the dolphins in a tight circle or, if this proves impossible, to keep them in close ranks in the direction of the wind. Meanwhile, deeper down in the water, the tunas presumably are following the movements of the dolphins. If the dolphins swim against the wind, the tunas precede them and then are more difficult to catch.

The net is then closed, capturing the dolphins and the tunas together. When this technique was first employed, the fishermen did not know quite how to go about getting rid of the dolphins. They hauled them aboard, separated them from the tunas, and then threw them back into the sea, dead or injured. Obviously, this took a great deal of time, and required much extra work. To move a 300- or 400-pound dolphin, whether it is dead or alive, is not an easy task. The American Government has notified the Pacific fishing fleets that they will no longer be allowed to operate unless they develop a method which allows dolphins to escape unharmed from their nets.

In the past few years, fishing fleets have begun to adopt a more efficient and less cruel method of disposing of the dolphins. This technique is known as "backing down." Half the net is hoisted aboard. Then, the tunas are at the forward end of the net, and the dolphins at the rear end, as far as possible from the ship. Upon an order of the captain, who is positioned in a crow's-nest, the ship's engines are reversed. This maneuver causes the far end of the net to sink, and the dolphins are able to escape.

This technique is not as simple as it sounds. The tunas can also escape from the net by following the dolphins. The captain must therefore, at the proper moment, give the order for the boat to resume its forward movement so that the net is raised again and the tunas are trapped.

These are dangerous maneuvers so far as the dolphins are concerned. Some of them become entangled in the net's openings and drown. There are always fatalities among the dolphins during a catch. Some of the fishermen try to free the dolphins caught in the net and, in so doing, run serious risks.

Among the dolphins who play an important role in the fishing for tunas in tropical waters, specialists have distinguished three species. One of them has not yet been identified. The other two are the *Stenella graffmani*, and the *Stenella longirostris*. Fishermen call the former the Spotted Dolphin — obviously because of its spots. The latter is known to them as the Spinner Dolphin, from its habit of leaping and spinning in the air. It is not known whether this peculiar gymnastic is simply a sign of exuberance, or an amorous demonstration, or a distress signal. Trainers have taught the Bottlenosed Dolphin to perform the same maneuver, but in this case it is a matter of special training. No free dolphin, except the Spinner Dolphin, performs this kind of acrobatic spontaneously.

Protection

Off the West Coast of the United States, modern fishing vessels catch 45,000 tons of tuna every year. At the same time, it was estimated that tuna fishing, in 1971, cost the lives of 250,000 dolphins. In other words, the American tuna-fishing fleet alone was responsible for the deaths of a quarter of a million dolphins — and there is no reason to think that the fleets of the other tuna-fishing nations are any more concerned about dolphins than the Americans are. The total number of dolphins killed every year by tuna-fishing must therefore be enormous.

On October 21, 1972, the Congress enacted a bill entitled "The Marine Mammal Protection Act," the provisions of which were entrusted to the National Fishery Service for enforcement.

In January 1973, the Pacific fishing fleet sailed from San Diego carrying

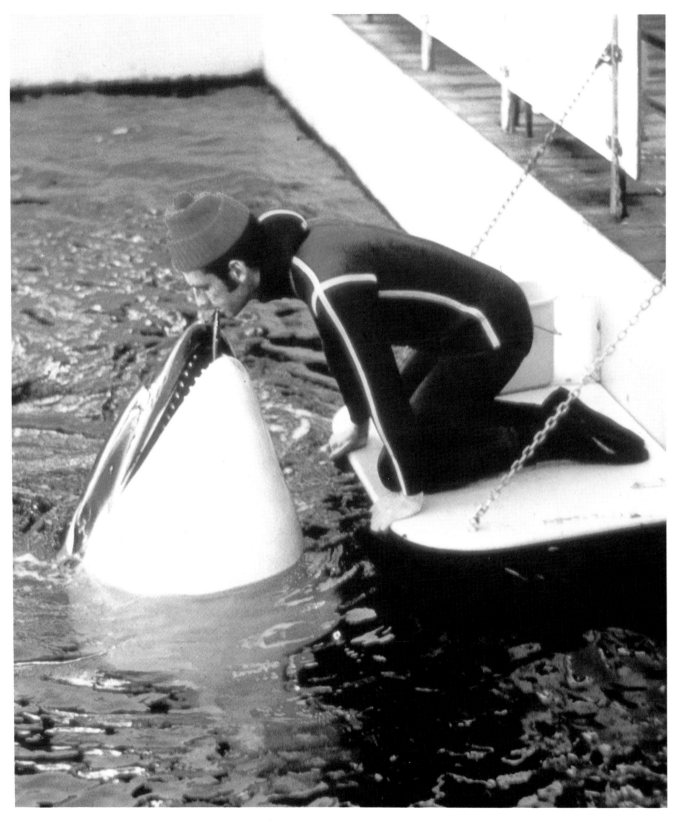

Louis Prezelin, one of Calypso's divers, presents a fish to Aida, a killer whale at the Vancouver Aquarium.

three representatives of the Service. The assignment of these representatives was to compute the number of dolphins killed and to study the means suitable for eliminating, or at least for reducing, that massacre.

At the same time, an aerial survey was undertaken in an attempt to determine the present dolphin population. Thus, far, this laudable project has not led to any conclusive results.

Various proposals have been submitted describing ways to reduce the number of dolphin deaths during tuna fishing. The most notable of these suggests the use of a net designed to allow the dolphins to escape more easily.

Dr. Fish is conducting experiments in California with a view toward installing underwater transmitters aboard fishing boats. These transmitters are intended to reproduce the cries of killer whales — the dolphins' most feared enemies. It is possible that the killer whale's war cry, broadcast at the proper moment, might inspire the dolphins to escape more rapidly from the net.

The Misfortunes of the Beluga Whale

In Europe, in the years following World War I, there was a veritable campaign, as absurd as it was groundless, waged against the Beluga whale, which was accused of stealing the catch and destroying the equipment of fishermen. The uproar smacked of mass hysteria based upon a misuse of terms, for the true Beluga is very rarely found in European waters. At the mouth of the Loire, for example, there is only one instance of a Beluga ever having been washed ashore. The word "Beluga," in fact, was used as a popular catch-all to designate any marine animal suspected of interfering with the fishing industry; and the French Navy had standing orders, for several years, to use their cannon against any such animals.

The real Beluga whale inhabits the polar regions and only rarely leaves the waters of the Arctic. "In one hundred and forty years," Professor Budker says, "only twelve Belugas were washed up on British shores, and these were mostly in the North."

The word "Beluga" means "white" in Russian. The Beluga is a toothed whale and is often called the "white whale." Adults reach a length of fifteen to seventeen feet. The Beluga has no dorsal fin, but it is one of the rare Delphinidae which has the semblance of a neck. It feeds on fish, mollusks, and crustaceans. It is hunted along the Canadian coast and in Alaskan waters — in the White Sea and the Sea of Okhotsk — for its oil and meat. Its hide is highly prized, for it is one of the very few cetaceans to yield a usable leather. A young white whale is dark gray and becomes lighter as it matures.

Beluga hunting has been sufficiently widespread for the Canadian government to pass legislation designed to protect the species from extinction.

A Marineland Boarder

The pilot whale is also a dolphin, but one of more than usual size since it attains a length of nineteen to twenty-two feet, while the more usual size for dolphins is six to eight feet.

The pilot whale, or *Globicephala melaena*, is black — whence its popular name of Blackfish. It is also known as the Ca'ing Whale. On its underside, it has a large white marking. Its head, different in shape from that of the dolphin, is round and has no snout or beak. And, compared to the face of the dolphin, it has no "expression."

The pilot whale has a talent for adaptation and understanding which makes it a desirable boarder in marinelands, especially since, in addition to those advantages, it is of much more impressive size than the dolphin. It seems to bear up well in captivity, and the many pilot whales in American institutions are able to perform the same tricks and stunts as dolphins — that is, they are able to catch balls, ring bells, answer to their names, etc. This ability comes as something of a surprise, for the pilot whale's blank face seems somehow less alert than that of the dolphin.

The taming and training of the pilot whale is due largely to the efforts of the Marineland of the Pacific, in California. The results already obtained show great promise for the future and lead one to hope that the pilot whale may be destined for something better than life as a circus performer. It is already being used by the U. S. Navy to recover practice torpedoes.

Free pilot whales live in schools which comprise as many as several hundred individuals. The movements of the school seem to be controlled by a leader who swims at the head of the school.

Several times during *Calypso*'s expeditions we encountered pilot whales, but they proved to be even more difficult to approach than dolphins.

In 1948, we accompanied Professor Piccard aboard the *Elie Monnier* when he dived in his bathyscaphe, the FNRS II. I have told the story elsewhere of how we succeeded in getting the bathyscaphe down to a depth of 5,500 feet. As it turned out, the bathyscaphe's only defect was that it was not seaworthy — for it was damaged, not in the great depths of the sea, but on the surface, by the swell. Nonetheless, we demonstrated that the FNRS II could go down and then rise again under its own power. That demonstration made possible the use of all the other bathyscaphes which have been built since that

(Above) A beluga whale at the Vancouver Aquarium inspects his visitors through a porthole. (Photo, Vancouver Aquarium.)

(Right) This killer whale was photographed by Louis Prezelin.

time.

On the return trip, we were passing through the Gibraltar straits when we sighted a school of pilot whales. The weather was exceptionally good, and I did not want to miss the opportunity to film these mammals. Therefore,

Philippe Cousteau encountered a pilot whale off Catalina Island. The whale was willing to be photographed.

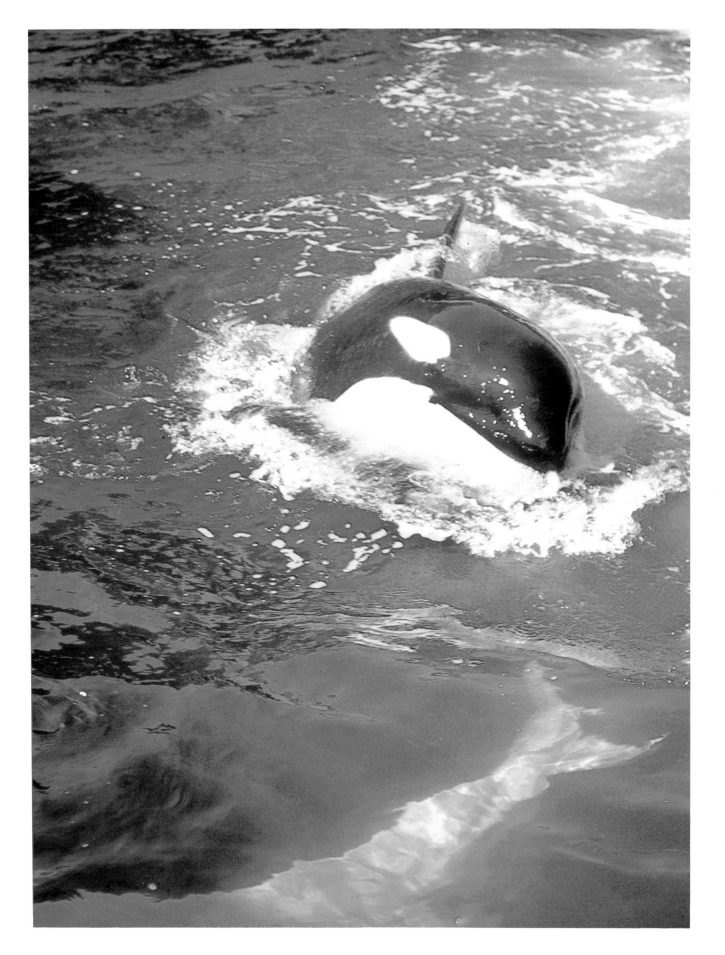

Frédéric Dumas and I set out in a small boat, with a sailor manning the oars. Whenever we attempted to get close to the pilot whales, however, they dived and disappeared, only to reappear a few minutes later at a greater distance. The game of hide-and-seek continued for several hours. We tried to foresee where the animals would come to the surface again, but we were always wrong. Finally, we managed to guess correctly, and we were on the spot when the school surfaced. Our guess was a bit too accurate, perhaps, for it turned out that we were in the middle of the school. One of the whales surfaced alongside the boat, and he was so frightened by what he saw that, with a flip of his tail, he sent everything flying into the air: the boat, the sailor, Dumas, myself, and the camera. We waited there in the water, while the school sped away, until the *Elie Monnier* came to fish us out.

Cuttlefish Eaters

Shortly before that incident, during the same expedition in 1948, we had another interesting experience with pilot whales. We were off the Cape Verde Islands, taking soundings in deep water. The bottom was some 12,000 feet below us, and, for the first time, we were getting echo readings from the D.S.L. — the deep scattering layer. The layer was especially thick at about 850 feet, and it was of that characteristic black which might lead one to believe that it was the bottom of the sea rather than a layer of animals. The only indication that it was indeed the latter was that, in certain places, the layer was very thick, and at others it was thin.

While we were busy with our soundings, we noticed a group of pilot whales near our vessel. There were about twenty of them, and they seemed to be swimming at an unusually slow pace. They did not appear to be going anywhere in particular. Instead, they swam around in the same area, occasionally disappearing in a dive.

Remember that this was in 1948. We still had much to learn, not only about life in the sea but also about ourselves. Without feeling a single twinge of conscience, we harpooned one of the animals to try to find out the reason for this strange behavior. We hauled the whale aboard and proceeded to dissect him. In his stomach we found the remains of several hundred cuttlefish. This was an interesting discovery from two viewpoints. It proved that

(Right) Two beluga whales in their tank at the Vancouver Aquarium.

pilot whales hunted for food at a depth of 1,200 feet, in the D.S.L composed of cephalopods. It also demonstrated that cuttlefish do not live solely in coastal waters, but that they are pelagic animals which are found in great numbers in deep water. Pilot whales also feed on squids.

We were astonished at the enormous quantity of undigested cuttlefish beaks in the whale's stomach. He and his companions obviously had stuffed themselves and were allowing their food to digest, which explained why they were moving so slowly. For once, they did not seem particularly eager to get away from us.

One occasionally hears reference to the "suicide" of pilot whales. This "suicide" refers to the fact that these mammals are sometimes beached in great numbers along the coast of northern England. It has been said that some of these accidents are intentionally provoked by fishermen from the Faeroe and the Shetland islands. The fishermen herd one or two individuals of the school toward land, and the rest of the school follows. Other instances of beached pilot whales have occurred on the coasts of France.

In 1973, thirty or so pilot whales were washed up near Charleston, South Carolina. The entire group was immediately hauled out to sea again, but only a few of them remained there. The rest returned to the beach. Once more they were towed out into the open water. And once more they all returned to the beach. A strange phenomenon, for which there is no adequate explanation.

Representatives of the Smithsonian Institution visited the site and removed the organs of the pilot whales, thinking that there might be a physiological reason for this mass suicide — an epidemic of some kind, for example. An examination, however, revealed that the animals were in normal health.

It is interesting to note that these beachings always occur in the same areas. One explanation offered is that the topological configuration in such areas interferes with the pilot whales' echolocation signals. But if this were so, it seems unlikely that, when stranded animals are towed far out into the open, they would immediately return to the beach.

There are instances, as we know, of captive dolphins allowing themselves to die, or even of causing their own deaths. But there is no obvious reason why pilot whales, living at liberty in the sea, should engage in mass suicide.

Researchers at the Smithsonian Institution have made an interesting discovery at one of the areas where pilot whales regularly allow themselves to be beached. They have excavated a large number of fossilized pilot-whale bones which appear to be several millions of years old. The mass suicide of

(Right) At the Vancouver Aquarium, a killer whale shows his teeth. The killer whale, unlike the dolphin, has no built-in "smile."

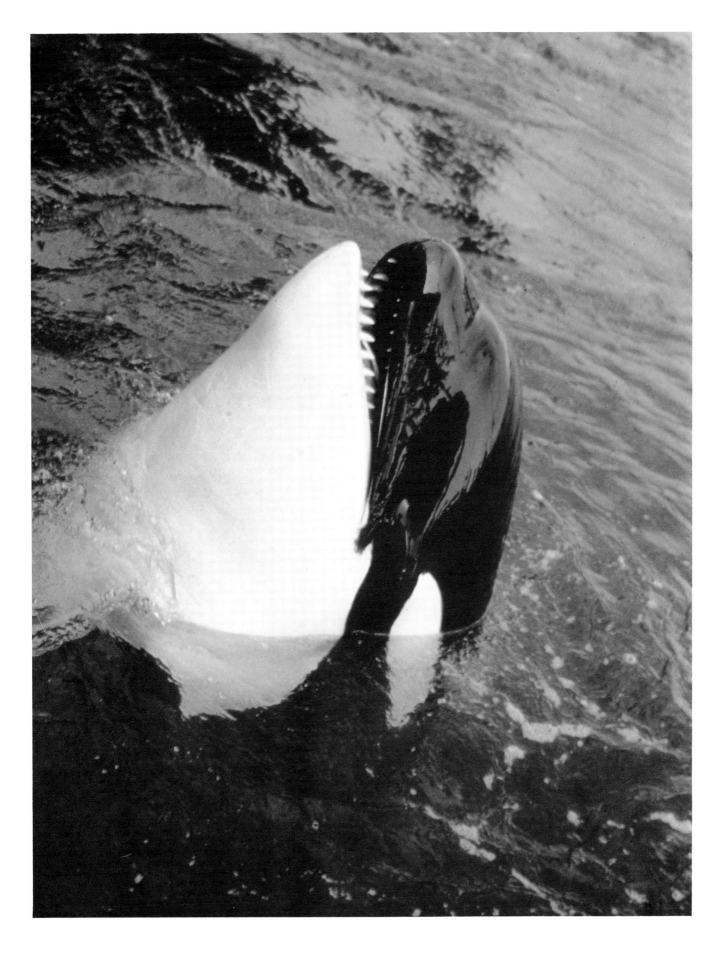

pilot whales, therefore, is not a recent phenomenon. Indeed, it antedates man on the earth. Thus, it can be explained neither as a consequence of commercial fishing nor as that of pollution.

Pilot whales, like dolphins, are creatures of sentiment. There is no instance we know of where a pilot whale became attached to humans, as Dolly and Nina did. But there is at least one case of a whale being passionately fond of a dolphin. The two mammals lived in the same tank in an aquarium. They played together and remained constantly side by side. After several years, the dolphin died of an infection. For several days, the pilot whale kept the corpse of his friend afloat at the surface, and allowed no one to take it away from him. Finally, he was tricked into surrendering it. Then the pilot whale refused to eat. He began to lose weight and was obviously wasting away. The management of the aquarium decided to release the pilot whale in the sea, hoping that this would save the animal's life. Even then, it was difficult to cope with the animal. He remained next to the boat, looking at the men with that expression of puzzled despair sometimes observed on the faces of animals who suffer without understanding what is happening to them. It was a mute, pathetic appeal from the injustice of life and death.

Of all the toothed whales, perhaps the narwhal is the most bizarre. It has a "tusk," which is actually a disproportionately long tooth on the left side of the upper jaw. The narwhal sometimes reaches a length of twelve or thirteen feet, but the average length is about nine feet. The tusk may reach a length of eight to nine feet. It is spirally twisted from right to left. It happens occasionally that a specimen may have a second tusk on the right side.

Only the males have the tusk, the function of which is obscure. It seems not be be used in hunting for food, for the female narwhal, who has no tusk, feeds herself without difficulty. Nor is it a weapon, since the narwhal is not an aggressive animal. Certain specialists hypothesize that the tusk is, in fact, a secondary sexual attribute.

Narwhals live in arctic waters in groups of approximately ten individuals. They are hunted by the Eskimos for the sake of their tusks, which fetch a good price in the ivory market.

These, in brief, are the members of the Delphinidae group. All members of the group have attractive characteristics, or exceptional abilities, or some rare attribute like the spiral "horn" of the narwhal. We can only hope that the public sympathy, which is slowly developing toward this family, may awaken in us the respect due to the intelligence and the innocuous character of its members. Then, perhaps the absurd massacres of the past will never again be repeated.

Chapter Twelve

AN ANCIENT FRIENDSHIP

The bond between dolphins and humans is very old, perhaps as old as that between the dog and man. It goes back, in any event, to the prehistoric period, even though it is difficult to assign an exact date to its beginning. One indication of this fact is the recent discovery, in South Africa, of prehistoric engraved images of dolphins. One can discern the figure of a man swimming among the dolphins.*

The artists of the Aegean civilization have left us handsomer and more precise representations of dolphins. In the palace at Knossos, the bathroom of the queen was decorated with a frieze of dolphins.

It seems certain that the people of ancient Crete were familiar with marine animals to an extent that would be forgotten until the twentieth century. The innumerable vases decorated with images of the octopus, also bear witness to the sympathy of the Aegeans for an animal often despised and feared among other peoples, and that we have tried to rehabilitate.

So far as the dolphin is concerned, an interesting question has been raised. Were dolphins more than mere images and mere subjects for artistic works? Some historians believe that the Cretans had tamed dolphins. Today,

*David K. Caldwell and Melba C. Caldwell, *World of the Bottle-Nosed Dolphin.* Philadelphia, 1972.

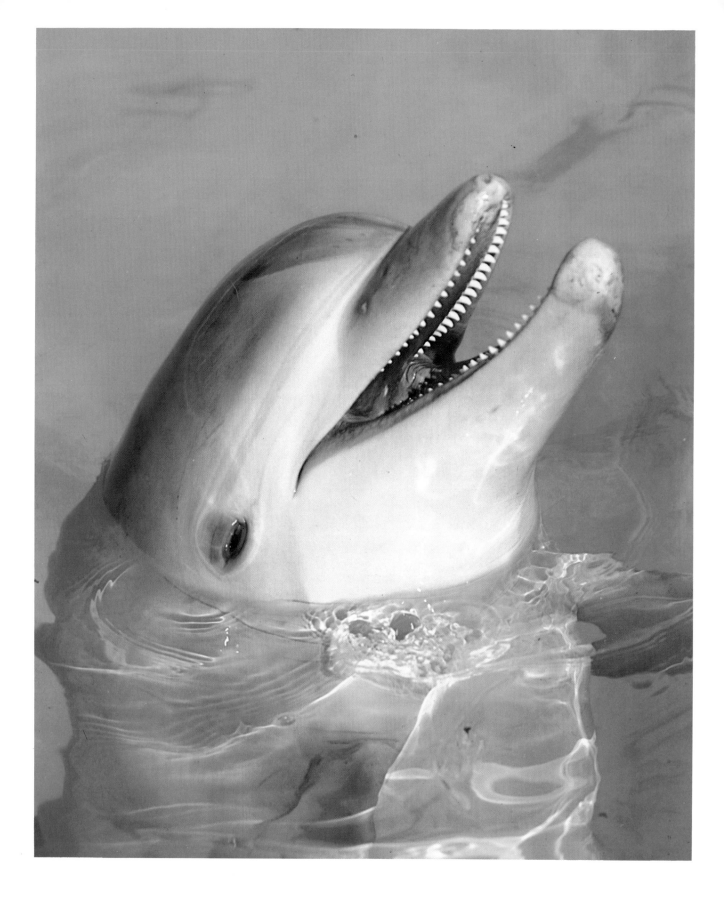

we know that it is possible to do so. The ships of Crete, says Gustave Glotz, "which would not have ventured onto the sea without having a fish tied to its prow, could not have found a better pilot than the dolphin."†

And it was the Cretans who, having learned that, to the South of Parnassus, on the heights dominating the Gulf of Corinth, there was an ancient sanctuary, established there a new sanctuary to which they gave the name of the dolphin: Delphi. They had been guided to that spot by their dolphin-god.

Delphi is the most famous sanctuary of Greece. It was thought to be the center of the world. It was there that the famous oracle spoke. And it was there that Apollo, the god of light, had his sanctuary. For, according to a legend older than that of the Minoans, the place had been given the name Delphi because the god had first appeared there in the form of a dolphin. This was the reason why the dolphins of pre-Hellenic Crete were honored as gods.

Dolphins apparently were more numerous in the Mediterranean in the second millennium before Christ than they are now, and they always showed signs of that willingness to fraternize with man which we see today. The Minoans and the Mycenaeans, being seafaring peoples, no doubt responded to these advances, and a friendship was born. That friendship would blossom and die, not to be recalled until the twentieth century when man and dolphin renewed their ancient contact.

Theseus the Diver

The maritime heirs of the Aegeans were the Phoenicians and the Greeks. The heritage they received included both the Aegeans' secrets of navigation and naval architecture and their respect for the dolphin and their belief in his role as protector. For centuries, the peoples of the Mediterranean believed that a dolphin's presence in the vicinity of a ship was a good omen, and that the animal's disappearance announced a forthcoming storm. When a ship was lost, the way to safety lay in following the course of a dolphin. Everyone knew that the animal would lead them safely home.

If it happened that fishermen accidentally caught a dolphin in their nets, the animal was released immediately.

†G. Glotz, *La Civilization égéenne.*

(Left) A picture of Snoopy, one of the dolphins at the Marineland of Antibes. (Photo, Jose Dupont, Marineland d'Antibes.)

The image of the dolphin is found everywhere on Greek ceramics. Theseus is depicted as surrounded by them, and sometimes they are represented as mounts for warriors. On the famous Euphronius cup, dating from the fifth century B.C. (now in the Museum of the Louvre) there is an image of Theseus at the bottom of the sea, surrounded by dolphins, receiving a golden crown from the hands of Amphitrite, goddess of the sea. The crown was the prize won by the first diver.

The Etruscans, a race of excellent seamen from Lydia, often depicted dolphins in their funeral frescoes. One famous example is found in a Tarquinian tomb of the sixth century B.C., where the dolphins are shown leaping out of the water around a fishing boat.

The dolphin appears, above all, on the coins of the ancients — coins being the essential tool of maritime commerce. On silver pieces of Syracuse, for instance, the nymph Arethusa is shown surrounded by dolphins.

The famous Taranto dolphin, which serves as the mount for the hero Taras (who gave the city of Taranto its name), in addition to its religious, commercial, and maritime significance, also serves to record a legend which may or may not be true: Taras, son of the sea-god Neptune, is supposed to have founded Taranto on the spot to which he was carried by a dolphin.

Some forty Greek cities used the image of the dolphin on their coins. The animal's form, more or less stylized, is also found on anchors, and it was used as the trademark of various prominent Greek and Roman shipowners. Following a model which probably goes back to the ninth, or eighth, century B.C., the Phoenicians showed the dolphin's body twisted around an anchor or a trident. This emblem was chosen by the celebrated Venetian printing house of Aldo Manuzio, in the sixteenth century, for their sumptuous editions of the Greek and Latin authors.

The anchor and the trident are also attributes of the god Poseidon and are used to indicate that the dolphin is the lord of navigation, by virtue of his power and speed as a swimmer, and also of his wisdom and prudence.

The Romans too showed the dolphins in their works of art. On a mosaic in Ostia, we can see dolphins swimming among the ships of a commercial fleet, looking very benevolent and vaguely amused. Their presence indicates that the Roman fleet was actually animated by Greek beliefs and traditions. From the port of Knossos to Ostia, port of Rome, dolphins have survived the ships which once honored them.

It would be wrong for us to think that the Aegeans, Etruscans, Greeks, and Romans used the dolphin to decorate their walls, shields, vases, cups, and coins simply because the dolphin's shape lends itself to ornamental use. Such an approach to art may be characteristic of the twentieth century, but it was

A silver coin of ancient Syracuse, depicting the goddess Arethusa surrounded by four dolphins.

(Above) A dolphin fresco in the Queen's chamber at the Palace of Knossos. The fresco dates from *c.* 1600 B.C. (Musee Archeologique d'Heraklion. Candie.)

(Left) A Greek dolphin ceramic from the fourth century B.C. (Louvre Museum.)

(Right) Fishermen accompanied by a dolphin. Note that the fishermen's boat is itself in the shape of a dolphin, as depicted in this Etruscan representation of the sixth century B.C. (Photo, Giraudon.)

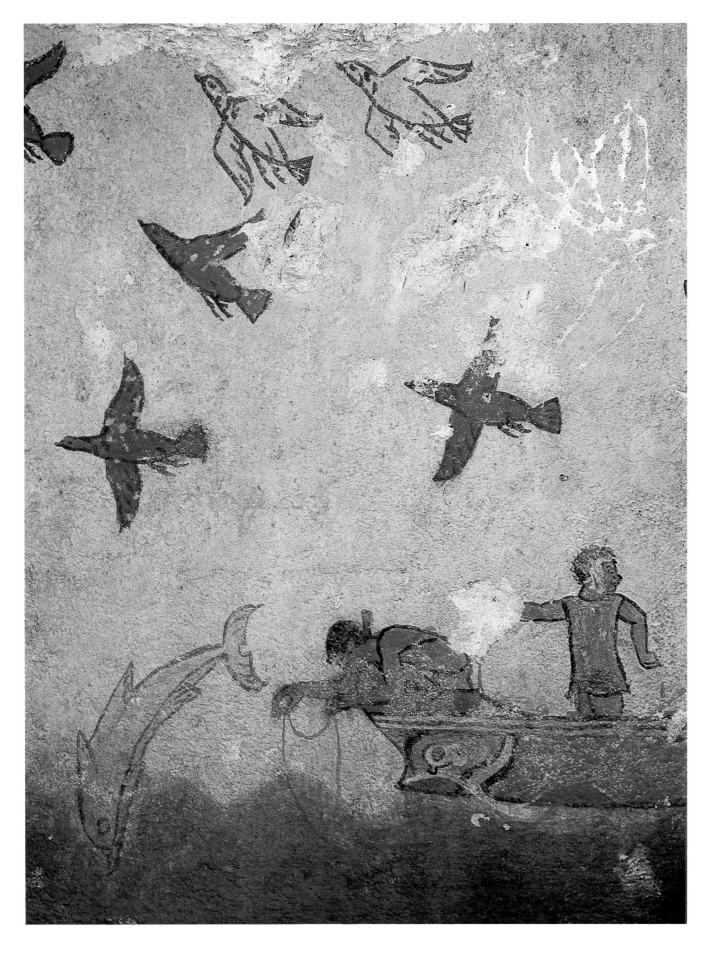

alien to the people of the ancient world. These images have a meaning, and perhaps several meanings. They are symbolic of something else — but of what, we can only guess. Lacking any precise text or inscription, we sense a funereal meaning in these images, but we do not know for certain. Many ancient symbols having to do with the sea and with water had such a meaning. One indication of the significance of the dolphin symbol is found on a mosaic in the Museum of Antioch. This mosaic shows dolphins carrying the souls of the departed to the Isle of the Blessed. The concept may have been part of the Aegean heritage, for the people of Crete assigned that same role to dolphins.

The symbolism of the dolphin, as it existed in the Mediterranean basin for some four thousand years, is not explained by the Greek and Latin texts that we possess. The only information we have comes to us almost solely from anecdotes and testimonials which illustrate the good will of dolphins toward man.

According to the Greeks, this good will was explained by the fact that dolphins were actually men who had been transformed into marine mammals, in the following circumstances: "Dionysos, having borrowed a ship to go to Naxos, saw that the sailors were heading toward Asia, no doubt with the intention of selling him into slavery. Therefore he turned their oars into serpents, filled the ship with ivy, and commanded invisible flutes to play. The ship was held motionless in the twisting vines, and the sailors, driven mad by what they had seen, threw themselves into the sea, where they were transformed into dolphins."‡ Dolphins, therefore, are friendly to man because they are repentant pirates.

From the time of Homer, classical literature abounded with stories of this kind, which have generally been regarded as fables or myths. Today, since we know more about the behavior of marine mammals, we may choose to judge them otherwise.

Several of these legends, in fact, in the light of modern knowledge, take on a certain element of truth. For example, Telemachus, the son of Ulysses, when still a child, fell into the water and was rescued by a dolphin. For that reason, Ulysses always wore a ring engraved with the image of a dolphin. Today, we know that dolphins do rescue drowning humans, and that they seem particularly fond of children.

In the fourth century B.C., Aristotle gave an accurate description of the anatomy and the behavior of dolphins. He noted that the dolphin was a mammal and could not be classified among the fishes.

‡Grimal, *Dictionnaire de la mythologie grecque et romaine.* Paris, 1963.

A *skyphos* representing six warriors mounted on dolphins. (Photo, Museum of Fine Arts, Boston.)

In Pliny's *Natural History*, we find the following: "They [dolphins] are solicitous for each other's well-being. A dolphin was captured by a king of Caria and leashed to the port. The other dolphins assembled in a crowd, attempting, by showing their sorrow, to excite the king's mercy. Finally, the king ordered the captive to be released. Moreover, young dolphins are always accompanied by an older dolphin, who serves as a guardian. And witnesses have seen a dolphin carried by his companions so that he would not fall prey to the monsters of the sea."

Many readers in past centuries have simply shrugged their shoulders, when perusing Pliny's writings, and accused the old Roman of naiveté. Yet, there is little that Pliny says that cannot be verified by our own experience. "The dolphin," Pliny states, "is friendly to man and is charmed by music, by harmonious instruments, and particularly by the sound of the hydraulic or-

(Above) An Italian cup from the fourth century B.C., representing Apollo in his chariot. To the left is a dolphin — the animal sacred to Apollo. (Louvre Museum.)

(Left) A pair of dolphins in the open sea.

gan. He does not regard man as a hostile being, but swims forward of ships, leaps playfully around them, runs races with them, and, no matter how full the sails, always outdistances them."

We know that dolphins are sensitive to music. Aboard *Calypso*, our two guitar players, Louis Prezelin and Dr. Millet, on several occasions attracted dolphins by music.

It is also Pliny who tells us the story of a dolphin who lived in Lake Lucrino. A boy, the son of a poor man who lived in a town near Naples, came every day to feed the dolphin. The boy and the dolphin became friends, and every morning the dolphin carried the child on his back across the lake to

A Greek plate depicting Thetis and the dolphins. (Museum of Fine Arts, Boston.)

school. In the afternoon, he would meet the child and carry him back so that the boy would not have to walk around the lake. One day, the child did not come. He had died during the night. The dolphin waited. When he realized that his friend would come no more, he died of sorrow.

Pliny's nephew, known as Pliny the Younger, in a letter to Caninium Rufus, relates the story of a young boy at Hippo who had been saved from drowning by a dolphin. The two became fast friends, and the boy rode on the dolphin's back, played and jumped and dived with him as the whole city crowded on the beach to watch this spectacle. The dolphin allowed other children, and even adults, to pet him.

This, of course, is exactly what happened with Nina at La Corogna, and with Opo in New Zealand, almost two thousand years later.

The dolphin, after having been a symbol among the Cretans, Etruscans,

A Greek ceramic cup decorated with the figures of three dolphins. (Louvre Museum.)

Greeks, and Romans, was assimilated into the Christian bestiary and into the heraldic art of the West. He became the symbol of rebirth. He was the intercessor who guided and supported man in the sea and allowed him to return to land cleansed of his sins. He was the guide who saved the shipwrecked man and carried him to port, that is, to salvation.

It should come as no surprise, therefore, that Christ the Saviour, like Apollo, was often represented in the form of a dolphin. There are several

(Following page left) The dolphin, when swimming, moves alternately beneath and above the surface.

(Following page right) Falco capturing a dolphin at *Calypso*'s stem.

animals with which man has had an intimate association since the dawn of history. The bond between man and some of these animals — the dog, for instance, and the horse — is reasonably well defined. In the case of other animals (and I am speaking particularly of the dolphin), it is nebulous and precarious. Surely there was a good reason why the peoples of the ancient world chose to surround themselves with images and representations of dolphins. Certainly, the general belief that dolphins were man's helpers and protectors in the sea was not without some foundation in fact. Yet, beyond the few stories contained in the works of Pliny and other ancient writers, we know very little about how the dolphin came to play such a notable role in the artistic and religious life of the ancient Mediterranean world. Is it possible that now, in the mid-twentieth century, we are just beginning to unveil a "secret" that was no secret at all to our ancestors? Can it be that the dolphin is not a new friend in the sea, but a very old friend whom chance — or destiny — has once more led us to recognize?

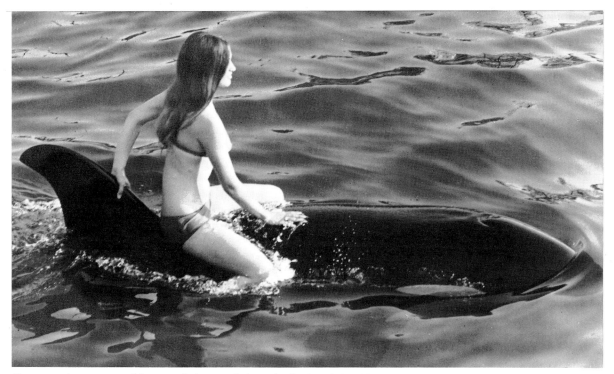

For centuries, reports of humans being carried on the backs of dolphins were treated as legends. The photograph above, however, shows a dolphin at the Marineland of Antibes carrying a young girl on his back. (Photo, Gilbert Pressenda.) Below, a Greek vase of the fifth century B.C. shows a Nereid mounted on a dolphin. (Louvre Museum.)

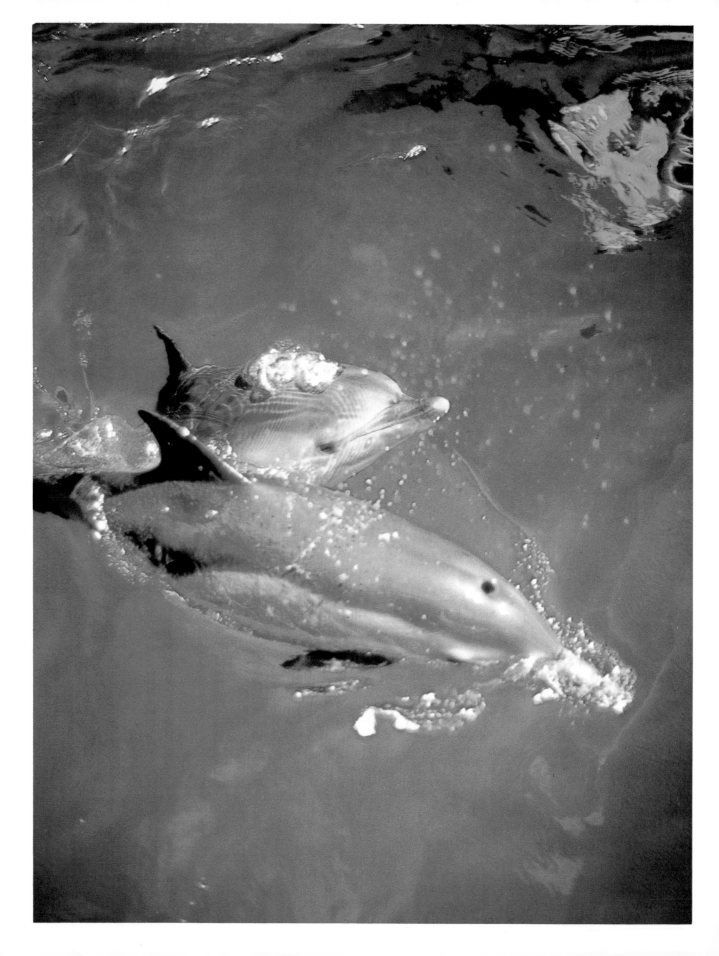

Chapter Thirteen

THE PROMISE OF THE FUTURE

What does the future hold for dolphins?

In twenty years, or in fifty years, if the good will and curiosity now shown them continues, there is little doubt that they will be living in increasingly close contact with man.

At that time, diving will constitute a considerable part of man's scientific, industrial, and social activities. There will be increased contact between divers and marine mammals. And, since the dolphin is a well-equipped animal from a physiological standpoint, these encounters will have an effect upon him and will influence him, educate him, and change his behavioral patterns.

Rats and other animals living in cities change their behavior in accordance with man's routine. Rats know at what time one's garbage is put outside, for example. And, in England, tits have learned to use their beaks to pierce the cardboard or metal covers on the milk bottles left outside one's door. We can only speculate what effect man's intervention in the sea will have on dol-

(Left) These two dolphins are "talking" to one another. Notice the bubbles rising from the blowhole of one of the dolphins.

phins, killer whales, Belugas, and sea lions. How will these animals profit from that intervention? And how will they use what they learn?

The number of animals trained for missions in the sea will no doubt be much larger than it is now. They will serve as guides and as liaison agents with their fellow dolphins still roaming the sea in schools.

Finally, one must think of what is happening, and of what will happen, in our aquariums and marinelands. Surely, the number of these establishments will be greatly increased. More animals will be held captive. And it is in captivity that animals are modified and changed. Domestic animals, after all, are wild animals which have been first confined and then bred by man. They are new animals, transformed animals, only in the sense that such animals do not exist in nature. Thus, in Mesopotamia, in the Indus valley, and in Egypt, five or six thousand years ago, man created hogs, goats, and cattle totally different from wild animals. So far as the dog is concerned, it took sixty thousand years to make him what he is.

Experimental Biology

The origin of the dog combines in the mists of time with that of man. The dog seems linked to man. He is man's perennial companion. What makes this possible is the dog's extreme polymorphism, his versatility which renders him susceptible to any metamorphosis. The dog's size, shape, color, and behavior have been changed by accident, by mutations, and by breeding.

Are cetaceans as amenable to change as dogs? It is still too early to tell. In any event, there has been an important event to which too little attention has been paid. Two species of dolphin — a Bottlenosed Dolphin and a Steno — have interbred in captivity. Hybridization is an essential tool of breeders. By crossbreeding, the breeder is able to develop certain qualities and to eliminate certain defects. It is the means by which man changes life and attains mastery over the other animals — a mastery which constitutes the most important chapter in human history and which has been called "a vast undertaking in experimental biology."

Will this work be undertaken in systematic fashion by zoologists? If so, where will it lead? Will we be given a companion and helper to take our place in the water and to work with us in the sea? Very probably. We are almost at

(Right) Yves Omer and Falco attach an underwater camera to a dolphin's dorsal fin.

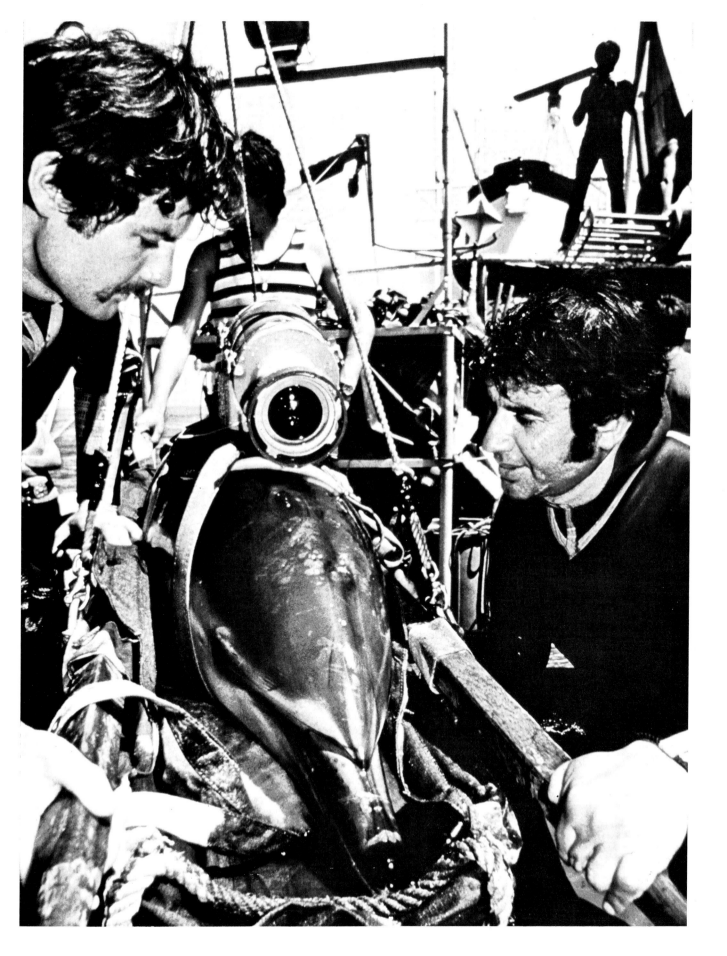

that stage now. We do not have the ability to locate objects in cloudy water, or to find the source of a sound. Our senses do not function well under water, while those of the dolphin are miracles of effective performance. The use of those senses on our behalf may render us invaluable service. The dolphin may become our great helpmate in the sea, the equivalent of the horse on land as it was almost four thousand years ago.

The Ultimate Step

The brain of the dolphin — its development and its structures — presents a major problem. What will become of that organ after fifty or a hundred years of close association between dolphins and men? The dolphin's brain is capable of memory, of associating ideas. It may, someday, be capable of language, like that of the primates.

Throughout this book, we have been especially careful to avoid exaggerating the mental potential of the dolphin even at the risk of disappointing the reader. When necessary, we have gone out of our way to demythologize dolphins and to strip away elements which, however appealing they may be, are redolent more of folklore than of fact. Even so, we must remember that what is not true today may be true tomorrow. Today, the dolphin is an animal. Tomorrow, human contact may make the dolphin something more than an animal. What promise the future holds for us — and what responsibility!

A mosaic decorating a basin of the fourth century A.D. found at Utica, in North Africa.

Acknowledgments

We acknowledge a debt of gratitude to a number of scientists who have given us the benefit of their advice in the preparation of this work. Our special thanks go to the following:

Professor Paul Budker, Director, Laboratory of Cetacean Biology, École Pratique des Hautes Études

Professor René-Guy Busnel, Director, Laboratory of Acoustical Physiology, CNRS, Jouy-en-Josas;

Mr. Charles Roux, Assoicate Director, Laboratory of Reptiles and Fishes, National Museum of Natural History;

Mr. Albin Dziedzic, Laboratory of Acoustical Physiology, CNRS, Jouy-en-Josas.

Photo Credits

The photographs appearing in this book were taken by Henri Alliet, Ron Church, Jan and Philippe Cousteau, François Dorado, Marie-Noëlle Favier, Ivan Giacoletto, Andrée Laban, Edmond Laffont, Jean-Jacques Languepin, Yves Omer, Louis Prezelin, André Ragiot, Jacques Renoir, and Jean-Clair Riant.

Several of the photographs taken at the surface were chosen from the private collections of *Calypso*'s team.

The line drawings appearing in the appendices and glossary were executed by Jean-Charles Roux.

Iconography: Marie-Noëlle Favier.

APPENDICES

From top to bottom: *Delphinus delphis*; *Tursiops truncatus*; *Phocoena cephalorhynchus*.

APPENDIX I

The Delphinidae Family

Throughout this book, we have sometimes referred to dolphins in general terms; and sometimes we have mentioned the names of some species which are rather less known to the public than the *Tursiops truncatus*, or Bottlenosed Dolphin. This practice, however necessary it may have been, may have caused some confusion in the reader's mind — not a surprising development, certainly, even when dealing with animals so distinct from each other in shape and size. It may be helpful, therefore, for us to supply some clarifications.

When dealing with dolphins — or with cetaceans generally — the first problem we encounter is one of nomenclature. "For English-language authors," Professor Paul Budker has observed, "any Odontocete [toothed whale] less than fifteen feet in length is a dolphin if it has a beak; and if it has a rounded snout, it is called a porpoise." It does not simplify matters that, in the United States, the popular name for the most famous species of dolphins, the Bottlenosed, is "porpoise," while the British reserve that term exclusively for the Harbor Porpoise (*Phocaena phocaena*).

It would be easy to multiply examples of such confusions. For our purposes, suffice it to say that the Delphinidae are the most numerous family of cetaceans, comprising some forty-eight species. "There is no such thing as a dolphin," Professor Budker says. "There are only dolphins."

The largest member of the Delphinidae clan is the Killer Whale, which attains a length of twenty-five to twenty-eight feet and weighs about a ton. This dolphin has a rounded head, a very large dorsal fin, and white markings. It is the mortal enemy of other dolphins, and even of baleen whales. However, its proverbial ferocity is held in abeyance so far as man is concerned. Killer Whales are easily trained and are star performers in aquariums and marinelands. Their "intelligence" is remarkable — undoubtedly superior to that of Bottlenosed Dolphins.

The Bottlenosed Dolphin grows to a length of nine to twelve feet. It is very common in the Atlantic, and, so far as the general public is concerned, it is the prototypal dolphin, immediately recognizable by its beak and the rictus which gives the dolphin the appearance of wearing a perpetual smile.

The Common Dolphin (*Delphinus delphis*) is slightly smaller than the Bottlenosed. It is found in all warm and temperate seas, such as in the Mediterranean and in the Black Sea. The Common Dolphin was the species with which the ancients were most familiar and which they depicted in their artifacts.

The coloration of dolphins varies according to species. *Stenella* is spotted (its popular name is Spotted Dolphin), while the *Lagenorhynchus acutus* has white flanks and *Lagenorhynchus albirostris* has a white snout. The genus *Cephalorhynchus* is of small size, with a non-prominent beak. Its body is black and white. It is found mostly in southern waters, where it feeds on jellyfish and shrimp.

River dolphins (Platanistidae), or fresh-water dolphins, have long, narrow snouts. The Stenodelphia is found in South American waters, but a member of the Delphinidae family is found in the Mekong: the *Orcaella*. Many of these fresh-water dolphins are blind. (See Appendix III.)

The porpoise, properly speaking, is not a dolphin at all, but belongs to another genus: Phocaena. It is a cetacean of relatively small size, with a slightly developed dorsal fin and a short snout. The Common Porpoise (*Phocaena phocaena*), which attains a length of four to six feet, is found in almost all parts of the world.

Beluga Whales and Narwhals are not members of the Delphinidae family. They belong to the Monodontidae. The Beluga (*Delphinapterus leucas*) inhabits cold waters and is from ten to twelve feet in length. It is white, with a comparatively prominent neck. It is known as the White Whale, and sometimes as the White Porpoise. The Narwhal (*Monodon monoceros*) attains a length of from twelve to eighteen feet. It feeds on starfish, cuttlefish, and fishes. In the male Narwhal, a single tooth, located on the left side of the lower jaw, grows disproportionately long and sometimes reaches a length of six feet.

The *Hyperoodon rostratus*, or Northern Bottlenosed Whale, belongs to the family Ziphiidae or "beaked whales." It is being trained, with some success, in several aquariums. It is said to be the most capable diver of all the cetaceans. The giant of the family is the *Berardius*, some specimens of which reach a length of thirty-six feet.

The Pilot Whale (*Globicephala scammonii*), (family Delphinidae), also called the Blackfish and the Ca'ing Whale, may be from eighteen to twenty-two feet in length. They are found in all the oceans. They travel in groups of several hundred individuals, all closely following the leader of the group. They are black, with a white marking on their underside. Pilot Whales adapt to captivity, and several specimens have been trained successfully.

The Sub-Committee on Small Cetaceans of the International Whaling Commission, at a meeting held in Montreal on April 1–10, 1974, decided that it was necessary to review the number of Delphinidae species recognized as such. A certain number of these species are no longer to be considered as geographic variants.

From top to bottom: Bottlenosed Whale; Killer Whale; Beluga Whale.

APPENDIX II

The Cetaceans*

Cetaceans are marine mammals. They are warm-blooded creatures, and, as Aristotle noted more than two thousand years ago, they breathe by means of lungs. Fertilization and gestation are internal, and female whales nurse their offspring.

The relationship of cetaceans to land mammals is obvious, although there are anatomical differences among cetaceans which have allowed them to adapt perfectly to marine life. The fossil remains of the land ancestors of the cetaceans have not been discovered, but small bones enclosed within the muscles of some cetaceans are vestiges of a pelvic structure and sometimes represent a rudimentary femur or a tibia.

The dorsal fin, which is characteristic of all cetaceans except the sperm whale, seems to have developed within comparatively recent times, and it has no connection with the skeleton.

All cetaceans are equipped with tails that spread horizontally rather than, as in the case of fish, vertically. Also they have a blowhole or vent, at the

*This appendix is based upon the works of Kenneth S. Norris, Dr. Harrison Matthews, Dr. F. C. Fraser, David K. and Melba C. Caldwell, Ernest P. Walker, and upon the classification of the International Whaling Commission.

top of their heads, through which they breathe. The position and shape of the blowhole varies according to the species.

The order of cetaceans includes approximately one hundred species and is divided into two suborders: the Mystacoceti, which are the baleen or whalebone cetaceans; and the Odontoceti, or toothed cetaceans.

The Odontoceti

The number of teeth varies. The Goosebeak Whale has two, some species of dolphin have 260. All species are carnivorous. (Formerly, it was thought that the fresh-water dolphins of American waters fed on aquatic plants.) There are five families of Odontoceti, which include the majority of the species of cetaceans:

(1) The Delphinidae, which contains nineteen genera: *Delphinus* with *Delphinus delphis* or Common Dolphin, *Tursiops, Grampus, Lagenorhynchus, Feresa, Cephalorhynchus, Orcaella, Lissodelphis, Lagenodelphis, Steno, Sousa, Sotalia, Stenella, Phocaena* (porpoise), *Phocaenoides* (Pacific porpoise), *Neomeris* (the Southeast Asian porpoise), *Pseudorca, Orcinus* (Killer Whale), and *Globicephala* (Pilot Whale).

Gestation lasts about twelve months among *Tursiops* and Killer Whales; eleven months for the Common Dolphin; and thirteen to sixteen months for the Pilot Whale.

(2) The Platanistidae are fresh-water dolphins, living exclusively or partially in fresh water, often in the estuaries of large rivers. They are divided into *Platanista* (Ganges Dolphin), *Inia* (Amazon Dolphin), *Lipotes* (found in China), and *Stenodelphis*, the La Plata River Dolphin.

(3) The Monodontidae, comprising two genera: *Delphinapterus*, the Beluga Whale found especially in the arctic seas around North America, whose period of gestation is about one year; and *Monodon*, the Narwhal.

(4) The Ziphiidae, which are characterized by a beak-shaped snout, include five genera: *Mesoplodon, Ziphius, Tasmacetus, Berardius, Hyperoodon*. Gestation lasts ten months only for the big *Berardius*.

(5) The Physeteridae are the sperm whales, divided into two genera: the

The Narwhal (above) and the Pilot Whale (below).

Kogia, or Pygmy Sperm Whale, and the *Physeter*, or Sperm Whale (Cachalot).

Of all the Odontoceti, the sperm whale is instantly recognizable because of its oblique spout. It has two blowholes, but the left opening is the only working one. The sperm whale is characterized especially by its massive head and squared snout. The head accounts for one third of the cachalot's body length. Only the lower jaw has teeth — but each tooth is ten inches long and weighs over two pounds.

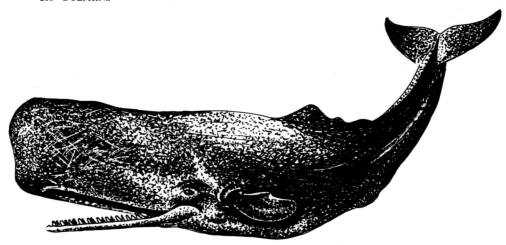

The Cachalot, or Sperm Whale, has no dorsal fin. Note, however, the bony ridge or "crest" on its back.

The sperm whale has no dorsal fin, but it does have a sort of "crest."

It is usually dark in color, with spots that lighten as it grows older.

The largest cachalots — always males — reach a maximum length of sixty feet. They weigh between thirty-five and fifty tons and feed principally on giant squid, which they seek out in the great depths of the sea.

Gestation lasts sixteen months, and the calf nurses for twelve months. A single calf is born every three years. Sperm whales live in family groups, or harems, of twenty to fifty individual whales.

The Mystacoceti

The Mystacoceti, or baleen whales, are characterized by the presence in the upper jaw of plates of whalebone (baleen), the fringed edges of which act as a sieve through which water is strained to remove the small animals on which the whale feeds. The spacing of the fringe depends upon the size of the animals on which a particular species normally preys. There are three families of Mystacoceti:

(1) The Balaenidae, which, in turn, comprises three genera:
(a) *Balaena*, of which the species *Balaena mysticetus*, or the right whale, is best known.

The right whale grows to a length of fifty to sixty feet and has black skin, except for the throat and chin which are cream-colored. One third of its body length is taken up by the enormous mouth. It has no dorsal fin and no ventral

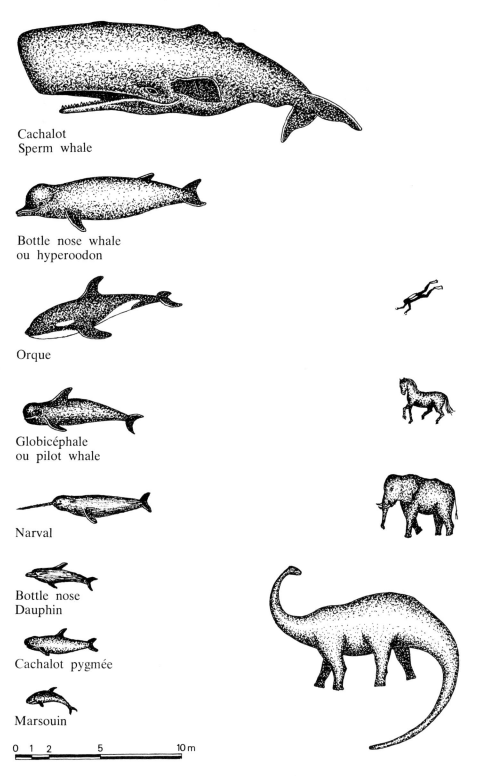

Cachalot
Sperm whale

Bottle nose whale
ou hyperoodon

Orque

Globicéphale
ou pilot whale

Narval

Bottle nose
Dauphin

Cachalot pygmée

Marsouin

0 1 2   5   10 m

The baleen whales: (from top to bottom) Blue Whale, Finback Whale, Right Whale, Sei Whale, Humpback Whale, Gray Whale, Dwarf Right Whale, small Finback Whale.

furrows. The right whale is able to suspend breathing for from ten to thirty minutes. Its gestation period is nine or ten months, and its principal food is krill.

Right whales were still abundant in arctic waters at the beginning of the nineteenth century. By the twentieth century, however, the species was almost extinct. They are now protected by international agreement.

(b) *Eubalaena*, whose external characteristics are the same as those of the right whale except for the mouth, which is smaller and accounts only for one quarter of the total body length. *Eubalaena* includes the following species: *Eubalaena glacialis*, which frequents the North Atlantic and which, because of its modest size (forty to fifty-five feet) was hunted by the Basques as early as the ninth century. Specimens are extremely rare, and the species has been protected for the past thirty-five years. *Eubalaena australis*, which lives in the waters of the Antarctic. Fifty years ago, this species counted its members in the hundreds of thousands. Whalers almost destroyed the species, however, and, at the present time, after thirty-five years of absolute protection, there are once again a few schools in the South Atlantic, in the neighborhood of the Cape of Good Hope, and off South Georgia (an island of Antarctica).

(c) *Caperea*, to which only one species belongs: *Caperea marginata*, or the pygmy right whale, which has a dorsal fin.

(2) The Eschrichtiidae, which includes only the *Eschrichtius gibbosus* — the California gray whale, which is found near the American and Korean coasts. The gray whale has no dorsal fin. It reaches a length of between thirty-five and forty-five feet and weighs between twenty-four and thirty-seven tons. Its color is black, or slate, and its skin is mottled with grayish patches of barnacles. (The grayish cast of its skin is the result of wounds inflicted by parasites.) Sexual maturity is attained at four and one half years, and gestation lasts from eleven to twelve months. A single calf is born every two years.

(3) The Balaenopteridae, of which there are two genera:

(a) Balaenoptera, comprising the following species:

Balaenoptera borealis, or Sei Whale;

Balaenoptera acutorostrata, or lesser rorqual;

Balaenoptera edeni, or Bryde's whale; and

Balaenoptera physalus, or finback whale (also known as the common rorqual). The finback whale measures sixty to seventy-five feet in length and weighs some fifty tons. Its back is grayish. There is a clearly distinguishable dorsal fin, rather high and triangular in shape. The finback whale travels in schools of twenty to one hundred individuals. It feeds on plankton, crustaceans, and small fishes. This species mates during the winter, and the period of gestation lasts between ten and twelve months. The male attains sexual maturity at five years; and the female, between three and eight years. Physical maturity, however, is not reached until the age of fifteen. Full-grown specimens may remain without breathing for from twenty to fifty minutes. The finback whale has been one of the principal victims of whalers, and it is estimated that 90 per cent of the species has been destroyed. In 1955, there were still approximately 110,000 specimens in the Atlantic. Today, there are probably no more than 30,000.

(b) *Balaenoptera musculus*, or blue whale (also known as the sulphur-bottomed whale), is the largest of the cetaceans and the largest animal that has ever existed on earth. It reaches lengths of between eighty and one hundred feet, and the largest specimen known weighed 120 tons.

The blue whale winters in tropical waters and spends its summers in polar seas. The skin is slate blue. Blue whales travel singly rather than in schools, and they are able to remain underwater for periods of from ten to twenty minutes. Their basic food is krill.

They mate during May and June, and gestation lasts eleven months. One calf is born every two years. Sexual maturity is reached at the age of four and one half years.

The blue whale was the most avidly hunted of the great cetaceans because it yielded the greatest quantity of oil. In 1930, it was estimated that there were between 30,000 and 40,000 blue whales in the Antarctic. Today, the most optimistic estimate sets the number at 2,000 — and perhaps fewer. The blue whale is now a totally protected species.

(c) *Megaptera*, of which there is a single species: *Megaptera novaeangliae*, the humpback whale. The humpback whale, along with the gray whale, is the only species to live in coastal waters.

The humpback's average length is forty feet; its average weight, thirty tons. The upper part of the body is black, and the throat and chest are white. It is recognizable by its large white flippers, which measure a third of the length of the body. Crustaceans form its normal diet.

Gestation lasts ten months. Sexual maturity is attained at the age of three, but full physical growth is not reached until the tenth year. A calf is born every two years.

During the 1930s, the Antarctic's humpback population was estimated at 22,000. Now, there are probably not more than 3,000 specimens in the Antarctic. In the northern Pacific, however, there are an additional 5,000 specimens. Today, the species is totally protected.

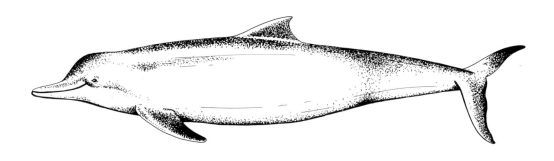

From top to bottom: *Inia geoffrensis*, Gagentic dolphin; *Sotalia fluviatilis*.

APPENDIX III

Fresh-water Dolphins

Certain species of dolphin live exclusively or partially in fresh water. These are the Platanistidae and three genera of Delphinidae (*Sousa, Sotalia,* and *Orcaella* of the Mekong, which is found both in rivers and in coastal waters).

Platanista, which inhabits the waters of the Ganges, the Brahmaputra, and the Indus, is notable for its long beak lined with many teeth and for its clearly distinguishable neck. It eats shrimp and bottom-living fishes which it digs out of the bottom. It does not venture beyond the limits of fresh water.

It is sightless. The eyes have no crystallin and no pigmented epithelium. The optical nerve is greatly reduced. Yet, by means of its acoustical equipment, it can easily locate its prey in the water and in the mud of the bottom, and it is very difficult to capture with nets.

These dolphins sometimes hunt for food in no more than eight inches of water, where they move by swimming on their side. Sometimes, small groups of Platanista live near human installations.

Among the Platanistidae, *Inia geoffrensis* or bouto dolphin of the Amazon and the Orinoco is remarkable for its small eyes, pink skin, long beak, and humped back. David and Melba Caldwell have designated it "the ugly dolphin." Occasionally, when the water is high, the bouto leaves the riverbed and ventures into the flooded forests. Unlike most fresh-water dolphins, this species lives in schools of twelve to twenty individuals, and they show signs of great social solidarity.

One species of Delphinidae, *Sotelia fluviatilis*, is a near relative of *Tursiops*. It is a small dolphin, not longer than five or six feet, and inhabits the Amazon and Orinoco basins from Brazil to Venezuela. Certain local tribes regard it as a sacred animal.

The dolphin of the Rio de La Plata, *Stenodelphis*, leaves fresh water in winter and moves into coastal waters. It feeds on shrimp, squid, and on fishes. It is also a small animal, and its skin is gray. Because of the latter trait, it is known in Uruguay as "Franciscana" — the Franciscan.

The *Sousa* dolphin is found in southern Asia, along the eastern and western coasts of Africa, at Senegal, in the Cameroons, and at Zanzibar.

The Chinese dolphin, *Lipotes* or pei ch'i, inhabits Lake Tung-t'ing. Its eyes are atrophied, and it seems almost totally without sight. It feeds on eel-shaped herbs buried in the bottom of the lake. Practically nothing is known of this species.

APPENDIX IV

Protective Legislation

In the United States:

A law for the protection of marine mammals was enacted by Congress on October 21, 1972, to become effective on December 21 of the same year. The Department of Commerce and the Department of the Interior are responsible for the enforcement of this legislation.

This new law forbids the capturing or importing of marine mammals into the United States. It also prohibits the importing of products made from any part of marine mammals.

A special permit is mandatory for the use of marine mammals in scientific experimentation or in public displays.

An exception to the law is the furred seals of the Pribiloff Islands which, since they are the victims of systematic commercial exploitation, are not protected.

Also, Eskimos and Indians who hunt cetaceans for their livelihood are specifically permitted to continue to do so.

Congress has also authorized a research program to study ways and means of reducing the numbers of dolphins killed during tuna-fishing expeditions. A separate research program is under way to determine the number of individuals belonging to the sixty-two species of marine mammals which are of vital interest to the United States.

In France:

The following is the text of the law prohibiting the capture or killing of dolphins:

"In view of the law of January 9, 1852, on maritime fishing, and particularly of Article 3 of said law;

"In view of the ordinance of June 3, 1944, regarding the reorganization of maritime fishing, especially Article 4 of said Ordinance;

"And taking into account the contribution of the Delphinidae to the ecological equilibrium of the seas and their utilization in the domain of scientific and technological research:

"Article One. It is forbidden to kill, to pursue or to capture, by any means whatever, even without the intention of harming, any marine mammals of the Delphinidae family (dolphins and porpoises).

"Article Two. The above dispositions do not apply to operations undertaken solely for purposes of scientific research.

"Article Three. The directors of maritime affairs at Le Havre, Saint-Servan, Nantes, Bordeaux, and Marseilles are responsible, each of his own territorial jurisdiction, for the execution of the present decree, which shall be published in the official Journal of the French Republic and made part of the official Bulletin of the Merchant Marine.

"Paris, October 20, 1970."

Appendix V

DOLPHINS IN THE CIRCUS AND IN THE LABORATORY

Among the institutions and establishments which breed, train, or study dolphins in captivity, we have listed those which are commercial in nature and which organize exhibitions or shows of trained animals, as well as centers for scientific research. Some marinelands, however, engage in both activities, and, in such cases, they have been listed in both categories.

MARINELANDS AND AQUARIUMS

United States.

Steinhart Aquarium, San Francisco, California
ABC Marine World, Redwood City, California
Marineland of the Pacific, California
Sea World, San Diego, California
Marineland of Florida, Florida
Ocean World, Fort Lauderdale, Florida
Miami Seaquarium, Miami, Florida
Aquarium of St. Petersburg Beach, Florida

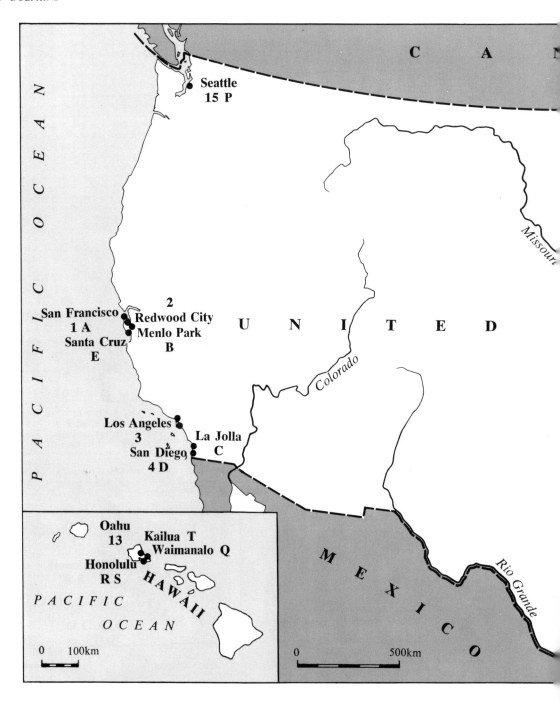

Marinelands are designated by numbers, and the various laboratories and dolphin research centers, by letters

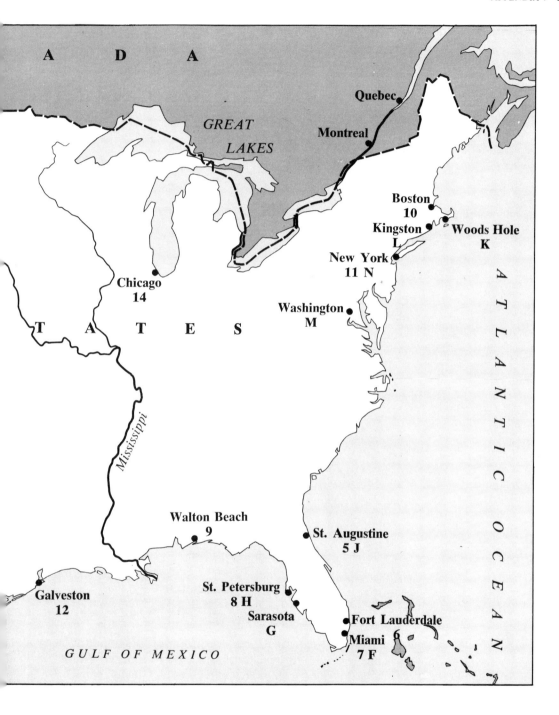

A   D   A

GREAT
LAKES

Quebec

Montreal

Boston
10

Kingston
L

Woods Hole
K

New York
11 N

Washington
M

Chicago
14

T   A   T   E   S

A T L A N T I C   O C E A N

Mississippi

Walton Beach
9

St. Augustine
5 J

Galveston
12

St. Petersburg
8 H

Sarasota
G

Fort Lauderdale
6

Miami
7 F

GULF OF MEXICO

Florida's Gulfarium, Walton Beach, Florida
New England Aquarium, Boston, Massachusetts
New York Aquarium, Coney Island, New York
Sea-Arama Marineworld, Galveston, Texas
Sea Life Park, Oahu, Hawaii
Sea World, Chicago, Illinois
Seattle Marine Aquarium and Namu Inc., Seattle, Washington

Other Countries

Australia: Coolangatta, Queensland
Belgium: Anvers Zoological Garden
Canada: Niagra Falls · Vancouver Public Aquarium, British Columbia
France: Marineland d'Antibes
Germany: Duisburg Zoological Garden
Great Britain: Flamingo Park, Malton, Yorkshire · Whipsnade Zoological
   Gardens, Bedfordshire
Holland: Harderwijk
Japan: Enoshima Marineland · Ito Aquarium, Ito · Mitor Aquarium,
   Numazu · Toba Aquarium, Toba · Iruka Jima Yvenchi, Toba · Shimonse
   Aquarium, Shimonoseki · Numazu Aquarium, Numazu
New Zealand: Marineland of New Zealand, Napier.
South Africa: Durban Aquarium · The Oceanarium, Port Elizabeth
Spain: Barcelona Zoological Garden
Switzerland: Berne Zoological Garden
Canada: Niagara Falls · Vancouver Public Aquarium,
   British Columbia

Laboratories and Centers for Experimental Research

United States

Steinhart Aquarium, California Academy of Sciences, San Francisco, Cali-
   fornia.
Stanford Research Institute, Menlo Park, California.
Scripps Institution of Oceanography, La Jolla, California.
Naval Undersea Research and Development Center, San Diego, California.
University of California, Santa Cruz, California.

School of Marine and Atmospheric Sciences, University of Miami, Florida.

Mote Marine Laboratory, Sarasota, Florida.

Marine Research Laboratory, Florida Dept. of Natural Resources, St. Petersburg, Florida.

Marineland Research Laboratory, St. Augustine, Florida.

Woods Hole Oceanographic Institution, Woods Hole, Massachusetts.

Narragansett Marine Laboratory, University of Rhode Island, Kingston, Rhode Island.

Smithsonian Institution, Washington, D.C. (Marine Mammals Study Center.)

Rockefeller Institute, New York, New York

Makapuu Oceanic Center, Waimanalo, Hawaii.

U. S. Navy Marine Biosystem Division, Honolulu, Hawaii.

Dept. of Psychology, University of Hawaii, Honolulu.

Naval Undersea Research and Development Center, Hawaii Laboratory, Kailva, Hawaii.

Other Countries

Australia: Arthur Rylah Institute for Environmental Research, Heidelberg, Victoria. • School of Biological Sciences, University of Sydney

Canada: Arctic Biological Station, Fisheries Research Board of Canada, St. Anne de Bellevue, Quebec. • Marine Ecology Laboratory, Fisheries Research Board of Canada, Bedfort Institute, Dartmouth, Nova Scotia • Department of Zoology, University of Guelph, Guelph, Ontario.

France: Centre d'Etudes des Cetaces, Museum d'Histoire Naturelle, La Rochelle. • Laboratoire de Physiologie Acoustique, INRA, ERA CNRS, Jouy-en-Josas 78.

Great Britain: Department of Mammalogy, British Museum (Natural History), London. Whale Research Unit, Institute of Oceanographic Science's c/o British Museum (Natural History), London.

Holland: Museum of Natural History, Leyden. • Zoological Museum, Institute of Taxonomic Zoology, Amsterdam.

Japan: Ocean Research Institute, Tokyo University. • Whaling Research Institute, Tokyo. • Faculty of Fisheries, Nagasaki University, Nagasaki-Ken.

New Zealand: Department of Zoology, Victoria University of Wellington.

Switzerland: Brain Research Institute, Berne.

U.S.S.R.: Institute of Morphology of the Academy of Sciences, Moscow. · Institute for the Study of Nervous Activity, University of Moscow. · Faculty of Biology, University of Moscow. · Institute of Developmental Biology, Academy of Sciences, Moscow.

Illustrated Glossary

Adjutage

An apparatus designed to fit the opening of a water or gas main and used to control the flow of the gas or liquid.

Apnea

The more or less prolonged suspension of breathing.

Aqua-Lung®

The Aqua-Lung®, or diving gear, was designed in 1943 by Jacques-Yves Cousteau and Emile Gagnan, an engineer.

The principal characteristic of this apparatus is that it is an "open-circuit" device. That is, the used air is expelled directly into the water, and fresh air is provided, not in continuous fashion but whenever the diver inhales.

The air itself is stored in one or more air tanks (or "bottles" or "cylinders") which are strapped to the diver's back. Its flow is controlled by a regulator, which delivers air when the diver inhales and which assures that the pressure of the air is the same as that of the water surrounding the diver. When the diver exhales, the used air is fed into the water by means of an exhaust located under the hood of the regulator. Two flexible tubes run from a mouthpiece to the regulator. One of these is for inhalation; the other, for exhalation.

This simple and safe apparatus, entirely automatic and easily mastered, has, in effect, opened the sea to man and made it possible for a large segment of the public to experience the thrill of diving. The invention of the Aqua-Lung®, therefore, was a decisive step forward in man's conquest of the sea, and even in the history of human progress.

The Cousteau-Gagnan independent diving unit was a revolutionary departure from the old "hard-hat" diving rig which most of us recall from the movies of the thirties. The hard-hat rig — so-called because of the heavy copper helmet that it included — was complicated to use, uncomfortable, and dangerous. It required a longer period of training, and it limited the diver's field of action to a small area of the bottom. If, in the past two decades, man has truly been able to go down into the sea, it is because of the independent diving gear — and its accessory equipment, such as the "fins" invented by Commandant de Corlieu, the mask, and the weight belt — which has proved its value as a means of exploration and scientific research even more than as a piece of sporting equipment.

Yet even though man has now learned to operate autonomously in the sea, he is still susceptible to two of the dangers with which hard-hat divers had always to contend: rapture of the deep and decompression accidents.

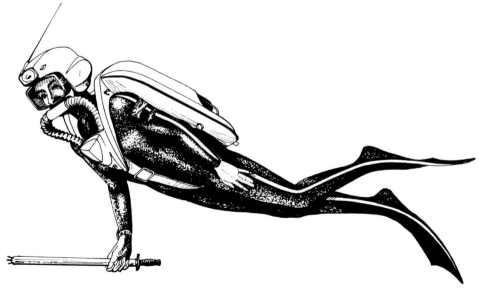

The Cousteau-Gagnon Aqua-Lung®.

Artiodactyls

A suborder of ungulate mammals the soles of whose paws bear an even number of digits. Ruminants and the pig family are artiodactyls.

Azimuth

The azimuth of a ship at sea is the angle formed by its bearing with respect to North.

Bathyscaphe

The first bathyscaphe was designed and perfected by Auguste Piccard. The bathyscaphe's first real dive took place on October 31, 1948, along the African coast off Dakar. On that occasion, the bathyscaphe, carrying no passengers, descended to a depth of 4,600 feet.

In October, 1950, an agreement between the French Navy and the Belgian National Research Foundation (Fonds National de la Recherche Scientifique) resulted in the construction of a new cable buoy and a new hull around the steel bell of the old *FNRS II*. This new design, called the FNRS III, was tested on February 15, 1954, off Dakar. With Commandant Nicolas-Maurice Houot and an engineer of the French Navy named Pierre-Henri Willm as passengers, the *FNRS III* attained a depth of 13,500 feet. In 1954 and 1958, it was used for deep dives in the Mediterranean, in the Atlantic, and in Japanese waters. After its ninety-fourth dive, the FNRS III was retired from active service.

Auguste and Jacques Piccard designed and built another bathyscaphe, the *Trieste*, which was tested in September, 1953, and which reached a depth of 10,000 feet. The *Trieste* was later acquired by the U. S. Navy and on January 23, 1960, it was used to reach the deepest known point in the sea: 36,380 feet, off the island of Guam.

Meanwhile, the French Navy, with the co-operation of the National Center for Scientific Research and the Belgian National Research Foundation, had undertaken the construction of an improved bathyscaphe. This new vehicle, christened the *Archimède*, was launched at the Toulon shipyard on July 28, 1961. In July 1962, in a series of six dives off the Kurile Islands in the North Pacific, the *Archimède* reached a depth of 30,000 feet. Since then, it has been used for deep-water research at various locations, from Puerto Rico to Madeira.

Blowhole

The blowhole is a valve located at the top of a cetacean's head. The two nostrils are situated within the blowhole. The sperm whale has two blowholes, but only one of them is functional. This organ has no connection with the alimentary canals of cetaceans, and it constitutes a major anatomical enigma.

Within the blowhole, the opening of which is controlled by a powerful muscle, there are inflatable air pockets on either side of the aperture. Two internal "lips" control exhalation and may contribute to the modulation of sound. In addition, a fleshy lamella, shaped like a tongue, serves as a cork, allowing the whale to close the blowhole more or less hermetically.

Bogue

The common name of a fish of the Sparidae family found in great abundance in the Mediterranean. Its flesh is not generally regarded as edible.

Calypso

Calypso is a former mine sweeper built in the United States in 1942 for the British Navy. She is a vessel of 350 tons, with a double hull of wood and two engines which give her a maximum speed of ten knots.

Calypso was found by Captain Cousteau in a naval-surplus yard on Malta, shortly after the close of World War II. The old mine sweeper was acquired through the generosity of a British patron, Mr. Loël Guinness.

She is remarkably easy to handle, and her shallow draft enables her to maneuver in and out of treacherous coral reefs with a minimum of trouble.

Extensive alterations were necessary before the ship could become a floating oceanographic laboratory. An underwater observation chamber was added: a well which descends to eight feet below the waterline and which is equipped with five portholes. This chamber is sometimes referred to as *Calypso*'s "false nose." Among the other changes and modifications was the addition of a double mast of light metal which was installed as far forward as possible on the deck. This mast serves as a radar antenna mount, as a sort of upper bridge from which to observe and direct a difficult passage, and as a crow's-nest from which to observe the larger marine animals in the water.

Catamaran

A sailing vessel characterized by the presence of two connected hulls.

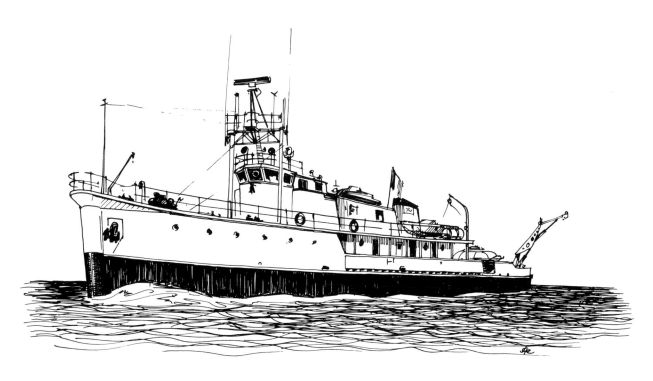

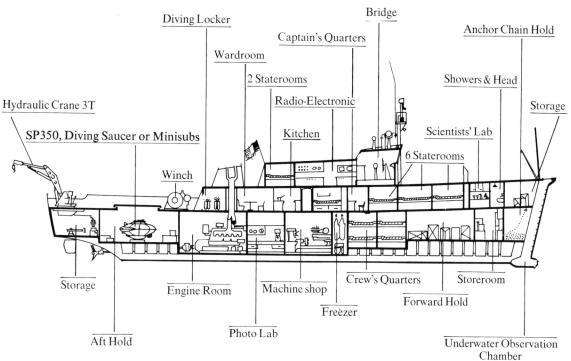

Hydraulic Crane 3T

SP350, Diving Saucer or Minisubs

Diving Locker

Wardroom

2 Staterooms

Radio-Electronic

Kitchen

Winch

Captain's Quarters

Bridge

Anchor Chain Hold

Showers & Head

Storage

Scientists' Lab

6 Staterooms

Storage

Engine Room

Machine shop

Crew's Quarters

Storeroom

Aft Hold

Photo Lab

Freèzer

Forward Hold

Underwater Observation
Chamber

Calypso. She is 140 feet long and has a draught of seven and a half feet. She is equipped with two 500 hp engines and has a cruising speed of 10 knots. Displacement: 800 tons. She normally carries a team of twenty-nine men.

Cerebral Cortex

The uppermost layer of the cerebral hemispheres. The word "cortex" is derived from the Latin word for "bark" (of a tree).

Cochlea

A spiral canal which is part of the inner ear.

Crete

An island of the eastern Mediterranean, about 3,500 square miles in area. The civilization of Crete was the forerunner of all later major civilizations of the Mediterranean basin. It disappeared, quite suddenly and mysteriously, in the second millennium before Christ. Most scholars now believe that foreign invasion was responsible for this cataclysm.

Curare

A poison derived from various American flora of the Strychnos genus. Curare induces death by destroying all motor nerves.

Cuttlefish

The cuttlefish belongs to the family Sepiidae, order Sepioidea, subclass Coleoidea. It lives in coastal waters among vegetation and on sandy bottoms, where it finds the shrimps which are its usual diet. There are approximately eighty species of cuttlefish, most of which are found in the tropical and subtropical waters of the Indo-Pacific. There are only a few Atlantic species; however, cuttlefish are abundant in the western Pacific and in the Indian Ocean. There are none in American waters.

The body of the cuttlefish is oval in shape. At the edge of the mantle, there is a ribbonlike fin running the length of the body. Around the head, there are eight arms and two tentacles, which are used to capture prey. Ordinarily, the two tentacles are retracted into two cavities under the cuttlefish's eyes.

The body of the cuttlefish is reinforced by an internal shell, the "cuttle-fish bone," which contains chambers filled with gas and which serves as the cuttlefish's hydrostatic equipment in swimming and floating.

The best-known species is the common cuttlefish, *Sepia officinalis*. This species was observed and commented upon by Aristotle some twenty-three centuries ago. It is found in the coastal waters of the Mediterranean, and all authorities agree that it is a strictly coastal species which is rarely found in water deeper than 450 feet.

Only a part of the cuttlefish population reaches the age of three or even four years. Its ordinary life span appears to be between two and two and one-half years.

The length of the cuttlefish's mantle is rarely more than sixteen to twenty inches. The smallest cuttlefish is the *Hemisepius typicus*, which is about 2-3/4 inches long. The largest species is *Sepia latimanus*, which reaches a length of five and one-half feet.

The mating season is in spring and summer.

Deep Scattering Layer, or D.S.L.

Deep Scattering Layer, which was so named during World War II, is a mysterious layer detected by the echo from sonar equipment at various depths and in various regions in the sea.

It has been observed that these layers rise toward the surface during the hours of darkness and then sink again during daylight. Professor H. E. Edgerton, of the Massachusetts Institute of Technology, working from *Calypso*, has succeeded in photographing these layers by using an electronic flash which he designed.

The constitutive elements of these layers are principally copepods, jellyfish, siphonophores, and eggs and larvae.

False Nose

Calypso's "*false nose*" is her underwater observation chamber. This chamber is one of the modifications which was necessary before the World War II mine sweeper could be used for oceanographic purposes. It is a metal well which goes down eight feet below the waterline and which is equipped with five portholes. The portholes are used for observing and filming marine life, even while *Calypso* is in motion.

Flippers

The flippers, or pectoral limbs, of cetaceans serve to remind us of the land origins of these marine mammals. An X ray of a flipper reveals the bones of five "fingers" (except in the case of the rorqual, or finback whale), of a "wrist," and of an "arm."

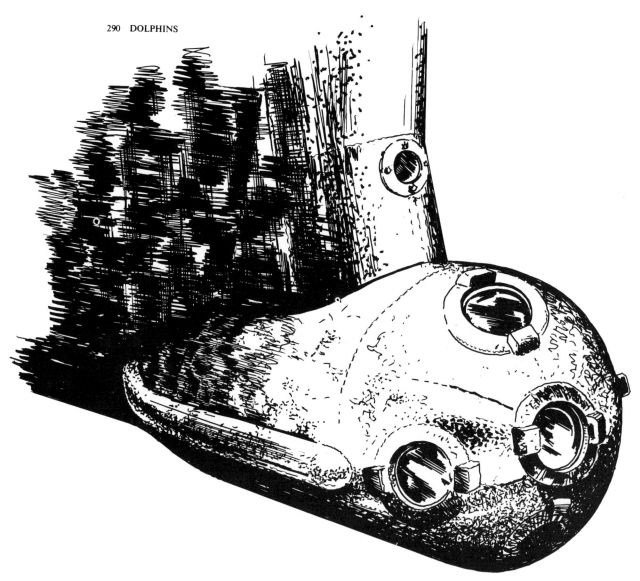

Calypso's "false nose" is a metallic well which leads to an observation chamber located eight feet beneath the waterline. This chamber has five portholes, which are useful not only in observing marine life, but also in photographing and filming it.

Flourescein

Fluorescein is a phthalein-based coloring agent. In solution, it is fluorescent.

Grouper

Groupers are sedentary fish that live in grottos and coral indentations, preferably on sandy bottoms, in water of various depths. They are adept hunters and attack their victims with great speed.

Groupers were once very numerous along the coasts of the Mediterranean, where they were hunted to excess because of their value as food. They are still abundant in African waters and also off the shores of both North and South America.

There are many species of groupers of various colors in tropical waters. In its proper meaning, the term "grouper" designates only members of the family Serranidae — which includes many fishes: *Ephinephelus, Cephalopholis*, etc. — but especially those belonging to the genera *Sterolepis* and *Promicrops*. The latter, which may reach an adult size of ten feet, is found along the coasts of Africa and also in American waters, where it is known as the Pacific jewfish or the giant sea bass.

Harpoon

The harpoon has been used since the dawn of history for fishing and hunting. In primitive times, it was made of wood or bone, with either one or two rows of barbs.

The *harpé*, as the Greeks called it (the word was derived from the Semitic *hereb*), is depicted on monuments dating from the third millennium before Christ. In the language of the Basques, those intrepid hunters of whales, the word *arpoi* (taken from the Greek root) means to "capture alive."

The present form of the harpoon is described in a text dating from 1474.

An important modern improvement was the addition of a pivoted crosspiece to the head, which prevents a harpooned animal from shaking the weapon loose.

Hawser

A line composed of several strands which is used for docking a ship or boat.

Hydrophone

A microphone designed for use in recording sounds in a liquid milieu.

Keeling

To keel a vessel is to turn up its keel, in dry dock, so as to scrape algae and barnacles from its hull, to inspect its condition, to paint it, or to effect repairs. Depending upon the work to be undertaken, keeling is classified either as major or minor.

La Méduse

On June 17, 1816, a French frigate named *La Méduse* left the Island of Aix, with three other vessels, bound for the colony of Senegal in West Africa. On July 2, *La Méduse* ran aground along the Arguin Bank. The crew tried for five days to get the ship afloat again. Then they constructed a raft, sixty feet in length and twenty feet in width, and 149 of the survivors were loaded aboard. The rest of the crew was distributed among five lifeboats secured to the raft by lines. Seventeen men, too drunk to take part in the evacuation of the ship, were left aboard *La Méduse*, which sank shortly thereafter.

The survivors drifted for twelve days without food or water. At the end of that time, they were rescued; but, by then, only fifteen of them were alive. The others had been devoured by sharks, or by the other occupants of the raft.

The Raft of La Méduse, a celebrated painting by Géricault, first exhibited in 1819, hangs today in the Louvre Museum.

Lamparo

Lamparo is a Provençal word meaning "lamp." It is used (especially by Mediterranean fishermen) to designate a fishing session in which a light is used to attract the fish.

Level Reef

A level reef is a coral plateau, more or less long and unbroken, which extends along a shoreline or on top of another reef that is completely surrounded by water. Level reefs are found in tropical shallows.

Minisub

There are several types of minisubs, or diving saucers, designed by Captain Cousteau and developed by the Center of Higher Marine Studies at Marseilles:

The *SP-350*, a two-passenger vehicle, is equipped with a cinematographic camera, a still camera, a hydraulically operated pincer and lift, and a storage basket. It has been used in over 600 dives. One *SP-350* can be parked in the rear hold of the *Calypso*.

The *SP-1000*, or sea flea, carries only one man but is designed to be used in conjunction with a second *SP-1000*. It has two exterior cameras (16mm. and 35mm.), both controlled from within, and tape recorders for recording underwater sounds. It has been used in over 100 dives. Two *SP-1000s* can be taken aboard the *Calypso*.

The *SP-4000*, or Deepstar, is capable of diving to 4,000 feet. It was built for Westinghouse and was launched in 1966. Since then, it has participated in over 500 dives. It is a two-man vehicle, with a speed of three knots.

The *SP-3000* was built for CNEXO. It attains a speed of three knots and carries three passengers.

Minoan Period

The Minoan is a period of Cretan history running from the third millennium B.C. to 1100 B.C. It is divided into the Upper Minoan (2400–2000B.C.), the Middle Minoan (1900–1600), and the Lower, or Recent, Minoan (1550–1100).

Mullet

The mullet is a member of the Mugilidae family and is classified as a bony fish. It is a coastal fish and is very common in temperate seas. It grows to two feet in length and reaches a weight of about twelve pounds. Its lateral line is not clearly visible, and its belly is white and soft. Mullets have flat, wide heads. They have very small teeth, or no teeth at all. Their scales are large, shiny, and well defined.

Mullets live in schools.

Mycenaean

The adjective Mycenaean is used to designate the ancient city of Mycenae in Argolis, or the civilization typified by the people of that city. The Mycenaean civilization followed that of the Minoans and dominated a large part of Greece, spreading into the islands of the Aegean and into Asia Minor. The Mycenaeans controlled the western Mediterranean, and their ships ventured into the North Sea and the Baltic to trade for amber and tin.

The empire of the Mycenaeans attained its peak *c.* 1400 B.C., then disappeared quite suddenly *c.* 1100 B.C. It was at the latter point in time that the Mycenaean citadel was completely destroyed.

Neurone

A nerve cell together with its processes.

Octopus

The octopus is a cephalopod mollusk having eight arms of equal length. The arms are equipped with sucker discs. Although it is a mollusk, the "shell" of the octopus is vestigial, or altogether absent.

There are numerous species of octopus - - all generally sedentary animals — found in every sea. The largest specimens attain a size of between six and seven feet. In some species, the salivary glands secrete a strong poison; and the bite of one species, native to Australian waters, is fatal to humans.

The third arm of the male octopus contains a channel or groove along its length. The animal's spermatophores pass down this groove. The arm is called the hectocotylus, and it is used to fertilize the female by introducing the spermatozoids into her pallial cavity.

Pelvis

An anatomical term for the usually basinlike bones to which the hind limbs are attached. In man and other land-living animals it is part of the nearly rigid structure involving the spine; in dolphins it is greatly reduced in size.

Pinnipeds

An order of animals comprising three familes:
Otaridae: sea lions, furred seals;
Odobaenidae: walrus;
Phocidae: seals and elephant seals.

Port

The nautical term used to designate the left side of a vessel when one is facing forward toward the stem.

Red Mullet, or Surmullet

The red mullet, commonly known as the bearded mullet, is easily recogniz-able by its iridescent red and yellow scales and by its two "whiskers," which are actually exploratory and tactile organs.

Rorqual, or Blue Whale

The rorqual *Balaenoptera physalus* is a baleen whale which belongs to the *Balaenoptera* genus of the Balaenopteridae family. It takes its common name of "finback" from its large, well-developed dorsal fin. Its lower jaw projects beyond the upper, and its underside is marked by a number of parallel ven-tral furrows.
The Blue Whale, *Balaenoptera musculus,* may attain a length of between 60 and 75 feet and a weight of 50 to 100 tons. The largest specimen known was a hundred feet in length. "The Blue Rorqual," says Professor Budker, "holds a record which has never been beaten. It is the largest, the most massive, and the heaviest creature that has ever existed on land or in the sea."
(See Appendix II, "The Cetaceans.")

Scrotum

The external bag, or pouch, which, in most mammals, contains the testicles.

Seine

A seine is a large net used for fishing. The two ends of the net are maneuvered

The Blue Whale — the largest living creature existing either on land or in the sea.

in such a way as to close gradually, shutting either the entire net or a section of it where the fishes have gathered.

Semantic

In language, that which is signified by a sign (or word). The study of such meanings is a function of the science of linquistics.

Sharks

The name "shark" is generally applied to fish belonging to the Elasmobranch, or Selachian, group.

Since sharks have no bones (their skeletons are composed entirely of cartilage), they are usually thought of as primitive animals. Yet, the nervous system of the shark is highly developed. There is a great variety in the ways in which various species reproduce, and some of these methods are especially well developed.

Among the Selachians, fertilization is internal, and there is a true mating. Professor Budker, an expert on sharks, writes: "So far as the mating of the species of large, pelagic sharks is concerned, it is impossible to formulate any hypotheses, since it is so difficult to observe such matings and the opportunity for such observation is so infrequent."

Among the smaller species, however, observation is possible, and we have more data. We know, for example, that the male dogfish swims in a tight circle near the female, while the latter remains stretched out and completely motionless.

Among the Carcharhinidae, especially, the young are always born live, and the foetus is connected to the mother's uterus by a kind of placenta. The number of sharks in a litter may vary from four to forty.

The heads and bodies of sharks are generously equipped with sensory organs — the "pit organs" described by Professor Budker in 1938 — which furnish them with an abundance of precise information on their environment. Work is currently under way to determine the roles of the different sensory organs which seem to make it possible for the shark to measure hydrostatic pressure, to perceive sonic and ultrasonic waves, to detect the chemical composition of water, etc. It is already known that a shark is able to perceive the presence of blood in the sea at a great distance, probably by means of its nostrils and the organs of taste with which the animal is equipped.

The shark enjoys the use of senses which man lacks, and thus it is much better equipped than a human diver for survival in the seas. This is particularly true at night, for the shark's eye, while it is not very effective in distinguishing the details or colors of a fixed object, is capable of perceiving and recognizing anything that moves in the water. Its field of vision is constant, even when the shark suddenly twists and turns in the water.

For more detailed information on the shark, and for a description of various experiments on the behavior of sharks, the reader is referred to *The Shark: Splendid Savage of the Sea*, by Jacques-Yves Cousteau and Philippe Cousteau, Doubleday & Co., Inc., and Cassell, 1970.

Sonar

"Sound Navigation Ranging" equipment, used in underwater detection and communication. It is analogous to radar and is based upon the reflection of sonic and supersonic waves.

Sphincter

A circular muscle surrounding, and able to contract or close, a natural opening or passage.

Spout

When a cetacean rises to the surface to breathe, it gives off, through one or two blowholes, a spout which is visible from a distance. It is a whitish spray, which cannot be attributed solely to the condensation of vapor in cold air, for it is visible even in tropical waters and climates.

As there is no passageway between its mouth and its blowhole, a whale cannot blow water out while exhaling.

Paul Portier, a French biologist, has offered the following hypothesis: the expansion in the open air of air which has been compressed in the thorax of a whale causes the condensation of the water vapor when the whale exhales.

F. C. Fraser and P. E. Purves have noted the presence in the whale's lungs of very small drops of oil and mucus, which may explain the visibility of its spout. This oil in the whale's respiratory tract may also play a part in the absorption of nitrogen.

Each species of whale has a distinctive spout. That of the blue whale and of the common rorqual is a single geyser that rises from eighteen to thirty feet above the surface. The right whale's spout is double. That of the sperm whale is single and emerges from the blowhole to the left of the whale and at a 45-degree angle.

The dolphin's spout, on the other hand, is barely visible above the water.

Squid

The squid is a cephalopod of the Loliginidae family, suborder Myopsida, order Teuthoidea, subclass Coleoidea.

The *Loligo vulgaris*, or common squid, is cigar-shaped and tapers to a point.

Squids have two triangular lateral fins and a horny, transparent internal element known as a "pen." They are common in the Atlantic, the North Sea, the Mediterranean, and the Red Sea. Most specimens of *Loligo vulgaris*, both in the Atlantic and in the Mediterranean, live to a probable age of between twenty-four and thirty months. The body of the male reaches a length of about eight inches. That of the female is of comparable length, but the arms of the male are longer. Certain species of squid, belonging to other genera, are true giants.

The *Loligo opalescens* has been the subject of a film made by the Cousteau team.

Stages of Ascent

Decompression accidents, during a diver's ascent to the surface, result from the diver's breathing of compressed air and from the gases that are dissolved in his system, by water pressure, during the ascent. The faster a diver rises, the larger are the air bubbles that may be generated. (The depth of the dive, and its duration, are also factors.) These bubbles block the circulatory system and may result in what is known as "gas embolism."

The diver's ascent is therefore slowed in order to allow these gases sufficient time to dissolve. Tables have been worked out which show the number and duration of the stops a diver must make during his ascent, in relation to the depth of the dive and the time spent at that depth. These mandatory stops are the "stages of ascent."

Starboard

The right side of a ship or boat, when one is looking forward, toward the stem.

Stays

Stays (also known as "shrouds" or "guys") are the lines of hemp or steel which run from the top of the masts of a ship to the hull. They serve to steady the masts. The term "to stay" or "to guy" means to steady a spar by means of lines.

Stem, or Stem Post

The specially sturdy piece to which sides of a ship or boat are secured in the bow. The prow.

Tuna

There are two commercial varieties of tuna: the white tuna (Thunnus, [or Germo] alalunga), and the red or true tuna (Thunnus thynnus). Both varieties are members of the Tunnidae family.

The giant tuna of Nova Scotia attains a length of thirteen feet and a weight of 1,500 pounds.

Undersea Houses

Captain Cousteau's first experiment with undersea houses (Conshelf I) took place in the Mediterranean, off Marseilles, in 1962, where two divers remained at a depth of 35 feet for eight days.

The second experiment (Conshelf II) was in the Red Sea, at Shab Rumi, in 1963. There, two oceanauts lived for a week at 80 feet, and eight others lived for a month at 37 feet.

The latest experiment took place in 1965 and was called Conshelf III. On that occasion, six divers remained at over 300 feet for three weeks, in an undersea house built in the open water off Cape Ferrat.

Bibliography

Alpers, Antony. *Dolphins, the Myth and the Mammal.* Boston, 1961.

Anthonioz, Raphaelle. "Les Imragen, pêcheurs nomades de Mauritanie". *Bulletin de l'IFAN.* t. XXIX (1967), t. XXX (1968).

Budker, Paul. "Dauphin," "La Mer," Encyclopedie Alpha, Paris, 1973.

Busnel, Rene-Guy, Moles, A., and Gilbert, M. "Un Cas de langue sifflee utilisee dans les Pyrenees francaise." *Logos,* V5-2, October 1962.

—————— "Le dauphin, nouvel animal de laboratoire," in *Sciences et Techniques*, III, 1966.

——————(ed.)*Les systemes sonars animaux.* Laboratoire de physiologie acoustique, Jouy-en-Josas, 1967.

—————— "Symbiotic Relationship between Man and Dolphins," *Meeting of the Section of Psychology*, N. Y. Academy of Sciences, 1972.

Caldwell, David K., and Melba C. *"World of the Bottle-Nosed Dolphin"* in *Sciences,* No. 108, 1966.

——————————. *The Ugly Dolphin.* St. Augustine, Florida.

——————————. *The World of the Bottlenosed Dolphin.* Philadelphia, 1972.

Classe, Andre. "L' Etrange language siffle des Iles Canaries," in *Courrier de l'Unesco.* Nov. 1957, No. 11.

Fraser, F. C. *British Whales, Dolphins and Porpoises*. London, 1966.

Green, R. E., Perrin, W. F., and Patrick, B. P. *The American Tuna Pure Seine Fishery*. London (n.d.)

Herald, Earl S. *Field and Aquarium Study of the Blind River Dolphin*, 1969.

Hershkovitz, P. *Catalog of Living Whales*. Washington, D.C., 1966.

Irvine, Blair. "Conditioning Marine Mammals to Work in the Sea," in *M. T. S. Journal*, Vol. 4, No. 3, May–June 1970.

Jonsgard, A., and Lyshoel, P. B. "A Contribution to the Knowledge of the Killer Whale," in *Nouveau Journal de Zoologie*, 1970.

Kellogg, W. N. *Porpoises and Sonar*. Phoenix, 1961.

Lilly, John C. *Man and Dolphin*. New York, 1961.

––––––. *The Mind of the Dolphin: A Non-human Intelligence*. New York, 1967.

Matthews, L. H. *The Whale*. London, 1968.

McNeely, Richard L. "The Pure Seine Revolution in Tuna Fishing," in *Pacific Fisherman*, June, 1961.

Norris, Kenneth S. "Trained Porpoise Released in Open Sea." *Science*, 147 (3661), pp. 1048–50.

––––––, ed. *Whales, Dolphins and Porpoises*. Berkeley and Los Angeles, 1966.

Perrin, William F. "Using Porpoise to Catch Tuna," in *World Fishing*, Vol. 18, No. 16 (1969).

Pilleri, G. *Observations on the Behavior of Platanista gangetica in the Indus and Brahmaputra rivers*. 1970.

Rice, D. W., and Scheffer, V. B. *A List of the Marine Mammals of the World*. Washington, D. C., 1968.

––––––––. *Recent Mammals of the World*. New York, 1967.

Riedman, Sarah R., and Gustafson, Elton T. *Home Is the Sea for Whales*. New York, 1966.

Slijper, E. J. *Whales*. London, 1962.

Index